INDEX TO REVIEWS, SYMPOSIA VOLUMES AND MONOGRAPHS IN ORGANIC CHEMISTRY

International Series of Monographs on ORGANIC CHEMISTRY

General Editors: D. H. R. BARTON, F.R.S., *and* W. VON E. DOERING

VOLUME 1 VISTAS IN FREE-RADICAL CHEMISTRY
Edited by W. A. Waters, F.R.S.

VOLUME 2 BORON FLUORIDE
and Its Compounds as Catalysts in Organic Chemistry
by A. V. Topchiev, S. V. Zavgorodnii *and* Ya. M. Paushkin
Translated from the Russian by J. T. Greaves

VOLUME 3 SYNTHETIC ANALGESICS
Part 1. Diphenylpropylamines
by P. A. J. Janssen

VOLUME 4 HOMOLYTIC AROMATIC SUBSTITUTION
by G. H. Williams

VOLUME 5 APPLICATIONS OF NUCLEAR MAGNETIC RESONANCE SPECTROSCOPY IN ORGANIC CHEMISTRY
by L. M. Jackman

SMALL RING COMPOUNDS
by E. Vogel

MOLECULAR ENERGETICS
by T. Heilbronner *and* J. D. Dunitz

ORGANIC SULFUR COMPOUNDS
Volume 1
Edited by Norman Kharasch

INDEX TO REVIEWS, SYMPOSIA VOLUMES AND MONOGRAPHS IN ORGANIC CHEMISTRY

For the Period 1940-1960

Compiled and Edited by

NORMAN KHARASCH

and

WALTER WOLF

University of Southern California
Los Angeles 7, California

and

ELAINE C. P. HARRISON

Technical Editor
Los Angeles, California

PERGAMON PRESS

NEW YORK • OXFORD • LONDON • PARIS • LOS ANGELES

1962

PERGAMON PRESS INC.
122 East 55th Street, New York 22, N.Y.

PERGAMON PRESS LTD.
Headington Hill Hall, Oxford
4 and 5 Fitzroy Square, London W.1.

PERGAMON PRESS S.A.R.L.
24 rue des Écoles, Paris V^e

PERGAMON PRESS G.m.b.H.
Kaiserstrasse 75, Frankfurt am Main

Copyright © 1962
Pergamon Press Inc.

Library of Congress Card No. 61-18796

Printed in U.S.A. by Edwards Bros., Ann Arbor, Mich.

FOREWORD

While preparing a resumé of monographs, reviews and symposia lectures for a volume on Organic Sulfur Compounds,[1] I had occasion to jot down references to hundreds of other summary works which I wanted to "pin down" for later use. This group of references, together with an earlier one, was then combined with a much more thorough list, prepared in collaboration with Elaine C. P. Harrison, and distributed, in 1960, as a private edition to friends and colleagues. The favorable response to the preliminary edition of this index led us to the next step, and the present, more complete version thus resulted, greatly aided by support of our publisher, Mr. Robert Maxwell of Pergamon Press, and the assistance of my research associate, Dr. Walter Wolf.

Our manuscript copy of this Index has proved quite useful to us and to our students, suggesting that it will also be a valuable desk-aid to thousands of other research workers, teachers and students. We also hope that it will assist editors and authors to select specific areas which require critical review.

We have adopted the plan of listings by symposia volume or journal, backed up by the total subject and author indexes. In this way the user can readily locate a particular article through the author index or the subject index; or should he recall that an article appeared in a particular source, the chronological listing in that source can be scanned quickly. As shown by the title, we have not listed references earlier than 1940, but an exception was made with Chemical Reviews, for which all organic reviews therein published are included.

While we stress the feature of time-saving as a prime one which may justify this Index, we suggest that equally important, perhaps, the Index gives a convenient overview of the accomplishments of organic chemists during this very prolific period of the growth of our science. Frequently, several articles on the same or similar subject appear, hence the historical perspective can be sensed by rapid evaluation of the reviews selected.

While the most recent reviews will be the ones of first interest, we have purposely not eliminated the earlier ones from the present edition. This is because we believe that they should be equally-easily available for inspection, on the one hand, and also because they may contain ideas and discussions which are not emphasized by later authors, but which may prove significant. Thus, we hope that this Index will be an effective invitation and aid to those who would browse and cogitate, for it would then not only be a source of reference, but a catalyst for begetting new research ideas as well.

Our selections are limited to papers published in French, German and English. Of course, valuable review articles, symposia and monographs appear in many other languages; but limitations of space and of our own efforts made the above restriction necessary. With a view to possible revision, however, (which we anticipate) we would truly welcome citations to those outstanding reviews or monographs in other languages which might otherwise be generally overlooked.

We believe that the Index has a high degree of accuracy, since, with very few exceptions, every article and book was actually seen in the original by one of us prior to inclusion. For each of the approximately seven thousand references given, we have included the full reference source and the actual page listings. In the case of multiple authorship, however, only the first three authors (as appeared in the article) were generally included in the Index listings. Nevertheless we have tried to include the name of *all* authors in the author index, with cross-references to the first-cited author. A list of addresses of publishers has also been included in the Appendix.

---

[1] *Organic Sulfur Compounds,* Volume 1, edited by N. Kharasch, Pergamon Press (1961).
[2] *Bibliography of Chemical Reviews,* edited by the staff of Chemical Abstracts; published by the American Chemical Society. Volumes 1 and 2 cover 1958 and 1959, respectively.

The idea for this Index was conceived and the work was in full progress when we learned of the parallel effort for the years 1958-onward by the staff of Chemical Abstracts.[2] We believe that our Index will fit in well with the ones prepared by the Abstracts staff, and that it will provide, for organic chemistry, a useful key to the earlier literature. For those who are interested specifically in organic chemistry and its closely allied fields, and because of differences in emphasis and arrangement, the present Index may also have additional justification.

Besides the question of selection, the subject index is necessarily and equally the critical feature of this Index. We have tried to make this fully comprehensive and adequately cross-indexed. The inclusion of extensive listings under Reactions, Rearrangements, Alkaloids, Hydrocarbons, etc. are indicative of the depth of the subject index. We will, however, appreciate notations concerning errors or omissions, either in the subject or author indexes and, of course, in the text.

A convenient list of the published monographs for 1940-1960, dealing with organic chemistry, should prove valuable. While the list included in this Index is already fairly extensive, we recognize that many borderline books on physical chemistry, inorganic chemistry, and biochemistry — as well as some textbooks, could be justifiably included. On the whole, we have listed all research monographs which are classified in the 547-file of the Library of Congress, and tried to add, selectively, such other titles as may be of general interest to organic chemists. Admittedly, this list is still quite incomplete, and once again, further suggestions will be welcomed. In connection with the list of monographs, we acknowledge, particularly, the kind assistance of Mr. Herman Henkle of the John Crerar Library in Chicago, who made available to us a photostatic record of the total 547-file of this famous and complete library.

Several other persons have helped this project and we wish to acknowledge their assistance. We thank Professors C. M. Buess, T. L. Geissman, R. L. Shriner, R. A. Raphael, J. A. Berson and E. W. Warnhoff, and Drs. George S. Schmid and Leon Goodman, among others, for their interest and specific suggestions. Mrs. E. Dolbee, librarian, and Professor W. G. McMillan, of the University of California at Los Angeles, assisted us by arranging library facilities for Mrs. Harrison, which made much of the work on the first edition most convenient and pleasant. Mr. Laszlo Tokes kindly gave us partial assistance in preparing the subject index and the Pergamon staff cooperated fully in making all publication arrangements.

We are particularly indebted also to Elenora Kharasch, Gladys Wolf and Irene Campbell, whose able and cheerful assistance with the library work and in checking of references and typing of the manuscript were of greatest value.

It is intended to keep this Index up to date by issuing an annual volume. Since the one covering the year 1961 is already in preparation, we will appreciate suggestions from users of the present work.

Los Angeles, California
January, 1962

Norman Kharasch
with
Walter Wolf and
Elaine C. P. Harrison

CONTENTS

PART I. REVIEWS IN JOURNALS AND PERIODIC PUBLICATIONS

ADVANCES IN ANALYTICAL CHEMISTRY AND INSTRUMENTATION	1
ADVANCES IN CANCER RESEARCH	1
ADVANCES IN CARBOHYDRATE CHEMISTRY	2
ADVANCES IN CATALYSIS AND RELATED SUBJECTS	6
ADVANCES IN CHEMICAL PHYSICS	7
ADVANCES IN CLINICAL CHEMISTRY	7
ADVANCES IN ENZYMOLOGY AND RELATED SUBJECTS OF BIOCHEMISTRY	8
ADVANCES IN INORGANIC CHEMISTRY AND RADIOCHEMISTRY	9
ADVANCES IN ORGANIC CHEMISTRY: METHODS AND RESULTS	9
ADVANCES IN PROTEIN CHEMISTRY	10
ADVANCES IN SPECTROSCOPY	12
ANALYST, THE	13
ANGEWANDTE CHEMIE	14
ANNALLES PHARMACEUTIQUES FRANÇAISES	26
ANNUAL REVIEW OF BIOCHEMISTRY	27
ANNUAL REVIEW OF NUCLEAR SCIENCE	30
ANNUAL REVIEW OF PHYSICAL CHEMISTRY	31
ANTIBIOTICA AND CHEMOTHERAPIA	32
BULLETIN DE LA SOCIÉTÉ DE CHIMIE BIOLOGIQUE	32
BULLETIN DE LA SOCIÉTÉ CHIMIQUE DE FRANCE	33
CHEMICAL REVIEWS	40
CHEMISCHE BERICHTE	53
CHEMISTRY AND INDUSTRY	54
CHIMIA	60
ENDEAVOUR	63
EXPERIENTIA	64
FORTSCHRITTE DER CHEMIE ORGANISCHER NATURSTOFFE	66
FORTSCHRITTE DER CHEMISCHEN FORSCHUNG	70
JOURNAL DE CHIMIE PHYSIQUE ET PHYSICO-CHIMIE BIOLOGIQUE	71
JOURNAL OF CHEMICAL EDUCATION	72
JOURNAL OF CHROMATOGRAPHY	76
JOURNAL OF MEDICINAL AND PHARMACEUTICAL CHEMISTRY	77
JOURNAL OF PHARMACY AND PHARMACOLOGY	78
MICROCHEMICAL JOURNAL	80
DIE NATURWISSENSCHAFTEN	81
ORGANIC ANALYSIS	83
ORGANIC REACTIONS	85
PROCEEDINGS OF THE CHEMICAL SOCIETY (LONDON)	89
PROGRESS IN INORGANIC CHEMISTRY	92
PROGRESS IN ORGANIC CHEMISTRY	93

PROGRESS IN THE CHEMISTRY OF FATS AND OTHER LIPIDS..................................95
QUARTERLY REVIEWS 96
RECORD OF CHEMICAL PROGRESS...101
RESEARCH APPLIED TO INDUSTRY..105
REVIEWS OF PURE AND APPLIED CHEMISTRY..107
LA REVUE SCIENTIFIQUE..109
THE ROYAL INSTITUTE OF CHEMISTRY JOURNAL..110
TETRAHEDRON 111
VITAMINS AND HORMONES..112
ZEITSCHRIFT FÜR VITAMIN-, HORMON- UND FERMENT-FORSCHUNG...........114

PART II. REVIEWS IN SYMPOSIA, COLLECTIVE VOLUMES AND NON-PERIODICAL PUBLICATIONS

ADVANCES IN CHEMISTRY SERIES..116
ADVANCES IN COLLOID SCIENCE..118
ADVANCES IN MASS SPECTROMETRY..119
ADVANCING FRONTS IN CHEMISTRY..120
THE ALKALOIDS, CHEMISTRY AND PHYSIOLOGY..121
ANNALS OF THE NEW YORK ACADEMY OF SCIENCES.....................................124
ANTIBIOTICS — THEIR CHEMISTRY AND NON-MEDICAL USES........................131
BIOCHEMICAL SOCIETY SYMPOSIA..132
CAHIERS DE SYNTHÈSE ORGANIQUE..134
THE CARBOHYDRATES — CHEMISTRY, BIOCHEMISTRY AND PHYSIOLOGY...135
THE CHEMICAL SOCIETY (LONDON) SPECIAL PUBLICATIONS.........................136
CHEMISORPTION 139
CHEMISTRY OF CARBON COMPOUNDS...140
CHEMISTRY OF COORDINATE COMPOUNDS..144
THE CHEMISTRY OF HETEROCYCLIC COMPOUNDS...145
CHEMISTRY OF MICROBIAL PRODUCTS (THE SQUIBB LECTURES)................147
THE CHEMISTRY OF NATURAL PRODUCTS 147
THE CHEMISTRY OF PENICILLIN...148
THE CHEMISTRY OF PETROLEUM HYDROCARBONS.......................................150
CHOLESTEROL 152
CIBA FOUNDATION COLLOQUIA ON ENDOCRINOLOGY...................................153
CIBA FOUNDATION SYMPOSIA..154
LES COLLOQUES DU CENTRE NATIONAL DE LA RECHERCHE SCIENTIFIQUE...158
CONFERENCE ON HYPERCONJUGATION...164
CONTRIBUTION TO THE STUDY OF MOLECULAR STRUCTURE......................165
CURARE AND CURARE-LIKE AGENTS..165
CURRENT TRENDS IN HETEROCYCLIC CHEMISTRY...166
DETERMINATION OF ORGANIC STRUCTURES BY PHYSICAL METHODS........167

FARADAY SOCIETY — DISCUSSIONS	168
L. FARKAS MEMORIAL VOLUME	173
FERMENTE-VITAMINE-HORMONE	174
FESTSCHRIFT ARTHUR STOLL	175
FLUORINE CHEMISTRY	178
FORMATION AND TRAPPING OF FREE RADICALS	179
FRONTIERS IN CHEMISTRY	180
HETEROCYCLIC COMPOUNDS	181
HIGH POLYMERS	184
HYDROGEN BONDING	186
INTERNATIONAL CONGRESSES OF BIOCHEMISTRY	187
INTERNATIONAL CONGRESSES OF PURE AND APPLIED CHEMISTRY	189
INTERNATIONAL SYMPOSIUM ON MACROMOLECULAR CHEMISTRY	191
ION EXCHANGES IN ORGANIC CHEMISTRY AND BIOCHEMISTRY	192
A LABORATORY MANUAL OF ANALYTICAL METHODS OF PROTEIN CHEMISTRY (INCLUDING POLYPEPTIDES)	193
MATTHEWS' TEXTILE FIBERS	194
MEDICINAL CHEMISTRY	195
METHODEN DER ORGANISCHEN CHEMIE	196
MICROCHEMISTRY: INTERNATIONAL SYMPOSIUM	200
MODERN COORDINATION CHEMISTRY, PRINCIPLES AND METHODS	200
MOLECULAR STRUCTURE AND ORGANOLEPTIC QUALITY	201
NON-BENZENOID AROMATIC COMPOUNDS	201
NMR AND EPR SPECTROSCOPY	202
NUCLEIC ACIDS	202
ORGANIC CHEMISTRY, AN ADVANCED TREATISE	203
ORGANOMETALLIC CHEMISTRY	204
THE ORIGIN OF LIFE ON EARTH	205
PERSPECTIVES IN ORGANIC CHEMISTRY	206
THE PETER C. REILLY LECTURES IN CHEMISTRY	207
PHOTOCHEMISTRY IN THE LIQUID AND SOLID STATES	207
PHYSICAL CHEMISTRY OF THE HYDROCARBONS	208
RADIOACTIVITY APPLIED TO CHEMISTRY	209
RADIOBIOLOGY SYMPOSIUM	209
RECENT PROGRESS IN HORMONE RESEARCH	210
THE ROGER ADAMS SYMPOSIUM	211
THE ROYAL INSTITUTE OF CHEMISTRY OF GREAT BRITAIN AND IRELAND	212
STERIC COURSE OF MICROBIOLOGICAL REACTIONS	213
STERIC EFFECTS IN CONJUGATED SYSTEMS	214
STERIC EFFECTS IN ORGANIC CHEMISTRY	215
SYMPOSIA ON COMPARATIVE BIOLOGY	216
A SYMPOSIUM ON MOLECULAR BIOLOGY	216
SYMPOSIUM ON PROTEIN STRUCTURE	217

THE STRATEGY OF CHEMOTHERAPY...217
TECHNIQUE OF ORGANIC CHEMISTRY..218
THEORETICAL ORGANIC CHEMISTRY...223
TRAITÉ DE CHIMIE ORGANIQUE..224
UBER STERINE, GALLENSÄURE UND VERWANDTE NATURSTOFFE.........................232
VISTAS IN FREE-RADICAL CHEMISTRY...233
OTHER SYMPOSIA AND COLLECTIVE VOLUMES (ADDENDUM).................................234

PART III.

MONOGRAPHS ON ORGANIC CHEMISTRY: 1940-1960..236

    Author Index 256
    Subject Index 291
    Appendix 343

PART I
REVIEWS IN JOURNALS AND PERIODIC PUBLICATIONS
Pages 1-114

ADVANCES IN ANALYTICAL CHEMISTRY AND INSTRUMENTATION

This is an annual collection of review articles in English, edited by C.N. Reilley and published by Interscience Publishers, Inc., New York.

Title	Author	Reference
Tetraphenylboron (TPB) as an analytical reagent	H. Flaschka and A. J. Barnard	$\underline{1}$, 1-117 (1960)
New ideas in organic microanalysis. Part I. C-H, O, N, halogens, S, and other elements	W. Schöniger	$\underline{1}$, 199-240 (1960)
The analytical chemistry of thioacetamide	E. H. Swift and F.C. Anson	$\underline{1}$, 293-345 (1960)
Near infra-red spectrophotometry	R. F. Goddu	$\underline{1}$, 347-424 (1960)

ADVANCES IN CANCER RESEARCH

This is an annual collection of review articles, in English. Edited by J. P. Greenstein and A. Haddow, and published by Academic Press, New York. In 1957, 1959 and 1960 no volumes appeared. Volume 6 is scheduled for 1961.

Title	Author	Reference
Electronic configuration and carcinogenesis	C.A. Coulson	$\underline{1}$, 2-56 (1953)
Carcinogenic aminoazo dyes	J. A. Miller and E. C. Miller	$\underline{1}$, 340-396 (1953)
Chemistry of cytotoxic alkylating agents	W. C. J. Ross	$\underline{1}$, 397-450 (1953)
Reactions of carcinogens with macromolecules	P. Alexander	$\underline{2}$, 2-71 (1954)
Chemical constitution and carcinogenic activity;	G.M. Badger	$\underline{2}$, 73-128 (1954)
Electronic structure and carcinogenic activity; aromatic molecules. New developments	A. Pullman and B. Pullman	$\underline{3}$, 117-169 (1955)
Relation between carcinogenic activity and the physical and chemical properties of angular benzacridines	A. Lacassagne N.P. Buu-Hoï R. Daudel and F. Zajdela	$\underline{4}$, 316-369 91956)
Chemistry, carcinogenicity and metabolism of 2-fluorenamine and related compounds	E.K. Weisburger and J.H. Weisburger	$\underline{5}$, 333-431 (1958)

An annual collection of review articles, in English. Volumes 1 to 4 were edited by W.W. Pigman and M.L. Wolfrom; volumes 5 to 7 by C.S. Hudson, M.L. Wolfrom and S.M. Cantor and volume 8 by C.S. Hudson and M.L. Wolfrom. The present editors are M.L. Wolfrom and R.S. Tipson (from volume 9 onwards). Published by Academic Press, New York.

Title	Author	Reference
Fischer Cyanohydrin Synthesis and the Configurations of Higher-Carbon Sugars and Alcohols	C.S. Hudson	1, 1-36 (1945)
Altrose Group of Substances	N.K. Richtmyer	1, 37-76 (1945)
Carbohydrate Orthoesters	E. Pacsu	1, 77-127 (1945)
Thio- and Seleno-Sugars	A.L. Raymond	1, 129-145 (1945)
The carbohydrate components of the Cardiac Glycosides	R.C. Elderfield	1, 147-192 (1945)
The chemistry of the nucleic acids	R.S. Tipson	1, 193-245 (1945)
The fractionation of starch	T.J. Schach	1, 247-277 (1945)
Preparation and properties of starch esters	R.L. Whistler	1, 279-307 (1945)
Cellulose esters of organic acids	C.R. Fordyce	1, 309-327 (1945)
Melezitose and turanose	C.S. Hudson	2, 1-36 (1946)
Chemistry of anhydro sugars	S. Peat	2, 37-77 (1946)
Analogs of ascorbic acid	F. Smith	2, 79-106 (1946)
Synthesis of hexitols and pentitols from unsaturated polyhydric alcohols	R. Lespieau	2, 107-118 (1946)
Chemistry of mucopolysaccharides and mucoproteins	M. Stacey	2, 161-201 (1946)
Bacterial polysaccharides	T.H. Evans and H. Hibbert	2, 203-233 (1946)
Chemistry of pectic materials	E.L. Hirst and J.K.N. Jones	2, 235-251 (1946)
Polyfructosans and difructose anhydrides	E.J. McDonald	2, 253-277 (1946)
Cellulose ethers of industrial significance	J.F. Haskins	2, 279-294 (1946)
Historical aspects of Emil Fischer's fundamental conventions for writing stereo-formulas in a plane	C.S. Hudson	3, 1-22 (1948)
Structure and reactivity of the hydrazone and osazone derivatives of the sugars	E.G.V. Percival	3, 23-44 (1948)
Chemistry and configuration of the cyclitols	H.G. Fletcher Jr.	3, 45-77 (1948)
Trityl ethers of carbohydrates	B. Helferich	3, 79-111 (1948)
Glutose and the unfermentable reducing substances in cane molasses	L. Sattler	3, 113-128 (1948)
Halogen oxidation of simple carbohydrates, excluding the action of periodic acid	J.W. Green	3, 129-184 (1948)
Molecular constitution of cellulose	J. Compton	3, 185-228 (1948)
Polysaccharides of mycobacterium tuberculosis	M. Stacey and P.W. Kent	3, 311-336 (1948)
Chemistry of streptomycin	R.U. Lemieux and M.L. Wolfrom	3, 337-384 (1948)
Structure and configuration of sucrose	I. Levi and C.B. Purves	4, 1-35 (1949)
Blood group polysaccharides	H.G. Bray and M. Stacey	4, 37-55 (1949)
Apiose and the glycosides of the parsley plant	C.S. Hudson	4, 57-74 (1949)

Title	Author(s)	Vol.	Pages	Year
Biochemical reductions at the expense of sugars	C. Neuberg	4,	75-117	(1949)
Acylated nitriles of aldonic acids and their degradation	V. Deulofeu	4,	119-151	(1949)
Wood saccharification	E.E. Harris	4,	153-188	(1949)
Use of boric acid for the determination of the configuration of carbohydrates	J. Böeseken	4,	189-210	(1949)
The hexitols and some of their derivatives	R. Lohmar and R.M. Goepp Jr.	4,	211-241	(1949)
Plant gums and mucilages	J.K.N. Jones and F. Smith	4,	243-291	(1949)
Applications in the carbohydrate field of reductive desulfurization by Raney nickel	H.G. Fletcher Jr. and N.K. Richtmyer	5,	1-28	(1950)
Enzymatic synthesis of sucrose and other disaccharides	W.Z. Hassid and M. Doudoroff	5,	29-48	(1950)
Relative crystallinity of celluloses	R.F. Nickerson	5,	103-126	(1950)
Methyl ethers of D-glucose	E.J. Bourne and S. Peat	5,	145-190	(1950)
Anhydrides of the Pentitols and hexitols	L.F. Wiggins	5,	191-228	(1950)
Xylan	R.L. Whistler	5,	269-290	(1950)
Methyl ethers of D-galactose	D.J. Bell	6,	11-25	(1951)
Synthesis of oligosaccharides	W.L. Evans D.D. Reynolds and E.A. Talley	6,	27-81	(1951)
Formation of furan compounds from hexoses	F.H. Newth	6,	83-106	(1951)
Cuprammonium-glycoside complexes	R.E. Reeves	6,	107-134	(1951)
Chemistry of ribose	R.W. Jeanloz and H.G. Fletcher Jr.	6,	135-174	(1951)
2-(Aldo-polyhydroxyalkyl)benzimidazoles	N.K. Richtmyer	6,	175-203	(1951)
Aconitic acid, a by-product in the manufacture of sugar	R.E. Miller and S.M. Cantor	6,	231-249	(1951)
Friedel-Crafts and grignard processes in the carbohydrate series	W.A. Bonner	6,	251-289	(1951)
Nitromethane and 2-nitroethanol syntheses	J.C. Sowden	6,	291-318	(1951)
Methyl ethers of the aldopentoses and of Rhamnose and fucose	R.A. Laidlaw and E.G.V. Percival	7,	1-36	(1952)
1,6-Anhydrohexofuranoses, a new class of hexosans	R.J. Dimler	7,	37-52	(1952)
Fructose and its derivatives	C.P. Barry and J. Honeyman	7,	53-98	(1952)
Psicose, sorbose and tagatose	J.V. Karabinos	7,	99-136	(1952)
Acetals and ketals of the tetritols, pentitols and hexitols	S.A. Barker and E.J. Bourne	7,	137-207	(1952)
Glycals	B. Helferich	7,	209-245	(1952)
Chemistry of the 2-amino-sugars (2-amino-2-deoxy-sugars)	A.B. Foster and M. Stacey	7,	247-288	(1952)
Size and shape of some polysaccharide molecules	C.T. Greenwood	7,	289-332	(1952)
Relative reactivities of hydroxyl groups of carbohydrates	J.M. Sugihara	8,	1-44	(1953)
Chemistry of the 2-desoxy-sugars	W.G. Overend and M. Stacey	8,	45-105	(1953)
Sulfonic esters of carbohydrates	R.S. Tipson	8,	107-215	(1953)

Methyl ethers of D-mannose	G.O. Aspinall	8,	217-230 (1953)
Chemical synthesis of D-glucuronic acid	C.L. Mehltretter	8,	231-249 (1953)
D-glucuronic acid in metabolism	H.G. Bray	8,	251-275 (1953)
The substituted-sucrose structure of melezitose	E.J. Hehre	8,	277-290 (1953)
Seaweed polysaccharides	T. Mori	8,	316-350 (1953)
Some implications in carbohydrate chemistry of theories relating to the mechanisms of replacement reactions	R.U. Lemieux	9,	1-57 (1954)
Alkali-sensitive glycosides	C.E. Ballou	9,	59-95 (1954)
2-Hydroxyglycals	M.G. Blair	9,	97-129 (1954)
Methyl ethers of hexuronic acids	G.O. Aspinall	9,	131-148 (1954)
Raffinose family of oligosaccharides	D. French	9,	149-184 (1954)
Conjugates of D-glucuronic acid of animal origin	R.S. Teague	9,	186-246 (1954)
Color and turbidity of sugar products	R.W. Liggett and V.R. Deitz	9,	247-284 (1954)
Carboxymethylcellulose	J.V. Karabinos and M. Hindert	9,	285-302 (1954)
Paper chromatography of carbohydrates and related compounds	G.N. Kowkabany	9,	303-353 (1954)
Stereochemistry of cyclic derivatives of carbohydrates	J.A. Mills	10,	1-53 (1955)
Column chromatography of sugars and their derivatives	W.W. Binkley	10,	55-94 (1955)
Glycosylamines	G.P. Ellis and J. Honeyman	10,	95-168 (1955)
The Amadori rearrangement	J.E. Hodge	10,	169-205 (1955)
Glycosyl halides and their derivatives	L.J. Haynes and F.H. Newth	10,	207-256 (1955)
Methyl ethers of the aldopentoses and of rhamnose and fucose	G.G. Maher	10,	257-272 (1955)
Methyl ethers of D-galactose	G.G. Maher	10,	273-282 (1955)
Polysaccharides associated with wood cellulose	W.J. Polglase	10,	283-333 (1955)
Chemistry of heparin	A.B. Foster and A.J. Huggard	10,	335-368 (1955)
Periodate oxidations of carbohydrates	J.M. Bobbitt	11,	1-41 (1956)
The osones	S. Bayne and J.A. Fewster	11,	43-96 (1956)
Reactions of monosaccharides with beta-ketonic esters and related substances	F. García González	11,	97-143 (1956)
Kojic acid	A. Beélik	11,	145-183 (1956)
Nucleic acids	G.R. Barker	11,	285-333 (1956)
Infrared spectra of carbohydrates	W.B. Neeley	12,	13-33 (1957)
Saccharinic acids	J.C. Sowden	12,	35-79 (1957)
Zone electrophoresis of carbohydrates	A.B. Foster	12,	81-115 (1957)
Sugar nitrates	J. Honeyman and J.W.W. Morgan	12,	117-135 (1957)
Benzyl ethers of sugars	C.M. McCloskey	12,	137-156 (1957)
Methyl and phenyl glycosides of the common sugars	J. Conchie, G.A. Levvy and C.A. Marsh	12,	157-187 (1957)
The Schardinger dextrins	D. French	12,	189-260 (1957)

Molecular structure of glycogens	D.J. Manners	12,	261-298 (1957)
Biosynthesis of Hyaluronic acid	R.L. Whistler and E.J. Olson	12,	299-319 (1957)
Formation and cleavage of the oxygen ring in sugars	F. Shafizadeh	13,	9-61 (1958)
Lobry de Bruyn - Alberda von Ekenstein transformation	J.C. Speck Jr.	13,	13-103 (1958)
Formazan reaction in carbohydrate research	L. Mester	13,	105-167 (1958)
Four-carbon saccharinic acids	J.D. Crum	13,	169-188 (1958)
Methyl ethers of 2-amino-2-deoxy sugars	R.W. Jeanloz	13,	189-214 (1958)
Glycosyl ureides	I. Goodman	13,	215-236 (1958)
The nonulosaminic acids. Neuroaminic acids and related compounds (sialic acids)	F. Zilliken and M.W. Whitehouse	13,	237-263 (1958)
Alkaline degradation of polysaccharides	R.L. Whistler and J.N. BeMiller	13,	289-329 (1958)
Starch nitrate	G.V. Caesar	13,	331-345 (1958)
Action of lead tetraacetate on sugars	A.S. Perlin	14,	9-61 (1959)
Maillard reaction	G.P. Ellis	14,	63-134 (1959)
Cyclitols	S.J. Angyal and L. Anderson	14,	136-212 (1959)
Amino-sugars	A.B. Foster and D. Horton	14,	213-281 (1959)
Pyrimidine nucleosides	J.J. Fox and I. Wempen	14,	283-380 (1959)
Structural chemistry of the hemicelluloses	G.O. Aspinall	14,	429-468 (1959)
Constitution and physicochemical properties of carbohydrates	B. Capon and W.G. Overend	15,	11-51 (1960)
Methods in structural polysaccharide chemistry	H.O. Bouveng and B. Lindberg	15,	53-89 (1960)
The carbonates and thiocarbonates of carbohydrates	L. Hough J.E. Priddle and R.S. Theobald	15,	91-158 (1960)
Tables of properties of 2-amino-2-deoxy sugars and their derivatives	D. Horton	15,	159-200 (1960)
Bacterial nucleosides and nucleotides	J. Jonsen and S. Laland	15,	201-234 (1960)
The biosynthesis of aromatic compounds from D-glucose	D.B. Sprinson	15,	235-270 (1960)
Polysaccharides of gram-negative bacteria	D.A.L. Davies	15,	271-340 (1960)
Dextran: structure and synthesis	W.B. Neely	15,	341-369 (1960)
Chitin	A.B. Foster and J.M. Webber	15,	371-393 (1960)

ADVANCES IN CATALYSIS AND RELATED SUBJECTS

This is an annual collection of review articles, in English. The editors for volumes 1 to 8 were W.G. Frankenburg, V.I. Komarewsky and E.K. Rideal; volume 9 was edited by A. Farkas and volume 10 by D.D. Eley, W.G. Frankenburg and V.I. Komarewsky. Present editors (from volume 11 onwards) are D.D. Eley, P.W. Selwood and P.B. Weisz. Published by Academic Press, New York.

Title	Author	Reference
Alkylation of isoparaffins	V.N. Ipatieff and L. Schmerling	1, 27-64 (1948)
The Fischer-Tropsch and related processes for synthesis of hydrocarbons by hydrogenation of carbon monoxide	H.H. Storch	1, 115-156 (1948)
The catalytic activation of hydrogen	D.D. Eley	1, 157-199 (1948)
Isomerization of alkanes	H. Pines	1, 201-256 (1948)
The mechanism of the polymerization of alkenes	L. Schmerling and V.N. Ipatieff	2, 21-80 (1950)
Catalytic cracking of pure hydrocarbons	V. Haensel	3, 179-197 (1951)
Acid-base catalysis and molecular structure	R.P. Bell	4, 151-210 (1952)
The specific reactions of iron in some hemo-proteins	P. George	4, 367-428 (1952)
Hydrogenation of organic compounds with synthesis gas	M. Orchin	5, 385-415 (1954)
The uses of Raney nickel	E. Lieber and F.L. Morritz	5, 417-455 (1954)
Noble metal-synthetic polymer catalysts and studies on the mechanism of their action	W.P. Dunworth and F.F. Nord	6, 125-141 (1954)
Commercial isomerization	B.L. Evering	6, 197-239 (1954)
Catalytic syntheses of ketones	V.I. Komarewsky and J.R. Coley	8, 207-217 (1956)
Polymerization of olefins from cracked gases	E.K. Jones	8, 219-238 (1956)
Reaction paths and energy barriers in catalysis and biocatalysis	D.D. Eley	9, 273-283 (1957)
Sulfur dioxide, a versatile homogeneous catalyst	H.I. Waterman and C. Boelhouwer	9, 294-301 (1957)
Catalytic technology in the petroleum industry	A.G. Oblad, H. Shalit and H.T. Tadd	9, 510-530 (1957)
Homogeneous metal carbonyl reactions and their relation to heterogeneous catalysis	I. Wender and H.W. Sternberg	9, 594-608 (1957)
The nature of active centers and the kinetics of catalytic dehydrogenation	A.A. Balandin	10, 96-129 (1958)
The structure of the active surface of cholinesterases and the mechanism of their catalytic action in ester hydrolysis	F. Bergmann	10, 130-164 (1958)
Commercial alkylation of paraffins and aromatics	E.K. Jones	10, 165-195 (1958)
The kinetics of the stereospecific polymerization of α-olefins	G. Natta and I. Pasquon	11, 1-66 (1959)
The catalytic exchange of hydrocarbons with deuterium	C. Kemball	11, 223-262 (1959)
The catalytic activation of hydrogen in homogeneous, heterogeneous, and biological systems	J. Halpern	11, 301-370 (1959)
Base catalyzed reactions of hydrocarbons	H. Pines and L.A. Schaap	12, 117-148 (1960)

ADVANCES IN CHEMICAL PHYSICS

Annual collection of review articles, published in English
Edited by I. Prigogine, Interscience Publishers Inc., New York.

Title	Author	Reference
Relation between structure and chemical reactivity of aromatic hydrocarbons with particular reference to carcinogenic properties	R. Daudel	1, 165-201 (1958)
Recent advances in polymer chemistry	M. Szwarc	2, 147-186 (1959)

ADVANCES IN CLINICAL CHEMISTRY

Annual collection of review articles, in English. Edited by H. Sobotka and C.P. Stewart. Published by Academic Press, New York.

Title	Author	Reference
Paper electrophoresis: principles and techniques	H. Peeters	2, 2-134 (1959)
Determination and significance of natural estrogens	J.B. Brown	3, 158-235 (1960)
Folic acid, its analogs and antagonists	R.H. Girdwood	3, 236-287 (1960)

ADVANCES IN ENZYMOLOGY AND RELATED SUBJECTS OF BIOCHEMISTRY

Volumes 1 to 5 of this annual collection of review articles, published in English (except for very unusual exceptions), were edited by C.H. Werkman. Succeeding volumes were edited by F.F. Nord. The series is published by Interscience Publishers, New York.

Title	Author	Reference
Protein structure	H.B. Bull	1, 1-42 (1941)
Vitamin K, its chemistry and physiology	H. Dam	2, 285-324 (1942)
The chemistry of glycogen	K.H. Meyer	3, 109-135 (1943)
The chemistry and biochemistry of pantothenic acid	R.J. Williams	3, 253-287 (1943)
The chemistry and biochemistry of biotin	K. Hofmann	3, 289-313 (1943)
Photochemistry of enzymes, proteins and viruses	A.D. McLaren	9, 75-170 (1949)
Chemistry and enzymology of nucleic acid	F. Schlenk	9, 455-535 (1949)
Chemical investigations of alliin, the specific principle of garlic	A. Stoll and E. Seebeck	11, 377-400 (1951)
The present status of starch chemistry	K.H. Meyer and G.C. Gibbons	12, 341-377 (1951)
Reaction of borate with substances of biological interest	C.A. Zittle	12, 493-527 (1951)
The structure of coenzyme A	J. Baddiley	16, 1-21 (1955)
Activation of amino acids (in German)	Th. Wieland and G. Pfleiderer	19, 235-266 (1957)
The chemistry and function of lipoic acid	L.J. Reed	18, 319-347 (1957)
Lignification	W.J. Schubert and F.F. Nord	18, 349-378 (1957)
Pectic substances and pectic enzymes	H. Deuel and E. Stutz	20, 341-382 (1958)
Folic acid coenzymes and one-carbon metabolism	F.M. Huennekens and M.J. Osborn	21, 370-446 (1959)
The synthesis of nucleotide coenzymes	J. Baddiley and N.A. Hughes	22, 157-204 (1960)

ADVANCES IN INORGANIC CHEMISTRY AND RADIOCHEMISTRY

Annual collection of review articles, in English
Edited by H.J. Eméléus and A.G. Sharpe, Academic Press, New York

Title	Author	Reference
Compounds of aromatic ring systems and metals	E.O. Fischer and H.P. Fritz	*1*, 55-115 (1959)
Phosphonitrilic halides and their derivatives	N.L. Paddok and H.T. Searle	*1*, 348-382 (1959)
Organometallic compounds	J. Eisch and H. Gilman	*2*, 61-103 (1960)
Fluorine-containing compounds of sulfur	G.H. Cady	*2*, 105-157 (1960)
Amides and imides of the oxyacids of sulfur	M. Becke-Goehring	*2*, 159-193 (1960)
Structures of compounds containing chains of sulfur atoms	O. Foss	*2*, 237-278 (1960)

ADVANCES IN ORGANIC CHEMISTRY METHODS AND RESULTS

Collection of review articles, in English. Edited by R.A. Raphael, E.C. Taylor and H. Wynberg. Interscience Publishers, New York.

Title	Author	Reference
The Kolbe electrolytic synthesis	B.C.L. Weedon	*1*, 1-34 (1960)
Polyphosphoric acid as a reagent in organic chemistry	F. Uhlig and H.R. Snyder	*1*, 35-81 (1960)
The Wittig reaction	S. Trippett	*1*, 83-102 (1960)
Hydroxylation methods	F.D. Gunstone	*1*, 103-148 (1960)
The selective degradation of proteins	E.O.P. Thompson	*1*, 149-238 (1960)
Optical rotatory dispersion and the study of organic structures	W. Klyne	*1*, 239-348 (1960)
Alkenylmagnesium halides	H. Normant	*2*, 1-65 (1960)
Dialkoxydihydrofurans and diacyloxydihydrofurans as synthetic intermediates	N. Elming	*2*, 67-115 (1960)
Ethynyl ethers and thioethers as synthetic intermediates	J.F. Arens	*2*, 117-212 (1960)
Ketene in organic synthesis	R.N. Lacey	*2*, 213-263 (1960)
Nuclear magnetic resonance in organic structural elucidation	H. Conroy	*2*, 265-328 (1960)
Hydrogenation-dehydrogenation reactions	L.M. Jackman	*2*, 329-366 (1960)
Ultraviolet photochemistry of simple unsaturated systems	P. de Mayo	*2*, 367-425 (1960)
The chemistry of muscarine	C.H. Eugster	*2*, 427-455 (1960)

These volumes appear annually and include review articles written in English. Volumes 1-5 were edited by M.L. Anson and J.T. Edsall, Volume 6 by M.L. Anson, J.T. Edsall and K. Bailey and Volumes 7 to 11 by M.L. Anson, K. Bailey and J.T. Edsall. Volumes 12 to the latest one were edited by C.B. Alfinsen, Jr., M.L. Anson, K. Bailey and J.T. Edsall. The publisher is Academic Press Inc., New York.

Title	Author	Reference
Lipoproteins	E. Chargaff	<u>1</u>, 1-24 (1944)
Structural proteins of cells and tissues	F.O. Schmitt	<u>1</u>, 25-68 (1944)
The interaction between the alkali earth cations, particularly calcium, and proteins	D.M. Greenberg	<u>1</u>, 121-151 (1944)
The purification and properties of certain protein hormones	B.F. Chow	<u>1</u>, 153-185 (1944)
Nucleoproteins	J.P. Greenstein	<u>1</u>, 209-287 (1944)
Analytical chemistry of the proteins	A.J.P. Martin and R.L.M. Synge	<u>2</u>, 1-83 (1945)
The amino acid composition of food proteins	R.J. Block	<u>2</u>, 119-134 (1945)
Terminal amino acids in peptides and proteins	S.W. Fox	<u>2</u>, 156-177 (1945)
The copper proteins	C.R. Dawson and M.F. Mallette	<u>2</u>, 179-248 (1945)
Mucoids and glycoproteins	K. Meyer	<u>2</u>, 249-277 (1945)
The reactions of formaldehyde with amino acids and proteins	D. French and J.T. Edsall	<u>2</u>, 277-335 (1945)
Protein denaturation and properties of protein groups	M.L. Anson	<u>2</u>, 361-386 (1945)
X-ray diffraction and protein structure	I. Fankuchen	<u>2</u>, 387-405 (1945)
Ferritin and apoferritin	L. Michaelis	<u>3</u>, 53-66 (1947)
Adsorption analysis of amino acid mixtures	A. Tiselius	<u>3</u>, 67-93 (1947)
The chemical determination of proteins	P.L. Kirk	<u>3</u>, 139-167 (1947)
Reactions of native proteins with chemical reagents	R.M. Herriott	<u>3</u>, 169-225 (1947)
The preparation and criteria of purity of the amino acids	M.S. Dunn and L.B. Rockland	<u>3</u>, 295-382 (1947)
The plasma proteins and their fractionation	J.T. Edsall	<u>3</u>, 383-479 (1947)
The interactions of proteins and synthetic detergents	F.W. Putnam	<u>4</u>, 79-122 (1948)
Preparative electrophoresis and ionophoresis	H. Svensson	<u>4</u>, 251-295 (1948)
Stereochemistry of amino acids	A. Neuberger	<u>4</u>, 297-383 (1948)
X-ray studies of amino acids and peptides	R.B. Corey	<u>4</u>, 385-406 (1948)
Heme proteins	J. Wyman Jr.	<u>4</u>, 407-531 (1948)
The synthesis of peptides	J.S. Fruton	<u>5</u>, 1-82 (1949)
Amino acid composition of purified proteins	G.R. Tristram	<u>5</u>, 83-153 (1949)
Synthetic fibers made from protein	H.P. Lundgren	<u>5</u>, 305-351 (1949)
Some protein-chemical aspects of tanning processes	K.H. Gustavson	<u>5</u>, 353-421 (1949)
Proteins, lipids and nucleic acids in cell structures and functions	A. Claude	<u>5</u>, 423-440 (1949)
Poly-α-amino acids	E. Katchalski	<u>6</u>, 123-185 (1951)

Title	Author(s)	Volume, Pages (Year)
Natural and artificial iodoproteins	J. Roche and R. Michel	6, 253-297 (1951)
Cross linkages in protein chemistry	J. Bjorksten	6, 343-381 (1951)
The arrangement of amino acids in proteins	F. Sanger	7, 1-67 (1952)
Infrared analysis of the structure of amino acids, polypeptides and proteins	G.B.B.M. Sutherland	7, 291-318 (1952)
Ultraviolet absorption spectra of proteins and amino acids	G.H. Beaven and E.R. Holiday	7, 319-386 (1952)
Naturally occurring peptides	E. Bricas and C. Fromageot	8, 4-125 (1953)
Peptide bond formation	H. Borsook	8, 127-174 (1953)
Peanut protein, isolation, composition and properties	J.C. Arthur Jr.	8, 393-414 (1953)
Zone electrophoresis	A. Tiselius and P. Flodin	8, 461-486 (1953)
Resolution of racemic α-amino acids	J.P. Greenstein	9, 121-202 (1954)
Formation, composition and properties of keratins	W.H. Ward and H.P. Lundgren	9, 243-297 (1954)
Molecular structure of simple substances related to the proteins	S.I. Mizushima	9, 299-324 (1954)
Protein-protein interaction	D.F. Waugh	9, 325-437 (1954)
Nature of phosphorus linkages in phosphoproteins	G.E. Perlmann	10, 1-30 (1955)
Zinc and metalloenzymes	B.L. Vallee	10, 317-384 (1955)
Protein structure in relation to function and biosynthesis	C.B. Anfinsen and R.R. Redfield	11, 1-100 (1956)
Hormones of the anterior pituitary gland. Part I. Growth and adrenocorticotropic hormones	C.H. Li	11, 101-190 (1956)
Column chromatography of peptides and proteins	S. Moore and W.H. Stein	11, 191-236 (1956)
Countercurrent distribution in protein chemistry	P. von Tavel and R. Signer	11, 238-308 (1956)
Complex formation between metallic cations and proteins, peptides, and amino acids	F.R.N. Gurd and P.E. Wilcox	11, 311-427 (1956)
Measurement and interpretation of diffusion coefficients of proteins	L.J. Gosting	11, 429-554 (1956)
X-ray analysis and protein structure	F.H.C. Crick and J.C. Kendrew	12, 133-214 (1957)
Hormones of the anterior pituitary gland. Part II. Melanocyte-stimulating and lactogenic hormones	C.H. Li	12, 269-317 (1957)
The chemical nature of antibodies	H.C. Isliker	12, 387-463 (1957)
The synthesis of peptides	M. Goodman and G.W. Kenner	12, 465-638 (1957)
Protein-carbohydrate complexes	F.R. Bettelheim-Jevons	13, 36-105 (1958)
The silk fibroins	F. Lucas, J.T.B. Shaw and S.G. Smith	13, 107-242 (1958)
Synthesis and chemical properties of poly-α-amino acids	E. Katchalski and M. Sela	13, 244-475 (1958)
Some factors in the interpretation of protein denaturation	W. Kauzmann	14, 1-63 (1959)

ADVANCES IN PROTEIN CHEMISTRY (Contd.)

Title	Author	Reference
Zone electrophoresis in starch gels and its application to studies of serum proteins	O. Smithies	14, 65-113 (1959)
The specificity of protein biosynthesis	M. Vaughan and D. Steinberg	14, 115-173 (1959)
Structural aspects of tobacco mosaic virus	H. Fraenkel-Conrat and L.K. Ramachandran	14, 175-229 (1959)
The sulfur chemistry of proteins	R. Cecil and G.R. McPhee	14, 255-389 (1959)
Protamines	K. Felix	15, 1-56 (1960)

ADVANCES IN SPECTROSCOPY

Annual collection of review articles, in English. Edited by A.W. Thompson, Interscience Publishers, New York.

Title	Author	Reference
The infrared spectra of polymers	A. Elliot	1, 214-287 (1959)
Rotational isomerism about C-C bonds in saturated molecules as studied by vibrational spectroscopy	N. Sheppard	1, 288-353 (1959)

THE ANALYST

This journal appears monthly and has included review articles since 1955. It has been published since 1876 under the auspices of the Society of Public Analysts and other analytical chemists. The present name of the Society was adopted in 1954.

Title	Author	Reference
Zone electrophoresis on filter-paper	L.F.J. Parker	80, 637-651 (1955)
The development of polarographic analysis	J. Heyrovský	81, 189-192 (1956)
The investigation of various chemical systems by electron-spin resonance	D.J.E. Ingram	81, 681-687 (1956)
The determination of 17-oxo steroids (17-keto steroids) and 17-oxogenic steroids (17-ketogenic steroids)	A.E. Kellie	82, 722-734 (1957)
Recent advances in the preparation and uses of ion-exchange resins	D.K. Hale	83, 3-9 (1958)
The analysis of synthetic detergents	W.B. Smith	84, 77-89 (1959)
The infra-red analysis of solid substances	G. Duyckaerts	84, 201-214 (1959)
Gas chromatography and its analytical applications	B.A. Rose	84, 574-595 (1959)
Light-scattering methods for the chemical characterization of polymers	F.W. Peaker	85, 235-244 (1960)
The determination of vitamin B_{12}	W.H.C. Shaw and C.J. Bessell	85, 389-409 (1960)
Analysis of organo-silicon compounds, with special reference to silanes and siloxanes	J.C.B. Smith	85, 465-474 (1960)
The changing aspect of chemical analysis	H.N. Wilson	85, 540-550 (1960)

Edited by Gesellschaft Deutscher Chemiker; Verlag Chemie GMBH, Weinheim. This journal appears bimonthly, publishes both review articles and short preliminary communications, all in German. Angewandte Chemie was originally called Zeitschrift fur Angewandte Chemie (1890-1931). From 1932 - 1941 it was named Angewandte Chemie, but during 1942-1945 "Die Chemie". No volume appeared in 1946. Since 1947 the current name has again applied.

Title	Author	Reference
Substitution, addition and elimination	W. Hückel	53, 49-54 (1940)
Progress in coal-tar research in the last thirty years	O. Kruber	53, 69-74 (1940)
Structure of internal complex salts	P. Pfeiffer	53, 93-98 (1940)
Synthetic estrogens	F. Wessely	53, 197-202 (1940)
New methods of preparative organic chemistry. 1. Syntheses with organo-lithium compounds	G. Wittig	53, 241-247 (1940)
New methods of preparative organic chemistry. 2. Meerwein-Ponndorf reductions and Oppenauer oxidations	Th. Bersin	53, 266-271 (1940)
New methods of preparative organic chemistry. 3. Oxidations with lead tetraacetate and periodic acid	R. Criegee	53, 321-326 (1940)
New methods of preparative organic chemistry. 4. The chromatographic adsorption	H. Brockmann	53, 385-390 (1940)
Bile-dyes	W. Siedel	53, 397-403 (1940)
New methods of preparative organic chemistry. 5. Fluorination of organic compounds	W. Bockemüller	53, 419-424 (1940)
Progress in microchemistry. 1. Quantitative organic microanalysis	H. Roth	53, 441-449 (1940)
New methods of preparative organic chemistry. 6. The use of biological oxidations and reductions for preparative purposes	F.G. Fischer	53, 461-471 (1940)
Transformation of steroids into aromatic compounds	H.H. Inhoffen	53, 471-475 (1940)
New methods of preparative organic chemistry. 8. New procedures of purification of proteins	G. Schramm	54, 7-19 (1941)
Pantothenic acid	J. Mittermaier	54, 51-55 (1941)
New methods of preparative organic chemistry. 9. Substitution on aliphatic compounds	J. Nelles	54, 77-85 (1941)
New methods of preparative organic chemistry. 10. Syntheses with diazomethane	B. Eistert	54, 99-105 (1941) 121-131 55, 118-121 (1942)
New methods of preparative organic chemistry. 11. Oxidations with selenium oxide	G. Stein	54, 146-152 (1941)
Organic thiocyanogen compounds	H.P. Kaufmann	54, 168-169 (1941)
New methods of preparative organic chemistry. 12. Methods of thiocyanation of organic compounds	H.P. Kaufmann	54, 195-199 (1941)
New methods of preparative organic chemistry. 13. Hydrogenation with Raney-catalysts	R. Schröter	54, 229-234 (1941) 252-260
New methods of preparative organic chemistry. 14. Boron fluoride as catalyst of chemical reactions	D. Kästner	54, 273-281 (1941) 296-304
Furfural	A.v. Wacek	54, 453-458 (1941)
Formation and structure of phenoplasts	H. von Euler	54, 458-461 (1941)

New methods of preparative organic chemistry. 15. Hydrogenation with copper-chromium oxide catalysts	Ch. Grundmann	54, 469-474 (1941)
New methods of preparative organic chemistry. 16. The diene synthesis	K. Alder	55, 53-58 (1942)
New research on arrow poisons	B. Witkop	55, 85-97 (1942)
New methods of preparative organic chemistry. 17. Dehydrogenation with sulfur, selenium and platinum metals	Pl. A. Plattner	55, 131-137 (1942) 154-158
Deamination, amination and transamination	Th. Wieland	55, 147-151 (1942)
Direct introduction of a sulfo-group into aliphatic compounds with the help of chlorine-sulfur dioxide mixtures and of sulfuryl chloride	J. H. Helberger	55, 172-174 (1942)
New objectives in terpene chemistry	W. Hückel	55, 227-232 (1942)
Phthalocyanine dyes	A. Sander	55, 255-260 (1942)
Azulenes	H. Arnold	56, 7-10 (1943)
Toad venoms	H. Behringer	56, 83-90 (1943)
Formation and degradation of biogenic amines	E. Werle	56, 141-148 (1943)
Advances in the chemistry of pyrroles	W. Siedel	56, 169-174 (1943) 185-190
The utilization of lower aliphatic hydrocarbons	C. T. Kautter	56, 225-230 (1943)
Inositols	T. Ploetz	56, 231-233 (1943)
On the pigments of butterflies	R. Purrmann	56, 253-258 (1943)
The alkaloids of the indole group	B. Witkop	56, 265-271 (1943)
The relation between constitution, reactivity and color of aromatic hydrocarbons	E. Clar	56, 293-300 (1943)
New methods of preparative organic chemistry. II. The use of hydrogen fluoride for organic chemistry reactions	K. Wiechert	56, 333-342 (1943)
Isomorphism and miscibilities of typical organic substances	A. Neuhaus	57, 33-40 (1944)
Mixed crystals and spatial structure of organic compounds	J. Pirsch	57, 40-43 (1944)
Chemistry and biology of hydroxy-amino acids	L. Birkofer	57, 135-139 (1944)
Regularities in the steric development of catalytic hydrogenation	H. A. Weidlich	58, 30-34 (1945)
Synthesis of higher aliphatic compounds	Th. A. Lennartz	59, 10-16 (1947) 49-55 77-82
Folic acid, a new active principle in the vitamin-B group	R. Tschesche	59, 65-68 (1947)
Modern moth repellants	H. Stötter	59, 145-150 (1947)
Synthetic medicinals with morphine activity	R. Grewe	59, 194-199 (1947)
The pathway from cholesterol to estradiol	H. H. Inhoffen	59, 207-212 (1947)
Synthesis of models for unsaturated steroids of the ergosterin type	K. Dimroth	59, 215-218 (1947)
On the constitution of colchicines	H. Lettré	59, 218-224 (1947)
Plant heart-venoms	R. Tschesche	59, 224-227 (1947)
Polyurethane resins (di-isocyanate addition reactions)	O. Bayer	59, 257-272 (1947)
Review on attempted synthesis of rotenoids and pyrethrins	H. A. Offe	60, 9-14 (1948)
Progress in the field of sensitizing dyes for photographic halogen-silver emulsions	K. Kainrath	60, 36-42 (1948)

Title	Author(s)	Citation
The condensation of aromatic compounds with formaldehyde. A new group of reactive formaldehyde resins	R. Wegler	60, 88-96 (1948)
New sulfur-containing chemotherapeutics	R. Behnisch F. Mietzsch and H. Schmidt	60, 113-115 (1948)
Cellulose chemistry III	F. Schütz P. Sarten and H. Meyer	60, 115-125 (1948)
The constitution of sulfur dyes	W. Zerweck H. Ritter and M. Schubert	60, 141-147 (1948)
The autoxidation of aldehydes and their inhibition	G. Wittig	60, 169-173 (1948)
Fundamental reactions of phenol resin formation	K. Hultzsch	60, 179-184 (1948)
Further developments in the chemotherapy of antimony compounds (Solustibosan)	H. Schmidt	60, 261-263 (1948)
Vinylacetylene	A. Treibs	60, 289-297 (1948)
The imidazole group	W. Langenbeck	60, 297-299 (1948)
Prediction of rules in the substitution reactions of substituted benzenes and pyridines	F. Seel	60, 300-305 (1948)
New syntheses of sulfur-containing amino acids	A. Schöberl	60, 308-311 (1948)
Reactions of heterocyclic compounds with reactive methylene groups	M. Coenen	61, 11-17 (1949)
Malaria and synthetic malaria remedies	A. Wingler	61, 49-54 (1949)
Half century of ionic reactions in organic chemistry	G. Hesse	61, 161-168 (1949)
Twenty-five years of "Contributions to the chemistry of trivalent carbon"	K. Ziegler	61, 168-179 (1949)
The action of diazonium salts on unsaturated aliphatic compounds. Extension of the Meerwein reaction	E. Müller	61, 179-183 (1949)
The chemistry of acrylonitrile	O. Bayer	61, 229-241 (1949)
The syntheses of tryptophane	H. Hellmann	61, 352-357 (1949)
Problems of the precise structures of heterocyclic oxo-compounds	F. Arndt	61, 397-400 (1949)
Constitution and vitamin A activity	F. Bohlmann	62, 4-7 (1950)
Synthesis and transformation products of acroleins	H. Schulz and H. Wagner	62, 105-118 (1950)
P. Pfeiffer's contribution to the development of complex chemistry	R. Wizinger-Aust	62, 201-205 (1950)
Complex compounds as catalysts in preparative organic chemistry	G. Hesse	62, 237-241 (1950)
Inner complex formation in dye chemistry	H. Pfitzner	62, 242-246 (1950)
The present state of research in the field of azulenes	H. Pommer	62, 281-289 (1950)
New urea-addition products	W. Schlenk	62, 299-301 (1949)
Introduction of sulfo-groups into alkanes by means of SO_2 and oxygen (Sulfoxydation)	L. Orthner	62, 302-305 (1949)
Phospho-organic compounds as new insecticides	G. Schrader	62, 471-473 (1950)
Steric hindrance and cis-trans isomerism in the diene reactions of conjugated unsaturated fatty acids.	J.D. von Mikusch	62, 475-480 (1950)
Strychnos alkaloids. A survey of half a century of alkaloid research	R. Huisgen	62, 527-534 (1950)
Chemistry and technology of nitroalkanes	O. von Schickh	62, 547-556 (1950)
Peptide synthesis	Th. Wieland	63, 7-14 (1951)
Ylides and ylid-reactions	G. Wittig	63, 15-18 (1951)

The stereochemistry of natural steroids	A. Heusner	63,	59-70 (1951)
The present status of phenol resin chemistry	K. Hultzsch	63,	168-171 (1951)
Ultraviolet light absorption of proteins	H. Dannenberg	63,	208-217 (1951)
Ionic chain polymerization	K. Hamann	63,	231-240 (1951)
Chemotherapy of tuberculosis	F. Mietzsch	63,	250-258 (1951)
Aromatization reactions in the bile acid series and their possible relations to the cancer problem	H.H. Inhoffen	63,	297-300 (1951)
Molecular rearrangement of some tricentric systems of the hydrofuran and hydropyran series	R. Paul	63,	301-305 (1951)
The ultraviolet spectrum as a function of the constitution of organic compounds	F. Korte	63,	370-377 (1951)
The chemistry of glycosides possessing cardiac activity	T. Reichstein	63,	412-421 (1951)
Chemistry and biology of mitosis inhibitors	H. Lettré	63,	421-430 (1951)
Tropolone and its derivatives	G. Huber	63,	501-508 (1951)
Odor and constitution	F. Nerdel and I. Spaeth	63,	545-550 (1951)
Problems relating to synthetic photochemistry	G.O. Schenck	64,	12-23 (1952)
The complete synthesis of natural steroids	A. Mondon	64,	121-128 (1952)
The characteristics and the importance of free radicals	E. Müller	64,	233-247 (1952)
Aluminum-organic synthesis in the field of olefinic hydrocarbons	K. Ziegler	64,	323-329 (1952)
Formazans and tetrazolium salts, their syntheses and importance as reduction indicators and vital stains	W. Ried	64,	391-396 (1952)
Fundamental and critical remarks concerning the theory of the keto-enol conversion	G. Briegleb and W. Strohmeier	64,	409-417 (1952)
Inclusion compounds	F. Cramer	64,	437-447 (1952)
Positive halogen	Ph. Fresenius	64,	470-478 (1952)
New highly elastic materials "Vulkollan". Part II.	E. Müller O. Bayer S. Petersen H.-F. Piepenbrink F. Schmidt and E. Weinbrenner	64,	523-531 (1952)
On the polymerization of unsaturated dioxolanes	H. Orth	64,	544-553 (1952)
Recent views on the structure of nucleic acids	A.R. Todd	65,	12-15 (1953)
Hyperconjugation	F. Becker	65,	97-107 (1953)
Theory and practice of the Sandmeyer reaction	E. Pfeil	65,	155-158 (1953)
Theory and fact in polymerization reactions	F. Patat	65,	173-178 (1953)
The historical development of the concept of mesomerism and biradicalism	E. Müller	65,	315-319 (1953)
The polyenes	F. Bohlmann	65,	385-389 (1953)
Configurations of cyclohexane substitution products having one to twelve mutually identical substituents	R. Riemschneider and P. Geschke	65,	390-392 (1953)
The chemistry of senecio-alkaloids and related compounds	R. Adams	65,	433-442 (1953)
Carbon-alkylation with tertiary amines and quaternary ammonium salts	H. Hellmann	65,	473-485 (1953)

Preparation of aldehydes from carboxylic acids	F. Weygand, G. Eberhardt, H. Linden, F. Schäfer and I. Eigen	65, 525-531 (1953)
Syntheses using pyridine salts	F. Kröhnke	65, 605-626 (1953)
Progress in the field of organic anionic chemistry	G. Wittig	66, 10-17 (1954)
Chemistry and technology of silicones	W. Noll	66, 41-55 (1954)
Ferment models and their relations to the incorporation compounds	W. Lautsch, W. Broser, W. Biedermann and H. Gnichtel	66, 123-135 (1954)
The chemistry of organic ring systems with urotropine structure	H. Stetter	66, 217-229 (1954)
Production and properties of polymers containing fluorine	G. Bier, R. Schäff and K.-H. Kahrs	66, 285-292 (1954)
Development work in the arsenic field	W. Herrmann and H. Hilmer	66, 349-359 (1954)
New derivatives of 1,2,4-triazine as tuberculostatics	R.E. Hagenbach, E. Hodel and H. Gysin	66, 359-363 (1954)
The development of antihistamines and centrally damping preparations	F. Mietzsch	66, 363-371 (1954)
Recent investigations of natural and synthetic tropane derivatives	A. Stoll and E. Jucker	66, 376-386 (1954)
The rauwolfia alkaloids	E. Schlittler, J.A. Schneider and A.J. Plummer	66, 386-390 (1954)
The history of the development of naphthol-AS dyes	W. Kirst and W. Neumann	66, 429-434 (1954)
Polyphosphoric acid - a new cyclization agent in preparative organic chemistry	F. Uhlig	66, 435-436 (1954)
Peptide syntheses II	Th. Wieland	66, 507-512 (1954)
Peroxide derivatives of acetaldehyde	J. D'Ans, K. Dossow and S. Mattner	66, 633-635 (1954)
Radicals, quasi radicals, meriquinoid compounds and quinhydrone. A contribution to color theory	E. Weitz	66, 658-677 (1954)
The development of the concept of quinhydrone and quinhydrone-like compounds	R. Kuhn	66, 678-679 (1954)
Recent chemistry of fluorine. Organometallic and organometalloid compounds of fluorine	R.N. Haszeldine	66, 693-701 (1954)
150 years of morphine and 15 years of synthetic analgesics having effects similar to morphine	O. Schaumann	66, 765-768 (1954)
Some problems of polymerization kinetics	P.D. Bartlett	67, 45-52 (1955)
Production and properties of several block and branch mixed polymers	H. Mark	67, 53-56 (1955)
Chemical transformations of high polymer substances	G. Smets	67, 57-60 (1955)
Phenolic disinfectants with several halogenated benzene nuclei	D. Jerchel and H. Oberheiden	67, 145-153 (1955)
Synthesis of simple quinone derivatives with fungicidal, bacteriostatic or cytostatic properties	S. Petersen, W. Gauss and E. Urbschat	67, 217-231 (1955)

ANGEWANDTE CHEMIE (Contd.)

Title	Author(s)	Citation
Modern structural chemistry. Nobel Lecture 1954	L. Pauling	67, 241-244 (1955)
Rapid methods in the organic microanalytical laboratory	W. Schöniger	67, 261-265 (1955)
Nitration of saturated hydrocarbons with nitrogen dioxide in the liquid phase	G. Geiseler	67, 270-273 (1955)
Recent developments in furan chemistry	G.-H. Schmidt	67, 317-326 (1955)
Recent studies on curare - especially on Calabash curare - and on alkaloids from barks of strychnos trees	P. Karrer and H. Schmid	67, 361-373 (1955)
Organic ionic reactions	H. Meerwein	67, 374-380 (1955)
New amino acids and keto acids in green plants, and the biosynthesis of amino acids	A.I. Virtanen	67, 381-388 (1955)
Naturally occurring polyacetylene compounds	F. Bohlmann	67, 389-394 (1955)
New methods of preparative organic chemistry II. 1. Syntheses with acetoacetic aldehyde	W. Franke and R. Kraft	67, 395-399 (1955)
Recent ideas on the nature of heterogeneous catalysis	G.-M. Schwab	67, 433-438 (1955)
Established facts and recent information on aliphatic diazo compounds	R. Huisgen	67, 439-463 (1955)
N-substituted amides of the phosphorus and phosphoric acids and their application in the building of peptide bonds	S. Goldschmidt and H.L. Krauss	67, 471-475 (1955)
Metallic compounds of cyclopentadiene and indene	E.O. Fischer	67, 475-482 (1955)
Bridge reactions in the case of amino acids and fiber proteins	H. Zahn	67, 561-572 (1955)
The catalysis of the autoxidation of unsaturated compounds	W. Kern and H. Willersinn	67, 573-581 (1955)
Chemistry of the polyepoxides	R. Wegler	67, 582-592 (1955)
Purification of hydrocarbons as solvents for ultraviolet spectroscopy	G. Hesse and H. Schildknecht	67, 737-739 (1955)
Purification of solvents for spectroscopic work Part II.	M. Pestemer	67, 740-741 (1955)
New methods of preparative organic chemistry. II. 2. Production of long chain carboxylic acids starting with cyclohexane-1,3-diones	H. Stetter	67, 769-784 (1955)
Recent developments in the chemistry of natural substances	R.B. Woodward	68, 13-20 (1956)
Lignin within the group of polymeric natural substances	K. Freudenberg	68, 84-92 (1956)
Natural tannins	O.Th. Schmidt and W. Mayer	68, 103-115 (1956)
Inclusion compounds	F. Cramer	68, 115-120 (1956)
Isoindolenines as intermediate products of the phthalocyanin synthesis	F. Baumann B. Bienert G. Rösch H. Vollmann and W. Wolf	68, 133-150 (1956)
Spectroscopic studies of simple unsaturated ketones	R. Mecke and K. Noack	68, 150-151 (1956)
New methods of preparative organic chemistry. II. 3. The preparative importance of cyclopentanone o-carboxylic acid ester	R. Mayer	68, 169-174 (1956)
New developments in furane chemistry	C.H. Schmidt	68, 175-176 (1956)
Recent developments in the chemistry of porphin dyes	K. Zeile	68, 193-201 (1956)

Oligomers of polyamides and polyesters	H. Zahn et. al.,	68,	229-238 (1956)
Aminomethylation. Interpretation and classification of the Mannich reaction	H. Hellmann and G. Opitz	68,	265-272 (1956)
New natural amino acids	H. Musso	68,	313-323 (1956)
Chemistry and biochemistry of neuraminic acid	E. Klenk	68,	349-352 (1956)
New methods of preparative organic chemistry. II. 4. Ketene in preparative organic chemistry	G. Quadbeck	68,	361-370 (1956)
Stereospecific catalyses and isotactic polymers	G. Natta	68,	393-403 (1956)
The chemistry of acyl cyanides	J. Thesing and D. Witzel	68,	425-435 (1956)
New methods of preparative organic chemistry. II. 5. The Preparative and analytical importance of tertiary phosphines and related compounds	L. Horner and H. Hoffmann	68,	473-485 (1956)
On the quantitative determination of organic peroxides. Part II. Testing of the methylene blue method	G. Sorge and K. Ueberreiter	68,	486-491 (1956)
Origin and development of phosphine alkylene chemistry	G. Wittig	68,	505-508 (1956)
Contributions to lignin research	K. Freudenberg	68,	508-512 (1956)
Vitamin A and the carotinoids	O. Isler	68,	547-553 (1956)
Chemistry and physiology of biogenic zinc compounds	G. Weitzel	68,	566-573 (1956)
New methods of preparative organic chemistry. II. 6. Reduction of carbonyl compounds by complex hydrides	H. Hörmann	68,	601-604 (1956)
Polycarbonates, a group of new types of thermoplasts (production and properties of aromatic polyesters of carbonic acid)	H. Schnell	68,	633-640 (1956)
The tropylium ion	W.v.E. Doering and H. Krauch	68,	661-667 (1956)
New developments in organometallic synthesis	K. Ziegler	68,	721-729 (1956)
Electronic and nuclear resonance as a method for molecular research	K.H. Hausser	68,	729-746 (1956)
The development of the chemistry of the ergot alkaloids	S.Cl. Schopf	69,	1-5 (1957)
New developments in the chemistry of pyrrolizidine alkaloids	R. Adams and M. Gianturco	69,	5-16 (1957)
Ommochromes, a class of natural phenoxazone dyestuffs	A. Butenandt	69,	16-23 (1957)
Amino sugars	R. Kuhn	69,	23-33 (1957)
Aromatic erthrina alkaloids	V. Prelog	69,	33-39 (1957)
The chemistry of ajmalin	R. Robinson	69,	40-44 (1957)
The toxic agents of the death cup	Th. Wieland	69,	44-50 (1957)
Structure and biogenesis of the macrolides	R.B. Woodward	69,	50-58 (1957)
Structure and reactivity of the acetylene linkage	F. Bohlmann	69,	82-86 (1957)
New methods of preparative organic chemistry. II. 7. Alkylation of aromatic amines	R. Stroh J. Ebersberger H. Haberland and W. Hahn	69,	124-131 (1957)
Short-lived radicals as intermediate products	S. Goldschmidt	69,	132-135 (1957)
Synthetic macromolecular substances with reactive groups	W. Kern and R.C. Schulz	69,	153-171 (1957)
Paper chromatography of polynuclear aromatic substances	Th. Wieland and W. Kracht	69,	172-174 (1957)
Determination of the constitution of peptides and proteins	G. Braunitzer	69,	189-197 (1957)

Title	Author(s)	Citation
Kinetics of stereospecific polymerization of propene to isotactic polymers	G. Natta, I. Pasquon and E. Giachetti	69, 213-219 (1957)
Modes of formation and reactions of benzyne (cyclohexadiene-yne)	G. Wittig	69, 245-251 (1957)
Further investigations of ethyleneiminoquinones and related compounds	W. Gauss and S. Petersen	69, 252-257 (1957)
Spectroscopic analysis of saturated hydrocarbons	H. Luther and H. Oelert	69, 262-266 (1957)
Autoxidation of hydrocarbons and the phenol synthesis via cumene	H. Hock and H. Kropf	69, 313-321 (1957)
New knowledge about carbon radicals	W. Theilacker et. al.	69, 322-333 (1957)
New contributions to the chemistry of medium-sized rings	R. Huisgen	69, 341-359 (1957)
Peptide syntheses, Part III	Th. Wieland and B. Heincke	69, 362-371 (1957)
Lactone acetals, a new class of carboxyl derivatives	R. Kuhn and D. Weiser	69, 371-376 (1957)
Chemical syntheses of intermediate products of sugar metabolism	H.O.L. Fischer	69, 413-419 (1957)
Contributions to the chemistry of starch and cycloglucanes (Schardinger dextrins)	K. Freudenberg	69, 419-422 (1957)
Progress in the field of oligosaccharides	M.G. Blair and W. Pigman	69, 422-433 (1957)
Amidomethylations	H. Hellmann	69, 463-471 (1957)
Organic complex compounds of molybdenum	G. Spengler and J. Gänsheimer	69, 523-529 (1957)
Tasks and possibilities of preparative radiation chemistry	G.O. Schenck	69, 579-599 (1957)
New methods of preparative organic chemistry. II. 8. Selective catalytic oxidations by means of noble metal catalysts	K. Heyns and H. Paulsen	69, 600-608 (1957)
New methods of preparative organic chemistry. II. 10. Alkylation of phenols by olefins	R. Stroh, R. Seydel and W. Hahn	69, 699-706 (1957)
Some problems of chain reactions and combustion theory	N.N. Semenov	69, 767-777 (1957)
Synthesis of di- and tricarboxylic acids of aromatic ring systems by shifting of carboxylic groups	B. Raecke	70, 1-5 (1958)
Pyridazines in drug synthesis	J. Druey	70, 5-13 (1958)
Thermochromic, piezochromic, photochromic and photomagnetic phenomena	G. Kortijm	70, 14-20 (1958)
One hundred years of organic structural chemistry	H.A. Staab	70, 37-41 (1958)
Formation of complexes and reactivity in metal-organic chemistry	G. Wittig	70, 65-71 (1958)
Studies of transannular eliminations and substitutions by means of isotopes	V. Prelog	70, 145-150 (1958)
Stereochemical considerations on reactions of alkali-organic compounds	R.L. Letsinger	70, 151-154 (1958)
Recent investigations on oxidations by means of lead tetraacetate	R. Criegee	70, 173-179 (1958)
Kinetic isotope effects and their application in the investigation of azo couplings	H. Zollinger	70, 204-210 (1958)
The reduction of aromatic diazo compounds by means of ethers, 1,3-dioxolanes and tertiary amines	H. Meerwein et. al.,	70, 211-215 (1958)

Title	Authors	Citation
Heterocyclic azo dyes by oxidative coupling	S. Hünig et.al.,	70, 215-222 (1958)
Neutral dyeing tricyclic and pentacyclic pre-metallized azo dyestuffs	G. Schetty and H. Ackermann	70, 222-231 (1958)
Introduction of copper into o-hydroxy azo dyes by oxidation	H. Pfitzner and H. Baumann	70, 232-238 (1958)
Azo phosphonic acid esters	F. Suckfüll and H. Haubrich	70, 238-240 (1958)
Stability and decomposition products of diazotated aminoazobenzene	J. Ribka	70, 241-244 (1958)
Peroxides of ethers, carbonyl compounds, and ozonides	A. Rieche	70, 251-266 (1958)
Beilstein's Handbook - 75 years of organic chemical documentation	F. Richter	70, 279-284 (1958)
Recent results of organotin research	G.J.M. van der Kerk et.al.,	70, 298-306 (1958)
Mass spectrographic examinations of the reactions and properties of free radicals and atoms	H.D. Beckey	70, 327-339 (1958)
New methods of preparative organic chemistry. II. 11. Reactions of sulfur with araliphatic and aliphatic compounds	R. Wegler E. Kühle and W. Schaefer	70, 351-367 (1958)
Phenol-formaldehyde-condensates of defined constitution and uniform molecular size	H. Kämmerer	70, 390-398 (1958)
Recent results in azulene chemistry	K. Hafner	70, 419-430 (1958)
Neighbor group effects in organic chemistry	W. Lwowsky	70, 483-495 (1958)
Course of low pressure polymerization of α-olefins. Complex polymerization I.	F. Patat and Hj. Sinn	70, 496-500 (1958)
Studies in the field of nucleotide synthesis (Nobel lecture)	A. Todd	70, 527-531 (1958)
Synthesis and breakdown of cytostatically active N-phosphamide esters of the bis-(β-chloroethyl)-amine	H. Arnold and F. Bourseaux	70, 539-544 (1958)
Experimental transitions between tropane derivative and the group of tropilidenes, tropones and tropolones	A. Heusner	70, 639-644 (1958)
Recent results of the calabash-curare research	P. Karrer et.al.,	70, 644-645 (1958)
Simple syntheses and chemical behavior of recently discovered heterocyclic ring systems	F. Asinger and M. Thiel	70, 667-683 (1958)
The absolute configuration of atropisomeric diaryl compounds	K. Mislow	70, 683-689 (1958)
Tetraalkyl-monothiopyrophosphates. Their preparation and properties	G. Schrader W. Lorenz and R. Mühlmann	70, 690-694 (1958)
New methods of preparative organic chemistry. II. 12. Introduction of substituents into the pyridine ring	K. Thomas and D. Jerchel	70, 719-737 (1958)
Vitamin K_1 and K_2	O. Isler	71, 7-15 (1959)
Chemical action of ionizing rays	A. Henglein	71, 15-28 (1959)
Recent investigations concerning the electron gas model of organic dyestuffs	H. Kuhn	71, 93-101 (1959)
Advances in the high polymer field in the U.S.A.	S.M. Atlas and H. Mark	71, 110-119 (1959)
Developments and problems of organic macromolecules	O. Bayer	71, 145-152 (1959)
Catalytic reactions of olefins on platinum metal compounds	J. Smidt et.al.,	71, 176-182 (1959)
Stereospecific polymerization of vinyl ethers	G. Natta et.al.,	71, 205-210 (1959)

Title	Author	Citation
Photo nitrosation and oximation of saturated hydrocarbons	E. Müller et. al.,	71, 229-236 (1959)
Isotope labelling of organic compounds by neutron irradiation	A.P. Wolf	71, 237-243 (1959)
Development of carotenoid chemistry	E. Jucker	71, 253-259 (1959)
New methods of preparative organic chemistry. II. 13. Carbonyl-olefination by means of triphenyl phosphine methylenes. Wittig reaction	U. Schöllkopf	71, 260-273 (1959)
The reaction of fluorosilicates with some organic halides	J. Dahmlos	71, 274-276 (1959)
Measurement of ^{14}C and ^{3}H in the gas phase	H. Simon, H. Daniel and J.F. Klebe	71, 303-308 (1959)
New kinds of hydrazines with basic substituents, and their application in the synthesis of pharmaceuticals	E. Jucker	71, 321-333 (1959)
New methods of preparative organic chemistry. II. 14. N-bromosuccinimide, its properties and types of reaction	L. Horner and E.H. Winkelmann	71, 349-365 (1959)
Chemistry of di-α-halogeno ethers	H. Baganz	71, 366-371 (1959)
Chemical action of ionizing rays. 2. Nuclear radiation chemistry of hydrocarbons	A. Henglein	71, 393-401 (1959)
Chemistry of polypeptides. Syntheses of peptides. IV	Th. Wieland	71, 417-425 (1959)
^{14}C-labelled dyestuffs via benzene from ^{14}C-acetylene	H. Baddenhausen, H. Götte and L. Wiesner	71, 444-445 (1959)
Reactions with carbenes and imines as intermediates	W. Kirmse	71, 537-541 (1959)
The mechanism of autoxidation of organo-metallic compounds	H. Hock, H. Kropf and F. Ernst	71, 541-545 (1959)
Constitutional exactness in macromolecular chemistry	W. Kern	71, 585-589 (1959)
Correlations between the kinetics of elementary processes and the constitution of macromolecules in the field of radical polymerizations	G.V. Schulz	71, 590-595 (1959)
Structural investigation of three-dimensional cross-linked macromolecules by means of degradation reactions (Example: Cured polyester resins)	K. Hamann, W. Funke and H. Gilch	71, 596-603 (1959)
Organo-metallic titanium compounds as polymerization catalysts	C. Beermann and H. Bestian	71, 618-623 (1959)
Polymerization (of ethylene) by means of metal alkyls of the 1st to 3rd group	K. Ziegler	71, 623-625 (1959)
Synthesis of colchicine	J. Schreiber et. al.,	71, 637-640 (1959)
New methods of preparative organic chemistry. II. 15. The acyl-lactone rearrangement for preparation of heterocyclic systems	F. Korte and K.H. Büchel	71, 709-722 (1959)
The mechanism of the Clemmensen reduction	D. Staschewski	71, 726-736 (1959)
New methods of preparative organic chemistry. II. 16. Syntheses with acid amides, in particular with formamide	H. Bredereck et. al.,	71, 753-774 (1959)
Small carbon rings	E. Vogel	72, 4-26 (1960)
Complex acetylides of transition metals	R. Nast	72, 26-31 (1960)
Coupled reactions in the dyeing process	W. Luck	72, 57-70 (1960)
Neucleofugal and electrofugal escape	J. Mathieu, A. Allais and J. Valls	72, 71-74 (1960)
Syntheses using carbon monoxide	G.P. Chiusoli	72, 74-76 (1960)
Nucleophilic aromatic substitution via arines	R. Huisgen and J. Sauer	72, 91-108 (1960)

ANGEWANDTE CHEMIE (Contd.)

Syntheses with chloramine in organic chemistry	W. Theilacker and E. Wegner	72, 127-131 (1960)
Substitution at the bridgehead of bicyclic compounds	U. Schöllkopf	72, 147-159 (1960)
Chemical behavior and bonding of boron hydride derivatives	A.B. Burg	72, 183-193 (1960)
The mechanism of the formation of the metal-carbon bond and the reactivity of organometallic compounds of heavy metals	O.A. Reutow	72, 198-208 (1960)
The development of the Diene synthesis (In memory of Kurt Alder)	M. Günzl and W. Günzl	72, 219-224 (1960)
Preparation of esters, amides and anhydrides of phosphoric acid	F. Cramer	72, 236-249 (1960)
Thermally resistant polymers	S.M. Atlas and H.F. Mark	72, 249-255 (1960)
Nucleophilic aromatic substitutions via additive mechanisms	J. Sauer and R. Huisgen	72, 294-315 (1960)
Chemistry and fine-structure of natural silk	H. Spoor and K. Ziegler	72, 316-321 (1960)
Aromatic compounds from pyrylium salts	K. Dimroth	72, 331-342 (1960)
The chemistry of depsipeptides	M.M. Schemjakin	72, 342-345 1960
Thermal stability and aromatic character: Ring opening of azoles	R. Huisgen	72, 359-372 (1960)
Lipoids of mycobacteria	E. Lederer	72, 372-379 (1960)
Polymeric hydrocyanic acid	Th. Volker	72, 379-384 (1960)
The formation of the acetylene bond	W. Franke W. Ziegenbein and H. Meister	72, 291-400 (1960)
Electron transition by means of light absorption and emission in electron donator/acceptor complexes	G. Briegleb and J. Czekalla	72, 401-413 (1960)
Application of polarography in organic chemistry	H.W. Nurnberg	72, 433-449 (1960)
Fully automatic quantitative amino acid determination	G. Braunitzer	72, 485-489 (1960)
New facts about polycyclic aromatic hydrocarbons	M. Zander	72, 513-520 (1960)
Determination of sugars and related materials on glass fiber paper	G. Jayme and G. Hahn	72, 520-522 (1960)
Syntheses using diazo-ketones	F. Weygand and H.J. Bestmann	72, 535-554 (1960)
Reaction gas chromatography	F. Drawert and G. Kupfer	72, 555-559 (1960)
Chemical action of ionizing rays	A. Henglein	72, 603-611 (1960)
IR-Spectroscopic detection of the addition of catalytically active electron donators and acceptors to molecules with multiple bonds	M. Pestemer and D. Lauerer	72, 612-618 (1960)
The history of sterol and vitamin research (In memory of Adolf Windaus)	A. Butenandt	72, 645-651 (1960)
Total synthesis of chlorophyll	R.B. Woodward	72, 651-662 (1960)
Hydride complexes of the transition metals	M.L.H. Green	72, 719-725 (1960)
Recent results in the field of total synthesis of steroids	L. Velluz G. Nomine and J. Mathieu	72, 725-730 (1960)
Formation of terephthalate by rearrangement of carboxylic groups in an $^{14}CO_2$ atmosphere	O. Riedel and H. Kienitz	72, 738-740 (1960)
Termination in free radical reactions	S.J. Lapporte	72, 759-766 (1960)
Relationships between constitution and color of simple nitro dyestuffs	E. Merian	72, 766-770 (1960)

ANGEWANDTE CHEMIE (Contd.)

Alcohol synthesis according to W. Reppe	N. von Kutepow and H. Kindler	72, 802-805 (1960)
The gangliosides of brain	R. Kuhn et.al.,	72, 805-811 (1960)
Syntheses in the vitamin-A series	H. Pommer	72, 811-819 (1960)
Practical and theoretical aspects of organometallic synthesis of higher aliphatic compounds from lower olefins	K. Ziegler	72, 829-835 (1960)
Amide chlorides and carbamide chlorides	H. Eilingsfeld M. Seefelder and H. Weidinger	72, 836-845 (1960)
Contribution to the chemistry of antirachitic vitamins	H.H. Inhoffen	72, 875-881 (1960)
3,6-Didesoxyhexoses chemistry and biology	O. Westphal and O. Luderitz	72, 881-891 (1960)
Reactions and syntheses of some natural aminohydroxy acids	T. Wieland	72, 892-895 (1960)
Determination of definite conformations by means of X-rays and reactivity of medium rings	J.D. Dunitz and V. Prelog	72, 896-902 (1960)
Recent results of carotinoid research	A. Winterstein	72, 902-910 (1960)
Syntheses in the carotinoid series	H. Pommer	72, 911-915 (1960)
Synthesis of a nonadecapeptide showing high corticotropic activity	R. Schwyzer et.al.,	72, 915-917 (1960)
Polymerization of tetrahydrofuran	H. Meerwein D. Delfs and H. Morschel	72, 927-934 (1960)
The principle of synthesis of urethan elastomers; "Vulkollan"	O. Bayer and E. Müller	72, 934-939 (1960)
Actinomycines	H. Brockmann	72, 939-947 (1960)
Recent results in the vitamin-A series	K. Eiter E. Truscheit and H. Oediger	72, 948-955 (1960)
The reaction of cyanuric chloride with dimethyl formamide	H. Gold	72, 956-959 (1960)
Contribution to the knowledge of cycloammonium rearrangement	H. Henecka U. Horlein and K.H. Risse	72, 960-963 (1960)
Dicyano-dithia-cyclohexene, a new heterocyclic dinitrile for the preparation of phthalocyanines	W. Wolf E. Degener and S. Petersen	72, 963-966 (1960)
Ring splitting of azopyrazolones to form osazones and their oxidative coupling, with color developments	W. Pelz, et.al.,	72, 967-973 (1960)

ANNALES PHARMACEUTIQUES FRANCAISES

This is a monthly journal, in French. It is the official bulletin of the Societies of Pharmacy of Paris and the provinces. Published by Masson et Cie (Paris).

Title	Author	Reference
Chemical structure and pharmacodynamical activity of synthetic antihistamines	D. Bovet and F. Walthert	<u>2</u>, 1-43 (1944) (Suppl.)
Methionine	P. Gonnard	<u>5</u>, 18-333 (1947)
My work on methyl-pentoses	E. Votocek	<u>6</u>, 1-12 (1948)
Some aspects of chemotherapy	E. Fourneau	<u>6</u>, 25-44 (1948) 282-298 (1948)
Structure of vitamin A	J. Guy	<u>6</u>, 299-317 (1948)
Chemistry of curare and related substances	E. Fourneau and M. Janot	<u>7</u>, 353-368 (1949)
Flavonoids	R. Paris and L. Beauquejne	<u>8</u>, 65-76 (1950) 148-152 228-237 322-342
Main research in antimicrobial chemotherapy grouped around some basic concepts and hypothesis	A. Lespagnol	<u>10</u>, 127-151 (1952)
Vitamins B_{12}	R.C. Moreau	<u>10</u>, 224-233 (1952)
Evolution of chemotherapy of tuberculosis	Ch. Gansser	<u>12</u>, 146-155 (1954)
Chemical studies of lipoic acids (thioctic acid)	J.R. Bissier and J.F. Miquel	<u>13</u>, 143-148 (1955)
Research in chemotherapy. Relation between chemical constitution, tolerance and amebicidal activity	J. Trefouel	<u>15</u>, 127-135 (1957)
Derivatives of thiosemicarbazide in anti-tuberculous chemotherapy	M. Girard and M.J. Laroche	<u>15</u>, 556-577 (1957)
Study of the isolation and chemical structure of gibberelic acid	F. Percheron	<u>16</u>, 769-777 (1958)
Synthetic reserpines	L. Velluz	<u>17</u>, 15-25 (1959)
Aspects of the biology of digitalis and their chemical constitution	P. Duquenois	<u>17</u>, 634-647 (1959)
Present development of steroids	L. Velluz	<u>18</u>, 229-244 (1960)

ANNUAL REVIEW OF BIOCHEMISTRY

This is an annual collection of review articles, in English, published since 1932 by Annual Reviews, Inc. (Palo Alto). J.M. Luck is the editor.

Title	Author	Reference
Chemistry of the carbohydrates and glycosides	H.S. Isbell	9, 65-92 (1940)
The chemistry of the acyclic constituents of natural fats and oils	J.A.B. Smith	9, 93-114 (1940)
The chemistry of the lipins	E. Kirk	9, 115-134 (1940)
The chemistry of the sterols	I.M. Heilbron and E.R.H. Jones	9, 135-172 (1940)
The chemistry and metabolism of the compounds of sulfur	G. Toennies	9, 199-230 (1940)
Hormones	F.C. Koch	9, 327-352 (1940)
Organic acids of plants	H.B. Vickery and G.W. Pucher	9, 529-544 (1940)
Chemistry of the carbohydrates and glycosides	A.G. Norman	10, 65-90 (1941)
Chemistry of amino acids and proteins	M.S. Dunn	10, 91-124 (1941)
The chemistry and metabolism of the compounds of sulfur	A. White	10, 125-150 (1941)
The chemistry of the acyclic constituents of natural fats and oils	T.P. Hilditch	11, 77-102 (1942)
The chemistry of the steroids	C.W. Shoppee	11, 103-150 (1942)
The chemistry of the proteins and amino acids	J.T. Edsall	11, 151-182 (1942)
Lignin	H. Hibbert	11, 183-202 (1942)
The chemistry and metabolism of the compounds of phosphorus	J.C. Sowden and H.O.L. Fischer	11, 203-216 (1942)
The chemistry of the hormones	J.J. Pfiffner and O. Kamm	11, 283-308 (1942)
The alkaloids	L.C. Craig	11, 569-594 (1942)
The chemistry of the proteins and amino acids. I.	L.F. Hewitt	12, 81-92 (1943)
The chemistry and metabolism of the compounds of sulfur	J.C. Andrews	12, 115-134 (1943)
The chemistry of the carbohydrates	H.S. Isbell	12, 205-232 (1943)
The chemistry of the lipins	S.J. Thannhauser and G. Schmidt	12, 233-250 (1943)
The chemistry of the hormones	H. Fraenkel-Conrat	12, 273-304 (1943)
Synthetic drugs	T.C. Daniels	12, 447-472 (1943)
The chemistry of the carbohydrates	W.Z. Hassid	13, 59-92 (1944)
The chemistry of the lipids	J.B. Brown	13, 93-116 (1944)
The chemistry of the proteins and amino acids	H. Neurath and J.P. Greenstein	13, 117-154 (1944)
Chemistry and metabolism of the compounds of phosphorus	A.A. Green and S.P. Colowick	13, 155-186 (1944)

The chemistry of the hormones	H. Jensen	<u>13</u>, 347-366 (1944)
The chemistry of the carbohydrates	C.D. Hurd	<u>14</u>, 91-112 (1945)
The chemistry of the lipids	H.E. Longenecker and B.F. Daubert	<u>14</u>, 113-144 (1945)
The chemistry of the amino acids and proteins	J. Steinhardt	<u>14</u>, 145-174 (1945)
The chemistry of the steroids	W.L. Ruigh	<u>14</u>, 225-262 (1945)
The chemistry and metabolism of the compounds of sulfur	J.W.H. Lugg	<u>14</u>, 263-282 (1945)
The chemistry and metabolism of the compounds of phosphorus	H.M. Kalckar	<u>14</u>, 283-308 (1945)
The chemistry of the triterpenes	C.R. Noller	<u>14</u>, 383-406 (1945)
The chemistry of antibiotic substances other than penicillin	A.E. Oxford	<u>14</u>, 749-772 (1945)
The chemistry of the lipids	J.B. Brown	<u>15</u>, 93-118 (1946)
The chemistry of the proteins and amino acids	T.L. McMeekin and R.C. Warner	<u>15</u>, 119-154 (1946)
The chemistry of the steroids	T. Reichstein and H. Reich	<u>15</u>, 155-192 (1946)
The chemistry of the hormones	H. Selye and H. Jensen	<u>15</u>, 347-360 (1946)
Organic insecticides	W.M. Hoskins and R. Craig	<u>15</u>, 539-572 (1946)
The chemistry of the carbohydrates	E.G.V. Percival	<u>16</u>, 55-78 (1947)
The chemistry and metabolism of the lipids	M.M. Piskur and H.W. Schultz	<u>16</u>, 79-104 (1947)
Phosphorus compounds	W.W. Umbreit	<u>16</u>, 105-124 (1947)
The chemistry of the proteins and amino acids	E. Brand and J.T. Edsall	<u>16</u>, 223-272 (1947)
The chemistry of the hormones	C.H. Li	<u>16</u>, 291-322 (1947)
The chemistry of the steroids	L.H. Sarett and E.S. Wallis	<u>16</u>, 655-688 (1947)
Chemistry of the carbohydrates	D.A. Prins and R.W. Jeanloz	<u>17</u>, 67-96 (1948)
X-ray crystallographic studies of compounds of biochemical interest	D. Crowfoot	<u>17</u>, 115-146 (1948)
The chemistry of the lipids	J. Folch-Pi and W.M. Sperry	<u>17</u>, 147-168 (1948)
The chemistry of the proteins and amino acids	K.O. Pedersen	<u>17</u>, 169-200 (1948)
The chemistry of penicillin	E. Chain	<u>17</u>, 657-704 (1948)
Carbohydrate chemistry	D.J. Bell	<u>18</u>, 87-96 (1949)
The chemistry of the lipids	J.A. Lovern	<u>18</u>, 97-114 (1949)
Chemistry of amino acids and proteins	H.P. Lundgren and W.H. Ward	<u>18</u>, 115-154 (1949)
Chemistry of the hormones	A. Wettstein and F. Benz	<u>18</u>, 355-390 (1949)
Chemistry of antibiotics	O. Wintersteiner and J.D. Dutcher	<u>18</u>, 559-594 (1949)
Carbohydrate chemistry	M.L. Wolfrom and J.M. Sugihara	<u>19</u>, 67-88 (1950)
Chemistry of lipids	H.J. Deuel, Jr.	<u>19</u>, 89-110 (1950)

ANNUAL REVIEW OF BIOCHEMISTRY (Contd.)

Title	Author(s)	Citation
The chemistry and metabolism of the steroid hormones	G. Pincus	19, 111-124 (1950)
The chemistry of amino acids and proteins	R.K. Cannan and M. Levy	19, 125-148 (1950)
Nucleic acids, purines and pyrimidines	G. Schmidt	19, 149-186 (1950)
Chemistry of the hormones	A. White	19, 261-276 (1950)
Carbohydrate chemistry	H.O.L. Fischer and D.L. MacDonald	20, 43-66 (1951)
Chemistry of the lipids	K.F. Mattil	20, 87-102 (1951)
The chemistry of amino acids and proteins	K. Bailey and F. Sanger	20, 103-130 (1951)
X-ray crystallographic studies of compounds of biological interest	R.B. Corey	20, 131-148 (1951)
Nucleic acids, purines and pyrimidines	J. Baddiley	20, 149-178 (1951)
Chemistry of the carbohydrates	R. Montgomery and F. Smith	21, 79-108 (1952)
Chemistry of lipids	H.J. Deuel, Jr. and R. Alfin-Slater	21, 109-128 (1952)
The chemistry and metabolism of the steroids	L.T. Samuels and H. Reich	21, 129-178 (1952)
The chemistry of amino acids and proteins	H.B. Bull	21, 179-208 (1952)
Nucleic acids, purines, and pyrimidines	D.O. Jordan	21, 209-244 (1952)
Carotenoids	G. MacKinney	21, 473-492 (1952)
The alkaloids	L.J. Sargent and L.F. Small	21, 493-520 (1952)
Chemistry of the carbohydrates	H.S. Isbell and H.L. Frush	22, 107-124 (1953)
Chemistry of the lipids	T.P. Hilditch	22, 125-140 (1953)
The chemistry of cortisone	C.W. Shoppee	22, 261-298 (1953)
Chemistry of amino acids, peptides, and proteins	Cl. Fromageot and M. Jutisz	22, 629-678 (1953)
Chemistry of the carbohydrates	R.L. Whistler O.I. McGilvray	23, 79-98 (1954)
Chemistry of the proteins, peptides and amino acids	W.L. Hughes and F.M. Sinex	23, 177-214 (1954)
Chemistry of the carbohydrates	J.K.N. Jones	24, 113-134 (1955)
Chemistry of the phosphatides	E. Baer	24, 135-156 (1955)
Chemistry of proteins, peptides and amino acids	A.G. Ogston	24, 181-206 (1955)
Carotenoids	T.W. Goodwin	24, 497-522 (1955)
Chemistry of the carbohydrates	E.J. Bourne and R. Stephens	25, 79-100 (1956)
Chemistry of the lipids	F.B. Shorland	25, 101-122 (1956)
The chemistry of proteins and peptides	H. Fraenkel-Conrat	25, 291-330 (1956)
The chemistry of proteins	D. Steinberg and E. Mihalyi	26, 373-418 (1957)
Chemistry of the carbohydrates	J.C. Sowden	26, 645-666 (1957)
Chemistry of the carbohydrates	R.E. Reeves	27, 15-34 (1958)
Chemistry and biochemistry of antibiotics	E.B. Chain	27, 167-222 (1958)
Chemistry of carbohydrates	W. Pigman K. Nisizawa and S. Tsuiki	28, 15-38 (1959)

ANNUAL REVIEW OF BIOCHEMISTRY (Contd.)

Title	Author	Reference
Chemistry of amino acids and peptides	P. Edman	28, 69-96 (1959)
The structure of proteins	R.L. Hill, J.R. Kimmel and E.L. Smith	28, 97-144 (1959)
Nucleic acids, purines, pyrimidines (Nucleotide synthesis)	S.C. Hartman and J.M. Buchanan	28, 365-410 (1959)
Chemistry of the carbohydrates	W.J. Whelan	29, 105-130 (1960)
The structure of proteins	G.E. Perlmann and R. Diringer	29, 151-182 (1960)
Chemistry of amino acids and peptides	R. Schwyzer	29, 183-206 (1960)

ANNUAL REVIEW OF NUCLEAR SCIENCE

This is an annual collection of review articles, in English. The editors are E. Segrè, L.I. Schiff, G. Friedlander and W.E. Meyerhof. Published by Annual Reviews in cooperation with the National Research Council of the National Academy of Sciences.

Title	Author	Reference
Isotopic tracers in chemical systems	R.R. Edwards	1, 301-342 (1952)
The production and distribution of natural radiocarbon	E.C. Anderson	2, 63-78 (1953)
Isotope effects in chemical reactions	P.E. Yankwich	3, 235-248 (1953)
Mass spectra and the chemical species produced by the impact of low energy electrons	M. Krauss, A.L. Wahrhaftig and H. Eyring	5, 241-268 (1955)
Applications of oxygen isotopes in chemical studies	H. Taube	6, 277-303 (1956)
Labelling of organic compounds by recoil methods	A.P. Wolf	10, 259-290 (1960)

ANNUAL REVIEW OF PHYSICAL CHEMISTRY

This is an annual collection of review articles, published in English. Volumes 1 to 6 were edited by G.K. Rollefson, and volumes 7 to the present by H. Eyring. Publisher: Annual Reviews, Inc., Palo Alto, California.

Title	Author	Reference
Effect of oxygen on the physical and chemical properties of polymers	H.F. Mark and R.B. Mesrobian	1, 325-336 (1950)
Copolymerization	H.F. Mark and T. Alfrey Jr.	1, 337-346 (1950)
Spectroscopy	L.G.S. Brooker and W.T. Simpson	2, 121-150 (1951)
Experimental molecular structure	W.L. Roth	2, 217-234 (1951)
Homogeneous chemical kinetics	M. Kilpatrick	2, 255-286 (1951)
Reaction kinetics	R.E. Powell	3, 309-338 (1952)
Experimental molecular structure	L.O. Brockway	3, 375-384 (1952)
Experimental molecular structures	S.H. Bauer and P. Andersen	4, 233-252 (1953)
Experimental molecular structure	R.L. Livingston	5, 395-412 (1954)
Experimental molecular structure and crystallography	E.W. Hughes	6, 261-280 (1955)
Polymerization kinetics and polymer properties	W.H. Stockmayer, F.W. Billmeyer Jr. and J.K. Beasley	6, 359-380 (1955)
Experimental molecular structure	S. Mizushima and T. Shimanouchi	7, 445-464 (1956)
Kinetics of polymerization	F.W. Peaker	8, 199-204 (1957)
Organic reaction mechanisms	J.D. Roberts G.S. Hammond and D.J. Cram	8, 299-330 (1957)
Physical organic chemistry	R.W. Taft Jr. N.C. Demo and P.S. Skell	9, 287-314 (1958)
Optical rotatory power	W. Kuhn	9, 417-438 (1958)
Block and graft copolymers	G.M. Burnett	10, 103-122 (1959)
Physical organic chemistry	V. Gold	10, 169-190 (1959)
Electronic spectra of organic compounds	J.R. Platt	10, 349-388 (1959)
Thermochemistry and thermodynamic properties of substances	J.P. McCullough	11, 1-20 (1960)
Solutions of electrolytes in non-aqueous solvents and mixtures	E.C. Evers and R.L. Kay	11, 21-40 (1960)
Gaseous reactions	J.G. Calvert	11, 41-64 (1960)
Physical organic chemistry	J. Hine	11, 65-86 (1960)
Radiation chemistry	W.H. Hamill	11, 87-106 (1960)
Quantum theory of electronic structure of molecules	Per-Olav Löwdin	11, 107-132 (1960)

ANNUAL REVIEW OF PHYSICAL CHEMISTRY (Contd.)

Title	Author	Reference
Molecular electronic spectroscopy	W.C. Price	11, 133-148 (1960)
Kinetics of reactions in solution	M. Eigen and J.S. Johnson	11, 307-334 (1960)
Vibration-rotation spectroscopy	D.H. Whiffen	11, 335-346 (1960)
Chromatography	R.A. Keller, G.H. Stewart and J.C. Giddings	11, 347-368 (1960)
Nuclear and electron resonance	R. Bersohn	11, 369-390 (1960)
Photosynthesis	J.D. Spikes and B.C. Mayne	11, 501-530 (1960)

ANTIBIOTICA AND CHEMOTHERAPIA

A collection of reviews (in French, German or English), of clinical interest. Present editor: O. Gsell. Published by S. Karger A.G., Basel, Switzerland.

Title	Author	Reference
Chemistry of corticosteroids (in German)	R. Neher	7, 1-28 (1950)

BULLETIN DE LA SOCIÉTÉ DE CHIMIE BIOLOGIQUE

A monthly journal of the Biochemical Society of France. Most articles are experimental ones, but occasional lecture and conference summaries are included. Articles are in French. Edited until 1946 by M. Fontaine and since 1947 by Y. Raoul. Published by Masson et Cie., Paris.

Title	Author	Reference
Panthotenic acid, vitamins of the B group	L. Velluz	27, 17-39 (1945)
New results on carotenoids	P. Karrer	28, 688-699 (1946)
Stereoisomeric provitamins A	L. Zechmeister	31, 956-964 (1949)
Report of the chemistry of natural cyclitols	Th. Posternak	33, 1041-1058 (1951)
Phosphoric ethers of inositol	J. Courtois	33, 1075-1112 (1951)
Structure of insulin	F. Sanger	37, 23-36 (1955)
Chemistry of phosphatase	L. Tamayo	38, 983-1001 (1956)
Glycoproteins. Chemistry and biology	J. Montreuil	39, III-3 to III-92 (195)
Milk oligosaccharides	R. Kuhn	40, 297-314 (1958)

BULLETIN DE LA SOCIÉTÉ CHIMIQUE DE FRANCE

The French Chemical Society (Societé Chimique de France) publishes a monthly journal <u>in French</u> devoted to original articles as well as conferences and special reviews. Between 1949 and 1954 the latter were published in a special section, whose page number was preceded by D. Symposia were published in a C section. The present location of these pages in the bound volumes depends entirely on the fantasy of the binder of each library.

Title	Author	Reference
Synthetic rubbers	L. Denivelle	1-20 (1940)
Copper, catalyst for hydrogenation of benzene	N. Ipatieff	281-295 (1940)
Raney nickel	R. Paul	296-346 (1940)
Contribution of deuterium to organic chemistry	E. Darmois	445-462 (1941)
Substitute fuels	G. Dupont	629-643 (1941)
Present state of our knowledge of lignin chemistry	A. Guillemonat	589-597 (1942)
New industrial acetylenic compounds	P. Piganiol	749-758 (1942)
Relations between the structure, the chemical reactivity and the absorption spectra of organic compounds	P. Ramart-Lucas	850-871 (1942) 13-32 (1943)
The chemical constituents of lignin	H. Brunet	109-123 (1943)
Synthesis of molecules with lubrifying properties	P. Piganiol	301-310 (1943)
Hertzian spectra of polar molecules	P. Girard and P. Abadie	202-217 (1945)
Halohydrins of the α-glycols	M. Tiffeneau	453-476 (1945)
Structure and absorption of colored (in the visible) derivatives of triphenylmethane	P. Ramart-Lucas	477-505 (1945)
Selenium oxide, oxidizing agent in organic chemistry	J. Véne	506-516 (1945)
Problems of the relations between structure and vitaminic activity. The ideas of isomorphism and isostery	P. Meunier	517-527 (1945)
Applications of infrared absorption spectra to the analysis of hydrocarbons and to the determination of their molecular structure	J. Lecomte	706-750 (1945)
The experimental basis for the concept of mesomerism	P. Rumpf	1-14 (1946)
Quasicomplex organometallic compounds	A.N. Nesmeyanov	569-574 (1946)
Recent development of the chemistry of vitamins	P. Karrer	141-151 (1947)
The use of carbon monoxide in organic synthesis: the "oxo" reaction	A. Willemart	152-157 (1947)
Furfural and its hydrogenation products. Sources of starting materials in organic synthesis	R. Paul	158-176 (1947)
New developments in the chemistry of steroid hormones	L. Velluz	567-583 (1947)
Intramolecular forces and the hydrogen bond	P. Rumpf	211-230 (1948)
Some aspects of the synthesis and structure of polycyclic aromatic hydrocarbons	E. Bergmann	D19-D34 (1948)

BULLETIN DE LA SOCIÉTÉ CHIMIQUE DE FRANCE (Contd.)

Title	Author(s)	Pages
The cyanines	H. Wahl	726-734 (1948)
Synthesis of nucleotides	A.R. Todd	933-938 (1948)
Structure of proteins	P. Desnuelle	D251-D264 (1949)
Thiamides	P. Chabrier and S.H. Renard	D272-D296 (1949)
The condensation of carbonyl compounds with succinic acid	D. Billet	D297-D321 (1949)
Determination of the structure of some biphenyl compounds by polar moments	M. Lumbroso	D387-D393 (1949)
Molecular structure and estrogen activity	J. Jacques	D411-D442 (1949)
On the application of electric dipole moment measurements to the solution of problems in structural chemistry (Eng.)	L.E. Sutton	D448-D456 (1949)
Geometric configuration and dipole moment of conjugated hydrocarbons	G. Berthier and B. Pullman	D457-D465 (1949)
Diamagnetism of isomerides (in English)	W.R. Angus	D483-D488 (1949)
Problems of steroid nomenclature	A. Petit	D545-D565 (1949)
The use of aluminum chloride in organic chemistry	A. Willemart	559-567 (1949)
Conditions for existence and physical properties of free radicals	D. Voigt	679-683 (1949)
Properties of the sulfonyl group	H.J. Backer	729-737 (1950)
Origin and evolution of the discovery of mixed organo-magnesium compounds	R. Locquin	897-906 (1950)
Commemoration of the fiftieth anniversary of the reaction of Victor Grignard	P. Karrer	907-909 (1950)
History and particular aspects of the reaction of Victor Grignard	J. Colonge	910-918 (1950)
The structure of the organo-magnesium compounds of Victor Grignard	P. Jolibois and R. Kullmann	919-932 (1950)
Application of ozonolysis to the study of the structure of aromatic compounds	J.P. Wibaut	996-1005 (1950)
The isothiamides	P. Chabrier and S.H. Renard	D13-D21 (1950)
Mechanism of the Friedel-Crafts reaction; the isomerization and the exchange of hydrocarbons in the presence of acid reagents	G. Chiurdoglu and P.J.C. Fierens	D27-D34 (1950)
Rearrangement of α-haloketones to acids under the influence of alkaline reagent (Faworsky reaction)	R. Jacquier	D35-D45 (1950)
Derivatives of dithiocarbamic acid	P. Chabrier and G. Nachmias	D51-D65 (1950)

BULLETIN DE LA SOCIÉTÉ CHIMIQUE DE FRANCE (Contd.)

Recent progress of the chemistry and biochemistry of cortisone	R. Jeanloz	D67-D76	(1950)
Structure of acyloins and their ethers	R. Jacquier	D83-D92	(1950)
Present state of the chemistry of irones (methyl-6-ionones)	Y.R. Naves	D99-D113	(1950)
Cadmium derivatives in organic synthesis	J. Vène	D163-D165	(1950)
Recent progress of the chemistry of synthetic perfumes	Y.R. Naves	1-15	(1951)
Addition compounds of macromolecules	G. Champetier	153-162	(1951)
The industrial synthesis of papaverine and related compounds	H. Wahl	D1-D8	(1951)
The intermolecular association by inclusion	G. Zilberstein	D33-D38	(1951)
The tropolones	J. Chopin	D57-D64	(1951)
New developments in the chemistry of cortisone	L. Velluz	1-16	(1952)
A new method of separating organic substances: liquid-phase chromatography or Craig's counter-current method	D. Pillon	D1-D9	(1952)
Application of radioactive isotopes to the study of the chemical reaction mechanisms	P. Daudel	D23-D27	(1952)
The stereochemistry of β-phenylserines	D. Billet	D33-D38	(1952)
Oxyluminescence in organic chemistry, in solutions, and chemical structure; the types of reaction	A. Bernanose	D39-D42	(1952)
Nitrous acid in organic chemistry	C.K. Ingold	667-671	(1952)
Recent progress and possibilities of modern quantitative organic microanalyses	R. Levy	672-687	(1952)
Theoretical and practical aspects of paper chromatography	E. Lederer	815-821	(1952)
Amino acids and certain of their derivatives	M. Jutisz	821-830	(1952)
Peptides and proteins	P. Boulanger and G. Biserte	830-844	(1952)
Constituents of nucleic acids	P. Boulanger and J. Montreuil	844-852	(1952)
Nitrogen bases (alkaloids, amines, vitamins) and hydrosoluble organic acids	R. Munier	852-873	(1952)
Glycosides and related compounds	R. Dedonder	874-883	(1952)
Fatty acids, phosphotides, sterols and related substances	J. Asselineau	884-891	(1952)
Organic compounds labelled by radioisotopes	S. Lissitzky and R. Michel	891-903	(1952)
Determination of double bonds by peracids	W.R. Wragg	911-922	(1952)
Properties and structure of synthetic textile polymers	G. Champetier	233-246	(1953)

BULLETIN DE LA SOCIÉTÉ CHIMIQUE DE FRANCE (Contd.)

Recent progress in the chemistry of irones	Y.R. Naves	551-558 (1953)
The hydroxamic acids	F. Mathis	D9-D22 (1953)
On the scission and isomerization reactions of α-epoxy alcohols (glycosidic scission)	M. Darmon	D25-D39 (1953)
Organic oxyluminescence in solution and chemical structure, the types of reactions	A. Bernanose	D39-D42 (1953)
o-Dihydropyridines (or dihydro-1,2-pyridines)	J.J. Panouse	D53-D59 (1953)
Tetrahydro-1,2,5,6-pyridines (or $\Delta_{3,4}$-piperidines)	J.J. Panouse	D60-D66 (1953)
Methods of preparation of semicarbazides	L. Peyron	D12-D26 (1954)
Application of isotopes to the study of structures and reaction mechanisms	P. Bévillard	D40-D48 (1954) D55-D79
Rearrangements of ketones, alcamines, peroxides, ozonides and alkaloids in the indole series	B. Witkop	423-433 (1954)
Some aspects of the chemistry and biochemistry of cholesterol	L.F. Fieser	541-547 (1954)
Research on the acene series (anthracene and its linear benzologues)	C. Marshalk	878-892 (1954)
The stereochemistry of lupinic alkaloids	L. Marion	1193-1196 (1954)
Some aspects of the chemistry of pyrazolones	S. Veibel	307-313 (1955)
Recent progress in the chemistry of organic complexes of metalloides	W. Haegi	581-587 (1955)
The influence of the work of Tchitchibabin on the development of the chemistry of pyridine derivatives	J.A. Gautier and J. Renault	588-592 (1955)
Infrared spectrometric study of the carbonyl function principally in aldehydes and ketones	J. Lecomte	717-756 (1955)
Some non-classical aspects of the oxidizing action of periodic acid on organic compounds	P. Fleury	1126-1135 (1955)
Action of nucleophilic reagents on α-halogenated ketones	B. Tchoubar	1363-1383 (1955)
The polymerization of ethylene	K. Ziegler	1-6 (1956)
Restricted rotation in organic molecules. Thermodynamic aspect of the question	A. Pacault and P. Bothorel	217-229 (1956)
New aspects of the kinetics of polymerization	M. Magat	534-541 (1956)
Initiation of polymerization. Influence of the polymerizing system on the structure of the polymer	Y. Landler	542-546 (1956)
Furan and pyran derivatives as sources of starting materials in organic synthesis	R. Paul	838-850 (1956)
Structure and chemistry of natural and synthetic polyamides	G. Champetier	853-865 (1956)
Conformation and reactivity of structures	D.H.R. Barton	973-979 (1956)
Steric effects in substitution reactions	H.C. Brown	980-986 (1956)
Steric influence in asymmetric synthesis	V. Prelog	987-995 (1956)
The principle of the predominance of equatorial bonds in cyclohexane derivatives	R. Cornubert	996-1007 (1956)

Influence of vicinal substituents in the reactions of cyclohexane derivatives	M. Mousseron	1008-1019 (1956)
Conformational structure in the terpenes	Y.R. Naves	1020-1031 (1956)
Determination of the configuration of certain tertiary amines and organic quaternary ammonium salts	G. Fodor	1032-1039 (1956)
The steric effect in acylation of ketones	J.M. Conia	1040-1049 (1956)
Steric influence in the formation of erythro-threo pairs	H. Felkin	1050-1057 (1956)
Conformation and reactivity of simple carbonyl compounds	J.E. Dubois	1058-1061 (1956)
Problems of cyclization and ring closure in steroid chemistry	J. Mathieu	1062-1075 (1956)
The chemistry of silanes	A.D. Petrov	1098-1102 (1956)
New synthetic methods in corticosteroid chemistry	A. Fridenson and F.G. Robinet	1481-1498 (1956)
Infrared and raman spectrographic study of the imine group	J. Fabian M. Legrand and P. Poirier	1499-1509 (1956)
Mechanism of addition reactions to the carbonyl group	H. Felkin	1510-1524 (1956)
Isomerization of tertiary α-ketols. Mechanisms and stereochemistry	I. Elphimoff-Felkin	1845-1856 (1956)
Chromatography in the gas phase	P. Chovin	83-101 (1957)
Chemical kinetics as a tool of research	J.C. Jungers	855-865 (1957)
Structure and rotatory dispersion	C. Djerassi	741-750 (1957)
The chemical structure of calophyllolid	J. Polonsky	1079-1087 (1957)
Circular electronic transfer in the interpretation of certain organic reactions	J. Mathieu and J. Valls	1510-1541 (1957)
Determination of flavones	K. Yagi	1543-1550 (1957)
Use of N-substituted metallic dithiocarbamates: analysis, biological action, various applications	M. Delépine	5-15 (1958)
Dehydroabietic acid and some derivatives	G. Dupont	17-22 (1958)
The synthesis and reactions of quinone mono- and di-imides (Eng.)	R. Adams and W. Reifschneider	23-65 (1958)
Trivalency of the central carbon in the salts of trimethylsulfonylmethane	H.J. Backer	67-68 (1958)
The chemistry of vitamin A and related compounds (Eng.)	I. Heilbron and B.C.L. Weedon	83-97 (1958)
Calabash and strychnos alkaloids (Ger.)	P. Karrer	102-107 (1958)
The biogenesis of alkaloids	L. Marion	109-115 (1958)

Title	Author	Pages (Year)
Photochemistry of hexanone-2 in the gas phase	V. Brunet and W.A. Noyes, Jr.	121-123 (1958)
Chemistry of brazilin and haematoxylin (Eng.)	R. Robinson	125-134 (1958)
The physicochemical constants of pure organic compounds	J. Timmermans	135-142 (1958)
Alkylidene triphenylphosphoranes and the Wittig reaction	J. Levisalles	1021-1037 (1958)
Some aspects of the reactivity of the nitrile group (presented at the conference on nitrile compounds, November 1957)	F. Salmon-Legagneur	1052-1059 (1958)
The principal methods of preparing the dinitriles used in industry	J. Phelisse	1069-1073 (1958)
Nomenclature of organic compounds. Section A - hydrocarbons Section B - basic heterocyclic systems	Report	1208-1268 (1958)
Vinyl esters and imides	M. Hopff	1283-1289 (1958)
(Reactions of) Grignard reagents and nitriles	A. Bruylants	1291-1299 (1958)
Application of nuclear magnetic resonance phenomena in organic chemistry	H. Rivière	1630-1641 (1958)
The structure, formation and reactivity of organometallic solvates	C. Prévost et.al.,	679-688 (1959)
Nature of the hydrogen linkage	S. Diner	1021-1031 (1959)
Infrared spectroscopy in organic chemistry	J. Lecomte	1049-1079 (1959)
Infrared spectroscopy and its applications to qualitative and quantitative analysis	J. Lecomte	1080-1099 (1959)
Stereochemistry of vitamin B_{12}	G. Stora	1421-1430 (1959)
The influence of chelation on the catalytic activity of metals	G. Thuillier	1431-1438 (1959)
Magnetochemistry of hemoproteins. Applications of paramagnetic electronic resonance to the study of the structure of hemoproteins	P. Ricaud	1693-1701 (1959)
The use of vinylmagnesium in (organic) synthesis. Part I. Action of metallic and metalloidal halides. Part II. Action on organic compounds	H. Normant	1764-1768 (1959) 1768-1783
The chemistry of benzocyclobutene and benzocyclobutadiene	M.P. Cava	1744-1747 (1959)
The biochemistry and constitution of lignin	K. Freudenberg	1748-1753 (1959)
Trends in organic analysis	M. Pesez and M. Legrand	453-461 (1960)
Boat form in equilibria and reactions of 6-membered rings	J. Levisalles	551-562 (1960)
Recent progress in partition chromatography in the gas phase	P. Chovin	755-768 (1960)
Steroidal alkaloids of the apocynaceae	R. Goutarel	769-774 (1960)
Mendeleyeff periodic classification and organic chemistry	A.N. Nesmeyanov	987-1010 (1960)

Modern ideas on acidity and mobile hydrogen. Their interest in organic chemistry	J. A. Gautier	1263-1269 (1960)
A biogenetic classification of the organic constituents of plants	C. Mentler	1270-1278 (1960)
New magnesium syntheses of α, β-ethylenic carbonyl compounds	H. Normant	1280-1281 (1960)
Phenol thiazine and its derivatives. Chemical and pharmaco-dynamical aspects	A. Lespagnol	1291-1299 (1960)
The isotopes of oxygen in organic chemistry	H. Dahn	1875-1880 (1960)
The stereochemistry of oses and their derivatives	G. Michel	2173-2187 (1960)
Chromatographic analysis with elution gradients	P. Lebreton	2188-2200 (1960)

Title	Author	Reference
The constitution of polysaccharides	J.C. Irvine	<u>1</u>, 41-71 (1924)
Organic radicals	M. Gomberg	<u>1</u>, 91-141 (1924)
Some factors influencing substitution in the benzene ring	A.F. Holleman	<u>1</u>, 187-230 (1924)
The organic compounds of lead	G. Calingaert	<u>2</u>, 45-83 (1925)
Lactose	E.O. Whittier	<u>2</u>, 85-125 (1925)
Recent studies on reversible oxidation-reduction in organic systems	M. Clark	<u>2</u>, 127-178 (1925)
The configurational relationships of the sugars, hydroxy acids, amino acids and halogen acids	P.A. Levene	<u>2</u>, 179-216 (1925)
The manufacture of alcohols from hydrocarbons, with particular reference to petroleum as a raw material	B.T. Brooks	<u>2</u>, 369-394 (1926)
The electrochemical formulation of the irreversible reduction and oxidation of organic compounds	J.B. Conant	<u>3</u>, 1-40 (1926)
Chemical processes in fermentations	F.F. Nord	<u>3</u>, 41-79 (1926)
Directive influence in the benzene ring	A.W. Francis	<u>3</u>, 257-289 (1926)
Recent advances in the determination of the structure	E. Klarmann	<u>4</u>, 51-107 (1927)
Phosgene	G.M. Dyson	<u>4</u>, 109-165 (1927)
The structure of the methane molecule	V. Henri	<u>4</u>, 189-201 (1927)
Progress in the structural study of carbohydrates	J.C. Irvine	<u>4</u>, 203-229 (1927)
Static and dynamic isomerism in prototropic compounds	T.M. Lowry	<u>4</u>, 231-253 (1927)
Recent advances in cellulose and starch chemistry	H.LeB.Gray and C.J. Straud	<u>4</u>, 355-373 (1927)
Active glucose	P.A. Levene	<u>5</u>, 1-16 (1928)
The theory of partial polarity of the ethylene bond and the existence of electroisomerism	M.S. Kharasch and F.R. Darkis	<u>5</u>, 571-602 (1928)
The oxidation of the gaseous paraffin hydrocarbons	G. Egloff and R.E. Schaad	<u>6</u>, 91-141 (1929)
The chemistry of anthraquinone	M. Phillips	<u>6</u>, 157-174 (1929)
Phototropy	L. Chalkley Jr.	<u>6</u>, 217-280 (1929)
The mechanism of carbohydrate oxidation	W.L. Evans	<u>6</u>, 281-315 (1929)
Molecular association	G.G. Longinescu	<u>6</u>, 381-418 (1929)
The physico-chemistry of creatine and creatinine	H.E. Shiver	<u>6</u>, 419-444 (1929)
Molecular structure as interpreted by X-ray diffraction measurements in liquids	G.W. Stewart	<u>6</u>, 483-501 (1929)
Electric moment, molecular orientation and structure in aliphatic compounds	C.P. Smyth	<u>6</u>, 549-587 (1929)
The structure of molecules as revealed by dielectric constant data	J.W. Williams	<u>6</u>, 589-619 (1929)
Recent progress in the menthone chemistry	J. Read	<u>7</u>, 1-50 (1930)
The chemistry of rubber	H.L. Fisher	<u>7</u>, 51-138 (1930)
The reactions of halogens with compounds containing the carbonyl group	H.B. Watson	<u>7</u>, 173-201 (1930)
Some recent advances in theoretical organic chemistry	R.C. Fuson	<u>7</u>, 347-368 (1930)
The substitution of linked aromatic ring systems	W.A. Waters	<u>7</u>, 407-429 (1930)
The crystal structure of organic compounds	S.B. Hendricks	<u>7</u>, 431-477 (1930)
Carbon suboxide	L.H. Reyerson and K. Kobe	<u>7</u>, 479-492 (1930)

Title	Authors	Vol, Pages (Year)
A study of mercaptan chemistry	W.M. Malisoff, E.M. Marks and F.G. Hess	7, 493-547 (1930)
The halogenation of the paraffin hydrocarbons	G. Egloff, R.E. Schaad and C.D. Lowry Jr.	8, 1-80 (1931)
Polymerization	W.H. Carothers	8, 353-426 (1931)
Structure of divalent carbon compounds	N.V. Sidgwick	9, 77-88 (1931)
Azoxy compounds	H.E. Bigelow	9, 117-167 (1931)
The history of the discovery of the amino acids	H.B. Vickery and C.L.A. Schmidt	9, 169-318 (1931)
Epinephrine and related compounds: influence of structure on physiological activity	W.H. Hartung	9, 389-465 (1931)
Reactions of organic molecules in the gaseous state	F.O. Rice	10, 135-159 (1932)
The kinetics of certain bimolecular reactions in solution	E.A. Moelwyn-Hughes	10, 241-264 (1932)
Recent isoprene chemistry. Phytol, carotenoids, lipochromes, and vitamin A	M.A. Bogert	10, 265-294 (1932)
Auto-oxidation	N.A. Milas	10, 295-364 (1932)
Recent progress in stereochemistry	F. Richter	10, 365-426 (1932)
Reactions of ethyl alcohol	H.E. Morris	10, 465-494 (1932)
Organo-alkali compounds	C.B. Wooster	11, 1-91 (1932)
The cyanine dyes	M.Q. Doja	11, 273-321 (1932)
Nuclear substitution and orientation of furan types	H. Gilman and G.F. Wright	11, 323-367 (1932)
The chemistry of the alkali amides	F.W. Bergstrom and W.C. Fernelius	12, 43-179 (1933)
The determination of the structure of rotenone	F.B. Laforge, H.L. Haller and L.E. Smith	12, 182-214 (1933)
The Beckmann rearrangement	A.H. Blatt	12, 215-260 (1933)
The stereochemistry of diphenyls and analogous compounds	R. Adams and H.C. Yuan	12, 261-338 (1933)
The structure of dicarboxy compounds from dissociation and reaction velocity data	J. Greenspan	12, 339-361 (1933)
The mechanism of heterogeneous catalytic organic reactions. I. Catalytic hydrogenation	O. Schmidt	12, 363-417 (1933)
Pyrimidines: their amino and aminooxy derivatives	T.B. Johnson and D.A. Hahn	13, 193-303 (1933)
The chemistry of vitamins A and C	P. Karrer	14, 17-30 (1934)
Orienting influences in the benzene ring	J.S. Reese	14, 55-102 (1934)
The chemistry of lignin	M. Phillips	14, 103-170 (1934)
The Hofmann-Beckmann-Curtius-Lossen rearrangements	E.C. Franklin	14, 219-250 (1934)
Chloropicrin	K.E. Jackson	14, 251-286 (1934)
Thermal reactions of terpene hydrocarbons	G. Egloff et. al.,	14, 287-383 (1934)
Metallic salts of alcohols and alcohol analogs	O.C. Dermer	14, 385-430 (1934)
Significant studies in the organic chemistry of sulfur	D.T. Gibson	14, 431-457 (1934)
Principles of an electronic theory of organic reactions	C.K. Ingold	15, 225-274 (1934)

The haloform reaction	R.C. Fuson and B.A. Bull	15,	275-309 (1934)
The chemistry of bile acids and related substances	H. Sobotka	15,	311-375 (1934)
β,β'-dichloroethyl sulfide (mustard gas)	K.E. Jackson	15,	425-462 (1934)
The principle of vinylogy	R.C. Fuson	16,	1-27 (1935)
The improved synthesis of o-phenanthroline	G.F. Smith and C.A. Getz	16,	113-120 (1935)
The effect of structure on the reactivity of some organic halogen compounds	E. Wilson	16,	149-194 (1935)
Lachrymators	K.E. Jackson and M.A. Jackson	16,	195-242 (1935)
Semiquinones, the intermediate steps of reversible organic oxidation-reduction	L. Michaelis	16,	243-286 (1935)
Heterocyclic nitrogen compounds	E.C. Franklin and F.C. Bergstrom	16,	305-361 (1935)
The chlorovinylarsines	K.E. Jackson and M.A. Jackson	16,	439-452 (1935)
The decomposition of organic compounds from the standpoint of free radicals	F.O. Rice	17,	53-63 (1935)
The mechanism of some important organic reactions. The dissociation of carbon bonds	O. Schmidt	17,	137-154 (1935)
The natural tannins	A. Russell	17,	155-186 (1935)
The chemistry of the cardiac glycosides	R.C. Elderfield	17,	187-249 (1935)
Sternutators	K.E. Jackson	17,	251-292 (1935)
The Friedel-Crafts syntheses	N.O. Calloway	17,	327-392 (1935)
Raman spectra in organic chemistry	J.H. Hibben	18,	1-230 (1936)
The free energy relations among the paraffin and olefin hydrocarbons	G.S. Parks	18,	325-334 (1936)
The synthesis and structure of benzopyrylium (chromylium) salts	D.W. Hill	19,	27-54 (1936)
The thermal stability of paraffinic and olefinic hydrocarbons	G. Egloff and C.I. Parrish	19,	145-161 (1936)
Dipole moment and molecular structure	N.V. Sidgwick	19,	183-194 (1936)
The dielectric constant of solutions of dipolar ions	J. Wyman Jr.	19,	213-239 (1936)
Recent progress in determining the chemical structure of chlorophyll	C.C. Steele	20,	1-39 (1937)
Chlorophyll	H. Fischer	20,	41-68 (1937)
The male sex hormones	L. Ruzicka	20,	69-79 (1937)
Energy changes involved in the addition reactions of unsaturated hydrocarbons	J.B. Conant and G.B. Kistiakowsky	20,	181-194 (1937)
Reactions of solutions of metals in liquid ammonia	W.C. Fernelius and G.W. Watt	20,	195-258 (1937)
The hydrogen bond and association	E.N. Lassettre	20,	259-303 (1937)
The reactions of pure hydrocarbons in the presence of aluminum chloride	G. Egloff et.al.,	20,	345-411 (1937)
The chemistry of the alkali amides. II	F.W. Bergstrom and W.C. Fernelius	20,	413-481 (1937)
Isomerization of hydrocarbons	E. Wilson	21,	129-167 (1937)

CHEMICAL REVIEWS (Contd.)

Some organic reactions involving the occurrence of free radicals in solution	D.H. Hey and W.A. Waters	21, 169-208 (1937)
The kinetics of elementary reactions of the simple hydrocarbons	E.W.R. Steacie	22, 311-402 (1938)
Aliphatic diazo compounds, nitrones, and structurally analogous compounds. Systems capable of undergoing 1,3-additions	L.I. Smith	23, 193-285 (1938)
The chemistry of fluorene and its derivatives	G. Rieveschl Jr. and F.E. Ray	23, 288-389 (1938)
Oxidation and reduction of organic compounds at the dropping mercury electrode and the application of Heyrovsky's polarographic method in organic chemistry	O.H. Muller	24, 95-124 (1939)
The chemistry of retene	D.E. Adelson and M.T. Bogert	24, 135-176 (1939)
The dissociation constants of monocarboxylic acids; their measurement and their significance in theoretical organic chemistry	J.F.J. Dippy	25, 151-211 (1939)
The chemistry of aminoguanidine and related substances	E. Lieber and G.B.L. Smith	25, 213-271 (1939)
The color of organic substances	G.N. Lewis and M. Calvin	25, 273-328 (1939)
Alkylation and the action of aluminum halides on alkylbenzenes	D.V. Nightingale	25, 329-376 (1939)
Ammonolysis in liquid ammonia	W.C. Fernelius and G.B. Bowman	26, 3-48 (1940)
Sulfamic acid, sulfamide and related aquoammonsulfuric acids	L.F. Audrieth et.al.,	26, 49-94 (1940)
The investigation of synthetic linear polymers	C.S. Fuller	26, 143-167 (1940)
X-ray investigations of carbohydrates	H. Mark	26, 169-186 (1940)
Interatomic distances in proteins and related substances	R.B. Corey	26, 227-236 (1940)
A summary of the reactions of aldehydes with amines	M.M. Sprung	26, 297-338 (1940)
Structure and chemotherapeutic activities of sulfanilamide derivatives	E.H. Northey	27, 85-197 (1940)
The chemistry of vitamin E	L.E. Smith	27, 287-329 (1940)
A review of the Kjeldahl determination of organic nitrogen	R.B. Bradstreet	27, 331-350 (1940)
The peroxide effect in the addition of reagents to unsaturated compounds and in rearrangement reactions	F.R. Mayo and C. Walling	27, 351-412 (1940)
The Fries reaction	A.H. Blatt	27, 413-436 (1940)
The ozonization reaction	L. Long Jr.	27, 437-493 (1940)
The Claisen rearrangement	D.S. Tarbell	27, 495-546 (1940)
Reactions of hydrocarbons in electrical discharges	C.L. Thomas, G. Egloff and J.C. Morrell	28, 1-70 (1941)
The chemistry and toxicity of selenium compounds, with special reference to the selenium problem	E.P. Painter	28, 179-213 (1941)
Coordination compounds of olefins with metallic salts	R.N. Keller	28, 229-267 (1941)
Relationship between the structures and the bactericidal properties of phenols	C.M. Suter	28, 269-299 (1941)

Transannular peroxides	W. Bergmann and M.J. McLean	28, 367-394 (1941)
Vitamin K	E.A. Doisy, S.B. Binkley and S.A. Thayer	28, 477-517 (1941)
Substitution and orientation in the benzene ring	C.C. Price	29, 37-67 (1941)
Alkaloids of tobacco	K.E. Jackson	29, 123-197 (1941)
Composition and structural characteristics of glycerides in relation to classification and environment	H.E. Longenecker	29, 201-224 (1941)
The structure of the phospholipids	E.B. Working and A.C. Andrews	29, 245-255 (1941)
Synthetic fatty acid glycerides of known constitution	D.F. Daubert and C.G. King	29, 269-285 (1941)
Preparation and properties of optically active derivatives of glycerol	H.O.L. Fischer and E. Baer	29, 287-316 (1941)
Ultraviolet absorption spectra of fatty acids and their application to chemical problems	G.O. Burr and E.S. Miller	29, 419-438 (1941)
Isomerization of unsaturated hydrocarbons	E. Bergmann	29, 529-551 (1941)
Dipole moments as a tool in the determination of structure	E. Bergmann and A. Weizmann	29, 553-592 (1941)
The constituents of Derris and other rotenone-bearing plants	H.L. Haller, L.D. Goodhue and H.A. Jones	30, 33-48 (1942)
Indole	R.B. van Order and H.G. Lindwall	30, 69-96 (1942)
Naphthenic acids. II. Manufacture, properties and uses	E.R. Littmann and J.R.M. Klotz	30, 97-111 (1942)
The chemistry of quinolines	R.H. Manske	30, 113-144 (1942)
The chemistry of isoquinolines	R.H. Manske	30, 145-158 (1942)
Organobismuth compounds	H. Gilman and H.L. Yale	30, 281-320 (1942)
The addition of hydrogen to multiple carbon-carbon bonds	K.N. Campbell and B.K. Campbell	31, 77-175 (1942)
The Diels-Alder diene synthesis	J.A. Norton	31, 319-523 (1942)
Liquid ammonia research - 1941	G.W. Watt, W.B. Leslie and T.E. Moore	31, 525-536 (1942)
Some less familiar aspects of carbohydrate chemistry	W.L. Evans	31, 537-560 (1942)
The ultraviolet absorption spectra of aromatic hydrocarbons	R.N. Jones	32, 1-46 (1943)
Chemistry of the biologically important imidazoles	S.W. Fox	32, 47-71 (1943)
The chemistry of phenoxathiin and its derivatives	C.L. Deasy	32, 173-194 (1943)
Liquid ammonia research - 1942	G.W. Watt, W.B. Leslie and T.E. Moore	32, 219-229 (1943)
Organic compounds of polyvalent iodine	R.B. Sandin	32, 249-276 (1943)
The nitroparaffins	H.B. Hass and E.F. Riley	32, 373-430 (1943)
The reaction between ethylene derivatives and the halogens	S.V. Anantakrishnan and R. Venkataraman	33, 27-55 (1943)

Alicyclic-aromatic isomerization	E.C. Horning	33,	89-135 (1943)
The hydroxamic acids	H.L. Yale	33,	209-256 (1943)
Polyhydric alcohol esters of fatty acids	H.A. Goldsmith	33,	257-349 (1943)
The chemistry and utilization of cyclopentadiene	P.J. Wilson Jr. and J.H. Wells	34,	1-50 (1944)
Determination of oxygen in organic compounds	P.J. Elving and W.B. Ligett	34,	129-156 (1944)
Cis-trans isomerization and stereochemistry of carotenoids and diphenylpolyenes	L. Zechmeister	34,	267-344 (1944)
Catalysis from the viewpoint of the electronic theory of acids and basis	W.F. Luder and S. Zuffanti	34,	345-370 (1944)
The chemistry of isatin	W.C. Sumpter	34,	393-434 (1944)
Polyene synthesis	H. Sobotka and E. Bloch	34,	435-460 (1944)
The chemical behavior of the organoalkali compounds	A.A. Morton	35,	1-49 (1944)
Heterocyclic nitrogen compounds. Part IIA. Hexacyclic compounds: pyridine, quinoline and isoquinoline	F.W. Bergstrom	35,	77-277 (1944)
Conversion of hydrocarbons into butadiene	G. Egloff and G. Hulla	35,	279-333 (1944)
Kinetics and mechanism of the Beckmann rearrangement	B. Jones	35,	335-350 (1944)
The chemistry of the amidines	R.L. Shriner and F.W. Neumann	35,	351-425 (1944)
The chemistry of coumarins	S.M. Sethna and N.M. Shan	36,	1-62 (1945)
Conversion of oxygen derivatives of hydrocarbons into butadiene	G. Egloff and G. Hulla	36,	63-141 (1945)
Hyperconjugation	C.L. Deasy	36,	145-155 (1945)
The reactions of nitrogen tetroxide with organic compounds	J.L. Riebsomer	36,	157-233 (1945)
Selenium dioxide: preparation, properties and use as oxidizing agent	G.R. Waitkins and C.W. Clark	36,	235-289 (1945)
The sulfur dyes	W.N. Jones Jr.	36,	291-313 (1945)
Biological methylation	F. Challenger	36,	315-361 (1945)
Dipyrylenes, dichromylenes, dixanthylenes and their sulfur analogs	A. Schönberg and W. Asker	37,	1-14 (1945)
Carbonyl bridge compounds and related substances	C.F.H. Allen	37,	209-268 (1945)
The chemistry of cinnolines	N.J. Leonard	37,	269-286 (1945)
The alkylation of alkanes	G. Egloff and G. Hulla	37,	323-399 (1945)
The chemistry of the oxazoles	R.H. Wiley	37,	401-442 (1945)
The chemistry of oxindole	W.C. Sumpter	37,	443-479 (1945)
Synthetic estrogens and the relation between their structure and their activity	U.V. Solmssen	37,	481-598 (1945)
The reactions of unsaturated ketones and derivatives with amino compounds. Amino ketones	N.H. Cromwell	38,	83-137 (1946)
The Ullmann synthesis of biaryls	P.E. Fanta	38,	139-196 (1946)
Oxidation of lubrication oils	H.H. Zuidema	38,	197-226 (1946)
The synthesis of aromatic aldehydes	L.N. Ferguson	38,	227-254 (1946)

The chemistry of the diaryl ethers	H.E. Ungnade	38,	405-446 (1946)
Aromatic cyclodehydration	C.K. Bradsher	38,	447-449 (1946)
The isolation and synthesis of the naturally occurring α-amino acids	R.J. Block	38,	501-571 (1946)
Thiones and thials	E. Campaigne	39,	1-77 (1946)
Fundamental principles of condensation polymerization	P.L. Flory	39,	137-197 (1946)
The sulfurization of unsaturated compounds	H.E. Westlake Jr.,	39,	219-239 (1946)
The sulfenic acids and their derivatives	N. Kharasch S.J. Potempa and H.L. Wehrmeister	39,	269-332 (1946)
The entropies and related properties of branched paraffin hydrocarbons	K.S. Pitzer and J.E. Kilpatrick	39,	435-447 (1946)
The use of organocadmium reagents for the preparation of ketones	J. Cason	40,	15-32 (1947)
The chemical composition of barks	E.F. Kurth	40,	33-49 (1947)
The actions of elementary fluorine upon organic compounds	L.A. Bigelow	40,	51-115 (1947)
Anomalous nitration reactions	D.V. Nightingale	40,	117-140 (1947)
Reactions of non-enolizable ketones in sunlight	A. Schönberg and A. Mustafa	40,	181-200 (1947)
The gas-phase photochemical decomposition of the simple aliphatic ketones	W. Davis Jr.	40,	201-250 (1947)
The Sandmeyer reaction	H.H. Hodgson	40,	251-277 (1947)
The pyrazines	I.J. Krems and P.E. Sporri	40,	279-358 (1947)
Recent advances in the chemistry of carbazole	N. Campbell and B.M. Barclay	40,	359-380 (1947)
Reactions of the halogens with the silver salts of carboxylic acids	J. Kleinberg	40,	381-390 (1947)
The chemistry of the tetrazoles	F.R. Benson	41,	1-61 (1947)
The chemistry of the pteridines	M. Gates	41,	63-95 (1947)
The present state of organosilicon chemistry	C.A. Burkhard and E.G. Rochow	41,	97-149 (1947)
The effects of alkyl substitution on the spectra and ionization potential of some fundamental chromophores	W.C. Price	41,	257-272 (1947)
The near-ultraviolet absorption spectra of monoalkyl-substituted benzenes. Hyperconjugation and the Baker-Nathan effect	F.A. Matsen W.W. Robertson and R.L. Chuoke	41,	273-279 (1947)
Electronic transitions in trisubstituted benzenes in the near ultraviolet	H. Sponer	41,	281-291 (1947)
Electronic transitions in the simple unsaturated hydrocarbons	E.P. Carr	41,	293-299 (1947)
Absolute absorption intensities of alkylbenzenes in the 2250-1700 A° region	J.R. Platt and H.B. Klevens	41,	301-310 (1947)
Intensities of electronic transitions in aliphatic ketones in the vacuum ultraviolet	R.S. Holdsworth and A.B.F. Duncan	41,	311-316 (1947)
The correlation of resonance structure with ultraviolet absorption in nitro-substituted organic molecules	W.H. Rodebush	41,	317-323 (1947)

Steric hindrance to planarity in dye molecules	L.G.S. Brooker et. al.,	41, 325-351 (1947)
The ultraviolet absorption spectra of anthracene derivatives	R.N. Jones	41, 353-371 (1947)
The effect of salts and proteins on the spectra of some dyes and indicators	I.M. Klotz	41, 373-399 (1947)
The chemistry of monocyclic α- and γ-pyrones	L.F. Cavalieri	41, 525-584 (1947)
The α-keto acids	K.L. Waters	41, 585-598 (1947)
Properties of alkylbenzenes	A.W. Francis	42, 107-162 (1948)
The chemistry of the resin acids	H.H. Zeiss	42, 163-187 (1948)
The preparation of nitriles	D.T. Mowry	42, 189-283 (1948)
Curariform activity and chemical structure	L.E. Craig	42, 285-410 (1948)
Synthesis of steroids of the progesterone series	M. Ehrenstein	42, 457-489 (1948)
Inhibition and retardation of vinyl polymerization	F.A. Bovey and I.M. Kolthoff	42, 491-525 (1948)
The chemistry of the pyrrocolines and the octahydropyrrocolines	E.T. Borrows and D.O. Holland	42, 611-643 (1948)
Structure and synthesis of cardiac genins	R.B. Turner	43, 1-42 (1948)
The chemistry of 4-hydroxyquinolines	R.H. Reitsema	43, 43-68 (1948)
The chemical reactions of pentaerythritol and its derivatives	S.F. Marrian	43, 149-202 (1948)
The chemistry of the organic isocyanates	J.H. Saunders and R.J. Slocombe	43, 203-218 (1948)
Liquid-phase alkylation of aromatic hydrocarbons	A.W. Francis	43, 257-269 (1948)
Brominations with N-bromosuccinimide and related compounds. The Wohl-Ziegler reaction	C. Djerassi	43, 271-317 (1950)
On doisynolic acids, a new class of estrogens	K. Miescher	43, 367-384 (1948)
Relationship between absorption spectra and chemical constitution of organic molecules	L.N. Ferguson	43, 385-446 (1948)
The chemistry of the phthalazines	W.R. Vaughan	43, 447-508 (1948)
The chemistry of the spiropyrans	A. Mustafa	43, 509-523 (1948)
The relationship between performance and constitution of pure organic explosive compounds	W.C. Lathrop and G.R. Handrick	44, 419-445 (1949)
The chemistry of the oxazolines	R.H. Wiley and L.L. Bennett Jr.	44, 447-476 (1949)
Organic peracids	D. Swern	45, 1-68 (1949)
The reaction of monomeric styrenes	W.S. Emerson	45, 183-345 (1949)
The preparation of substituted styrenes by methods not involving hydrocarbon cracking	W.S. Emerson	45, 347-383 (1949)
Cleavages and rearrangements involving oxygen radicals and cations	J.E. Leffler	45, 385-417 (1949)
The ketone acetals	S.M. McElvain	45, 453-492 (1949)
The behavior of conjugated systems containing aromatic double bonds towards organometallic reagents	R. Gaertner	45, 493-521 (1949)
The chemistry of the vicinal triazoles	F.R. Benson and W.L. Savell	46, 1-68 (1950)
Hydrocarbon autoxidation	C.E. Frank	46, 155-169 (1950)
The chemistry of phenanthridine and its derivatives	R.S. Theobald and K. Schofield	46, 171-189 (1950)

Copolymerization	F.R. Mayo and C. Walling	46, 191-287 (1950)
Reactions of organic and organometallic compounds with solutions of metals in liquid ammonia	G.W. Watt	46, 317-379 (1950)
The chemistry of the hydantoins	E. Ware	46, 403-470 (1950)
The preexponential factor for some reactions of methyl radicals	L.M. Dorfman and R. Gomer	46, 499-516 (1950)
The absorption spectra of chlorophyll and related compounds	S. Arnoff	47, 175-195 (1950)
Recent investigations on Ergot alkaloids	A. Stoll	47, 197-218 (1950)
Bredt's rule of double bonds in atomic-bridged-ring structures	F.S. Fawcett	47, 219-274 (1950)
The naphthydridines	C.F.H. Allen	47, 275-305 (1950)
Antihistamine drugs	B. Idson	47, 307-527 (1950)
The addition compounds of olefins with mercuric salts	J. Chatt	48, 7-43 (1951)
The preparation of sulfinic acids	W.E. Truce and A.M. Murphy	48, 69-124 (1951)
New developments in the chemistry of war gases	M.F. Sartori	48, 225-257 (1951)
The germanes and their organo derivatives	O.H. Johnson	48, 259-297 (1951)
The structure of the aromatic triazenes	T.W. Campbell and B.F. Day	48, 299-317 (1951)
Nitrosyl chloride	L.J. Beckman, W.A. Fessler and M.A. Kise	48, 319-396 (1951)
The chemistry of the benzimidazoles	J.B. Wright	48, 397-541 (1951)
The chemistry and physiological action of Khellin and related products	C.P. Huttrer and E. Dale	48, 543-579 (1951)
Cleavage of the carbon-sulfur bond in divalent sulfur compounds	D.S. Tarbell	49, 1-90 (1951)
The Elbs persulfate oxidation	S.M. Sethna	49, 91-101 (1951)
The chemistry of eight-membered carbocycles	L.E. Craig	49, 103-236 (1951)
Aromatic nucleophilic substitution reactions	J.F. Bunnett and R.E. Zahler	49, 273-412 (1951)
The reaction between Grignard reagents and the oxirane ring	N.G. Gaylord and E.I. Becker	49, 413-533 (1951)
Sulfonylureas and sulfonylthioureas	F. Kurzer	50, 1-46 (1952)
Orientation of substitution in the benzene nucleus	L.N. Ferguson	50, 47-67 (1952)
The azulenes	M. Gordon	50, 127-200 (1952)
The Strecker degradation of α-amino acids	A. Schönberg and R. Moubacher	50, 261-277 (1952)
Some aspects of the organic chemistry of selenium	T.N. Campbell, H.G. Walker and G.M. Coppinger	50, 279-349 (1952)
The chemistry of fluoranthene	S.H. Tucker and M. Whalley	50, 483-538 (1952)
Dimerizations in sunlight	A. Mustafa	51, 1-23 (1952)
Some thermodynamic properties of formic acid	W. Waring	51, 171-183 (1952)
Nitroguanidines	A.F. McKay	51, 301-346 (1952)
The kinetics of the diazo coupling reaction	H. Zollinger	51, 347-361 (1952)
Allophanates	H.W. Blohm and E.I. Becker	51, 471-504 (1952)
The olefin-aldehyde condensation. The Prins reaction	E. Arundale and L.A. Mikeska	51, 505-555 (1952)

Relationships between analogous organic compounds of silicon and carbon	H. Gilman and G.E. Dunn	52, 77-115 (1952)
The critical properties of elements and compounds	K.A. Kobe and R.E. Lynn	52, 117-236 (1952)
The reactions of aliphatic acid chlorides	N.O.V. Sonntag	52, 237-416 (1952)
Ultraviolet absorption of steroids	L. Dorfman	53, 47-144 (1953)
The chemistry of carbodiimides	H.G. Khorana	53, 145-166 (1953)
The fulvenes	J.H. Day	53, 167-189 (1953)
A re-examination of the Hammett equation	H.H. Jaffe	53, 191-261 (1953)
The oxazolidines	E.D. Bergmann	53, 309-352 (1953)
The dehydrocyclization reaction	C. Hansch	53, 353-396 (1953)
The parachors of organic compounds. An interpretation and catalogue	O.R. Quayle	53, 439-589 (1953)
Alkyl and aryl azides	J.H. Boyer and F.C. Canter	54, 1-58 (1954)
The chemistry of the Pechmann dyes	E. Klingsberg	54, 59-77 (1954)
Organolead compounds	R.W. Leeper L. Summers and H. Gilman	54, 101-167 (1954)
The chemistry of sultones and sultams	A. Mustafa	54, 195-223 (1954)
Determination of the concentration of intermediates and of rate constants in radical reactions	G.M. Burnett and H.W. Melville	54, 225-288 (1954)
Oxidation of liquid aldehydes by molecular oxygen	J.R. McNesby and C.A. Heller Jr.	54, 325-346 (1954)
The stereoisomerism of cyclohexane derivatives	H.D. Orloff	54, 347-447 (1954)
The chemistry of the alkali amides. III. Part II. Alkali amides as reagents for organic reactions	R. Levine and W.C. Fernelius	54, 467-573 (1954)
The vapor-phase catalytic hydrogenation of olefins	H.E. Hoelscher W.G. Poynter and E. Weger	54, 575-592 (1954)
The chemistry of the 2-imidazolines and imidazolidines	R.J. Ferm and J.L. Riebsomer	54, 593-613 (1954)
Aromatic molecular complexes of the electron donor-acceptor type	L.J. Andrews	54, 713-776 (1954)
The cleavage of ethers	R.L. Burwell Jr.	54, 615-685 (1954)
The chemistry of phenothiazine	S.P. Massie	54, 797-833 (1954)
Methods of preparation of organometallic compounds	R.G. Jones and H. Gilman	54, 835-890 (1954)
Organic hypohalites	M. Anbar and D. Ginsburg	54, 925-958 (1954)
Chelate complexes of 1,10-phenanthroline and related compounds	W.W. Brandt F.P. Dwyer and E.D. Gyarfas	54, 959-1017 (1954)
The chemistry of quinolizines	B.S. Thyagarajan	54, 1019-1064 (1954)
Displacement reactions at bridgeheads of bridged polycarbocyclic systems	D.E. Applequist and J.D. Roberts	54, 1065-1089 (1954)
Tropones and tropolones	P.L. Pauson	55, 9-136 (1955)
The Nef reaction	W.E. Noland	55, 137-156 (1955)
Thioureas	D.C. Schroeder	55, 181-228 (1955)
The Friedel-Crafts acylation reaction and its application to polycyclic aromatic hydrocarbons	P.H. Gore	55, 229-282 (1955)
The α-haloethyl ethers	L. Summers	55, 301-354 (1955)

The chemistry of formazans and tetrazolium salts	A.W. Aineham	55,	355-483 (1955)
The chemistry of the nitrate esters	R. Boschan, R.T. Merrow and R.W. van Dolah	55,	485-510 (1955)
The chemistry of N-acyldihydroquinaldonitriles and N-acyldihydroisoquinaldonitriles (Reissert compounds)	W.E. McEwen and R.L. Cobb	55,	511-550 (1955)
Alkyls and aryls of transition metals	F.A. Cotton	55,	551-594 (1955)
The cis-trans isomerization of conjugated compounds	G.M. Wyman	55,	625-658 (1955)
Tiglic and angelic acids	R.E. Buckles, G.V. Mock and L. Locatell Jr.	55,	659-678 (1955)
Partition chromatography of steroids	E. Heftmann	55,	679-712 (1955)
The deuterium isotope effect	K.B. Wiberg	55,	713-744 (1955)
The concept of electronegativity	H.O. Pritchard and H.A. Skinner	55,	745-786 (1955)
The use of trifluoroacetic anhydride and related compounds in organic syntheses	J.M. Tedder	55,	787-828 (1955)
Nuclear and electronic spin magnetic resonance	J.E. Wertz	55,	829-956 (1955)
The naturally occurring lignans	W.M. Hearon and W.S. MacGregor	55,	957-1068 (1955)
The preparation of organometallic and organo metalloidal compounds by the diazoalkane method	D. Seyferth	55,	1155-1175 (1955)
Bond hybridization and structure in the metal carbonyls	J.W. Cable and R.K. Sheline	56,	1-26 (1956)
The Pschorr synthesis	P.H. Leake	56,	27-48 (1956)
The primary photochemical process in simple ketones	W.A. Noyes Jr., J.B. Porter and J.E. Jolley	56,	49-94 (1956)
Biuret and related compounds	F. Kurzer	56,	95-197 (1956)
Protein-iodine interaction	L.K. Ramachandran	56,	199-218 (1956)
The degradation of carboxylic acid salts by means of halogen. The Hunsdiecker reaction	R.G. Johnson and R.K. Ingham	56,	219-269 (1956)
The reactions of 8-quinolinol	J.P. Phillips	56,	271-297 (1956)
The properties of metalloporphyrins	R.J.P. Williams	56,	299-328 (1956)
The methoxyl group	L.A. Wiles	56,	329-385 (1956)
The radiation chemistry of organic substances	E. Collinson and A.J. Swallow	56,	471-568 (1956)
Solvolytic displacement reactions at saturated carbon atoms	A. Streitwieser Jr.	56,	571-752 (1956)
Substitution and rearrangement reactions of allylic compounds	R.H. DeWolfe and W.G. Young	56,	753-901 (1956)
Organic compounds of boron	M.F. Lappert	56,	959-1064 (1956)
Carbon-functional silicones	F.D. George, M. Prober and J.R. Elliott	56,	1065-1219 (1956)
Recent advances in isocyanate chemistry	R.G. Arnold, J.A. Nelson and J.J. Verbanc	57,	47-76 (1957)
Radical substitution in aromatic nuclei	O.C. Dermer and M.T. Edmison	57,	77-122 (1957)

Homolytic aromatic arylation	D.R. Augood and G.H. Williams	57, 123-190 (1957)
Recent developments in the synthesis of fatty acids	W.J. Gensler	57, 191-280 (1957)
Artificial estrogens	J. Grundy	57, 281-416 (1957)
The preparation and properties of phosphonic acids	L.D. Freedman and G.O. Doak	57, 479-523 (1957)
Comparison of phenanthridine with other azo-aromatic heterocycles	J. Eisch and H. Gilman	57, 525-581 (1957)
The Kolbe-Schmitt reaction	A.S. Lindsey and H. Jeskey	57, 583-620 (1957)
The chemistry of carbonyl sulfide	R.J. Ferm	57, 621-640 (1957)
The tetrahydrophthalic acids	R.E. Buckles	57, 641-663 (1957)
Polyethylene: preparation, structure and properties	S.L. Aggarwol and O.J. Sweeting	57, 665-742 (1957)
Metalations with organosodium compounds	R.A. Benkeser et.al.,	57, 867-894 (1957)
Stereochemistry and heterogeneous catalysis	R.L. Burwell Jr.	57, 895-934 (1957)
Application of the H_0 acidity function to kinetics and mechanisms of acid catalysis	F.A. Long and M.A. Paul	57, 935-1010 (1957)
Arylthiazathiolium salts and o-aminoaryl thiols. The Herz reaction	W.K. Warburton	57, 1011-1020 (1957)
The chemistry of quaternized hydrazine compounds	H.H. Sisler and G.M. Omietanski	57, 1021-1047 (1957)
2,4-Oxazolidinediones	J.W. Clark-Lewis	58, 63-99 (1958)
Melamine and derivatives of melamine	B. Brown and S.A. Miller	58, 131-172 (1958)
The chemistry of perchlorocyclopentenes and cyclopentadienes	H.E. Ungnade and E.T. McBee	58, 249-320 (1958)
Polyphosphoric acid as a reagent in organic chemistry	F.D. Popp and W.E. McEwen	58, 321-401 (1958)
Kinetics and mechanism of oxidation by permanganate	J.W. Ladbury and (in part) C.F. Cullis	58, 403-438 (1958)
Oxidations by ferricyanide	B.S. Thyagarjan	58, 439-460 (1958)
The chemistry of trichloromethanesulfenyl chloride	G. Sosnovsky	58, 509-540 (1958)
Polymerization of olefins by complex metal catalysts	J.K. Stille	58, 541-580 (1958)
Infrared intensities and molecular structure	T.L. Brown	58, 581-609 (1958)
Nitromethane. Physical properties, thermodynamics, kinetics of decomposition and utilization as fuel	A. Makovky and L. Lenji	58, 627-644 (1958)
Electronic transitions due to non-bonding electrons in carbonyl-aza-aromatic, and other compounds	J.W. Sidman	58, 689-713 (1958)
Alkyl polymerizations	R.C. Laible	58, 807-843 (1958)
Advances in the synthesis of glycerides of fatty acids	L. Hartman	58, 845-867 (1958)
The synthesis of substituted terphenyls	G.R. Ames	58, 895-923 (1958)
The reactions of ozone with organic compounds	P.S. Bailey	58, 925-1010 (1958)
Reactions of boron trichloride with organic compounds	W. Gerrard and M.F. Lappert	58, 1081-1111 (1958)
Syntheses of alkylated alkanedioic acids	D.G.M. Diaper and A. Kuksis	59, 89-178 (1959)
The chemistry of adrenochrome and related compounds	R.A. Heacock	59, 181-237 (1959)

CHEMICAL REVIEWS (Contd.)

The thermochemistry and reactivity of alkoxyl radicals	P. Gray and A. Williams	59, 239-328 (1959)
Unsymmetrical 1,6-additions to conjugated systems	J.W. Ralls	59, 329-344 (1959)
The furoxans	J.V.R. Kaufman and J.P. Picard	59, 429-461 (1959)
High-resolution nuclear magnetic resonance and molecular structure	S. Brownstein	59, 463-496 (1959)
Nitrous acid and nitrosation	T.A. Turney and G.A. Wright	59, 497-513 (1959)
Scission of the sulfur-sulfur bond	A.J. Parker and N. Kharasch	59, 583-628 (1959)
Near infrared spectra of organic compounds	O.H. Wheeler	59, 629-666 (1959)
The chemistry of the glycocyamidines	C. Lempert	59, 667-736 (1959)
Mechanisms of epoxide reactions	R.E. Parker and N.S. Isaacs	59, 737-799 (1959)
Synthesis and chemistry of cyanogen	T.K. Brotherton and J.W. Lynn	59, 841-883 (1959)
Constituents of tobacco and tobacco smoke	R.A.W. Johnstone and J.R. Plimmer	59, 885-936 (1959)
Anthraquinone-acridones	C.F.H. Allen	59, 983-1030 (1959)
Diterpenoids	M. Tsutsui and E.A. Tsutsui	59, 1031-1075 (1959)
Cleavage and rearrangement of sulfonamides	S. Searles and S. Nukina	59, 1077-1103 (1959)
Basic functions of oxygen in certain organic compounds	W. Gerrard and E.D. Macklen	59, 1105-1123 (1959)
The hydride-transfer reaction	N.C. Deno, H.J. Peterson and G.S. Saines	60, 7-14 (1960)
The chemistry of ninhydrin	D.J. McCaldin	60, 39-51 (1960)
Mechanisms of catalysis of nucleophilic reactions of carboxylic acid derivatives	M.L. Bender	60, 53-113 (1960)
The coordination chemistry of the actinides	A.E. Comyns	60, 115-146 (1960)
The chemistry of sodium nitromalonaldehyde	P.E. Fanta and R.A. Stein	60, 261-266 (1960)
The expansion of the sulfur outer shell	G. Cilento	60, 147-167 (1960)
The Reimer-Tiemann reaction	H. Wynberg	60, 169-184 (1960)
The preparation and properties of tertiary and secondary phosphine oxides	K.D. Berlin and G.B. Butler	60, 243-260 (1960)
The preparation, reactions, and properties of triphenylenes	C.M. Buess and D.D. Lawson	60, 313-330 (1960)
Pyrolytic cis eliminations	C.H. DePuy and R.W. King	60, 431-457 (1960)
Organotin compounds	R.K. Ingham, S.D. Rosenberg and H. Gilman	60, 459-539 (1960)
Long-chain derivatives of monosaccharides and oligosaccharides	G.R. Ames	60, 541-553 (1960)
Gossypol, a pigment of cottonseed	R. Adams, T.A. Geissman and J.D. Edwards	60, 555-574 (1960)
Applications of molecular spectroscopy to relationships between biological activity and structure	P.W. Sadler	60, 575-592 (1960)

CHEMISCHE BERICHTE

Published by Verein Deutcher Chemiker Verlag Chemie, GMBH. Until 1945, called Berichte der Deutchen Chemischen Gesselschaft and published by same. The section A, containing some reviews, was discontinued in 1945. All articles are in German.

Title	Author	Reference
The box-model theory and its application to aromatic compounds	O. Schmidt	73 A, 97-116 (1940)
New developments in carbohydrate research	G. Zemplén	74 A, 75-92 (1941)
New synthetic work in the camphor and terpene groups	G. Komppa	75 A, 1-13 (1942)
Contribution to the chemistry of carbohydrates	K. Freudenberg	76 A, 71-96 (1943)
Cytochromes	K. Zeile	76 A, 99-115 (1943)
Chemistry and metabolism of blood-dyes	W. Ziedel	77 A, 21-42 (1944)
Main results of my research in the chemistry of complexes	P. Pfeiffer	77 A, 59-73 (1944)

CHEMISTRY AND INDUSTRY

A weekly journal, published by the Society of Chemical Industry, London, in English. This journal publishes review articles, and short communications.

Title	Author	Reference
Plastics and coal	N.J.L. Megson and K.W. Pepper	247-253 (1940)
The constitution and physiological significance of carotene and allied pigments	R.A. Morton	301-307 (1940)
Mesomerism	R.C. Evans	518-521 (1940)
The hydrogen bond	H.J. Eméleus	583-585 (1940)
The role of free radicals in the mechanisms of gaseous explosions	A.R. Ubbelohde	657-659 (1940)
Bivalent hydrogen. Some new aspects of tautomerism	L. Hunter	32-37 (1941)
The development of polyvinyl resins	G.O. Morrison	209 (1941)
Correlations among cancer-producing compounds	J.W. Cook	242-243 (1941)
Diazotization	J. Kenner	443-447 (1941)
Proteins	W.T. Astbury	491-497 (1941)
"Through the looking glass"	G.N. Copley	631-635 (1941)
Vitamin-A and the biologically active carotenoids	R.F. Hunter	89-94 (1942)
The chemical structure of plastics	C.A. Redfarn	201-204 (1942)
Synthetic resins for surface and protective coatings	E.A. Bevan	261-267 (1942)
The light absorption of geometrical isomerides and the structure of vitamin-D	H.P. Koch	273-275 (1942)
Newer aspects of the chemical function of the vitamins	L.E. Booher	388-392 (1942)
Some of the recent developments in the field of thiocyanates	J.H. Clayton and B. Bann	420-422 (1942)
Aspects of the chemistry of flavouring materials	T.F. West	46-49 (1943)
Plastics from acetylene	J.I. Jones	66-71 (1943)
Mucopolysaccharides and related substances	M. Stacey	110-112 (1943)
The thiazoles and their uses in industry and medicine	R.F. Hunter	118-121 (1943)
Recent advances in organic chemical methods	E.R.H. Jones	178 (1943)
The physical states of rubber in relation to its molecular structure	L.R.G. Treloar	326-328 (1943)
Some aspects of the chemistry of antioxidants	F. Bergel	127-128 (1944)
The hydrogen bond	L. Hunter	155-157 (1944)
The pyrethrins and the role of pyrethrum in anti-pest measures. Part 1	T.F. West	290-294 (1944)
Developments of valency theory	E.J. Bowen	338-341 (1944)
The vitamin B_2 complex. Some recently characterized components. Part 1	F.A. Robinson	370-373 (1944)
The vitamin B_2 complex. Some recently characterized components. Part II	F.A. Robinson	386-389 (1944)
The X-ray examination of plastics	W.T. Astbury	114-116 (1945)
Macromolecular chemistry	S.H. Pinner	138-140 (1945)

CHEMISTRY AND INDUSTRY (Contd.)

The γ-isomer of hexachlorocyclohexane (Gammexane)	R.E. Slade	314-319 (1945)
Photography in colour	H. Baines	2-5 (1946)
Some recent developments in the chemistry of tea	A.E. Bradfield	242-244 (1946)
Ion exchange resins	C.W. Davies	51-54 (1948)
Biotin and related compounds	E. Ju-Hwa Chu	115-118 (1948)
Recent advances in antibiotic research	P.P. Regna	275-278 (1948) 295-297 (1948)
The relation between chemical structure and performance	W.D. Scott and D.S.P. Roebuck	627-631 (1948)
Some developments in organic chemical manufacture: dyestuffs	Wm. Smith and W.G. Reid	675-679 (1948)
Practical aspects of wetting and detergency	E.S. Paice	691-694 (1948)
A survey of steroid molecular rotations	D.H.R. Barton and W. Klyne	755-759 (1948)
Molecular structure and biological specificity	L. Pauling	1-4 (1948) Supplement
Some recent results in organic chemistry	P. Karrer	5-8 (1948) Supplement
Recent developments in electrophoresis	A. Tiselius	9-12 (1948) Supplement
The part of chemistry in the new therapeutics	H. Dale	17-22 (1948) Supplement
Chemical aspects of elastomers	H.W. Melville	83-86 (1949)
Recent advances in the chemistry of the phenol-aldehyde condensation	E.G.K. Pritchett	295-299 (1949)
Some aspects of the relationship between chemical constitution and physiological activity	F. Bergel	407-412 (1949)
The sugar cane as a source of raw materials for chemical industry	L.F. Wiggins	555-560 (1949)
The relation of physical characteristics and chemical structure of cellulose derivatives	E. Ott	915-922 (1949)
Synthetic fibres from natural proteins: Reactions with formaldehyde	D. Traill	23-30 (1950)
Progress in the science and technology of natural rubber	A. van Rossem	63-71 (1950)
Some recent advances in thermohardening resins	N.J.L. Megson	100-104 (1950)
The chemistry of photographic sensitizing dyestuffs	J.O. Kendall	121-124 (1950)
Symposium on amino-acids and protein hydrolysates: Introductory address	E.C. Dodds	135-143 (1950)
Displacement chromatography as a preparative method for amino-acids	S.M. Partridge	383-387 (1950)
The chemistry of thyroxine	B.A. Hems	663-666 (1950)
Recent progress in the chemistry of phenolic resins	S.R. Finn N.J.L. Megson and E.J.W. Whittaker	849-853 (1950)
Insecticidal phosphorus compounds	B. Topley	859-868 (1950)
Amino acid analysis	G.R. Tristram	868-873 (1950)
The chemistry of antihistamine and related drugs	D.W. Adamson	2-7 (1951)
The Meerwein-Ponndorff/Oppenauer reaction	W.A. Johnson and G.E.H. Skrimshire	380-384 (1951)
The chemical compositions and properties of pectins	J.K.N. Jones	430-431 (1951)
Trypanocides: A review	L.P. Walls	606-610 (1951)

The adrenocortical hormones	G.F. Marrian	804-807 (1951)
Nomenclature of some stereoisomeric compounds. Specification of configurations	W. Klyne	1022-1025 (1951)
Some recent developments in the academic fields of starch chemistry	E.J. Bourne	1047-1052 (1951)
Recent developments in the surface coating industry	F. Armitage and W.T.C. Hammond	1082-1087 (1951)
Streptomycin - its uses, properties and production	W.B. Emery	254-259 (1952)
The diamino-triazine group: some recent approaches and applications	G.V. Austerweil	372-375 (1952)
The possible nature of the synthesis of "Koresin" and the polyfunctional nature of certain naphthenates	E.G. Curphey	389-392 (1952)
Studies in chemical documentation. Part 1. Formula indexes; order of citation of elements	G.M. Dyson	676-684 (1952)
Acetylene in chemical industry	N. Booth	812-819 (1952)
The synthesis of peptides	B.L. Shapiro	1119-1125 (1952)
Some recent advances in fluorine chemistry	H.J. Eméleus	1235-1238 (1952)
The stereochemistry of alkaloids	R.C. Cookson	337-340 (1953)
Depolymerization reactions in vinyl polymers	N. Grassie	622-624 (1953)
The biochemistry of schradan	B.A. Kilby	856-861 (1953)
Recent research on oxidation of monoethenoid fatty acids and esters	J.H. Skellon	1047-1049 (1953)
Some chemical problems arising in the study of anthraquinone dyes	S. Coffey	1068-1074 (1953)
Ion exchange and its applications in the fine chemical industry	E.L. Streatfield	1214-1222 (1953)
Recent developments in the study of oxidative deterioration of lipids	C.H. Lea	1303-1309 (1953)
The chemistry of wood extractives	F.E. King	1325-1328 (1953)
Some relationships between chemical constitution and biological activity	W.A. Sexton	1356-1359 (1953)
The interpretation of organic chemical analyses with anti-composition tables	H.H. Hatt	30-32 (1954)
An analysis of the Friedel-Crafts reaction	H. Burton and P.F.G. Praill	90-92 (1954)
Recent advances in the structure of phenoplasts	R.F. Hunter	262-265 (1954)
Anticholinesterases. The relation between structure and activity of anticholinesterases containing quarternary-nitrogen groups	A.W.D. Avison	288-293 (1954)
Studies in chemical documentation. Part III. Mechanized documentation	G.M. Dyson	440-449 (1954)
Chemical and physical aspects of synthetic fibres	R. Hill	1083-1089 (1954)
The mechanism of hydrolysis at carbonyl carbon	C.A. Bunton T.A. Lewis and D.R. Llewellyn	1154-1155 (1954)
Carbon disulphide. Some applications in organic synthesis	E.G. Curphey	102-104 (1955)
A new isomeric change in the flavonoids	S.K. Mukerjee and T.R. Seshadri	271-275 (1955)
The stereochemistry of bimolecular substitution reactions	H.M.E. Cardwell	422-424 (1955)

CHEMISTRY AND INDUSTRY (Contd.)

Fluorine-containing lubricants	A.J. Rudge	452-461 (1955)
The representation of the so-called mesoionic compounds	A.R. Katritzky	521-522 (1955)
The alkaline degradation of carbonyl oxycelluloses and the significance of saccharinic acids for the chemistry of carbohydrates	J. Kenner	727-730 (1955)
The hydrolysis of organic phosphates	P.W.C. Barnard et. al.	760-763 (1955)
Recent chemistry of phosphine	N.L. Paddock	900-905 (1955)
Mechanism of the Wurtz-Fittig reaction between organic halides, tetrachlorosilane and sodium	H.G. Emblem, D. Ridge and M. Todd	905-906 (1955)
Meso-ionic compounds	W. Baker and W.D. Ollis	910-911 (1955)
On the structure of cyclic mesoionic compounds	T.I. Bieber	1055-1056 (1955)
Stability of glycosides to acid hydrolysis. A conformational analysis	J.T. Edward	1102-1104 (1955)
Nucleic acid structure and function	A. Todd	1139-1144 (1955)
X-rays and the molecule	L. Bragg	1164-1169 (1955)
Measurement of molecular weight by the light scattering method. The models of light scattering theory	D. Cleverdon, L. Harvey, D. Laker and P.G. Smith	1396-1398 (1955)
Monomeric and polymeric vinyl acetate and its derivatives	O. Horn	1748-1755 (1955)
The effect of ring size on the enolization and acidity of α-carbethoxy and α-acylcycloalkanones	P.B. Russell	326-327 (1956)
Phosphates in vital processes	A.R. Todd	802-807 (1956)
That heterocyclic nitrogen and oxygen may be less electron attracting than carbon	I.M. Bassett, R.D. Brown and A. Penfold	892-893 (1956)
Optical rotation and geometrical structure	D.H. Whiffen	964-968 (1956)
Polyester resins: Their chemical nature and industrial uses	L.H. Vaughan	996-1005 (1956)
The chromatographic separation of phospholipids	D.N. Rhodes	1010-1013 (1956)
The determination of small amounts of γ-picoline in aqueous solutions of γ-picoline by vapour phase chromatography	W.J. Murray and A.F. Williams	1020-1021 (1956)
Phospholipids in foods	J.N. Hawthorne	1171-1174 (1956)
Production and organic chemistry of chelating agents	J.K. Aiken	1334-1338 (1956)
Radiation as a tool in the synthesis of organic compounds	E.J. Bourne, M. Stacey and G. Vaughan	1372-1376 (1956)
Industrial and medical uses of carbohydrates	M. Stacey	1398-1408 (1956)
Phospholipids in foods. Classes and formulae of phospholipids	H.H. Hutt	1412-1414 (1956)
Applications of infrared spectroscopy in chemical industry. Recent advances in infrared structural analysis	L.J. Bellamy	26-28 (1957)
Applications of infrared spectroscopy in chemical industry. Applications of infrared spectroscopy to textile problems	C.G. Cannon	29-33 (1957)
Applications of infrared spectroscopy. The infrared spectroscopy of steroids	J.E. Page	58-63 (1957)
Applications of infrared spectroscopy. Some applications of infrared spectroscopy to carbohydrate chemistry	D.H. Whiffen	129-135 (1957)

Applications of infrared spectroscopy. Some applications of infrared spectroscopy to structural problems in the rubber industry	W.H.T. Davison	131-135 (1957)
The mechanism of hydrogenation reactions	F.J. McQuillin	251-252 (1957)
Modern methods of research	L.A. Jordan	306-318 (1957)
Achievements of industrial chemistry — hydrocarbon macromolecules	C.W. Bunn	404-410 (1957)
Recent work on the polymerization of acrylonitrile	J.C. Bevington	411-412 (1957)
The role of abnormal linkages in polymer degradation reactions	N. Grassie	537-542 (1957)
The chemistry and functions of vitamin B_{12}	E.L. Smith	572-577 (1957)
Some aspects of chelating and complexing resins	J.R. Millar	606-612 (1957)
Epoxide resins. Some aspects of the chemistry of epoxide resins in relation to their application	P. Bruin	616-621 (1957)
The study of biologically active agents as a vocation	F. Bergel	740-750 (1957)
The substituted urea herbicides	A.L. Abel	1106-1112 (1957)
Some new chemical and physical aspects of polyester resin technology	B.T. Hayes W.J. Read and L.H. Vaughan	1162-1170 (1957)
Industrial organic intermediates: past, present and future	D.A.W. Adams	1428-1432 (1957)
Isotactic polymers	G. Natta	1520-1530 (1957)
The use of radioactive isotopes and high-energy	H.W. Melville	1632-1638 (1957)
Theoretical chemistry: looking before and after	D.P. Craig	3-7 (1958)
Chemistry of hexachlorocyclopentadiene	C.W. Roberts	110-115 (1958)
Synthesis in the study of nucleotides	A.R. Todd	170-176 (1958)
One hundred years of diazo-compounds. Their impact and importance in the chemical industry	W.H. Cliffe	1248-1255 (1958)
The chemistry of insulin	F. Sanger	104-109 (1959)
Some developments in the field of chemical propellents	W.S. Wood	136-142 (1959)
Cortisone from hecogenin	B.A. Hems	442-448 (1959)
Surface activity of organo-silicon compounds	R.L. Bass	912-918 (1959)
Catalysis in industry	J.H. de Boer	934-941 (1959)
Organic chemical research in industry	R. Robinson	964-972 (1959)
Chemical structure and action of morphine-like analgesics and related substances	N.B. Eddy	1462-1468 (1959)
The present state of our knowledge in the field of elastomers	P. Baumann	1498-1504 (1959)
The cardiac glycosides of digitalis	A. Stoll	1558-1567 (1959)
A century of synthetic dyes for cellulosic fibres	S. Coffey	132-138 (1960)
The possibility of obtaining polymeric materials, based on polyacrylonitrile, with semiconducting properties	A.V. Topchiyev et.al.	184-186 (1960)
High polymers and molecular architecture	C.E.H. Bawn	388-391 (1960)
Chemical derivatives of fats for industrial utilisation	W.C. Ault	476-479 (1960)
The production of bulk organic chemicals	D.G. Smith	508-515 (1960)
Recent developments in the field of high polymers	H.F. Mark	568-571 (1960)
Co-ordination polymers: a review	C.N. Kenney	880-884 (1960)

Terephthalic acid by isomerisation and disproportionation	P.W. Sherwood	1096-1100 (1960)
Some new herbicides: developments in chemical weed control 1958-60	E.K. Woodford and L. Kasasian	1118-1125 (1960)
Pyrethrolone and related compounds	M. Elliott	1142-1146 (1960)
Polyurethane foams: methods of production, properties and applications	J.M. Buist R. Hurd and A. Lowe	1544-1558 (1960)

CHIMIA

This is a monthly journal, published in English, French and German by the "Schweizerischer Chemiker Verband". It contains both review articles and short communications.

Title	Author	Reference
Vitamins as building stones of enzymes (in German)	P. Karrer	<u>1</u>, 3-12 (1947)
Review of the chemistry and physics of pectic materials and discussion of the newer literature 1937-1946 (in German)	H. Pallman and H. Deuel	<u>1</u>, 27-33 (1947) 51-56
New methods of oil refinement as the modern basis of the heavy organic chemistry industry in the USA	J. Risi	<u>1</u>, 239-246 (1947)
Research in the field of polycyclic hydrocarbons (in German)	E. Bergmann	<u>2</u>, 45-51 (1948)
Progress in some fields of organic chemistry (in German)	P. Karrer	<u>2</u>, 101-109 (1948)
Products with musk odor and development of the large-ring chemistry (in French)	M. Stoll	<u>2</u>, 217-226 (1948)
Properties and activities of reductones (in German)	H. v. Euler	<u>3</u>, 209-213 (1949)
Progress in the chemistry of acetylene and carbon monoxide (in German)	W. Reppe	<u>3</u>, 233-237 (1949) 257-266
Chemistry of the suprarenal hormones (in German)	Th. Reichstein	<u>4</u>, 21-25 (1949) 47-53
Chemistry of vitamin A (in German)	O. Isler	<u>4</u>, 103-118 (1950)
Light absorption of organic compounds (in German)	H. Kuhn	<u>4</u>, 203-218 (1950)
Recent progress in the chemistry of terpenoid constituents of essential oils (in French)	Y.R. Navez	<u>4</u>, 227-232 (1951)
Lithium aluminum hydride in organic chemistry (in German)	U. Solms	<u>5</u>, 25-39 (1951)
Cardioactive glycosides (in German)	Th. Reichstein	<u>5</u>, 93-100 (1951)
Sebacic acid (in English)	H. Jones	<u>5</u>, 169-173 (1951)
Progress in organic microanalysis, especially in the determination of functional groups (in German)	H. Lieb	<u>6</u>, 34-39 (1952)
Synthesis of alkyl aryl sulfonates as intermediates with detergent action (in German)	A. v. Segesser and H. Stüpel	<u>6</u>, 84-86 (1952)
Growth-promoters and their antagonists (in German)	H. v. Euler	<u>6</u>, 253-258 (1952)
Reactivity and stereochemistry in the cyclohexane series (in French)	M. Mousseron	<u>7</u>, 108-111 (1953)
Structural analysis of polypeptide chains (in German)	M. Brenner	<u>7</u>, 198-206 (1953)
Chemistry of completely synthetic fibers (in German)	H. Zollinger	<u>7</u>, 222-230 (1953)
Stereochemical problems in organic chemistry (in German)	H. Dahn	<u>8</u>, 25-30 (1954)
Development and present status of chemical research on wood (in German)	H.F.J. Wenzl	<u>8</u>, 31-48 (1954)

CHIMIA (Contd.)

Title	Author	Vol.	Pages	Year
Polycyclic aromatic hydrocarbons and heterocyclics as new building stones in the synthesis of dyes (in German)	Th. Holbro	8,	57-64	(1954)
Hydroxylation of steroids by biological methods (in German)	K. Florey	8,	81-87	(1954)
New progress in the chemistry and industry of synthetic perfumes (in French)	Y.R. Navez	8,	175-178, 189-195	(1954)
Some new insecticides (in German)	H. Gysin	8,	205-210, 221-229	(1954)
Chemistry and biochemistry of tropan alkaloids (in German)	A. Stoll and E. Jucker	9,	25-36	(1955)
Progress in rubber science and rubber technology (in German)	R. Herzog	9,	149-161, 265-276	(1955)
Use of possible in-vivo alkaloid synthesis to some fields of drug synthesis	E. Jucker	9,	195-215	(1955)
Macromolecular chemistry (in German)	H. Staudinger	9,	225-232	(1955)
Scope of molecular physics in chemistry (in German)	H. Labhart	10,	125-132	(1956)
New developments in the chemistry of natural organic products (in English)	Ch. Tamm	10,	221-228	(1956)
Molecular architecture and living matter (in German)	A.S. Dreiding	11,	152-161	(1957)
Paper chromatography and paper electrophoresis (in German)	A. Grüne	11,	173-203, 213-256	(1957)
Ozonization and ozonolysis of aromatic and heterocyclic compounds in relation to the reactivity of the rings (in German)	J.P. Wibaut	11,	298-304, 321-328	(1957)
Synthesis in the field of the carotenoids (in French)	O. Isler and M. Montavon	12,	1-16	(1958)
Synthesis of active polypeptides (in German)	R. Schwyzer	12,	53-68	(1958)
The structure of osazones (in German)	G. Henseke and H.J. Binte	12,	103-112	(1958)
Chemical structure and activity of moth repellants containing the sulfonic acid group (in German)	H. Martin	12,	191-215	(1958)
Chemistry of aminonaphthoquinones (in German)	E. Merian	13,	181-191	(1959)
The influence of substituents on the chemical reactivity of aromatic compounds (in German)	A. v. Willi	13,	257-263, 285-291	(1959)
Spectropolarimetry (in German)	H.G. Lermann	14,	1-10	(1960)
Carbon monoxide (in German)	R. Grauer	14,	11-16	(1960)
Applications of high-resolution nuclear magnetic resonance spectroscopy to organic chemistry (In English)	N. Sheppard	14,	145-152	(1960)
Chemical applications of electron resonance	K.H. Hauser	14,	153-161	(1960)
The use of gas chromatography in the organic laboratory (in German)	W. Simon	14,	189-201	(1960)
Use of radioactive isotopes in the study of reaction mechanisms in organic chemistry (in German)	H. Schmid	14,	248-261	(1960)

CHIMIA (Contd.)

The application of mass spectrometry in amino-acid and peptide chemistry (in English)	K. Biemann	14, 293-301 (1960)
Use of X-ray methods for the identification of peptides (in German)	H. Zahn	14, 401-404 (1960)
The use of enzymatic reactions for purity-analysis and structural determination of peptides and proteins (in German)	H. Zuber	14, 405-418 (1960)

ENDEAVOUR

A quarterly review designed to record the progress of the sciences "in the service of mankind." In English. Published by Imperial Chemical Industries. Present editor is T.I. Williams.

Title	Author	Reference
Phthalocyanines	C.J.T. Cronshaw	1, 79-84 (1942)
The production of cancer by chemical compounds	A. Haddow	2, 26-33 (1943)
The hemp drugs	A.R. Todd	2, 69-72 (1943)
Paludrine - a new antimalarial drug	F.L. Rose	5, 65-69 (1946)
The fluorescence of organic compounds	N. Campbell	5, 155-159 (1946)
Organosilicon compounds and their industrial development	D.V.N. Hardy	6, 29-35 (1947)
Carotenoid pigments	P. Karrer	7, 3-8 (1948)
Chemical properties and structure of the penicillins. Part I	E. Chain	7, 83-91 (1948)
Chemical properties and structure of the penicillins. Part II	E. Chain	7, 152-158 (1948)
Mechanism of chemical reactions	M. Polanyi	8, 3-10 (1949)
Some aspects of terpene chemistry	L.N. Owen and J.L. Simonsen	8, 26-31 (1949)
Cyclo-polyolefines and related molecules	W. Baker	9, 35-39 (1950)
The reactivity of free radicals in solution	H.W. Melville	9, 98-101 (1950)
Molecular compounds	H.M. Powell	9, 154-158 (1950)
The chemistry of plant gums and mucilages	E.L. Hirst	10, 106-111 (1951)
Carotenoids and vitamin A - the end of a chapter	I. Heilbron	10, 175-182 (1951)
Fibres from aromatic polyesters	J.R. Whinfield	11, 29-32 (1952)
The biological importance of organic compounds of sulfur	F. Challenger	12, 173-181 (1953)
Some intramolecular electrical effects on the course of chemical change	R. Robinson	13, 173-183 (1954)
Organic compounds of the metals	W. Wardlaw and D.C. Bradley	14, 140-145 (1955)
Vitamin B_{12}	A.W. Johnson and A. Todd	15, 29-33 (1956)
The Perkin family of organic chemists	R. Robinson	15, 92-102 (1956)
New kinds of macromolecules	C.E.H. Bawn	15, 137-143 (1956)
The structure of insulin	F. Sanger and L.F. Smith	16, 48-53 (1957)
Nonulosaminic acids - complexes of carbohydrates and amino acids	M. Stacey	19, 43-49 (1960)

EXPERIENTIA

An international journal, published in English, French and German by Birkhauser Verlag (BASEL). This journal publishes both leading (review) articles and short communications in all fields of the natural sciences. Present editors are A.v. Muralt, L. Ruzicka and J. Weigle.

Title	Author	Reference
The ergot alkaloids (in French)	A. Stoll	$\underline{1}$, 250-262 (1945)
Hashish (in English)	A.R. Todd	$\underline{2}$, 55-60 (1946)
The mechanical properties of rubber (in French)	K.H. Meyer and A.J.A. Vanderwyk	$\underline{2}$, 117-126 (1946)
The chemical constitution of wood (in German)	A.v. Wacek	$\underline{2}$, 171-180 (1946)
The lignin sulfonic acids and their technical use (in German)	K. Kratzl	$\underline{2}$, 469-476 (1946)
Cortical steroids: configurations at C_{20} relative to C_{17} (in English)	L.F. Fieser and M. Fieser	$\underline{4}$, 285-295 (1948)
Curare (in English)	D. Bovet and F. Bovet-Nitti	$\underline{4}$, 325-348 (1948)
The Serini reaction (in English)	C.W. Shoppee	$\underline{4}$, 418-420 (1948)
The estrogenic hormones from their discovery to their complete synthesis (in French)	K. Miescher	$\underline{5}$, 1-11 (1949)
Recent progress in histamine and antihistamine research (in English)	C.P. Huttrer	$\underline{5}$, 53-65 (1949)
New developments in the field of acetylene and carbon monoxide (in German)	W. Reppe	$\underline{5}$, 93-110 (1949)
Chemical and biochemical studies of proteins of tumors (in German)	F. Kögl	$\underline{5}$, 173-180 (1949)
Studies on the influence of temperature and of catalysts on the substitution reactions of the aromatic ring (in German)	J.P. Wibaut	$\underline{5}$, 337-347 (1949)
The internal structure of protein molecules (in English)	F. Haurowitz	$\underline{5}$, 347-354 (1949)
Compounds of quinone structure as allergens and cancerogenic agents (in English)	R.L. Mayer	$\underline{6}$, 241-250 (1950)
The most important processes in color photography (in German)	J. Eggert	$\underline{6}$, 401-410 (1950)
A hundred years of ion exchange (in German)	V. Deuel and F. Hostettler	$\underline{6}$, 445-456 (1950)
The past and present of starch chemistry (in English)	K.H. Meyer	$\underline{8}$, 405-420 (1952)
Chemical binding and state of the electrons in molecules. Part I. (in German)	H. Kuhn	$\underline{9}$, 41-61 (1953)
Chemistry of snake venoms (in German)	K. Slotta	$\underline{9}$, 81-88 (1953)
The isoprene rule and the biogenesis of terpenic compounds (in English)	L. Ruzicka	$\underline{9}$, 357-367 (1953)
Some stereochemical aspects of polyenes (in English)	L. Zechmeister	$\underline{10}$, 1-11 (1954)
The constitutions of cevine and some related alkaloids (in English)	D.H.R. Barton O. Jeger V. Prelog and R.B. Woodward	$\underline{10}$ 81-90 (1954)

Chemistry of insecticides. Their development and present status (in German)	P. Müller and M. Spindler	10, 91-131 (1954)
The cardiotonic compounds of scilla maritima L. (in French)	A. Stoll	10, 282-297 (1954)
Advances in the field of adrenal cortical hormones (in English)	A. Wettstein and G. Anner	10, 397-416 (1954)
The specification of asymmetric configuration in organic chemistry (in English)	R.S. Cahn	12, 81-94 (1956)
The mechanism of electrophilic aromatic substitution (in English)	H.Ch. Zollinger	12, 165-175 (1956)
The order of stability of stereoisomeric hydrindenes and hydrindanone derivatives (in German)	G. Quinkert	13, 381-389 (1957)
The separation of fatty acids (in German)	R.T. Holman	14, 121-127 (1958)
Benzyne intermediates in nucleophilic aromatic substitution (in German)	E.F. Jenny M.C. Caserio and J.D. Roberts	14, 349-354 (1958)
Results and problems of organic anionic chemistry (in German)	G. Wittig	14, 389-395 (1958)
Alkaloid biosynthesis (in English)	E. Wenkert	15, 165-173 (1959)
The constitution of limonin (in English)	D. Arigoni D.H.R. Barton, E.J. Corey, O. Jeger et al.	16, 41-49 (1960)
The structure of limonin (in English)	S. Arnott et.al.,	16, 49-51 (1960)
Chemistry of natural products (in German)	A. Stoll	16, 85-100 (1960)
Catachenes and hydroxyflavandioles as tannin precursors (in German)	K. Freudenberg	16, 101-105 (1960)
Reactions of anthocyanidins upon pH changes and illumination (in German)	H. Kuhn and W. Sperling	16, 237-244 (1960)
A view of progress in the chemistry of indole alkaloids (in English)	E. Schlittler and W.I. Taylor	16, 244-248 (1960)
Description of steric relationships across single bonds (in English)	W. Klyne and V. Prelog	16, 521-523 (1960)

FORTSCHRITTE DER CHEMIE ORGANISCHER NATURSTOFFE

These review articles, edited by Professor L. Zechmeister of the California Institute of Technology, cover the recent advances in the chemistry of Natural Products. The articles are most frequently in English and German, and only occasionally in French. Published by Springer-Verlag, Vienna, since 1945.

Title	Author	Reference	
The chemistry of plant heart venoms, toad venoms, saponines and alkaloids of the steroid group (In German)	R. Tschesche	4,	1-27 (1945)
Contribution to the biochemistry of the vitamin B group. (Pantothenic acid and vitamin B_6) (in German)	Th. Wieland and I. Löw	4,	28-45 (1945)
Pterins (in German)	R. Purrmann	4,	64-86 (1945)
Carotenoid-epoxides and furanoid oxides of carotenoid dyes (in German)	P. Karrer	5,	1-19 (1948)
Azulenes	A.J. Haagen-Smit	5,	40-71 (1948)
Recent advances in the study of component acids and component glycerides of natural fats (in English)	T.P. Hilditch	5,	72-100 (1948)
Recent developments in the structural problem of cellulose. I. The linear structure of cellulose (in English)	E. Pacsu	5,	128-174 (1948)
Lignin (in English)	F.E. Brauns	5,	175-240 (1948)
The chemistry of the constituents of toad venoms (in English)	V. Deulofeu	5,	241-266 (1948)
Odors and perfumes of animals (in French)	E. Lederer	6,	87-153 (1950)
Cactus alkaloids and some related compounds	L. Reti	6,	242-289 (1950)
The constitution of triterpenes (in German)	O. Jeger	7,	1-86 (1950)
Constitution, configuration and synthesis of digitaloid aglycones and glycosides (in German)	H. Heusser	7,	87-166 (1950)
Thyroxine and related compounds (in English)	C. Niemann	7,	167-192 (1950)
Penicillin and its place in science (in English)	A.H. Cook	7,	193-247 (1950)
Sennosides A and B, the active principles of Senna (in English)	A. Stoll and B. Becker	7,	248-269 (1950)
The fine structure of cellulose (in English)	A. Frey-Wyssling and K. Mühlethaler	8,	1-27 (1951)
Sugar phosphates (in English)	L.F. Leloir	8,	47-95 (1951)
The chemistry of nucleotides (in English)	G.W. Kenner	8,	96-145 (1951)
The odoriferous substances from violets (in German)	H. Schinz	8,	146-206 (1951)
New developments in the field of lichen substances (in German)	Y. Asahina	8,	207-244 (1951)

FORTSCHRITTE DER CHEMIE ORGANISCHER NATURSTOFFE (Contd.)

Title	Author(s)	Vol., Pages (Year)
Lupin alkaloids and related compounds (in German)	F. Galinovsky	8, 245-277 (1951)
Ipecac alkaloids (in German)	M. Pailer	8, 278-309 (1951)
Synthetic chemistry of carotenoids (in German)	H.H. Inhoffen and H. Siemer	9, 1-40 (1952)
Synthesis and properties of vitamin A and some related compounds (in English)	J.G. Baxter	9, 41-87 (1952)
The antivitamins (in French)	P. Meunier	9, 88-113 (1952)
Recent investigations on ergot alkaloids (in English)	A. Stoll	9, 114-174 (1952)
The alkaloids of the merispermaceae plants (in German)	M. Tomita	9, 175-224 (1952)
Naturally occurring coumarins (in English)	F.M. Dean	9, 225-291 (1952)
Some current concepts of the chemical nature of antigens and antibodies (in English)	D.H. Campbell and N. Bulman	9, 443-484 (1952)
Application of the diene synthesis to the investigation of natural products (in German)	K. Alder and M. Schumacher	10, 1-118 (1953)
Chemistry of bacterial lipids (in French)	J. Asselineau and E. Lederer	10, 170-273 (1953)
Syntheses of cortisone (in English)	G. Rosenkranz and F. Sondheimer	10, 274-389 (1953)
Rauwolfia alkaloids (in English)	A. Chatterjee (née Mookerjee)	10, 391-422 (1953)
Insecticides occurring in higher plants (in English)	L. Feinstein and M. Jacobson	10, 423-476 (1953)
Starch: its constitution, enzymic synthesis and degradation (in English)	S. Peat	11, 1-42 (1954)
New developments in the field of lignin and lignification (in German)	K. Freudenberg	11, 43-82 (1954)
Problems and new results in the vitamin D chemistry (in German)	H.H. Inhoffen and K. Brückner	11, 83-123 (1954)
Naturally-occurring chromones (in German)	H. Schmid	11, 124-179 (1954)
The configuration of polypeptide chains in proteins (in English)	L. Pauling and R.B. Corey	11, 180-239 (1954)
Porphyrins in nature (in English)	R. Lemberg	11, 299-349 (1954)
The pteridines (in English)	A. Albert	11, 350-403 (1954)
Sesquiterpenes and diterpenes (in English)	A.J. Haagen-Smit	12, 1-43 (1955)
Tetracyclic triterpenes (in English)	E.R.H. Jones and T.G. Halsall	12, 44-130 (1955)

FORTSCHRITTE DER CHEMIE ORGANISCHER NATURSTOFFE (Contd.)

Title	Author(s)	Citation
The pyrrolizidine alkaloids (in English)	F.L. Warren	12, 198-269 (1955)
Iodinated amino acids and iodo proteins (in French)	J. Roche and R. Michel	12, 349-405 (1955)
Chemistry and biochemistry of snake venoms (in English)	K. Slotta	12, 406-465 (1955)
Gallotannins and ellagic tanning agents (in German)	O.T. Schmidt	13, 70-136 (1956)
New developments in the field of glycosidic heart poisons. Fundamentals and the aglycones (in German)	Ch. Tamm	13, 137-231 (1956)
Natural tropolones and some related troponoids (in English)	T. Nozoe	13, 232-301 (1956)
Alkaloids related to anthranilic acid (in English)	J.R. Price	13, 302-345 (1956)
Recent developments in the chemistry and pharmacology of rauwolfia alkaloids (in English)	A. Chatterjee S.C. Pakrashi and G. Werner	13, 346-443 (1956)
Synthesis of peptides (in German)	W. Grassmann and E. Wünsch	13, 444-559 (1956)
New developments in the field of glycosidic heart poisons: sugars and glycosides (in German)	Ch. Tamm	14, 71-140 (1957)
Photodynamic active plant dyes (in German)	H. Brockmann	14, 141-185 (1957)
The aminochromes (in English)	H. Sobotka N. Barsel and J.D. Chanley	14, 217-243 (1957)
Visual pigments (in English)	R.A. Morton and G.A.J. Pitt	14, 244-316 (1957)
Some in vitro conversions of naturally-occurring carotenoids (in English)	L. Zechmeister	15, 31-82 (1958)
The chemistry of podophyllum (in English)	J.L. Hartwell and A.W. Schrecker	15, 83-166 (1958)
X-ray analysis and the structure of vitamin B_{12} (in English)	D.C. Hodgkin	15, 167-220 (1958)
Catechines, other hydroxy flavanes and hydroxy flavenes (in German)	K. Freudenberg and K. Weinges	16, 1-25 (1958)
Recent progress in the chemistry of the aconite-garrya alkaloids (in English)	K. Wiesner and Z. Valenta	16, 26-89 (1958)
Structural chemistry of actinomycetes antibiotics (in English)	E.E. van Tamelen	16, 90-138 (1958)
The electron gas theory of the color of natural and artificial dyes: problems and principles (in English)	H. Kuhn	16, 169-205 (1958)
Flavones and isoflavones (in English)	K. Venkataraman	17, 1-69 (1959)
Progress in the chemistry of Vitamin D and its derivatives (in German)	H.H. Inhoffen and K. Irmscher	17, 70-123 (1959)

FORTSCHRITTE DER CHEMIE ORGANISCHER NATURSTOFFE (Contd.)

New developments in the chemistry of plant bitter substances (in German)	F. Korte H. Barkemeyer and I. Korte	17, 124-182 (1959)
Alkaloids of calebash-curare and South American strychnos varieties (in German)	K. Bernauer	17, 183-247 (1959)
Paleobiochemistry and organic geochemistry (in English)	P. H. Abelson	17, 379-403 (1959)
The electron gas theory of the color of natural and artificial dyes: applications and extensions (in English)	H. Kuhn	17, 404-451 (1959)
The actinomycins (in German)	H. Brockmann	18, 1-54 (1960)
Guanidilic derivatives of biological importance (in French)	N. van Thoai and J. Roche	18, 83-121 (1960)
Naturally derived isothiocyanates (mustard oils) and their parent glucosides (in English)	A. Kjaer	18, 122-176 (1960)
The dyes in the plumage of birds (in German)	O. Völker	18, 177-222 (1960)
Cis-trans isomerism of carotenoid pigments (in German)	L. Zechmeister	18, 223-349 (1960)
The gibberellins (in English)	P. W. Brian J. F. Grove and J. MacMillan	18, 350-433 (1960)

FORTSCHRITTE DER CHEMISCHEN FORSCHUNG

This series of review articles on advances in organic research publishes articles, mainly in German, and occasionally in English. Three volumes have appeared in the period 1949-1958, edited by S.G. Fischer, H.W. Kohlschutter and K. Schafer. Publishers: Springer Verlag, Berlin.

Title	Author	Reference
The chemistry of silicones (in German)	H.W. Kohlschütter	1, 1-60 (1949)
Size and shape of protein molecules (in English)	J.T. Edsall	1, 119-174 (1949)
Synthesis in carotenoid chemistry since 1939 (in German)	H.H. Inhoffen and F. Bohlmann	1, 175-210 (1949)
Separation and determination of natural amino acids (in German)	Th. Wieland	1, 211-291 (1949)
The free-radical nature of unsaturated compounds	E. Müller	1, 325-416 (1949)
Organic peroxides (in German)	R. Criegee	1, 508-566 (1950)
New fatty acids and fats (in German)	F.L. Dreusch	1, 567-612 (1950)
Action radii of atoms in molecules (in German)	G. Briegleb	1, 642-684 (1950)
Ester condensations (in German)	H. Henecka	1, 685-724 (1950)
Organic inclusion compounds (in German)	W. Schlenk Jr.	2, 92-145 (1951)
Growth substances and microbiological metabolic analysis (in German)	E.F. Möller	2, 146-228 (1951)
The oxo synthesis (in German)	C. Schuster	2, 311-374 (1951)
The chemistry of polythionic acids (in German)	M. Goehring	2, 444-483 (1952)
Chlorophyll (in German)	A. Stoll and E. Wiebemann	2, 538-608 (1952)
Recent advances in fluorine chemistry (in English)	H.J. Eméleus	2, 609-618 (1953)
Studies on natural lignins and lignification (in English)	G. de Stevens and F.F. Nord	3, 70-107 (1954)
Application of isotopes in organic chemistry (in German)	F. Weygand and H. Griesbach	3, 108-186 (1954)
Hyperconjugation (in German)	F. Decker	3, 187-252 (1955)
Some recent developments in thiophene chemistry (in English)	F.F. Nord A. Vaitiekunas and L.J. Owen	3, 309-333 (1955)
Progress in azulene chemistry since 1950 (in German)	W. Triebs W. Kirchhof and W. Ziegenbein	3, 334-410 (1955)
Small carbon rings (in German)	E. Vogel	3, 430-502 (1955)
Sensitization of photographic films by dyes (in German)	H. Wolff	3, 503-602 (1955)
Chemistry of amino sugars (in German)	H.H. Baer	3, 822-910 (1958)

JOURNAL DE CHIMIE PHYSIQUE ET DE PHYSICO-CHIMIE BIOLOGIQUE

This is a monthly journal, publishing original articles in French, as well as symposia and some review articles. Published by the "Societé de Chimie Physique", Paris.

Title	Author	Reference
Diamagnetism and molecular structure	B. Cabrera	<u>38</u>, 1-11 (1941)
Application of radioactive tracers to chemistry and biology. Review of previous work	P. Süe	<u>38</u>, 31-45 (1941)
Micelles and macromolecules. (Emulsions, soaps and proteins)	D.G. Dervichian	<u>38</u>, 58-77 (1941)
Recent progress in isotopic exchange	M. Haïssinsky	<u>47</u>, 957-982 (1950)
Change in shape of molecules during electronic excitation	C.K. Ingold	<u>53</u>, 472-479 (1956)
The dissociation energy of hydrocarbons	W. Heitler	<u>56</u>, 265-268 (1957)
General review of physical chemical studies of atoms and free radicals	M. Letort	<u>56</u>, 713-718 (1959)

JOURNAL OF CHEMICAL EDUCATION

A monthly journal, published by the division of Chemical Education of the American Chemical Society. In English.

Title	Author	Reference
Liquid ammonia research in 1939 - a review	G.W. Watt and N.O. Cappel	17, 274-282 (1940)
Phenolphthalein and methyl orange	C.A. Peters and B.C. Redmon	17, 525-528 (1940)
Some problems of chemotherapy	A. Burger	18, 58-61 (1941)
Flower coloration	T.A. Geissman	18, 108-110 (1941)
Steric hindrance in organic solids	B.S. Biggs	18, 224-226 (1941)
Recent advances in the chemistry of proteins	D.C. Carpenter	18, 274-276 (1941)
The history of nicotine	H.G. Fletcher Jr.	18, 303-308 (1941)
Emil Fischer's discovery of the configuration of glucose. A semi-centennial retrospect	C.S. Hudson	18, 353-357 (1941)
The reactive paraffins	E.E. Gilbert	18, 435-438 (1941)
The ethanolamines	C.B. Kremer	19, 80-81 (1942)
Acids and bases in organic chemistry	D. Davidson	19, 154-160 (1942)
Sulfanilamide and related chemotherapeutic agents	L.H. Amundsen	19, 167-171 (1942)
Magnetism and molecular structure	P.W. Selwood	19, 181-188 (1942)
The vitamins	C.R. Addinall	19, 203-214 (1942)
Carbonyl compounds as oxidizing agents	H. Adkins	19, 218-221 (1942)
The search for new insecticides	H.L. Haller	19, 315-321 (1942)
Plexiglas and other acrylic resins	C.B. Wooster	19, 430-434 (1942)
Structure of synthetic chain polymers as shown by X-rays	C.S. Fuller and W.O. Baker	20, 3-10 (1943)
Carl Julius Fritzsche and the discovery of anthranilic acid, 1841	F.E. Sheibley	20, 115-117 (1943)
Infrared spectroscopy as an organic analytical tool	R.C. Gore	20, 223-229 (1943)
The toxic principle of poison ivy and other related plants	D. Wasserman and C.R. Dawson	20, 448-453 (1943)
Synthetic rubber and plastics	E.A. Hauser	21, 15-17 (1944)
Nomenclature of organosilicon compounds	R.O. Sauer	21, 303-305 (1944)
Synthetic resin design	A.G. Chenicek	21, 495-501 (1944)
The Walden inversion in nucleophilic aliphatic substitution reactions	C.L. Deasy	22, 82-83 (1945)
Enolization: an electronic interpretation	S. Zuffanti	22, 230-234 (1945)
Adolf Lieben (December 3, 1836-June 6, 1914)	M. Kohn	22, 562-564 (1945)
A system of characterization of pure hydrocarbons. Refractometric analysis as a key to the evaluation of structure	R.T. Wendland	23, 3-15 (1946)
Silicon organics	H. Hausman	23, 16-21 (1946)
Reactions of sulfur dioxide with unsaturated hydrocarbons	O. Grummitt and A. Ardis	23, 73-77 (1946)
The chemistry of benzene hexachloride and its insecticidal properties	G.R. Chamlin	23, 283-284 (1946)

JOURNAL OF CHEMICAL EDUCATION (Contd.)

Title	Author(s)	Citation
A new system for the classification of compounds	E.L. Buhle et.al.,	23, 375-391 (1946)
Rearrangement of substituted benzopinacols. Application of electronic theories	G.H. Stempel Jr.	23, 434-438 (1946)
Patentability of organic compounds	I.J. Fellner	23, 555-558 (1946)
Otto Wallach: the first organizer of the terpenes	W.S. Partridge and E.R. Schierz	24, 106-108 (1947)
The concept of isosterism	H.L. Bradlow C.A. Vanderwerf and J. Kleinberg	24, 433-435 (1947)
Vitamins and carbohydrate metabolism	H.A. Lardy	25, 262-267 (1948)
Cellulose, glycogen and starch	T.J. Schoch	25, 626-631 (1948)
Charles Friedel (1832-1899)	A. Willemart	26, 3-9 (1949)
The chemistry of organo-metallic compounds	C.A. Kraus	26, 45-49 (1949)
Emulsion polymerization	W.B. Reynolds	26, 135-138 (1949)
Some applications of the Dysonian notation of organic compounds	G.M. Dyson	26, 294-303 (1949)
Victor Meyer and the thiophene compounds	M.D. Cameron	26, 521-524 (1949)
The story of dyes and dyeing	C. Decelles	26, 583-587 (1949)
Synthesis of isoprenoid compounds in plants	J. Bonner	26, 628-631 (1949)
The path of carbon in photosynthesis, VI	M. Calvin	26, 639-657 (1949)
The chemistry of flower color variation	T.A. Geissman	26, 657-665 (1949)
Organic reaction mechanisms with allylic compounds	W.G. Young	27, 357-364 (1950)
Catalytic hydrogenation using Raney nickel	S.H. Tucker	27, 489-493 (1950)
The chemical nature of thiophene and its derivatives	H.D. Hartough	27, 500-503 (1950)
A physical picture of covalent bonding and resonance in organic chemistry	C.R. Noller	27, 504-510 (1950)
Crystallization of organic compounds from solution	H. Svanoe	27, 549-553 (1950)
The discovery of the nitroparaffins by Victor Meyer	G. Schmidt	27, 557-559 (1950)
Dipole moments and molecular structure	H.R. Davidson	27, 598-603 (1950)
The DDT-type compound as source material in organic synthesis	F.A. Gunther and R.C. Blinn	27, 654-658 (1950)
A method of estimating the boiling points of organic liquids	D.E. Pearson	28, 60-62 (1951)
The scientific literature cited by Russian organic chemists	J.G. Tolpin et.al.	28, 254-258 (1951)
The history of barbituric acid	M.K. Carter	28, 524-526 (1951)
The mechanisms of the reactions of aliphatic hydrocarbons	L. Schmerling	28, 562-571 (1951)
The chemotherapy of tuberculosis	H.H. Fox	29, 29-33 (1952)
Castor oil as a starting material for laboratory preparations	X.A. Dominguez E. Speron and J. Slim	29, 446-448 (1952)
The high points in the development of cellulose chemistry since 1876	E. Heuser	29, 449-453 (1952)
The chemical properties of the methyl group	P.D. Bartlett	30, 22-31 (1953)
The Fischer indole synthesis	P.A. Roussel	30, 122-125 (1953)
Aspects of isomerism and mesomerism I. (a) Formulas and their meaning (b) mesomerism	R.L. Bent	30, 220-228 (1953)

Isotope studies in photosynthesis	J.A. Bassham, A.A. Benson and M. Calvin	30,	274-283 (1953)
Aspects of isomerism and mesomerism II. Structural isomerism	R.L. Bent	30,	284-290 (1953)
Aspects of isomerism and mesomerism III. Stereoisomerism	R.L. Bent	30,	328-340 (1953)
Predicting reactions of a resonance hybrid from minor canonical structures	A. Gero	31,	136-138 (1954)
Linear polymerization and synthetic fibers	R.W. Moncrieff	31,	233-237 (1954)
The mechanism of diazotization	R.G. Gillis	31,	344-346 (1954)
Theoretical chemistry in Russia	I.M. Hunsberger	31,	504-514 (1954)
Molecular association of organic substances	L.N. Ferguson	31,	626-630 (1954)
Organic fluorine chemicals	E.T. McBee and C.W. Roberts	32,	13-19 (1955)
Recent research on thyroid hormone	N. Kharasch	32,	192-194 (1955)
Porphyrins in petroleum	T. Muniyappan	32,	277-279 (1955)
Nucleophilic substitution in aromatic systems	R.G. Gillis	32,	296-300 (1955)
Frederic Swarts: Pioneer in organic fluorine chemistry	G.B. Kauffman	32,	301-303 (1955)
A notation for the study of certain stereochemical problems	M.S. Newman	32,	344-347 (1955)
Friedlieb Ferdinand Runge: A forgotten chemist of the nineteenth century	B. Anft	32,	566-574 (1955)
Aromatic substitution by free radicals	P.F. Nelson	32,	606-610 (1955)
Uses of isotopes in organic chemistry	D.A. Semenow and J.D. Roberts	33,	2-14 (1956)
Tetrazolium salts as chemical reagents	N.D. Cheronis and H. Stein	33,	120-125 (1956)
Hydrogen bonding and physical properties of substances	L.N. Ferguson	33,	267-271 (1956)
Rational approaches to drug structure	A. Burger	33,	362-372 (1956)
Urea in the history of organic chemistry. Isolation from natural sources	F. Kurzer and P.M. Sanderson	33,	452-459 (1956)
Chemistry of organic free radicals in the vapor phase. I: Detection and reactions of free alkyl radicals	H.E. de la Mare and W.E. Vaughan	34,	10-21 (1957)
Sir William Henry Perkin: Pioneer of chemical industry	R. Robinson	34,	54-58 (1957)
Chemistry of organic free radicals in the vapor phase. II: Reactions of alkoxy and alkylperoxy radicals: Energetics of some alkyl radical reactions	H.E. de la Mare and W.E. Vaughan	34,	64-70 (1957)
The use of mass spectrometry in organic analysis	E.L. Eliel, T.J. Prosser and G.W. Young	34,	72-77 (1957)
The study of free radical reactions through photochemistry	H.E. Gunning	34,	121-126 (1957)
Organic isocyanates - versatile chemical intermediates	R.G. Arnold, J.A. Nelson and J.H. Verbanc	34,	158-165 (1957)
Ferrocene: a novel organometallic compound	M. Rausch, M. Vogel and H. Rosenberg	34,	268-272 (1957)
Some aspects of organic molecules and their behavior. I: electronegativity	O. Reinmuth	34,	272-275 (1957)

Some aspects of organic molecules and their behavior. II: Bond energies	O. Reinmuth	**34**, 318-324 (1957)
Hydrogen bonding in high polymers and inclusion compounds	M.L. Huggins	**34**, 480-488 (1957)
S.N. Reformatskii and his reaction	A. Sementsof	**34**, 530-532 (1957)
Reactions in liquid dinitrogen tetroxide	H.S. Sisler	**34**, 555-561 (1957)
Structure of synthetic high polymers	F.C. McGrew	**35**, 178-186 (1958)
Peter Griess – discoverer of diazo compounds	V. Heines	**35**, 187-191 (1958)
Representation of polycyclic aromatic compounds	T.I. Bieber	**35**, 235-237 (1958)
Transformation of organic compounds by microorganisms	D. Perlman	**36**, 60-63 (1959)
Foundations of the structural theory	H.C. Brown	**36**, 104-110 (1959)
Fundamental processes of autoxidation	G.A. Russell	**36**, 111-118 (1959)
Base-catalyzed alkylations with alcohols	E.I. Becker	**36**, 119-122 (1959)
Contributions of vinyl polymerization to organic chemistry	F.R. Mayo	**36**, 157-160 (1959)
The geometry of giant molecules	C.C. Price	**36**, 160-163 (1959)
Kinetics of polymer formation by free radical mechanism	T.E. Ferington	**36**, 174-181 (1959)
The experimental basis of Kekulé's valence theory	E.N. Hiebert	**36**, 320-327 (1959)
Contributions of Butlerov to the development of structural theory	H.M. Leicester	**36**, 328-329 (1959)
The unraveling of geometic isomerism and tautomerism	A. Ihde	**36**, 330-336 (1959)
The contributions of Fritz Arndt to resonance theory	E. Campaigne	**36**, 336-339 (1959)
Radiation chemistry of high polymers	M. Dole	**36**, 353-359 (1959)
Recent advances in chemotherapy of cancer	R.B. Ross	**36**, 368-377 (1959)
The chemistry of molecular shapes	H.C. Brown	**36**, 424-431 (1959)
Japanese organic chemical nomenclature. Problems of translation and transliteration	Y. Urushibara revised by M. Nakamura	**36**, 482-485 (1959)
Nucleic acids, genes, and viruses	J.L. Fairley	**36**, 544-547 (1959)
Conformational analysis in mobile systems	E.L. Eliel	**37**, 126-133 (1960)
Antihypertensive and diuretic agents: past, present and future	A.J. Plummer and F.F. Yonkman	**37**, 179-184 (1960)
The hormones	L.H. Sarett	**37**, 184-189 (1960)
Use of metal complexes in organic dyes and pigments	O. Stallmann	**37**, 220-230 (1960)
The qualitative detection of olefins by ozonolysis	J.G. Sharefkin and A. Ribner	**37**, 296-297 (1960)
Determination of alkaloid structures. 1. Isolation, characterization, and physical methods	A.W. Sangster	**37**, 454-459 (1960)
Some recent advances in the field of steroids	R.E. Beyler	**37**, 491-494 (1960)
Determination of alkaloid structures. II. Chemical methods	A.W. Sangster	**37**, 518-525 (1960)
Hydrocarbons in petroleum	F.D. Rossini	**37**, 554-561 (1960)
Cyclopentadienyl compounds of metals and metalloids	M.D. Rausch	**37**, 568-578 (1960)

JOURNAL OF CHROMATOGRAPHY

This is a journal devoted to all aspects of chromatographic methods and their applications, publishing original articles, short communications, chromatographic data, as well as review articles. Articles are published in English, French or German. Edited by M. Lederer. Published by Elsevier Publishing Company, Amsterdam.

Title	Author	Reference
High voltage electrophoresis (in German)	H. Michl	<u>1</u>, 93-121 (1958)
Chromatography of sterols, steroids and related substances (in German)	R. Neher	<u>1</u>, 122-165 (1958) 205-258
Paper chromatography of chloroplast pigments (in English)	Z. Sestak	<u>1</u>, 293-308 (1958)
Review of gas-liquid chromatography (in English)	C.J. Hardy and F.H. Pollard	<u>2</u>, 1-43 (1959)
Starch electrophoresis. I. Starch block electrophoresis (in English)	H. Bloemendal	<u>2</u>, 121-135 (1959)
Paper chromatography of dinitrophenylamino acids (in French)	G. Biserte et. al.,	<u>2</u>, 225-271 (1959)
The chromatography of the flavonoid pigments (in English)	J.B. Harborne	<u>2</u>, 581-604 (1959)
Starch electrophoresis. II. Starch column electrophoresis (in English)	H. Bloemendal	<u>3</u>, 1-10 (1960)
Starch electrophoresis. III. Starch gel electrophoresis (in English)	H. Bloemendal	<u>3</u>, 509-519 (1960)
Chromatography of lipids on silicic acid (in English)	J.J. Wren	<u>4</u>, 173-195 (1960)

JOURNAL OF MEDICINAL AND PHARMACEUTICAL CHEMISTRY

A bimonthly journal, in English, containing original and review articles. Edited by A.H. Beckett and A. Burger. Published by Interscience Publishers Inc., New York.

Title	Author	Reference
Hypotensive hydrazinophthalazines and related compounds	J. Druey and A. Marxer	$\underline{1}$, 1-21 (1959)
The trifluoromethyl group in medicinal chemistry	H.L. Yale	$\underline{1}$, 121-133 (1959)
Chemistry and structure-activity relationships of amphenone analogues	W.L. Bencze and M.J. Allen	$\underline{1}$, 395-406 (1959)
Biological activity in compounds possessing thiophen rings	M. Martin-Smith and S.T. Reid	$\underline{1}$, 507-564 (1959)

JOURNAL OF PHARMACY AND PHARMACOLOGY

This is a monthly journal, in English, publishing both original articles and reviews. Published by the Pharmaceutical Society of Great Britain.

Title	Author	Reference
The antihistamine drugs	D.M. Dunlop	1, 1-10 (1949)
Some recent developments in the pharmacology of the anti-thyroid compounds	W.R. Trotter	1, 65-77 (1949)
Synthetic oestrogens	E.C. Dodds	1, 137-147 (1949)
The chemical estimation of digitalis and strophanthus glycosides	T. Canbäck	1, 201-210 (1949)
Anticoagulants	F.C. MacIntosh	1, 353-367 (1949)
Analgesics: some developments	A.D. MacDonald	1, 569-575 (1949)
The cardioactive glycosides	A. Stoll	1, 849-868 (1949)
Anti-epileptic compounds (in French)	R. Hazard and J. Cheymol	2, 1-9 (1950)
The determination of vitamin A	R.A. Morton	2, 129-144 (1950)
Folic acid, vitamin B_{12} and anaemia. I. Chemical aspects	E. Lester Smith	2, 409-417 (1950)
The nitrogen mustards	J.D.N. Nabarro	2, 865-879 (1950)
The chemotherapy of tuberculosis	J.B. Stenlake	3, 129-148 (1951)
The chemotherapy of human virus infections	G.M. Findlay	3, 193-214 (1951)
New antibiotics (chloramphenicol, aureomycin, terramycin and neomycin)	E.P. Abraham	3, 257-270 (1951)
Parasympathomimetics and anticholinesterases	F. Bergel	3, 385-399 (1951)
The chemistry and biochemistry of streptomycin and related compounds	J.H. Birkinshaw	3, 529-546 (1951)
Analgesics - a general survey	A.H. Beckett	4, 425-447 (1952)
Some steps in the development of stereochemistry	J. Read	5, 1-17 (1953)
Recent advances in the pharmacology of salicylates	M.J.H. Smith	5, 81-93 (1953)
Recent advances in the knowledge of the constituents of vegetable drugs	J.W. Fairbairn	5, 281-292 (1953)
The chemistry of cortisone	B.A. Hems	5, 409-437 (1953)
Ion exchange resins in organic analysis	L. Saunders	5, 569-579 (1953)
Alkaloid formation in plants	W.O. James	5, 809-822 (1953)
Adrenaline and noradrenaline	G.B. West	7, 81-98 (1955)
The active principles of the neurohypophysis	H. Heller	7, 225-247 (1955)
Attempts at chemotherapy of malignant diseases	F. Bergel	7, 297-313 (1955)
Stereoisomerism and biological action	A.H. Beckett and A.F. Casy	7, 433-455 (1955)
The alkaloids of curare	P. Karrer	8, 161-184 (1956)

JOURNAL OF PHARMACY AND PHARMACOLOGY (Contd.)

Title	Author(s)	Citation
Structure and synthesis of naturally-occurring peptides	F.A. Robinson	8, 297-308 (1956)
The rauwolfia alkaloids	J.J. Lewis	8, 456-494 (1956)
Antifolic acids and antipurines in chemotherapy	G.M. Timmis	9, 81-91 (1957)
The pharmacology of tropone compounds in relation to their steric structure	L. Gyermek and K. Nador	9, 209-229 (1957)
The story of muscarine	K. Bowden and G.A. Mogey	10, 145-156 (1958)
The chemotherapy of helminthiasis	T.I. Watkins	10, 209-227 (1958)
Chemotherapy of malaria	A.F. Crowther	10, 337-347 (1958)
Some chemical and medical aspects of the antibiotics	G.G.F. Newton and E.P. Abraham	10, 401-426 (1958)
Structure-activity relationships	W.A. Sexton	10, 465-482 (1958)

MICROCHEMICAL JOURNAL

A quarterly journal, in English, publishing mainly original articles on microchemical methods and their applications. An annual progress in Microchemistry issue is devoted to review articles. Interscience Publishers Inc., New York.

Title	Author	Reference
Chemical experimentation under the microscope	A.A. Benedetti-Pichler	2, 3-20 (1958)
Historical developments in quantitative organic micro analysis	A. Steyermark	2, 21-42 (1958)
The micro identification of organic compounds	N.D. Cheronis	2, 43-70 (1958)
Quantitative organic micro analysis below the milligram scale	W.J. Kirsten	2, 179-204 (1958)
The role of micro- and ultramicro-chemistry in the isolation of the first transuranium element: plutonium	M. Cefola	2, 205-217 (1958)
Progress in elemental quantitative organic analysis: 1958	A. Steyermark	3, 399-414 (1959)
Progress in functional group quantitative organic analysis: 1958	T.S. Ma	3, 415-432 (1959)
Progress in qualitative organic analysis: 1958	N.D. Cheronis	3, 433-458 (1959)
Progress in organic and inorganic microsynthesis: 1958	A.R. Ronzio	3, 459-465 (1959)
Progress in elemental quantitative organic analysis: 1959	A. Steyermark and B.E. McGee	4, 353-372 (1960)
Progress in organic functional group analysis: 1959	T.S. Ma	4, 373-386 (1960)

DIE NATURWISSENSCHAFTEN

This is a journal appearing twice monthly with review articles in all fields of the natural sciences, in German. Edited by F. Suffert until 1944, by A. Eucken from 1946 to 1949 and by E. Lamla since 1950. Published by Springer Verlag, Berlin.

Title	Author	Reference
Physical research on protein molecules	P. Jordan	<u>28</u>, 69-77 (1940)
Progress in the chemistry of chlorophyll	H. Fischer	<u>28</u>, 401-405 (1940)
Characterization and mechanisms of carcinogenic carbohydrates	O. Schmidt	<u>29</u>, 146-150 (1941)
The pigments of the ommin- and ommatin-group, a new class of natural dyes	E. Becker	<u>29</u>, 237-238 (1941)
Developments in the synthesis of natural steroids	A. Butenandt	<u>30</u>, 4-17 (1942)
History of terpene chemistry	W. Hückel	<u>30</u>, 17-30 (1942)
The formaldehyde condensation as an organic auto-catalysis	W. Langenbeck	<u>30</u>, 30-34 (1942)
Mitotic poisons and their relation to natural products	H. Lettré	<u>30</u>, 34-40 (1942)
Classical methods in the detailed structural analysis of organic compounds	A. Lüttringhaus	<u>30</u>, 40-45 (1942)
New developments in the chemistry of tumors	F. Kögl	<u>30</u>, 46-47 (1942)
The work of H. Wieland in the field of steroid chemistry	E. Dane	<u>30</u>, 333-342 (1942)
Enzymatic degradation and structure of nucleic acids	F.G. Fischer	<u>30</u>, 377-382 (1942)
Chemical, physical and physiological research in plant chemistry of lumi-auxons	F. Kögl	<u>30</u>, 392-398 (1942)
Phenyl-lithium, the key to the new chemistry of metallo-organic compounds	G. Wittig	<u>30</u>, 696-703 (1942)
Free atoms in photochemical reactions	P. Harteck	<u>31</u>, 409-412 (1943)
The chemistry of oriented growths of crystals of organic compounds	J. Willems	<u>32</u>, 324-333 (1944)
Results and problems of research on mitotic poisons	H. Lettré	<u>33</u>, 75-86 (1946)
Poisonous proteins (animal, plant and bacterial poisons)	F. Micheel	<u>33</u>, 239-243 (1946)
Oxidation of carbohydrates	W. Jost	<u>33</u>, 265-270 (1946) 297-301
The problem of the morphine synthesis	R. Greene	<u>33</u>, 333-336 (1946)
The "inorganic benzene" $B_3N_2H_6$ and its methyl analogs	E. Wiberg	<u>35</u>, 182-188 (1948) 212-218

DIE NATURWISSENSCHAFTEN (Contd.)

The protein molecule, its refined structure and its physico-chemical properties	G. Scheibe	35,	168-175 (1948)
Problems of reaction mechanisms in the formation of high polymeric vinyl substances	L. Kuchler	35,	105-110 (1948) 144-151
Isostery	J. Goubeau	35,	246-250 (1948)
Separation energies of organic molecules	E. Wicke	35,	335-343 (1948)
Relationships in the chemistry of natural products containing sulfur	A. Schöberl	36,	121-125 (1949) 149-153
New research on the phosphorescence of organic substances in solid solutions	Th. Förster	36,	240-245 (1949)
Electrophoresis and adsorption analysis as auxiliary tools for the research of high polymeric substances and their decomposition products	A. Tiselius	37,	25-33 (1950)
The natural occurrence and the primary action of auxines and heterauxines	H. v. Guttenberg	37,	65-67 (1950)
New procedures in the electrophoresis of proteins	W. Grassmann	38,	200-206 (1951)
50 years of chemistry of sterols	H.H. Inhoffen	38,	553-558 (1951)
Research on steroids	H.H. Inhoffen	40,	455-456 (1953)
Syntheses of uroporphyrins. III.	A. Treibs and W. Ott	40,	476-477 (1953)
Quinone derivatives of chemotherapeutic value	S. Petersen and G. Domagk	41,	10-12 (1954)
New developments related to bee- and snake-poisons	W. Neumann	41,	322-326 (1954)
The basis of macromolecular chemistry	H. Staudinger	42,	221-230 (1955)
The chemistry of macromolecular substances	K. Hamann	42,	230-237 (1955)
Chemistry of natural macromolecules	R. Signer	42,	265-270 (1955)
Nomenclature in organic chemistry	F. Richter	42,	593-600 (1955)
The carcinogenic carbohydrates as photosensibilizing agents. Contribution to the problem of phototoxic activity	G.O. Schenck	43,	71-72 (1956)
Research on the synthesis and properties of urea-acetaldehyde condensation products	F. Scheffer W. Ziechmann and H. Kuntze	44,	52-58 (1957)
Isotopes in organic chemistry	F. Weygand	44,	169-176 (1957)
Model research for the formation of organic products in an atmosphere of simple gases by means of an electrical discharge	K. Heyns W. Walter and E. Meyer	44,	385-389 (1957)
Energy transfer in organic systems	O. Neunhoeffer	45,	255-259 (1958)
Amino acid sequences in proteins	H. Tuppy	46,	35-43 (1959)
Pheromones (a proposal for the nomenclature for a class of active agents)	P. Karlson and M. Luscher	46,	63-64 (1959)
Active agents of insects	A. Butenandt	46,	461-471 (1959)
Future developments of reactors	A.J. Salmon	46,	520-529 (1959)

ORGANIC ANALYSIS

This is a periodical collection of review articles, in English. The editors are J. Mitchell, Jr., I.M. Kolthoff, E.S. Proskauer and A. Weissberger. Published by Interscience Inc., New York.

Title	Author	Reference
Determination of hydroxyl groups	V.C. Mehlenbacher	1, 1-65 (1953)
Determination of alkoxyl groups	A. Elek	1, 67-126 (1953)
Determination of the alpha-epoxy group	J.L. Jungnickel et. al.,	1, 127-154 (1953)
Organometallic compounds for the determination of active hydrogen	G.F. Wright	1, 155-195 (1953)
Diazomethane for the determination of active hydrogen	F.G. Arndt	1, 197-241 (1953)
Determination of carbonyl compounds	J. Mitchell, Jr.	1, 243-307 (1953)
Determination of acetals	J. Mitchell, Jr.	1, 309-328 (1953)
Determination of organic sulfur groups	S. Dal Nogare	1, 329-402 (1953)
Spectroscopic functional group analysis in the petroleum industry	N.D. Coggeshall	1, 403-450 (1953)
Microdetermination of carboxyl groups (Neutralization equivalent)	A. Steyermark	2, 1-18 (1954)
Determination of esters	R.T. Hall and W.E. Shaefer	2, 19-70 (1954)
Determination of nitro, nitroso, and nitrate groups	W.W. Becker and W.E. Shaefer	2, 71-122 (1954)
Applications of lithium aluminum hydride to organic analyses	T. Higuchi	2, 123-167 (1954)
Coulometric methods	W.D. Cooke	2, 169-193 (1954)
Application of polarography to organic analysis	P.J. Elving	2, 195-236 (1954)
Methods based on reaction rate	T.S. Lee	2, 237-252 (1954)
Phase solubility analysis	W.J. Mader	2, 253-275 (1954)
Countercurrent distribution	J.R. Weisiger	2, 277-326 (1954)
Determination of organic acids	J. Mitchell, Jr. B.A. Montague and R.H. Kinsey	3, 1-95 (1956)
Determination of acid anhydrides	C.W. Hammond	3, 97-128 (1956)
Determination of amines and amides and related compounds	E.F. Hillenbrand, Jr. and C.A. Pentz	3, 129-201 (1956)
Determination of olefinic unsaturation	A. Polgár and J.L. Jungnickel	3, 203-386 (1956)

ORGANIC ANALYSIS (Contd.)

Analytical mass spectrometry	V.H. Dibeler	<u>3</u>,	387-441 (1956)
Synthetic organic coating resins (analytical characterization and determination of some commercially important classes)	O.D. Shreve	<u>3</u>,	443-508 (1956)
Determination of organic peroxides	A.J. Martin	<u>4</u>,	1-64 (1960)
Enzyme analytical reactions	J.B. Neilands	<u>4</u>,	65-90 (1960)
Gas chromatography	S. Dal Nogare and L.W. Safranski	<u>4</u>,	91-227 (1960)
Application of nuclear magnetic resonance spectroscopy to organic analysis	H. Foster	<u>4</u>,	229-291 (1960)
Crystallographic methods of analysis (X-ray analysis and microscopy)	J. Krć, Jr.,	<u>4</u>,	293-360 (1960)
Application of differential thermal analysis to high polymers	B. Ke	<u>4</u>,	361-393 (1960)

ORGANIC REACTIONS

This series publishes quite exhaustive reviews, in English, on a number of the major reactions of organic chemistry. The series was initiated by Professor Roger Adams of the University of Illinois, with the aid of many associate editors in the following years. Publishers: John R. Wiley and Sons, Inc., New York. Volume I appeared in 1942.

Title	Author	Reference
The Reformatsky reaction	R.L. Shriner	<u>1</u>, 1-37 (1942)
The Arndt-Eistert synthesis	W.E. Bachmann and W.S. Struve	<u>1</u>, 38-62 (1942)
Chloromethylation of aromatic compounds	R.C. Fuson and C.H. McKeever	<u>1</u>, 63-90 (1942)
The amination of heterocyclic bases by alkali amides	M.T. Leffler	<u>1</u>, 38-62 (1942)
The Bucherer reaction	N.L. Drake	<u>1</u>, 105-128 (1942)
The Elbs reaction	L.F. Fieser	<u>1</u>, 129-154 (1942)
The Clemmensen reduction	E.L. Martin	<u>1</u>, 155-209 (1942)
The Perkin reaction and related reactions	J.R. Johnson	<u>1</u>, 210-265 (1942)
The acetoacetic ester condensation and certain related reactions	C.R. Hauser and B.E. Hudson Jr.	<u>1</u>, 266-302 (1942)
The Mannich reaction	F.F. Blicke	<u>1</u>, 303-341 (1942)
The Fries reaction	A.H. Blatt	<u>1</u>, 342-369 (1942)
The Jacobsen reaction	L.I. Smith	<u>1</u>, 370-384 (1942)
The Claisen rearrangement	D.S. Tarbell	<u>2</u>, 1-48 (1944)
The preparation of aliphatic fluorine compounds	A.L. Henne	<u>2</u>, 49-93 (1944)
The Cannizzaro reaction	T.A. Geissman	<u>2</u>, 94-113 (1944)
The formation of cyclic ketones by intramolecular acylation	W.S. Johnson	<u>2</u>, 114-177 (1944)
Reduction with aluminum alkoxides (the Meerwein-Ponadorf-Verley reduction)	A.L. Wilds	<u>2</u>, 178-223 (1944)
The preparation of unsymmetrical biaryls by the diazo reaction and the nitrosoacetylamine reaction	W.E. Bachmann and R.A. Hoffman	<u>2</u>, 224-261 (1944)
Replacement of the aromatic primary amino group by hydrogen	N. Kornblum	<u>2</u>, 262-340 (1944)
Periodic acid oxidation	E.L. Jackson	<u>2</u>, 341-375 (1944)
The resolution of alcohols	A.W. Ingersoll	<u>2</u>, 376-414 (1944)
The preparation of aromatic arsonic and arsinic acids by the Bart, Béchamp and Rosenmund reactions	C.S. Hamilton and J.F. Morgan	<u>2</u>, 415-454 (1944)

ORGANIC REACTIONS (Contd.)

Title	Author(s)	Volume, Pages (Year)
The alkylation of aromatic compounds by the Friedel-Crafts method	C.C. Price	3, 1-82 (1946)
The Willgerodt reaction	M. Carmack and M.A. Spielman	3, 83-107 (1946)
Preparation of ketenes and ketene dimers	W.E. Hanford and J.C. Sauer	3, 108-140 (1946)
Direct sulfonation of aromatic hydrocarbons and their halogen derivatives	C.M. Suter and A.W. Weston	3, 141-197 (1946)
Azlactones	H.E. Carter	3, 198-239 (1946)
Substitution and addition reactions of thiocyanogen	J.L. Wood	3, 240-266 (1946)
The Hofmann reaction	E.S. Wallis and J.F. Lane	3, 267-306 (1946)
The Schmidt reaction	H. Wolff	3, 307-336 (1946)
The Curtius reaction	P.A.S. Smith	3, 337-450 (1946)
The Diels-Alder reaction with maleic anhydride	M.C. Kloetzel	4, 1-59 (1948)
The Diels-Alder reaction: ethylenic and acetylenic dienophiles	H.L. Holmes	4, 60-173 (1948)
The preparation of amines by reductive alkylation	W.S. Emerson	4, 174-255 (1948)
The acyloins	S.M. McElvain	4, 256-268 (1948)
The synthesis of benzoins	W.S. Ide and J.S. Buck	4, 269-304 (1948)
Synthesis of benzoquinones by oxidation	J. Cason	4, 305-361 (1948)
The Rosenmund reduction of acid chlorides to aldehydes	E. Mosettig and R. Mozingo	4, 362-377 (1948)
The Wolff-Kishner reduction	D. Todd	4, 378-422 (1948)
The synthesis of acetylenes	T.L. Jacobs	5, 1-78 (1949)
Cyanoethylation	H.A. Bruson	5, 79-135 (1949)
The Diels-Alder reaction: quinones and other cyclenones	L.W. Butz and A.W. Rytina	5, 136-192 (1949)
Preparation of aromatic fluorine compounds from diazonium fluoborates: the Schiemann reaction	A. Roe	5, 193-228 (1949)
The Friedel and Crafts reaction with aliphatic dibasic acid anhydrides	E. Berliner	5, 229-289 (1949)
The Gattermann-Koch reaction	N.N. Crounse	5, 290-300 (1949)
The Leuckart reaction	M.L. Moore	5, 301-330 (1949)
Selenium dioxide oxidation	N. Rabjohn	5, 331-386 (1949)
The Hoesch synthesis	P.E. Spoerri and A.S DuBois	5, 387-412 (1949)
The Darzens glycidic ester condensation	M.S. Newman and B.J. Magerlein	5, 413-440 (1949)

ORGANIC REACTIONS (Contd.)

The Stobbe condensation	W.S. Johnson and G.H. Daub	6,	1-73	(1951)
The preparation of 3,4-dihydroisoquinolines and related compounds by the Bischler-Napieralski reaction	W.M. Whaley and T.R. Govindachari	6,	74-150	(1951)
The Pictet-Spengler synthesis of tetrahydroisoquinolines and related compounds	W.M. Whaley and T.R. Govindachari	6,	151-190	(1951)
The synthesis of isoquinolines by the Pomeranz-Fritsch reaction	W.J. Gensler	6,	191-206	(1951)
The Oppenauer oxidation	C. Djerassi	6,	207-272	(1951)
The synthesis of phosphonic acid and phosphinic acid	G.M. Kosolapoff	6,	273-338	(1951)
The halogen-metal interconversion reaction with organolithium compounds	R.G. Jones and H. Gilman	6,	339-366	(1951)
The preparation of thiazoles	R.H. Wiley D.C. England and L.C. Behr	6,	367-409	(1951)
The preparation of thiophenes and tetrahydrothiophenes	E. Wolf and K. Folkers	6,	410-468	(1951)
Reductions by lithium aluminum hydride	W.G. Brown	6,	469-510	(1951)
The Pechmann reaction	S. Sethna and R. Phadke	7,	1-58	(1953)
The Skraup synthesis of quinolines	R.H.F. Manske and M. Kulka	7,	59-98	(1953)
Carbon-carbon alkylations with amines and ammonium salts	J.H. Brewster and E.L. Eliel	7,	99-197	(1953)
The von Braun cyanogen bromide reaction	H.A. Hageman	7,	198-262	(1953)
Hydrogenolysis of benzyl groups attached to oxygen, nitrogen, or sulfur	W.H. Hartung and R. Simonoff	7,	263-326	(1953)
The nitrosation of aliphatic carbon atoms	O. Touster	7,	327-377	(1953)
Epoxidation and hydroxylation of ethylenic compounds with organic peracids	D. Swern	7,	378-434	(1953)
Catalytic hydrogenation of esters to alcohols	H. Adkins	8,	1-27	(1954)
The synthesis of ketones from acid halides and organometallic compounds of magnesium, zinc, and cadmium	D.A. Shirley	8,	28-58	(1954)
The acylation of ketones to form β-diketones or β-keto aldehydes	C.R. Hauser F.W. Swamer and J.T. Adams	8,	59-196	(1954)
The Sommelet reaction	S.J. Angyal	8,	197-217	(1954)
The synthesis of aldehydes from carboxylic acids	E. Mosettig	8,	218-257	(1954)

ORGANIC REACTIONS (Contd.)

Title	Author(s)	Volume, Pages (Year)
The metalation reaction with organolithium compounds	H. Gilman	8, 258-304 (1954)
β-Lactones	H.E. Zaugg	8, 305-363 (1954)
The reaction of diazomethane and its derivatives with aldehydes and ketones	C.D. Gutsche	8, 364-430 (1954)
The cleavage of non-enolizable ketones with sodium amide	K.E. Hamlin and A.W. Weston	9, 1-36 (1957)
The Gatterman synthesis of aldehydes	W.E. Truce	9, 37-72 (1957)
The Baeyer-Villiger oxidation of aldehydes and ketones	C.H. Hassall	9, 73-106 (1957)
The alkylation of esters and nitriles	A.C. Cope, H.L. Holmes and H.O. House	9, 107-331 (1957)
The reaction of halogens with silver salts of carboxylic acids	C.V. Wilson	9, 332-387 (1957)
The synthesis of β-lactams	J.C. Sheehan and E.J. Corey	9, 388-408 (1957)
The Pschorr synthesis and related diazonium ring closure reactions	D.F. DeTar	9, 409-462 (1957)
Coupling of diazonium salts with aliphatic carbon atoms	S.M. Parmerter	10, 1-142 (1959)
Japp-Klingemann reaction	R.R. Phillips	10, 143-178 (1959)
The Michael reaction	E.D. Bergman, D. Ginsburg and R. Pappo	10, 179-555 (1959)
The Beckmann rearrangement	L.G. Donamura and W.Z. Heldt	11, 1-156 (1960)
The Demjanov and Tiffeneau-Demjanov ring expansions	P.A.S. Smith and D.R. Baer	11, 157-188 (1960)
Arylation of unsaturated compounds by diazonium salts	C.S. Rondestvedt, Jr.	11, 189-260 (1960)
The Favorskii rearrangement of haloketones	A.S. Kende	11, 261-316 (1960)
Olefins from amines: the Hoffmann elimination reaction and amine oxide pyrolysis	A.C. Cope and E.R. Trumbull	11, 317-493 (1960)

PROCEEDINGS OF THE CHEMICAL SOCIETY (LONDON)

This periodical, which is associated by origin with the Journal of the Chemical Society, now publishes the various lectures of the Society. These include the Tilden Lecture, the Pedler Lecture and the Faraday, Liversidge and Simonsen Lectures, as well as the Presidential address. Prior to 1957, these lectures appeared in the Journal. Published by The Chemical Society, London.

Title	Author	Reference
Synthetic immunochemistry	C.R. Harington	119-128 (1940)
Some aspects of the chemotherapy of tuberculosis	R. Robinson	505-509 (1940)
A speculation regarding the ring structure of the sterols	R. Robinson	509-510 (1940)
The present state of valency theory	L.E. Sutton	544-553 (1940)
Mechanism of the benzidine transformation and some allied topics	R. Robinson	220-240 (1941)
Some themes in the chemistry of macromolecules	H.W. Melville	414-426 (1941)
Vitamins of the B group	A.R. Todd	427-432 (1941)
Complex formation	N.V. Sidgwick	433-443 (1941)
Recent progress in the chemistry of the pectic materials and plant gums	E.L. Hirst	70-78 (1942)
Some aspects of algal chemistry	I.M. Heilbron	79-89 (1942)
X-rays and the stoicheiometry of the proteins, with special reference to the structure of the keratin-myosin group	W.T. Astbury	337-347 (1942)
Fluorine	H.J. Eméleus	441-447 (1942)
The chemistry of the lignan group of natural products	R.D. Haworth	448-456 (1942)
The basis of stereochemistry	W.H. Mills	457-466 (1942)
The stereochemistry of labile compounds	W.H. Mills	194-199 (1943)
The scope and limitations of infra-red measurements in chemistry	H.W. Thompson	183-192 (1944)
Newer knowledge of the biochemistry of the thyroid gland	C.R. Harington	193-201 (1944)
Some aspects of the chemistry of nucleotides	J.M. Gulland	208-217 (1944)
Old and new views on some chemical problems	W.H. Mills	340-350 (1944)
Chemotherapy in tropical medicine	A.J. Ewins	351-355 (1944)
Some aspects of the organic chemistry of phosphorus and arsenic	F.G. Mann	65-73 (1945)
Diffraction methods in modern structural chemistry	J.M. Robertson	249-257 (1945)
Non-benzenoid aromatic hydrocarbons	W. Baker	258-267 (1945)
Reactions in monolayers	E.K. Rideal	423-428 (1945)
Some recent developments in the chemistry of free radicals	W.A. Waters	409-415 (1946)
Starch	W.N. Haworth	543-549 (1946)

PROCEEDINGS OF THE CHEMICAL SOCIETY (LONDON) (Contd.)

Synthesis in the study of nucleotides	A.R. Todd	647-653 (1946)
Substitution	E.D. Hughes	968-979 (1946)
Carbohydrate components of biologically active materials	W.N. Haworth	582-589 (1947)
Macromolecules synthesised by micro-organisms	M. Stacey	853-864 (1947)
The development of electrochemical theories of the course of reactions of carbon compounds	R. Robinson	1288-1301 (1947)
Structural relationships in the natural unsaturated higher fatty acids	T.P. Hilditch	243-252 (1948)
Recent developments in the vitamin A field	I. Heilbron	386-393 (1948)
Some aspects of the chemistry of hydrocarbons	C.N. Hinshelwood	531-538 (1948)
The occurrence and significance of the pentose sugars in nature, and their relationship to the hexoses	E.L. Hirst	522-533 (1949)
The structure and reactivity of free radicals	C.E.H. Bawn	1042-1050 (1949)
Three- and four-membered heterocyclic rings	F.E. King	1318-1328 (1949)
Concerning amino-acids, peptides, and purines	I. Heilbron	2099-2107 (1949)
Chemistry and biochemistry of some mammalian secretions and excretions	E. Lederer	2115-2125 (1949)
Newer developments of the chemistry of many-membered ring compounds	V. Prelog	420-428 (1950)
Acetylene and acetylenic compounds in organic synthesis	E.R.H. Jones	754-761 (1950)
Recent advances in the chemistry of the steroids	F.S. Spring	3352-3357 (1950)
Concepts in catalysis. The contributions of Paul Sabatier and of Max Bodenstein	E.K. Rideal	1640-1647 (1951)
A chemotherapeutic search in retrospect	F.L. Rose	2770-2788 (1951)
Some recent developments in the chemistry of free-radical reactions in solution	D.H. Hey	1974-1992 (1952)
Willstätter Memorial Lecture (Richard Willstätter)	R. Robinson	999-1026 (1953)
The stereochemistry of cyclohexane derivatives	D.H.R. Barton	1027-1040 (1953)
Autosynthesis	C. Hinshelwood	1947-1956 (1953)
Old and new ideas on saturated rearrangements	C.K. Ingold	2845-2852 (1953)
Discoveries among conjugated macrocyclic compounds	R.P. Linstead	2873-2884 (1953)
Aromaticity in seven-membered ring systems	A.W. Johnson	1331-1340 (1954)
Some applications of the separation of large molecules and colloidal particles	A. Tiselius	2650-2657 (1954)
The chemistry of intermolecular compounds	H.M. Powell	2658-2663 (1954)
Organometallic compounds containing fluorocarbon radicals	H.J. Eméleus	2979-2986 (1954)
The isoquinoline alkaloids	R.H. Manske	2987-2990 (1954)

PROCEEDINGS OF THE CHEMICAL SOCIETY (LONDON) (Contd.)

Signs of a new pathway in reaction mechanism and stereochemistry	C.K. Ingold	2991-2998 (1954)
Some newer aspects of the organic chemistry of nitrogen	G.R. Clemo	2057-2068 (1955)
The contributions of wave mechanics to chemistry	C.A. Coulson	2069-2084 (1955)
Some problems in the chemistry of the hemicelluloses	E.L. Hirst	2974-2984 (1955)
A problem in structural chemistry	W. Wardlaw	3569-3576 (1955)
Chemical effects of steric strains	H.C. Brown	1248-1268 (1956)
The photosynthetic carbon cycle	M. Calvin	1895-1915 (1956)
Recent progress in the chemistry of peptides	G.W. Kenner	3689-3700 (1956)
Reactions of radicals in gaseous systems	E.W.R. Steacie	3986-3996 (1956)
Alkoxides old and new	W. Wardlaw	4004-4014 (1956)
The role of the π-electron in aromatic chemistry	H.C. Longuet-Higgins	157-165 (1957)
The structure of addition compounds, especially those in which halogens act as electron-acceptors	O. Hassel	250-255 (1957)
The course of polar reactions in non-polar conditions	C.K. Ingold	279-287 (1957)
Isocyanates	A.C. Farthing	301-303 (1957)
Some aspects of sesquiterpenoid chemistry	D.H.R. Barton	61-66 (1958)
Design in high polymers	C.E.H. Bawn	139-144 (1958)
Some isothermal reactions of free radicals studied by kinetic spectroscopy	R.G.W. Norrish	247-255 (1958)
Structural representation of aromatic compounds	W. Baker	75-79 (1959)
Some recent advances in the chemistry of the D-vitamins	B. Lythgoe	141-149 (1959)
Nucleotides and bacterial cell wall components	J. Baddiley	177-182 (1959)
Faith and doubt: the theory of structure in organic chemistry	W.V. Farrar and K.R. Farrar	285-291 (1959)
History of the isoprene rule	L. Ruzicka	341-360 (1959)
Some recent advances in fluorocarbon chemistry	G.H. Cady	133-138 (1960)
Polyacetylenes	E.R.H. Jones	199-211 (1960)
Progress in the study of heterogeneous catalysis	C. Kemball	264-274 (1960)
Hydrocarbon metal carbonyls	P.L. Pauson	297-305 (1960)

PROGRESS IN INORGANIC CHEMISTRY

This is an annual collection of review articles, in English. Edited by F.A. Cotton. Published by Interscience Publishers, Inc. New York and London.

Title	Author	Reference
Cyclopentadienyl and arene metal compounds	G. Wilkinson and F.A. Cotton	1, 1-124 (1959)
Isocyanide complexes of metals	L. Malatesta	1, 233-379 (1959)
Metal alkoxides	D.C. Bradley	2, 303-361 (1960)

PROGRESS IN ORGANIC CHEMISTRY

This is a periodical publication, in English, edited by J.W. Cook and published by Academic Press, Inc., N.Y., and Butterworths Scientific Publications, London.

Title	Author	Reference
Molecular structure of strychnine, brucine and vomicine	R. Robinson	<u>1</u>, 1-21 (1952)
Chemistry of some heartwood constituents of conifers and their physiological and taxonomic significance	H. Erdtman	<u>1</u>, 22-63 (1952)
Photodynamically-active natural pigments	H.H. Brockmann	<u>1</u>, 64-82 (1952)
Chemicals from petroleum	S.F. Birch	<u>1</u>, 83-133 (1952)
Acetylene chemistry	B.C.L. Weedon	<u>1</u>, 134-172 (1952)
Drugs inhibiting symptomatic stimulators	F. Bergel and M.W. Parkes	<u>1</u>, 173-218 (1952)
Free radicals as intermediates in organic reactions	D.H. Hey	<u>1</u>, 219-247 (1952)
Starch and its products of amylolytic degradation	I.A. Preece	<u>1</u>, 248-279 (1952)
Some recent developments in theoretical organic chemistry	M.J.S. Dewar	<u>2</u>, 1-28 (1953)
Organic fluorine compounds	M. Stacey	<u>2</u>, 29-66 (1953)
The chemistry of the triterpenoids	D.H.R. Barton	<u>2</u>, 67-103 (1953)
The partial synthesis of cortisone and related compounds from accessible steroids	F.S. Spring	<u>2</u>, 104-130 (1953)
The relationship of natural steroids to carcinogenic aromatic compounds	H.H. Inhoffen	<u>2</u>, 131-155 (1953)
Some recent developments in pyridine chemistry	J.P. Wibaut	<u>2</u>, 156-199 (1953)
Total synthesis of steroids	J.W. Cornforth	<u>3</u>, 1-43 (1955)
Non-benzenoid aromatic compounds	W. Baker and J.F.W. McOmie	<u>3</u>, 44-80 (1955)
The fulvenes	E.D. Bergmann	<u>3</u>, 81-171 (1955)
Organic compounds of lithium	E.A. Braude	<u>3</u>, 172-217 (1955)
Indole alkaloids	V. Boekelheide and V. Prelog	<u>3</u>, 218-266 (1955)
Naturally occurring unsaturated fatty acids	F.D. Gunstone	<u>4</u>, 1-30 (1958)
Free valence in conjugated organic molecules	B. Pullman and A. Pullman	<u>4</u>, 31-71 (1958)
Oxygen-containing heterocyclic fungal metabolites	W.B. Whalley	<u>4</u>, 72-114 (1958)
Naturally occurring 2-acylcyclohexane-1,3-diones	C.H. Hassall	<u>4</u>, 115-139 (1958)
Degradation and synthesis of peptides and proteins	A.H. Cook and G. Harris	<u>4</u>, 140-216 (1958)
Heterocyclic derivatives of phosphorus, arsenic and antimony	F.G. Mann	<u>4</u>, 217-248 (1958)

PROGRESS IN STEREOCHEMISTRY

This is a collection of review articles, in English. Volume I was edited by W. Klyne, Volume II by W. Klyne and P.B.D. de la Mare. Published by Academic Press, New York and Butterworths Scientific Publications, London.

Title	Author	Reference
The shape of simple molecules	A.D. Walsh	1, 1-35 (1954)
The conformations of six-membered ring systems	W. Klyne	1, 36-89 (1954)
Stereochemical factors in reaction mechanisms and kinetics	P.B.D. de la Mare	1, 90-125 (1954)
The relationships between the stereochemistry and spectroscopic properties of organic compounds	E.A. Braude and E.S. Waight	1, 126-176 (1954)
The correlation of configurations	J.A. Mills and W. Klyne	1, 177-222 (1954)
The stereochemistry of the hydrogen bond	L. Hunter	1, 223-249 (1954)
The stereochemistry of compounds of high molecular weight	E.J. Ambrose	1, 250-284 (1954)
The stereochemistry of complex compounds	R.S. Nyholm	1, 322-360 (1954)
Crystallography and stereochemistry	J.C. Speakman	2, 1-38 (1958)
The stereochemistry of homolytic processes	G.H. Williams	2, 39-64 (1958)
The stereochemistry of displacements at unsaturated centres	P.B.D. de la Mare	2, 65-98 (1958)
Steric effects on mesomerism	B.M. Webster	2, 99-156 (1958)
The study of optically labile compounds	M.M. Harris	2, 157-195 (1958)
The stereochemistry of the Group V elements	F.G. Mann	2, 196-227 (1958)
Steric factors in immunochemistry	J.R. Marrack and E.S. Orlans	2, 228-260 (1958)

PROGRESS IN THE CHEMISTRY OF FATS AND OTHER LIPIDS

This is a collection of review articles, in English. Edited by R.T. Holman, W.O. Lundberg and T. Malkin and published by Pergamon Press, New York.

Title	Author	Reference
The molecular structure and polymorphism of fatty acids and their derivatives	T. Malkin	1, 1-17 (1952)
Sterols	W. Bergmann	1, 18-69 (1952)
Structure and properties of phosphatides	P. Desnuelle	1, 70-103 (1952)
Chromatography of fatty acids and related substances	R.T. Holman	1, 104-126 (1952)
Derivatives of the fatty acids	H.J. Harwood	1, 127-174 (1952)
The polymorphism of glycerides	T. Malkin	2, 1-50 (1954)
Autoxidation of fats and related substances	R.T. Holman	2, 51-98 (1954)
Urea inclusion compounds of fatty acids	H. Schlenk	2, 243-267 (1954)
Infrared absorption spectroscopy in fats and oils	D.H. Wheeler	2, 268-291 (1954)
Counter-current fractionation of lipids	H.J. Dutton	2, 292-325 (1954)
Applications of low temperature crystallization in the separation of the fatty acids and their compounds	J.B. Brown and D.K. Kolb	3, 57-94 (1955)
Synthetic detergents	W. Baird	3, 95-151 (1955)
Oxygenated fatty acids	D. Swern	3, 213-241 (1955)
Low pressure fractional distillation and its use in the investigation of lipids	K.E. Murray	3, 243-273 (1955)
The constitution and synthesis of fatty acids	F.D. Gunstone	4, 1-43 (1957)
The naturally occurring acetylenic acids	E.M. Meade	4, 45-62 (1957)
The synthesis of glycerides	T. Malkin and T.H. Bevan	4, 63-77 (1957)
Lipid waxes	A.H. Warth	4, 79-96 (1957)
The synthesis of phospholipids	T. Malkin and T.H. Bevan	4, 97-140 (1957)
Ultraviolet spectrophotometry of fatty acids	G.A.J. Pitt and R.A. Morton	4, 227-278 (1957)
Advances in technology	Collective Volume	5, 1-338 (1959)

QUARTERLY REVIEWS

This review journal, published by the Chemical Society (London), contains articles on all phases of chemistry. The articles are prepared to be of interest to the general reader. Edited by R.S. Cahn and L.C. Cross. In English.

Title	Author	Reference
Colour and constitution	A. Maccoll	1, 16-58 (1947)
Some thermodynamic properties of high polymers, and their molecular interpretation	G. Gee	1, 265-298 (1947)
Asymmetric transformation and asymmetric induction	E.E. Turner and M.M. Harris	1, 299-330 (1947)
Chemistry of the metal carbonyls	J.S. Anderson	1, 331-357 (1947)
The aliphatic nitro-compounds	N. Levy and J.D. Rose	1, 358-395 (1947)
Steric hindrance	E.D. Hughes	2, 107-131 (1948)
The chemistry of the penicillins	A.H. Cook	2, 203-259 (1948)
The interpretation of bond properties	T.L. Cottrell and L.E. Sutton	2, 260-276 (1948)
Aromatic nitration	R.J. Gillespie and D.J. Millen	2, 277-306 (1948)
Synthetic analgesics	F. Bergel and A.L. Morrison	2, 349-382 (1948)
The polarity of the C-H bond	W.L.G. Gent	2, 383-392 (1948)
Kinetics of olefin oxidation	J.L. Bolland	3, 1-21 (1949)
The chemistry of diterpenoids	D.H.R. Barton	3, 36-64 (1949)
Kinetics of thermal addition of halogens to olefinic compounds	P.B.D. de la Mare	3, 126-145 (1949)
Some aspects of the organic chemistry of derivatives of phosphorus oxyacids	F.R. Atherton	3, 146-159 (1949)
Some aspects of pyrimidine and purine chemistry	B. Lythgoe	3, 181-207 (1949)
Hyperconjugation	V.A. Crawford	3, 226-244 (1949)
Carbohydrate sulphates	E.G.V. Percival	3, 369-384 (1949)
The reduction of organic compounds by metal-ammonia solutions	A.J. Birch	4, 69-93 (1950)
Relation between the oxidation-reduction potentials of quinones and their chemical structure	M.G. Evans and J. DeHeer	4, 94-114 (1950)
Isotopic tracer techniques	H.R.V. Arnstein and R. Bentley	4, 172-194 (1950)
Some aspects of furan and pyran chemistry	D.G. Jones and A.W.C. Taylor	4, 195-216 (1950)

QUARTERLY REVIEWS (Contd.)

Organometallic compounds of the first three periodic groups	G.E. Coates	4,	217-235 (1950)
Some organic peroxides and their reactions	E.G.E. Hawkins	4,	251-271 (1950)
Rate constants in radical polymerisation reactions	G.M. Burnett	4,	292-326 (1950)
The cyanine dyes	F.M. Hamer	4,	327-355 (1950)
The nitration of heterocyclic nitrogen compounds	K. Schofield	4,	382-403 (1950)
Anionotropy	E.A. Braude	4,	404-425 (1950)
Bond dissociation energies	M. Szwarc	5,	22-43 (1951)
Some aspects of the chemistry of nitramines	A.H. Lamberton	5,	75-98 (1951)
The tropolones	J.W. Cook and J.D. Loudon	5,	99-130 (1951)
The mechanism of thermal decarboxylation	B.R. Brown	5,	131-146 (1951)
The aromatic bond	G.M. Badger	5,	147-170 (1951)
Reactions of halides in solution	E.D. Hughes	5,	245-269 (1951)
The configuration of flexible organic molecules	J.C. McCoubrey and A.R. Ubbelohde	5,	364-389 (1951)
The constitution of wool wax	E.V. Truter	5,	390-404 (1951)
Synthetic approaches to the morphine structure	E.S. Stern	5,	405-419 (1951)
The infra-red and raman spectra of hydrocarbons. Part I. Acetylenes and olefins	N. Sheppard and D.M. Simpson	6,	1-33 (1952)
Aromatic rearrangements	E.D. Hughes and C.K. Ingold	6,	34-62 (1952)
Molecular orbitals and organic reactions	R.D. Brown	6,	63-99 (1952)
Geometrical isomerism about carbon-carbon double bonds	L. Crombie	6,	101-140 (1952)
The polymerisation of aldehydes	J.C. Bevington	6,	141-156 (1952)
The pteridines	A. Albert	6,	197-237 (1952)
Polarography of organic compounds	J.E. Page	6,	262-301 (1952)
Reactions of organic cations	H. Burton and P.F.G. Praill	6,	302-318 (1952)
The free-electron approximation for conjugated compounds	N.S. Bayliss	6,	319-339 (1952)
Structural investigation of peptides and proteins	H.G. Khorana	6,	340-357 (1952)
Sandmeyer and related reactions	W.A. Cowdrey and D.S. Davies	6,	358-379 (1952)
Anodic syntheses with carboxylic acids	B.C. Weedon	6,	380-398 (1952)
The infra-red and raman spectra of hydrocarbons. Part II. Paraffins	N. Sheppard and D.M. Simpson	7,	19-55 (1953)
Recent developments in the preparation of natural and synthetic straight-chain fatty acids	F.D. Gunstone	7,	175-197 (1953)

QUARTERLY REVIEWS (Contd.)

The reactions of methyl radicals	A.F. Trotman-Dickenson	7,	198-220 (1953)
Stereochemistry of cyclohexane	O. Hassel	7,	221-230 (1953)
Steroidal alkaloids	J. McKenna	7,	231-254 (1953)
The association of carboxylic acids	G. Allen and E.F. Caldin	7,	255-278 (1953)
The synthesis of isotopically labelled organic compounds	S.L. Thomas and H.S. Turner	7,	407-443 (1953)
The behaviour of organic compounds in sulphuric acid	R.J. Gillespie and J.A. Leisten	8,	40-66 (1954)
The isoflavones	W.K. Warburton	8,	67-87 (1954)
Ionic polymerisation	D.C. Pepper	8,	88-121 (1954)
Olefin oxidation	L. Bateman	8,	147-167 (1954)
The structure of the ergot alkaloids	A.L. Glenn	8,	192-218 (1954)
The mechanism of catalytic hydrogenation and related reactions	G.C. Bond	8,	279-307 (1954)
Free-radical addition reactions of olefinic systems	J.I.G. Cadogan and D.H. Hey	8,	308-329 (1954)
The reactions of organic fluorine compounds	W.K.R. Musgrave	8,	331-354 (1954)
Modern aspects of the Friedel-Crafts reaction	G. Baddeley	8,	355-379 (1954)
The application of mass spectrometry to chemical problems	W.J. Dunning	9,	23-50 (1955)
The chemistry of 5-oxazolones	E. Baltazzi	9,	150-173 (1955)
Alkyl-oxygen heterolysis in carboxylic esters and related compounds	A.G. Davies and J. Kenyon	9,	203-228 (1955)
The estimation of thermodynamic properties for organic compounds and chemical reactions	G.J. Janz	9,	229-254 (1955)
The initiation of polymerisation processes by redox catalysts	R.G.R. Bacon	9,	287-310 (1955)
The action of ionising radiations on organic compounds	E. Collinson and A.J. Swallow	9,	311-327 (1955)
The tetracyclic triterpenes	R.M. Gascoigne and J.J.H. Simes	9,	328-361 (1955)
Ferrocene and related compounds	P.L. Pauson	9,	391-414 (1955)
Phenol tautomerism	R.H. Thomson	10,	27-43 (1956)
The principles of conformational analysis	D.H.R. Barton and R.C. Cookson	10,	44-82 (1956)
The indole alkaloids excluding harmine and strychnine	J.E. Saxton	10,	108-147 (1956)
Nuclear methylation of flavones and related compounds	A.C. Jain and T.R. Seshadri	10,	169-184 (1956)

QUARTERLY REVIEWS (Contd.)

Peptides: methods of synthesis and terminal-residue studies	H.D. Springall and H.D. Law	10, 230-257 (1956)
Oxidative-hydrolytic splitting of carbon-carbon bonds of organic molecules	M.M. Shemyakin and L.A. Shchukina	10, 261-282 (1956)
Tetra- and tri-chloroalkanes and related compounds	A.N. Nesmeyanov, R.Kh. Freidlina and L.I. Zakharkin	10, 330-370 (1956)
Acetylenic compounds as natural products	J.D. Bu'Lock	10, 371-394 (1956)
The chemistry of the aromatic heterocyclic $\underline{N}$-oxides	A.R. Katritzky	10, 395-406 (1956)
The stereochemistry of sub-group VI_B of the Periodic Table	S.C. Abrahams	10, 407-436 (1956)
Quantitative study of steric hindrance	C.K. Ingold	11, 1-14 (1957)
Meso-ionic compounds	W. Baker and W.D. Ollis	11, 15-29 (1957)
Carbohydrate phosphates	A.B. Foster and W.G. Overend	11, 61-85 (1957)
Grignard and organolithium reagents derived from dihalogen compounds	I.T. Millar and H. Heaney	11, 109-120 (1957)
Recent advances in sesquiterpenoid chemistry	D.H.R. Barton and P. de Mayo	11, 189-211 (1957)
The inositols	S.J. Angyal	11, 212-226 (1957)
Mechanism and reactivity in aromatic nucleophilic substitution reactions	J.F. Bunnett	12, 1-16 (1958)
Reduction by metal-amine solutions: applications in synthesis and determination of structure	A.J. Birch and H. Smith	12, 17-33 (1958)
Veratrum alkaloids	K.J. Morgan and J.A. Barltrop	12, 34-60 (1958)
Some thermodynamic and kinetic aspects of addition polymerisation	F.S. Dainton and K.J. Ivin	12, 61-92 (1958)
Chemistry of some newer antibiotics	N.G. Brink and R.E. Harman	12, 93-115 (1958)
The structure of carbonium ions	D. Bethell and V. Gold	12, 173-203 (1958)
Mechanisms for carbon-hydrogen bond breakage	E.S. Lewis and M.C.R. Symons	12, 230-249 (1958)
Mechanisms of oxidation by compounds of chromium and manganese	W.A. Waters	12, 277-300 (1958)
Chemistry of $\underline{p}$-xylylene, its analogues, and polymers	L.A. Errede and M. Szwarc	12, 301-320 (1958)
Structure and properties of $\underline{C}$-nitroso-compounds	B.G. Gowenlock and W. Lüttke	12, 321-340 (1958)

QUARTERLY REVIEWS (Contd.)

Compounds containing carbon-phosphorus bonds	P.C. Crofts	12,	341-366 (1958)
Sugar epoxides	F.H. Newth	13,	30-47 (1959)
Asymmetry: the non-conservation of parity and optical activity	T.L.V. Ulbricht	13,	48-60 (1959)
Oxidations by manganese dioxide in neutral media	R.M. Evans	13,	61-70 (1959)
Organosilylmetallic compounds: their formation and reactions, and comparison with related types	D. Wittenberg and H. Gilman	13,	116-145 (1959)
The mass spectrometry of free radicals	J. Cuthbert	13,	215-232 (1959)
Perfluoroalkyl derivatives of metals and non-metals	J.J. Lagowski	13,	233-264 (1959)
Newer aspects of the stereochemistry of carbohydrates	R.J. Ferrier and W.G. Overend	13,	265-286 (1959)
Infrared spectra of heteroaromatic compounds	A.R. Katritzky	13,	353-373 (1959)
Alkaloids of calabash-curare and strychnos species	A.R. Battersby and H.F. Hodson	14,	77-103 (1960)
Primary processes in photo-oxidation	R.M. Hochstrasser and G.B. Porter	14,	146-173 (1960)
Benzilic acid and related rearrangements	S. Selman and J.F. Eastham	14,	221-235 (1960)
Tetronic acids	L.J. Haynes and J.R. Plimmer	14,	292-315 (1960)
The chemistry of naturally-occurring 1,2-epoxides	A.D. Cross	14,	317-335 (1960)
The interaction of free radicals with saturated aliphatic compounds	J.M. Tedder	14,	336-356 (1960)
The pinacol rearrangement	C.J. Collins	14,	357-377 (1960)

RECORD OF CHEMICAL PROGRESS

This is a quarterly review journal, published in English, by Wayne State University, for the Kresge-Hooker Science Library Associates, since 1957. Founded in 1940 as a bulletin of the Kresge-Hooker Science Library, it started publication of review articles in 1946, and since 1949 (volume 10) these became its main objective. The foundation of the library and the journal is specially indebted to the efforts of Dr. Neil E. Gordon (see Record of Chemical Progress, 10, 140-151 (1949)). Present editor is W.H. Powell.

Title	Author	Reference
Hooker's researches on lapachol in relation to new developments in the field of chemotherapy	L.F. Fieser	7, 26-45 (1946)
Some polar factors affecting the properties of unsaturated compounds	C.C. Price	8, 5-8 (1947)
Recent progress in the field of theoretical organic chemistry	A.E. Remick	8, 25-34 (1947)
Advances in the field of pharmaceuticals and medicinals - 1946	T.G. Klumpp and J.B. Rice	8, 35-42 (1947)
Recent advances in nitro paraffins	H.B. Hass	8, 127-129 (1947)
Molecular structure in fiber systems	H.S. Taylor	9, 35-43 (1948)
Directive effects in aliphatic chlorination	A.B. Ash and H.C. Brown	9, 81-94 (1948)
Factors determining the mechanism of redox reactions	A.E. Remick	9, 95-103 (1948)
A quantitative theory of steric effects	F.H. Westheimer	10, 11-15 (1949)
Some special features of the stereochemistry of the metal ammines	J.C. Bailar, Jr.	10, 17-23 (1949)
Hydroarylation of some unsaturated compounds	W.S. Johnson	10, 53-57 (1949)
Advances in the field of pharmaceuticals and medicinals - 1948	T.G. Klumpp and J.B. Rice	10, 71-77 (1949)
Restricted rotation	R. Adams	10, 91-99 (1949)
Textile chemistry in 1948	J.F. Smith	10, 115-119 (1949)
Summary of the hydrocarbons isolated from one representative petroleum	F.D. Rossini, B.J. Mair and A.R. Glasgow, Jr.	10, 121-126 (1949)
Recent work on the mechanisms of peroxide reactions	P.D. Bartlett	11, 47-51 (1950)
Recent progress in the field of theoretical organic chemistry	A.E. Remick	11, 52-60 (1950)
Preparation and properties of some cyclopropane derivatives	L.I. Smith	11, 65-73 (1950)
Chemistry of eight-membered ring-compounds	A.S. Cope	11, 115-119 (1950)
Fundamental chemistry of the anthocyanins	R.L. Shriner	11, 121-127 (1950)

RECORD OF CHEMICAL PROGRESS (Contd.)

Allylic rearrangements during the synthesis of organic compounds	W.G. Young	11, 129-135 (1950)
Biosynthesis of isoprenoid compounds	J.R. Johnson	11, 137-144 (1950)
Bimolecular reduction of carbonyl compounds	R.C. Fuson	12, 1-7 (1951)
Mechanism of polar displacement reactions	C.G. Swain	12, 21-26 (1951)
Rearrangement of alkyl and aryl groups as anions	R.T. Arnold	12, 29-36 (1951)
Macromolecules containing long range periodicities	H.L. Mark	12, 139-146 (1951)
Configuration of polypeptide chains in proteins	L. Pauling	12, 155-161 (1951)
Polyalkylene sulfides	C.S. Marvel	12, 185-189 (1951)
Some recent advances in fluorine chemistry	H.J. Emeléus	13, 1-7 (1952)
Physicochemical studies on Vitamin B_{12}	H. Diehl et.al.,	13, 9-21 (1952)
Recent developments in the chemistry of organic carcinogens	N.P. Buu-Hoï	13, 23-29 (1952)
Halogenation of aromatic and heterocyclic compounds by means of N-halogenated amides	N.P. Buu-Hoï	13, 30-36 (1952)
Stereochemical research	W.R. Brode	13, 45-53 (1952)
Catalytic chemistry of hydrocarbons	A.V. Grosse	13, 55-63 (1952)
A useful notation for visualizing certain stereospecific reactions	M.S. Newman	13, 111-117 (1952)
Certain anionic aromatic substitution reactions	R.C. Elderfield	13, 119-129 (1952)
Constitution of the Grignard reagents	A.B. Garrett et.al.,	13, 155-159 (1952)
Developments in the synthesis of cortical hormones	M. Tishler	13, 161-177 (1952)
Recent work on polyacetylene	E.R.H. Jones	14, 1-5 (1953)
The chemical nature of fatty acids of bacterial origin	K. Hofmann	14, 7-17 (1953)
The chemistry of the veratrum alkaloids	O. Wintersteiner	14, 19-34 (1953)
The F-, B-, I- strains	H.C. Brown	14, 83-97 (1953)
Electrochemical fission of carbon-halogen bonds	P.J. Elving	14, 99-115 (1953)
The use of small-scale fractionation techniques for characterization of complex organic compounds	L.C. Craig	14, 177-189 (1953)
Some recent progress in the chemistry of caryophyllene	D.H.R. Barton	15, 19-25 (1954)
The toxic principle of poison ivy and related plants	C.R. Dawson	15, 39-53 (1954)
Quantitative separations by ion-exchange chromatography	Wm. Rieman III	15, 85-101 (1954)
Stereochemical control of organic reactions; differences in behavior of diastereoisomers	D.Y. Curtin	15, 111-128 (1954)
Reaction of aluminum with carbon tetrachloride	H.H. Uhlig	15, 129-130 (1954)
The primary act in photochemical reactions sensitized by polyatomic molecules	R. Livingston	16, 13-21 (1955)

RECORD OF CHEMICAL PROGRESS (Contd.)

Optical activity and configurational relations in carbon compounds	M.L. Wolfrom	16,	121-136 (1955)
Plant chemistry in Australia	J.R. Price	16,	153-163 (1955)
Mechanisms involved in pyridine nucleotide action	N.O. Kaplan	16,	177-195 (1955)
Erythrina alkaloids	V. Boekelheide	16,	227-239 (1955)
Reactions of oxy-anions in water solution	H. Taube	17,	25-33 (1956)
New small-ring compounds	J.D. Roberts	17,	95-107 (1956)
Transannular nitrogen-carbonyl interactions	N.J. Leonard	17,	243-257 (1956)
The formation and significance of the porphyrins	J.M. Orten	17,	259-266 (1956)
The chemistry of sphingosine	C.A. Grob	18,	55-66 (1957)
Vapor phase chromatography	R.H. Munch	18,	69-101 (1957)
The chemistry and stereochemistry of butyrospermol, a tetracyclic triterpenoid	F.S. Spring	18,	103-108 (1957)
The course of ozonization of unsaturated compounds	R. Criegee	18,	111-120 (1957)
Some recent advances in the chemistry of sesquiterpenoid lactones	D.H.R. Barton	18,	125-131 (1957)
Unsolved problems in flavonoid chemistry	T.S. Wheeler	18,	133-161 (1957)
Recent advances in peptide synthesis	M. Bodanszky	18,	187-199 (1957)
Investigations on the transannular effects in elimination and substitution reactions by tracer technique	V. Prelog	18,	247-260 (1957)
Aromatic substitution	M.J.S. Dewar	19,	1-11 (1958)
Synthetic studies related to lysergic acid and the ergot alkaloids	E.C. Kornfeld	19,	23-32 (1958)
Some aspects of the chemistry of ribose	H.G. Fletcher Jr.,	19,	147-164 (1958)
Studies on the synthesis of nucleosides	J.J. Fox	19,	173-190 (1958)
The stereochemistry of three-ring carbonyl compounds	N.H. Cromwell	19,	215-232 (1958)
The pyrrolizidine alkaloids. Comparative structure, biological synthesis and pharmacology	F.L. Warren	20,	13-21 (1959)
The chemistry of the thiocarbonyl group	N. Lozac'h	20,	23-32 (1959)
Transannular effects in paracyclophanes and related compounds	D.J. Cram	20,	71-93 (1959)
Some recent applications of optical rotatory dispersion studies to organic chemical problems	C. Djerassi	20,	101-145 (1959)
Synthetic pathways to naturally occurring polypeptides	R. Schwyzer	20,	147-167 (1959)
Chemical applications of pure quadruple spectroscopy	R. Livingston	20,	173-186 (1959)
Biogenesis of the tetracyclic triterpenes	P. Crabbe	20,	189-207 (1959)
New reactions of 1,1- and 1,2-di-substituted hydrazines	C.G. Overberger	21,	21-47 (1960)
Some recent developments in sesquiterpene chemistry	F. Šorm	21,	73-93 (1960)
Carbonium reactions in allylic systems	H.L. Goering	21,	109-121 (1960)
Alkyl and aryl derivatives of transition metals	J. Chatt	21,	147-157 (1960)
Organo-compounds of transition metals	D.C. Bradley	21,	179-188 (1960)

RECORD OF CHEMICAL PROGRESS (Contd.)

Some chemical applications of nuclear magnetic resonance	M.T. Rogers	21, 197-210 (1960)
Recent studies on the hydrolysis of aliphatic amides	A. Bruylants and F. Kezdy	21, 213-240 (1960)
The Kolbe electrolysis - current problems	G.W. Thiessen	21, 243-255 (1960)

RESEARCH
(Applied to Industry)

This journal is published, in English, each month by Butterworth Scientific Publications. The present editor is G.K.T. Conn.

Title	Author	Reference
Water soluble cellulose ethers	W.A. Caldwell and A.J. Watters	1, 248-253 (1948)
Molecular association	L. Hunter	1, 447-453 (1948)
Photosensitized reactions of hydrocarbons	E.W.R. Steacie	1, 541-547 (1948)
The chemistry of destructive hydrogenation	C.M. Cawley	1, 553-561 (1948)
Alcian blue, a new phthalocyanine dyestuff	N.H. Haddock	1, 685-689 (1948)
A new notation for organic chemistry	G.M. Dyson	2, 104-114 (1949)
Friedel-Crafts polymerizations	P.H. Plesch	2, 267-275 (1949)
Alkyl fluorophosphates and related compounds	B.A. Kilby	2, 417-422 (1949)
Vitamin B_6: Pyridine, pyridoxal and pyridoxamine	T. Urbański	2, 507-512 (1949)
X-ray structure analysis of complex organic compounds	J.D. Dunitz	3, 6-12 (1950)
Chemistry of lignin	H. Erdtman	3, 63-67 (1950)
Reaction between nitrous acid and amines	J.C. Earl	3, 120-127 (1950)
Applications of the electronic theory of organic reactions	M.J.S. Dewar	3, 154-159 (1950)
Carotenoids and vitamin A	R.F. Hunter	3, 453-461 (1950)
Orthoesters of silicon, titanium and zirconium	W. Wardlaw and D.C. Bradley	3, 462-465 (1950)
Recent advances in estimation of vitamins A	V.H. Booth	3, 497-504 (1950)
Stereochemistry of <u>cyclo</u>hexane	O. Hassel	3, 504-509 (1950)
Chemistry of specific, selective and sensitive reactions	F. Feigl	3, 550-557 (1950)
New features of catalytic hydrogenations and related processes	Z. Csürös	4, 52-60 (1951)
Recent studies of high polymers in relation to the properties of gelatin and glue	A.G. Ward	4, 119-125 (1951)
Synthesis of macromolecules with long range periodicities	H. Mark	4, 167-171 (1951)
Chemistry of the plant gums	E.L. Hirst and J.K.N. Jones	4, 411-417 (1951)
Microbiological approaches to the preparation of cortisone and hydrocortisone	D.H. Peterson	6, 309-319 (1953)
Sorting molecules by size and shape	E.V. Truter	6, 320-326 (1953)
Polymer research	I. Goodman	6, 428-433 (1953)
The polarizing microscope in organic chemistry and biology	A.E.J. Vickers	9, 67-78 (1956)
Chelating resins	D.K. Hale	9, 104-108 (1956)
Hydrogenation of benzene and alkylbenzenes	N.I. Shuykin and N.G. Berdnikova	9, 132-137 (1956)
Molecular structure of waxes	H.H. Hatt and J.A. Lamberton	9, 138-146 (1956)
Infrared spectroscopy	L.J. Bellamy	9, 147-152 (1956)

Isocyanate-based polymers	P. Merriman	9, 254-259 (1956)
The mass spectrometer in chemical analysis	J.D. Waldron	9, 306-316 (1956)
Isotactic polymers	J.W.S. Hearle	9, 461-465 (1956)
Living polymers - their preparation and application	J.H.S. Green	12, 232-237 (1959)
Organic semiconductors	D.D. Eley	12, 293-299 (1959)
The phosphonitrilic derivatives. Aromatics without carbon	N.L. Paddock	13, 94-100 (1960)
Modern dyes	C. Paine	13, 122-127 (1960)
Isolation and identification of volatile fruit-flavours	D.S. Bidmead and D. Welti	13, 295-299 (1960)
The scope of organotin compounds in industry	E.S. Hedges	13, 449-452 (1960)

REVIEWS OF PURE AND APPLIED CHEMISTRY

This quarterly journal is devoted to the publication of review articles pertaining to theoretical and applied chemistry. All articles are in English. Editor: A.L.G. Rees. Published by the Royal Australian Chemical Institute.

Title	Author	Reference
The impact of chemistry on biology and medicine	A.R. Todd	1, 14-24 (1951)
The pteridines	A. Albert	1, 51-63 (1951)
The mechanism of nucleophilic substitution in aromatic compounds	J. Miller	1, 171-185 (1951)
The chemistry of pedicin and related substances	T.R. Seshadri	1, 186-202 (1951)
Vitamin B_{12}	A.R. Todd and A.W. Johnson	2, 23-32 (1952)
Chemical applications of radiocarbon	G.M. Harris	2, 57-64 (1952)
The electropositivity of the halogens	K.D. Reeve	2, 108-124 (1952)
Syntheses of alkaloids under "Physiological Conditions" and their relation to alkaloid biogenesis	G.K. Hughes and E. Ritchie	2, 125-138 (1952)
The acid and alkaline hydrolysis of glycerides in homogeneous systems	H.H.G. Jellinek	2, 139-162 (1952)
The photolysis of the aliphatic aldehydes and ketones	A.J.C. Nicholson	2, 174-184 (1952)
The shape and reactivity of the cyclohexane ring	S.J. Angyal and J.A. Mills	2, 185-202 (1952)
The total synthesis of steroids	A.J. Birch	3, 61-82 (1953)
Amine oxides	C.C.J. Culvenor	3, 83-114 (1953)
The simple pyrimidines	D.J. Brown	3, 115-133 (1953)
The polarographic reduction of organic compounds	H.J. Gardner and L.E. Lyons	3, 134-178 (1953)
The electronic spectra of the simple aromatic hydrocarbons	D.P. Craig	3, 207-240 (1953)
Infra-red spectra and the structure of steroids	A.R.H. Cole	4, 111-132 (1954)
The biosynthesis of cholesterol	J.W. Cornforth	4, 275-302 (1954)
Recent additions to knowledge of the chemistry of citrus fruits	J.F. Kefford	5, 77-98 (1955)
The direct determination of molecular structure and configuration of moderately complex organic compounds	A. McL. Mathieson	5, 113-142 (1955)
Inclusion compounds	F.D. Cramer	5, 143-164 (1955)
The Kerr effect. Its measurement and applications in chemistry	G.G. Le Fèvre and R.J.W. Le Fèvre	5, 261-318 (1955)
The chemical mechanism of bile pigment formation	R. Lemberg	6, 1-23 (1956)
The chemical constitution of oxidized celluloses	A. Meller	6, 40-60 (1956)
The occurrence of acetylenic compounds in nature	P.C. Wailes	6, 61-98 (1956)
The slow oxidation of gaseous hydrocarbons	M.J. Ridge	6, 121-152 (1956)
The crystalline hydrates of alcohols and glycols	H.H. Hatt	6, 153-190 (1956)
The pentacyclic triterpenoids	D.E. White	6, 191-248 (1956)

REVIEWS OF PURE AND APPLIED CHEMISTRY (Contd.)

Chitin	M.V. Tracey	7,	1-14	(1957)
Intramolecular hydrogen bonding in organic chemistry	G.M. Badger	7,	55-68	(1957)
The ion- and electron-exchange properties of activated carbon in relation to its behavior as a catalyst and adsorbent	V.A. Garten and D.E. Weiss	7,	69-122	(1957)
Halogen addition to unsaturated compounds	P.W. Robertson	7,	155-164	(1957)
Aromatic ciné substitution	L.K. Dyall	8,	33-52	(1958)
Naturally occurring quinone methines and related compounds	R.G. Cooke and R.H. Thomson	8,	85-100	(1958)
The cytochromes	R.K. Morton	8,	161-220	(1958)
The configuration of proteins in solution	S.J. Leach	9,	33-85	(1959)
The ionization and coordination behavior of porphyrins	J.N. Phillips	10,	35-60	(1960)
Organic phosphorus compounds and their application	A.P. Childs	10,	81-94	(1960)

LA REVUE SCIENTIFIQUE

This is a French journal which formerly was dedicated to all the sciences, but whose nature has altered since 1950. All articles are in French. Published by "Editions de la Revue Scientifique, Paris".

Title	Author	Reference
Vitamins and catalysts	D.E. Green	78, 17-20 (1940)
Synthetic fats	Y. Mayor	78, 149-152 (1940)
Deuterium and molecular assymetry	D. Duveen and A. Willemart	78, 279-285 (1940)
Present state of chemotherapy of lepra	N.P. Buu Hoï, P. Cagniant and J. Janicaud	79, 433-439 (1941)
Use of physical methods to determine chemical structures	R. Truchet	80, 104-116 (1942)
Vitamins K - antihemorragic vitamins	J. Cheymol	80, 117-127 (1942)
Industrial synthesis of fatty acids	R. Truchet	80, 265-270 (1942)
Tartaric acids	M. Tiffeneau	80, 297-312 (1942)
Flavor and chemical structure. The synthetic "sweet" molecules	J.A. Gautier	81, 121-132 (1943)
General principles of magnetochemistry. Its applications to organic chemistry	A. Pacault	82, 465-479 (1944)
Study of ethylene-polysulfides by X-rays	R. Tertian and J.J. Trillat	83, 21-26 (1945)
Physicochemical theories on cancer	R. Daudel	84, 37-42 (1946)
Electronic structure and carcinogenic activity of organic molecules	A. Pullman and B. Pullman	84, 145-158 (1946)
Metallo-carbonyls	M. Lehne	84, 295-302 (1946)
Penicillin	E. Catelain	85, 169-181 (1947)
Free radicals	P. Chabrier	85, 240-246 (1947)
Structure of colchicine	L. Séris	85, 489-493 (1947)
Folic acid	P. Chauchard	85, 683-686 (1947)
Study of physical and chemical properties of polyphenyl substances with fused or separated rings	N.P. Buu Hoï et. al.,	85, 1041-1050 (1947)
Use of organic reagents in inorganic analysis	E. Cattelain	86, 234-241 (1948)
Tythricine	G. Roval	86, 369-376 (1948)
The concept of mesomerism and the evolution of the ideas concerning color in organic chemistry	P. Rumpf	87, 170-180 (1949)

THE ROYAL INSTITUTE OF CHEMISTRY JOURNAL

This is a monthly journal, in English. Since 1955, review articles and conferences have been published in full. Editor is E.M. Rodd.

Title	Author	Reference
The lotoflavin problem	T.S. Wheeler	79, 21-23 (1955)
Some aspects of aromatic substitution	F. Bell	79, 322-326 (1955)
Organic compounds of iron and other transition metals	P.L. Pauson	79, 363-367 (1955)
Some recent advances in organic chemistry	M. Stacey	79, 421-423 (1955)
Synthesis in the ergot alkaloid field	A. Cohen	79, 628-631 (1955)
Hydrogen transfer *in vitro* and *in vivo*	E.A. Braude	80, 71-73 (1956)
Avogadro (1776-1865), Gerhardt (1816-1856), and the development of organic chemistry	J.H.S. Green	80, 394-397 (1956)
Vitamin B_{12}	A.W. Johnson	80, 610-616 (1956)
Liquid ammonia as a solvent	A.J. Birch	81, 100-105 (1957)
Cozymase - a study in synthesis	A. Todd	82, 309-316 (1958)
A.S. Couper, F.A. Kekulé and the quadrivalence of carbon	J.H.S. Green	82, 518-525 (1958)
Some aspects of the chemistry of quinols	F. Wessely	83, 424-430 (1959)
The fluorescence of some aromatic compounds in aqueous solution	R.T. Williams	83, 611-626 (1959)
Progress in organic fluorine chemistry	M. Stacey	84, 11-14 (1960)
Aromatic character	A.W. Johnson	84, 90-94 (1960)

TETRAHEDRON

This is an international journal of organic chemistry, founded by Sir Robert Robinson in 1957. It is devoted to the publication of original articles and selected reviews concerning all fields of organic chemistry, in English, French or German. Published by Pergamon Press, Inc., London and New York

Title	Author	Reference	
Nomenclature problems in stereochemistry (in English)	A.P. Terentiev and V.M. Potatov	1,	119-128 (1957)
Stereochemistry of electrophylic and homolytic substitution at the olefinic carbon atom (in English)	A.N. Nesmeyanov and A.E. Borisov	1,	158-168 (1957)
Remarks on the nomenclature of triterpenes (in English)	S. Allard and G. Ourisson	1,	277-283 (1957)
Theory of electronic spectra of organic molecules (in English)	A. Burawoy	2,	122-139 (1958)
The organic chemistry of desoxynucleosides and desoxynucleotides (in English)	A.M. Michelson	2,	333-344 (1958)
Some mechanisms of oxidation (in English)	J. Kenner	3,	78-89 (1958)
Some aspects of the thermochemistry and thermodynamics of the fluorocarbons (in English)	C.R. Patrick	4,	26-35 (1958)
Bond lengths and bond energies in conjugation and hyperconjugation (in English)	R.S. Mulliken	6,	68-87 (1959)
Recent developments in the chemistry of the flavonoids (in English)	T.R. Seshadri	6,	169-200 (1959)
Selective reactions and modifications of functional groups in steroid chemistry (in English)	H.J.E. Loewenthal	6,	269-303 (1959)
Reactions of ions with molecules in the gas phase (in English)	F.W. Lampe and F.H. Field	7,	189-205 (1959)
Bond lengths in benzene derivatives (in English)	J. Trotter	8,	13-22 (1960)
Organometallic complexes as catalysts in ionic polymerizations (in English)	G. Natta and G. Mazzanti	8,	86-100 (1960)
Steric correlations by the quasi-racemate method (in English)	A. Fredga	8,	126-144 (1960)
Systematic review and nomenclature of the flavonoids (in German)	K. Freudenberg and K. Weinges	8,	336-349 (1960)
Steroid nomenclature (in English)	L. Fieser and M. Fieser	8,	360-366 (1960)
The application of the Hammett equation to the theory of tautomeric equilibrium (in English)	M.I. Kabachnik et al.	9,	10-29 (1960)
Conformational analysis of alicyclic compounds (in English)	R. Pauncz and D. Ginsburg	9,	40-52 (1960)
Carcinogenesis by thiophene isosteres of polycyclic hydrocarbons. Synthesis of condensed thiophenes (in English)	B.D. Tilak	9,	76-95 (1960)
Structure of aromatic diazo compounds (in English)	B.A. Porai-Koshits	11,	30-38 (1960)

VITAMINS AND HORMONES

This is an annual collection of review articles, in English. Volumes 1 to 9 were edited by R.S. Harris and K.V. Thimann; volumes 10 to the current one were edited by R.S. Harris, G.F. Marrian and K.V. Thimann. Published by Academic Press, New York.

Title	Author	Reference
Choline - chemistry and significance as a dietary factor	C.H. Best and C.C. Lucas	1, 1-51 (1943)
Physical methods for the identification and assay of vitamins and hormones	J.R. Loofbourow	1, 109-112 (1943)
The chemistry and physiological relationships between vitamins and amino-acids	H.H. Mitchell	1, 157-187 (1943)
The hormones of the adrenal cortex	T. Reichstein and C.W. Shoppee	1, 346-405 (1943)
The chemistry of biotin	D.B. Melville	2, 29-66 (1944)
The chemistry and physiology of vitamin A	I.M. Heilbron and W.E. Jones	2, 155-205 (1944)
X-ray crystallography and sterol structure	D. Crowfoot	2, 409-459 (1944)
Chemistry of anti-pernicious anemia substance of liver	A. Subbarow A.B. Hastings and M. Elkin	3, 238-293 (1945)
The synthesis of vitamin A and related products	N.A. Milas	5, 1-36 (1947)
The chemistry and biological action of pteroyl-glutamic acid and related compounds	B.L. Hutchings and J.H. Mowat	6, 1-22 (1948)
Vitamin P	H. Scarborough and A.L. Bachrach	7, 1-56 (1949)
Stereoisomeric provitamins A	L. Zechmeister	7, 57-79 (1949)
The chemistry of gonadotropic hormones	C.H. Li	7, 224-250 (1949)
The chemistry and physiology of adenohypophyseal luteotropin (Prolactin)	A. White	7, 254-288 (1949)
Infrared spectrometry applied to steroid structure and metabolism	N. Jones and K. Dobriner	7, 294-360 (1949)
The chemistry of the hormones of posterior lobe of the pituitary gland	R.L. Stehle	7, 383-388 (1949)
Steroid configuration	C.W. Shoppee	8, 255-303 (1950)
Antimetabolites of nucleic acid metabolism	L.D. Wright	9, 131-156 (1951)
The synthesis and metabolism of radioactively-labeled steroids	G.H. Twombly	9, 237-260 (1951)
The intermediary metabolism of the non-benzenoid steroid hormones	L.T. Samuels and C.D. West	10, 251-291 (1942)

VITAMINS AND HORMONES (Contd.)

Recent knowledge of the biochemistry of thyroid gland	J. Gross and R. Pitt-Rivers	11, 159-171 (1953)
Syntheses of cortisone and related steroids	C. Djerassi	11, 205-235 (1953)
Chemistry of vitamin B_2	K. Folkers and D.E. Wolf	12, 2-48 (1954)
Estrogens and related substances in plants	R.B. Bradbury and D.E. White	12, 207-230 (1954)
The biosynthesis of ascorbic acid	L.W. Mapson	13, 71-93 (1955)
Chemistry of vitamin B_{12}	A.W. Johnson and A. Todd	15, 1-27 (1957)
Total synthesis of carotenoids	O. Isler and P. Zeller	15, 33-69 (1957)
Carnitine	G. Fraenkel and S. Friedman	15, 74-118 (1957)
The biological synthesis of cholesterol	K. Bloch	15, 119-147 (1957)
Chemical structure in relation to biological activities of vitamin B_6	E.E. Snell	16, 78-122 (1958)
Chemistry and physiology of the thyroid-stimulating hormone	M. Sonenberg	16, 206-247 (1958)
Glucagon	O.K. Behrens and W.W. Bromer	16, 264-301 (1958)
Synthetic derivatives of cortical hormones	J. Fried and A. Borman	16, 304-369 (1958)
Chemistry and biochemistry of the K vitamins	O. Isler and O. Wiss	17, 54-87 (1959)
Ergothioneine	D.B. Melville	17, 156-204 (1959)
Biochemistry of vitamin E	F.D. Vasington S.M. Reichard and A. Nason	18, 43-87 (1960)
The chemistry and pharmacology of angiotensin	R. Schwyzer and H. Turrian	18, 237-288 (1960)
Symposium on vitamin A and metabolism, in honor of Professor P. Karrer		18, 291-571 (1960)
The synthesis and labelling of vitamin A and related compounds	O. Isler et.al.,	18, 295-313 (1960)
The conversion of β-carotene into vitamin A	J. Glover	18, 371-386 (1960)

ZEITSCHRIFT FÜR VITAMIN, HORMON- UND FERMENT-FORSCHUNG

This is a journal publishing research work and review articles, mainly in German. Edited by E. Abderhalden from 1947 to 1950, and since 1951 by R. Abderhalden. Published by Verlag Urban und Schwarzenberg G.M.B.H. (Wien).

Title	Author	Reference
Folic acid (pteroylglutamic acid) (in German)	R. Abderhalden	1, 163-185 (1947-48)
The essential fatty acids (in German)	K. Bernhard	1, 199-215 (1947-48)
Chromatographic methods in protein chemistry (in German)	F. Turba	2, 49-97 (1948-49)
Metabolites and their antagonists (in French)	L. Massart	2, 113-125 (1948-49)
Basis and methods for chemical determination of suprarenal hormones and the so-called "renal corticoids" (in German)	K.H. Pfeffer and Hj. Staudinger	5, 50-65 (1952-53)
Isolation and attempts to determine the structure of the vitamin B_{12} group (in German)	O. Schindler	5, 66-74 (1952-53)
Chemistry and pharmacology of steroid hormone esters (in German)	K. Junkmann and H. Witzel	9, 97-143 (1958) 227-257

PART II
REVIEWS IN SYMPOSIA, COLLECTIVE VOLUMES AND NON-PERIODICAL PUBLICATIONS
Pages 116-234

ADVANCES IN CHEMISTRY SERIES

This is the collection of the proceedings of national and international conferences sponsored by the American Chemical Society. Edited and published by the American Chemical Society, Applied Publications Division.

Title	Author	Reference
Agricultural control chemicals		<u>1</u>, 76 pp. (1950)
Chemical factors in hypertension		<u>2</u>, 59 pp. (1950)
Analytical methods in the food industry		<u>3</u>, 73 pp. (1950)
Searching the chemical literature		<u>4</u>, 171 pp. (1951)
Progress in petroleum technology		<u>5</u>, 392 pp. (1951)
Azeotropic data		<u>6</u>, 328 pp. (1952)
Agricultural applications of petroleum products		<u>7</u>, 104 pp. (1952)
Chemical nomenclature		<u>8</u>, 112 pp. (1953)
Fire retardant paints		<u>9</u>, 91 pp. (1954)
Literature resources for chemical process industries		<u>10</u>, 547 pp. (1954)
Natural plant hydrocolloids		<u>11</u>, 103 pp. (1954)
Use of sugars and other carbohydrates in the food industry		<u>12</u>, 132 pp. (1955)
Pesticides in tropical agriculture		<u>13</u>, 102 pp. (1955)
Nomenclature for terpene hydrocarbons		<u>14</u>, 98 pp. (1955)
Physical properties of chemical compounds. I.		<u>15</u>, 536 pp. (1955)
A key to pharmaceutical and medicinal chemistry literature		<u>16</u>, 243 pp. (1955)
Training of literature chemists		<u>17</u>, 144 pp. (1956)
Thermodynamic properties of the elements		<u>18</u>, 234 pp. (1956)
Handling and uses of the alkali metals		<u>19</u>, 177 pp. (1957)
Literature of the combustion of petroleum		<u>20</u>, 295 pp. (1958)
Ozone chemistry and technology		<u>21</u>, 465 pp. (1959)
Physical properties and chemical compounds. II.		<u>22</u>, 491 pp. (1959)
Metal-organic compounds		<u>23</u>, 371 pp. (1959)
Organometallic compounds	H. Gilman	<u>23</u>, 1-9 (1959)
Metal alkoxides	D.C. Bradley	<u>23</u>, 10-36 (1959)
Metal chelates	M. Knell	<u>23</u>, 37-45 (1959)
Manufacture, properties, and uses of organolithium compounds	D.L. Esmay	<u>23</u>, 46-57 (1959)
Reduction of organic compounds by lithium in amines of low molecular weight	R.A. Benkeser	<u>23</u>, 58-62 (1959)

ADVANCES IN CHEMISTRY SERIES (Contd.)

Organosodium compounds for preparation of other carbon-metal bonds	J.F. Nobis L.F. Moormeir and R.E. Robinson	23,	63-68	(1959)
Some aspects of sodium acetylide chemistry	K.L. Lindsay W.L. Perilstein and J.B. Zachry	23,	69-72	(1959)
Grignard reagents	T.D. and R.C. Waugh	23,	73-81	(1959)
Preparation of alkyl mercurials with tetraethyl lead	M.S. Whelen	23,	82-86	(1959)
Organoboron compounds	R.M. Adams	23,	87-101	(1959)
Preparation, properties, and uses of benzeneboronic acid	R.M. Washburn et. al.,	23,	102-128	(1959)
Preparation, properties, and uses of borate esters	R.M. Washburn et. al.,	23,	129-157	(1959)
Trimethoxyboroxine - an extinguishing agent for metal fires	J.D. Commerford, D.L. Chamberlain Jr. and J.W. Shepherd	23,	158-162	(1959)
Organoaluminum compounds	R.F. Schultz	23,	163-171	(1959)
Preparation and ignition properties of aluminum alkyls	C.J. Marsel et. al.,	23,	172-183	(1959)
Aluminum alcoholates and the commercial preparation and uses of aluminum isopropylate	G.C. Whitaker	23,	184-189	(1959)
Applications of organotin compounds	W.R. Lewis and E.S. Hedges	23,	190-203	(1959)
Organotin compounds	H.E. Hirschland and C.K. Banks	23,	204-211	(1959)
Arylsilanes	A.R. Anderson R.W. Lerner and W.E. Smith	23,	212-216	(1959)
Alkanolamine silicate derivatives	J.O. Koehler and H. Lamprey	23,	217-224	(1959)
Alkyl methoxysilane water repellents	H. Lamprey and J.O. Koehler	23,	225-232	(1959)
Redistribution of organochlorosilanes	B.A. Bluestein and H.R. McEntee	23,	233-245	(1959)
Direct process for preparation of arylhalosilanes	A.J. Barry J.W. Gilkey and D.E. Hook	23,	246-264	(1959)
Formation of alkyl and aryl titanium-carbon bond compounds	D.F. Herman	23,	265-271	(1959)

ADVANCES IN CHEMISTRY SERIES (Contd.)

Chemistry and uses of titanium organic compounds	J.H. Haslam	23, 272-281 (1959)
Properties and uses of organic titanates	H.H. Beacham	23, 282-289 (1959)
Preparation of tetraalkyl lead compounds from lead or its alloys	H. Shapiro	23, 290-298 (1959)
A new method for the synthesis of tetraethyl lead	T.H. Pearson et. al.,	23, 299-305 (1959)
Chemical reactions of tetraethyl lead	R.L. Milde and H.A. Beatty	23, 306-318 (1959)
Uses and economic preparation of organic arsenic compounds	R.M. Kary	23, 319-327 (1959)
Chemical corps experience in the manufacture of lewisite	G.N. Jarman	23, 328-337 (1959)
Chromium complexes	F.B. Hauserman	23, 338-356 (1959)
Molybdenum chelates, esters, and organometallics	J.G. Dean H. Kay and M.L. Larson	23, 357-367 (1959)
The amine method for preparing ferrocene	R.L. Pruett and E.L. Morehouse	23, 368-371 (1959)
Chemical marketing in the competitive sixties		24, 147 pp. (1959)
Physical functions of hydrocolloids		25, 103 pp. (1960)
Nonmilitary defence. Chemical and biological defenses in perspective		26, 100 pp. (1960)
Saline water conversion		27, 246 pp. (1960)

ADVANCES IN COLLOID SCIENCE

This collection of review articles in the field of colloid science was discontinued in 1950. Volume 1 was edited by E.O. Kraemer, F.E. Bastell and S.S. Kistler, Volume 2 by H. Mark and G.S. Whitby and Volume 3 by H. Mark and E.J.W. Verwey. The following articles relate to organic chemistry. Published by Interscience Publishers Inc., N.Y.

Title	Author	Reference
Recent developments in starch chemistry	K.H. Meyer	1, 143-181 (1941)
Vulcanization	E.H. Farmer	2, 299-363 (1946)
Surface chemistry and colloids	A.E. Alexander	3, 67-96 (1950)

ADVANCES IN MASS SPECTROMETRY

These are the proceedings of a conference held in London, 1958; edited by J.D. Walden, published by Pergamon Press, London.

Title	Author	Reference
Mass spectrometric identification of impurities in organic substances by means of additional fractionation at the inlet system	C. Bokhoven and H.J. Theuwen	222-231 (1959)
Theoretical aspects of the mass spectra of polyatomic molecules	G.R. Lester	287-307 (1959)
High resolution mass spectrometry of organic materials	J.H. Beynon	328-354 (1959)
Interpretation of mass spectra of organic molecules	F.W. McLafferty	355-364 (1959)
The mass spectra of some organic phosphates	R. Guayle	365-383 (1959)
Study of the rearrangement processes in mass spectrometry by means of labelled compounds	J. Collin	384-393 (1959)
Ionization potentials at alkyl and halogenated alkyl free radicals	F.P. Lossing, P. Kebarle and J.B. de Sousa	431-442 (1959)

ADVANCING FRONTS IN CHEMISTRY

This is a collection of review articles based on a series of lectures sponsored by Wayne University under the direction of Neil E. Gordon. Volume 1 was devoted to High Polymers, and edited by S.B. Twiss, Volume 2 to Chemotherapy, edited by W.H. Powers. Published by Reinhold Publishing Corporation, New York.

Title	Author	Reference		
Molecular structure and mechanical behavior of high polymers	H.F. Mark	1,	7-13	(1945)
The relation between structure and physical properties of high polymers	S.S. Kistler	1,	15-23	(1945)
Some applications of catalysis to hydrocarbon reactions of importance in the synthesis of high polymers	E.C. Pitzer	1,	25-35	(1945)
Some aspects of the mechanism of addition polymerization	C.C. Price	1,	37-45	(1945)
Polymerization as a study of reactions of free radicals	F.R. Mayo	1,	47-59	(1945)
Molecular size distribution in high polymers	W.H. Stockmayer	1,	61-73	(1945)
Effect of chain length on physical properties of cellulose derivatives	E. Ott	1,	75-103	(1945)
Nature of the solid state of chain polymers	W.O. Baker	1,	105-151	(1945)
Synthetic antispasmodics	F.F. Blicke	2,	29-35	(1946)
Chemistry of sulfa drugs	E.H. Northey	2,	37-51	(1946)
Organometallic compounds as chemotherapeutic agents	C.K. Banks	2,	71-103	(1946)

THE ALKALOIDS. CHEMISTRY AND PHYSIOLOGY

This is a collection of review articles in the field of alkaloid chemistry. Volumes 1 - 5 were edited by R.H.F. Manske and H.L. Holmes, and Volumes 6 and 7 were edited by R.H.F. Manske. Published by Academic Press Inc., New York.

Title	Author	Reference
Sources of alkaloids and their isolation	R.H.F. Manske	1, 1-14 (1950)
Alkaloids in the plant	W.O. James	1, 15-90 (1950)
The pyrrolidine alkaloids	L. Marion	1, 91-106 (1950)
Senecio alkaloids	N.J. Leonard	1, 108-164 (1950)
The pyridine alkaloids	L. Marion	1, 165-269 (1950)
The chemistry of the tropane alkaloids	H.L. Holmes	1, 271-374 (1950)
The strychnos alkaloids	H.L. Holmes	1, 375-500 (1950)
The morphine alkaloids. I	H.L. Holmes	2, 1-159 (1952)
The morphine alkaloids. II	H.L. Holmes and G. Stork	2, 161-217 (1952)
Sinomenine	H.L. Holmes	2, 219-260 (1952)
Colchicine	J.W. Cook and J.D. Loudon	2, 261-329 (1952)
Alkaloids of the amaryllidaceae	J.W. Cook and J.D. Loudon	2, 331-352 (1952)
Acridine alkaloids	J.R. Price	2, 353-368 (1952)
The indole alkaloids	L. Marion	2, 369-498 (1952)
The erythrina alkaloids	L. Marion	2, 499-511 (1952)
The strychnos alkaloids. Part II	H.L. Holmes	2, 513-551 (1952)
The chemistry of the cinchona alkaloids	R.B. Turner and R.B. Woodward	3, 1-63 (1953)
Quinoline alkaloids, other than those of cinchona	H.T. Openshaw	3, 65-99 (1953)
The quinazoline alkaloids	H.T. Openshaw	3, 101-118 (1953)
Lupin alkaloids	N.J. Leonard	3, 119-199 (1953)
The imidazole alkaloids	A.R. Battersby and H.T. Openshaw	3, 201-246 (1953)
The chemistry of solanum and veratrum alkaloids	V. Prelog and O. Jeger	3, 247-312 (1953)
-Phenethylamines	L. Reti	3, 313-338 (1953)
Ephedra bases	L. Reti	3, 339-362 (1953)
The ipecac alkaloids	M.M. Janot	3, 363-394 (1953)
The biosynthesis of isoquinolines	R.H.F. Manske	4, 1-6 (1954)
Simple isoquinoline alkaloids	L. Reti	4, 7-21 (1954)

THE ALKALOIDS. CHEMISTRY AND PHYSIOLOGY (Contd.)

Cactus alkaloids	L. Reti	4,	23-28 (1954)
The benzylisoquinoline alkaloids	A. Burger	4,	29-75 (1954)
The protoberberine alkaloids	R.H.F. Manske and W.R. Ashford	4,	77-118 (1954)
The aporphine alkaloids	R.H.F. Manske	4,	119-145 (1954)
The protopine alkaloids	R.H.F. Manske	4,	147-166 (1954)
Phthalideisoquinoline alkaloids	J. Stanek and R.H.F. Manske	4,	167-198 (1954)
Bisbenzylisoquinoline alkaloids	M. Kulka	4,	199-247 (1954)
The Cularine alkaloids	R.H.F. Manske	4,	249-252 (1954)
α-Naphthaphenanthridine alkaloids	R.H.F. Manske	4,	253-263 (1954)
The erythophleum alkaloids	G. Dalma	4,	265-273 (1954)
The aconitum and delphinium alkaloids	E.S. Stern	4,	275-333 (1954)
Narcotics and analgesics	H. Krueger	5,	1-77 (1955)
Cardioactive alkaloids	E.L. McCawley	5,	79-107 (1955)
Respiratory stimulants	M.J. Dallemagne and C. Heymans	5,	109-139 (1955)
Antimalarials	L.H. Schmidt	5,	141-161 (1955)
Uterine stimulants	A.K. Reynolds	5,	163-209 (1955)
Alkaloids as local anesthetics	T.P. Carney	5,	211-227 (1955)
Pressor alkaloids	K.K. Chen	5,	229-241 (1955)
Mydriatic alkaloids	H.R. Ing	5,	243-263 (1955)
Curare-like effects	L.E. Craig	5,	265-293 (1955)
The lycopodium alkaloids			
Minor alkaloids of unknown structure	R.H.F. Manske	5,	301-332 (1955)
Alkaloids in the plant	K. Mothes	6,	1-29 (1960)
The pyrrolidine alkaloids	L. Marion	6,	31-34 (1960)
Senecio alkaloids	N.J. Leonard	6,	35-121 (1960)
The pyridine alkaloids	L. Marion	6,	123-144 (1960)
The tropane alkaloids	G. Fodor	6,	145-177 (1960)
The strychnos alkaloids	J.B. Henrickson	6,	179-217 (1960)
The morphine alkaloids	G. Stork	6,	219-245 (1960)
Colchicine and related compounds	W.C. Wildman	6,	247-288 (1960)
Alkaloids of the amaryllidaceae	W.C. Wildman	6,	289-413 (1960)
The indole alkaloids	J.E. Saxton	7,	4-199 (1960)
The erythrina alkaloids	V. Boekelheide	7,	201-227 (1960)
Quinoline alkaloids, other than those of cinchona	H.T. Openshaw	7,	229-252 (1960)
Lupin alkaloids	N.J. Leonard	7,	253-317 (1960)

THE ALKALOIDS. CHEMISTRY AND PHYSIOLOGY (Contd.)

Steroid alkaloids: the holarrhena group	O. Jeger and V. Prelog	7, 319-342 (1960)
Steroid alkaloids: the Solanum group	V. Prelog and O. Jeger	7, 343-361 (1960)
Steroid alkaloids: veratrum group	O. Jeger and V. Prelog	7, 363-417 (1960)
The ipecac alkaloids	R.H.F. Manske	7, 419-432 (1960)
Phthalideisoquinoline alkaloids	J. Stanek	7, 433-438 (1960)
Bisbenzylisoquinoline alkaloids	M. Kulka	7, 439-472 (1960)
The diterpenoid alkaloids from aconitum, delphinium, and garrya species	E.S. Stern	7, 473-503 (1960)
The lycopodium alkaloids	R.H.F. Manske	7, 505-507 (1960)
Minor alkaloids of unknown structure	R.H.F. Manske	7, 509-521 (1960)

ANNALS OF THE NEW YORK ACADEMY OF SCIENCES

These are the proceedings of the conferences held by the Academy. Present editors are F.N. Furness, E.G. White and N. Halebsky. Each conference has its editor(s). Published by the New York Academy of Sciences.

Title	Author	Reference
Kinetics in solution, held February 1939		39, 299-408 (1940)
Prototropy and deuterotropy in pseudo acids	S.H. Maron and V.K. LaMer	39, 355-373 (1940)
Kinetics of the exchange of oxygen between organic compounds and water	I. Roberts	39, 375-394 (1940)
The kinetics of some amine catalyzed reactions	F.H. Westheimer	39, 401-407 (1940)
Organic free radicals, held November 1939		40, 37-132 (1940)
Occurrence and significance of semiquinone radicals	L. Michaelis	40, 39-76 (1940)
Quantum mechanical basis of the stability of free radicals	G.W. Wheland	40, 77-90 (1940)
Application of the dropping mercury electrode for the detection of intermediate radicals	O.H. Müller	40, 91-109 (1940)
The analogy between two-step oxidation and two-step ionization	M. Schubert	40, 111-122 (1940)
The free energy of O_2 in relation to the slowness of oxygen reactions	M.H. Gorin	40, 123-127 (1940)
Remarks on the estimation of semi-quinone radicals by the conversion of para-hydrogen	L. Farkas	40, 129-132 (1940)
Dielectrics, held April 1939		40, 289-482 (1940)
Rotation of some large organic molecules	S.O. Morgan	40, 357-369 (1940)
Polarization measurements on carboxylic acids in dilute solutions in non-polar solvents	H.A. Pohl, M.E. Hobbs and P.M. Gross	40, 389-428 (1940)
The dielectric constants of some organic crystals and glasses	W.O. Baker and C.P. Smyth	40, 447-481 (1940)
Crystalline protein molecules, held February 1940		41, 77-168 (1941)
Evidence from organic chemistry regarding the size and shape of protein molecules	H.B. Vickery	41, 87-120 (1941)
Evidence from physical chemistry regarding the size and shape of protein molecules from ultracentrifugation, diffusion, viscosity, dielectric dispersion and double refraction of flow	J.L. Oncley	41, 121-150 (1941)
The X-ray diffraction methods used in protein studies	B.E. Warren	41, 151-156 (1941)
Evidence from X-rays regarding the structure of protein molecules	I. Fankuchen	41, 157-168 (1941)

ANNALS OF THE NEW YORK ACADEMY OF SCIENCES (Contd.)

Title	Author	Citation
The primary process in photochemistry, held May, 1940		41, 169-240 (1941)
Asymmetric vibrations excited by an electronic transition	E. Teller	41, 173-186 (1941)
Photosensitization experiments with various metal vapors	E.W.R. Steacie	41, 187-202 (1941)
Primary processes in fluorescence and photosensitization, with particular reference to simple aromatic compounds	W. West	41, 203-230 (1941)
Photolysis of metal alkyls and their significance in photo processes	H.S. Taylor	41, 231-239 (1941)
The amphoteric properties of proteins, held November 1940		41, 241-328 (1941)
The amphoteric properties of egg albumin	R.K. Connan A. Kibrick and A.H. Palmer	41, 243-266 (1941)
The influence of pH on the mobility and diffusion of ovalbumin	L.G. Longsworth	41, 267-285 (1941)
Participation of anions in the combination of proteins with acids	J. Steinhardt	41, 287-320 (1941)
High polymers, held January 1943		44, 263-443 (1943)
Some aspects of the mechanism of addition polymerization	C.C. Price	44, 351-370 (1943)
Surface active agents, held January 1945		46, 347-530 (1946)
Certain aspects of the chemistry of surface active agents	D. Price	46, 407-426 (1946)
Folic acid, held May 1946		48, 255-350 (1946)
Structure and synthesis of the pteridine degradation products of the fermentation L. casei factor	J.H. Mowat et.al.,	48, 279-281 (1946)
Synthesis of pteroylglutamic acid (liver L. casei factor) and pteroic acid	C.W. Waller et.al.,	48, 283-287 (1946)
Chromatography, held November 1946		49, 141-326 (1948)
History, scope and methods of chromatography	L. Zechmeister	49, 145-160 (1948)
Chromatography: a problem in kinetics	H.C. Thomas	49, 161-182 (1948)
Frontal analysis and displacement development in chromatography	S. Claesson	49, 183-203 (1948)
Some experiments in systematic quantitative chromatography	W.A. Schroeder	49, 204-217 (1948)
Fractionation and analysis of hydrocarbons by adsorption	B.J. Mair	49, 218-219 (1948)
Stereochemistry and chromatography	L. Zechmeister	49, 220-234 (1948)
Chromatography in the streptomycin problem	R.L. Peck	49, 235-248 (1948)
Partition chromatography	A.J.P. Martin	49, 249-264 (1948)
Partition chromatography of amino acids on starch	S. Moore and W.H. Stein	49, 265-278 (1948)
A review of fractionation of mixtures by foam formation	L. Shedlovsky	49, 279-294 (1948)

ANNALS OF THE NEW YORK ACADEMY OF SCIENCES (Contd.)

Title	Author	Citation
Ion-exchange adsorbents as laboratory tools	N. Applezweig	49, 295-314 (1948)
The chemotherapy of filariasis, held October 1947		50, 19-170 (1948)
The chemistry of piperazine compounds in the chemotherapy of filariasis	S. Kushner et.al.,	50, 120-127 (1948)
Thyroid function, held January 1947		50, 279-508 (1949)
The formation of thyroxine in iodinated proteins	E.P. Reineke	50, 450-465 (1949)
Newer synthetic analgesics, held May 1948		51, 1-174 (1948)
Chemistry of natural and synthetic analgesics	L.F. Small	51, 12-20 (1948)
Antibiotics derived from bacillus polymyxa, held May 1948		51, 853-1000 (1949)
Chemical studies on polymyxin: comparison with "aerosporin"	P.H. Bell et.al.,	51, 897-908 (1949)
Chemical evidence for the multiplicity of the antibiotics produced by bacillus polymyxa	T.S.G. Jones	51, 909-916 (1949)
The chemistry of the polymyxin A	J.R. Catch T.S.G. Jones and S. Wilkinson	51, 917-923 (1949)
Infrared studies	R.C. Gore and E.M. Petersen	51, 924-934 (1949)
Terramycin, held June 1950		53, 221-460 (1950)
The chemical and physical properties of terramycin	P.P. Regna and I.A. Solomons	53, 229-237 (1950)
Specific methods of analysis, held May 1949		53, 995-1118 (1951)
The analytical specificity of countercurrent distribution	J.D. Gregory and L.C. Craig	53, 1015-1030 (1951)
Quantitative analysis by means of catalytic hydrogenation reactions	E.C. Dunlop	53, 1087-1092 (1951)
Analysis of mixtures based on rates of reaction	T.S. Lee and I.M. Kolthoff	53, 1093-1107 (1951)
Automatic paper chromatography	R.H. Muller and D.L. Clegg	53, 1108-1118 (1951)
Ion exchange resins in medicine and biological research		57, 61-324 (1953)
Synthesis of ion exchange resins	P.N. Craig	57, 67-78 (1953)
Cation exchange processes	J.I. Bregman	57, 125-143 (1953)
Anion exchange processes	S. Peterson	57, 144-158 (1953)
Non-ionic separations with ion exchange resins	R.M. Wheaton and W.C. Bauman	57, 159-176 (1953)
Ion exchange membranes	K. Sollner	57, 177-203 (1953)
The synthesis and physical-chemical properties of new aromatic amidines	M. Kuna and M.J. Kopac	58, 261-292 (1954)
Bioflavonoids and the capillary, held February 1955		61, 637-736 (1955)

ANNALS OF THE NEW YORK ACADEMY OF SCIENCES (Contd.)

Chemistry of bioflavonoids	W.E. Baier	61, 639-645 (1955)
Mercury and its compounds, held April 1956		65, 357-652 (1957)
Oxymercuration of alkenes	G.F. Wright	65, 436-453 (1957)
Relationship between chemical structure and biological activity in mercurial compounds	H.L. Friedman	65, 461-470 (1957)
The pharmacology of psychotomimetric and psychotherapeutic drugs, held April 1956		66, 417-840 (1957)
Neurochemistry and serotonin: a chemical fugue	I.H. Page	66, 592-598 (1957)
The chemical constitution and biochemical effects of psychotherapeutic and structurally related agents	L.G. Abood and L. Romanchek	66, 812-825 (1957)
Unstable chemical species: free radicals, ions and excited molecules		67, 447-670 (1957)
Photochemical reactions leading to unstable species	H.A. Taylor	67, 477-484 (1957)
Electronic spectra of polyatomic free radicals	D.A. Ramsay	67, 485-498 (1957)
Mass spectrometry of free radicals	F.P. Lossing	67, 499-517 (1957)
Stabilization of free radicals at low temperatures	H.P. Broida	67, 530-545 (1957)
Paramagnetic resonance of free radicals	G.K. Fraenkel	67, 546-569 (1957)
Vibrational energy transfer from collisional deactivation of simple molecules and fluorescence stabilization of complex molecules	B. Stevens and M. Boudart	67, 570-599 (1957)
The role of free radicals in organic reaction mechanisms	C. Walling	67, 633-647 (1957)
The role of free radicals in biological oxidations	E.S. Guzmán-Barrón	67, 648-660 (1957)
Some recent developments in the study of unstable species	R.A. Marcus	67, 661-669 (1957)
Comparative clinical and biological effects of alkylating agents		68, 657-1266 (1958)
Fundamental mechanisms of alkylation	C.C. Price	68, 663-668 (1958)
In vitro reactions of biological alkylating agents	W.C.J. Ross	68, 669-681 (1958)
Biological applications of infrared spectroscopy, held December 1956		69, 1-254 (1957)
Infrared intensity measurements applied to the determination of molecular structure	R.N. Jones et.al.,	69, 38-62 (1957)
Some simple hydrogen-bonding systems studied by infrared absorption	U. Liddel	69, 70-83 (1957)
The solid-state infrared absorption of the optically active and racemic straight-chain amino acids	R.J. Koegel et.al.,	69, 94-115 (1957)
Infrared studies of tissue lipids	H.P. Schwarz et.al.,	69, 116-130 (1957)
Infrared spectroscopy of serum lipids	N.K. Freeman	69, 131-144 (1957)
A bibliography of infrared spectra of biochemicals	C. Clark and M. Chianta	69, 205-253 (1957)
The role of I^{131}-labeled proteins in biology and medicine, held November 1956		70, 1-152 (1957)

ANNALS OF THE NEW YORK ACADEMY OF SCIENCES (Contd.)

Title	Author(s)	Citation
The chemistry of iodination	W. L. Hughes	70, 3-18 (1957)
Nuclear magnetic resonance, held November 1957		70, 763-930 (1958)
Magnetic resonance as a phenomenon	C. P. Slichter	70, 769-779 (1958)
Requirements and developments in nuclear magnetic resonance instrumentation	R. H. Sands	70, 780-785 (1958)
Chemical shifts and electron-coupled spin-spin interactions	H. S. Gutowsky	70, 786-805 (1958)
Analysis of the nuclear magnetic resonance spectra of pyridine and some deuterated pyridines	W. G. Schneider, H. J. Bernstein and J. A. Pople	70, 806-816 (1958)
Studies of hindered internal rotation in organic molecules by nuclear magnetic resonance	W. D. Phillips	70, 817-832 (1958)
Organic analytical application of nuclear magnetic resonance	A. A. Bothner-By and C. Naar-Colin	70, 833-840 (1958)
Some applications of C^{13} nuclear magnetic resonance spectra to organic chemistry	P. C. Lauterbur	70, 841-857 (1958)
Proton exchange behavior in some hydrogen-bonded systems	W. G. Schneider and L. W. Reeves	70, 858-869 (1958)
Nuclear magnetic resonance spectra of proteins	M. Saunders and A. Wishnia	70, 870-874 (1958)
Complementary use of nuclear magnetic resonance and infrared absorption studies in organic phosphorus chemistry	H. Finegold	70, 875-889 (1958)
Quantitative determination of organic structures by nuclear magnetic resonance: intensity measurements	R. B. Williams	70, 890-899 (1958)
Nuclear dipole-dipole interactions	J. S. Waugh	70, 900-926 (1958)
Recent nuclear magnetic resonance studies in England	G. R. Murray Jr.	70, 927-929 (1958)
Chlorothiazide and other diuretic agents, held November 1957		71, 321-478 (1958)
The chemistry of diuretics	J. M. Sprague	71, 328-343 (1958)
New steroid compounds with progestational activity, held October 1957		71, 479-806 (1958)
Some chemical and biological properties of 19-nor-17-ethynyltestosterone	D. A. McGinty and C. Djerassi	71, 500-515 (1958)
Quantum aspects of catalysis: oxidation and other reactions of ethylene	R. R. Myers	72, 339-351 (1958)
The analysis of mixtures of volatile substances, held April 1958		72, 559-785 (1959)
The movement of highly radioactive gases in adsorption tubes	E. Glueckauf	72, 562-591 (1959)
The development of highly efficient gas-liquid chromatographic columns	J. H. Purnell	72, 592-605 (1959)

ANNALS OF THE NEW YORK ACADEMY OF SCIENCES (Contd.)

Title	Authors	Citation
Chromatography in the gas-solid system	J. Janak	72, 606-615 (1959)
Gas-liquid chromatographic analysis of higher fatty acids and fatty acid methyl esters	R.K. Beerthuis et.al.,	72, 616-632 (1959)
Gas chromatography in amino acid analysis	M. Bier and P. Teitelbaum	72, 641-648 (1959)
Recent advances in the gas chromatographic separation of methyl esters of fatty acids	C.H. Orr and J.E. Callen	72, 649-665 (1959)
The 1,2-dibromo-1-propenes	L.F. Hatch and J.S. Payne, Jr.	72, 698-704 (1959)
Photoreception, held January 1958		74, 161-406 (1958)
The mechanism of bleaching rhodopsin	A. Kropf and R. Hubbard	74, 266-280 (1958)
The basic and clinical research of the new antibiotic, kanamycin, held July 1958		76, 17-408 (1958)
The chemistry of kanamycin	M.J. Cron et.al.,	76, 27-30 (1958)
Radiopaque diagnostic agents, held October 1958		
Chemical aspects of radiopaque agents	S. Archer	78, 720-726 (1959)
Electron group polarizability and molecular properties of organophosphorus compounds	H. Tolkmith	79, 187-232 (1959)
Amine oxidase inhibitors, held November 1958		80, 551-1045 (1959)
Structure and activity relationships of monoamine oxidase inhibitors	J.H. Biel et.al.,	80, 568-582 (1959)
Radiation and high-temperature behavior of textiles, held November 1958		82, 645-796 (1949)
The effects of very hot gas on organic materials	I.J. Gruntfest	82, 755-761 (1959)
Response of fibers to intense thermal radiation	A.J. McQuade E.T. Waldron and B.S. Farquhar	82, 762-773 (1959)
Effects of high energy radiation on polymers	A.A. Miller	82, 774-781 (1959)
The thermal stabilization of nylon fibers	I.A. Saad and F.R. Eirich	82, 782-795 (1959)
A decade of anti-inflammatory steroids, from cortisone to dexamethasone, held December 1958		82, 797-1014 (1959)
Synthesis of 16α- and 16β-methyl corticoids	E.P. Oliveto	82, 809-820 (1959)
Deuterium isotope effects in chemistry and biology, held May 1960.		84, 573-781 (1960)
Stereochemical and kinetic applications of deuterium isotope effects	A. Streitwieser Jr.,	84, 576-582 (1960)
Secondary deuterium isotope effects in chemical and biochemical reactions	V.J. Shiner Jr.	84, 583-595 (1960)
Acid-base studies with deuterium oxide	F.A. Long	84, 596-602 (1960)
Some aspects of deuterium isotope effects in mechanism studies	C.J. Collins	84, 603-607 (1960)

ANNALS OF THE NEW YORK ACADEMY OF SCIENCES (Contd.)

Helix-random coil transformations in deuterium macromolecules	H.A. Scheraga	84,	608-616 (1960)
Chelation phenomena, held December 1959		88,	281-532 (1960)
Chelation: stability and selectivity	A.E. Martell	88,	284-292 (1960)
Indicative properties of a ferric chelate	S. Soloway and F. Mies	88,	293-306 (1960)
Infrared spectra and correlations for the ethylenediaminetetraacetic acid metal chelates	D.T. Sawyer	88,	307-321 (1960)
Formation of polynuclear complexes in aqueous solution	R.L. Gustafson and A.E. Martell	88,	322-331 (1960)
Participation of chelating metals in carboxylation reactions	M. Stiles	88,	332-340 (1960)
The effect of structural modifications on polyamine-acetic acid chelating agents	H. Kroll and M. Gordon	88,	341-352 (1960)
Chelation and catalysis	A.K. Prince	88,	512-518 (1960)
Amino acids, peptides and proteins, held February 1960		88,	533-570 (1960)
Ion-exchange chromatography of insulin and other proteins in buffers containing urea	R.D. Cole and L. Mendiola	88,	549-570 (1960)
Homogeneity studies with insulin and related substances	L.C. Craig T.P. King and W. Konigsberg	88,	571-585 (1960)
Rapid determination of molecular weights of peptides and proteins	D.A. Yphantis	88,	586-601 (1960)
Phenylthiohydantoins in protein analysis	P. Edman	88,	602-610 (1960)
The structure of ribonuclease	C.H.W. Hirs	88,	611-641 (1960)
Stepwise synthesis of peptides by the nitrophenyl-ester method	M. Bodanszky	88,	655-664 (1960)
Activated cyclic derivatives of amino acids in peptide synthesis	J.C. Sheehan	88,	665-668 (1960)
Conformational aspects of low molecular weight peptides	M. Goodman and E.E. Schmitt	88,	669-675 (1960)
New approaches to peptide synthesis	G.W. Anderson	88,	676-688 (1960)
Synthesis of melanocyte-stimulating hormone derivatives	K. Hofmann	88,	689-707 (1960)
Synthetic aspects of ribosomes	R.B. Roberts	88,	752-769 (1960)
Conference on the actinomycins and their importance in the treatment of tumors in animals and man, held March 31 and April 1, 1960		89,	283-486 (1960)
Structural differences of the actinomycins and their derivatives	H. Brockmann	89,	323-335 (1960)
The chemistry of actinomycin D and related compounds	A.W. Johnson	89,	336-341 (1960)
Biochemistry and pharmacology of compounds derived from marine organisms, held April 1960		90,	615-950 (1960)

ANNALS OF THE NEW YORK ACADEMY OF SCIENCES (Contd.)

Title	Author	Reference
Some chemical properties of nereistoxin	Y. Hashimoto and T. Okaichi	90, 667-673 (1960)
Steroids in marine organisms	G.A.D. Haslewood	90, 877-883 (1960)
Sterols of some invertebrates	W. Bergman and I.I. Domsky	90, 906-909 (1960)
Chemistry of coelenterates. I. Occurrence of terpenoid compounds in gorgonians	L.S. Cierezko D.H. Sifford and A.J. Weinheimer	90, 917-919 (1960)
Chemistry of coelenterates. II. Occurrence of taurobetaine and creatine in gorgonians	L.S. Cierezko P.H. Odense and R.W. Schmidt	90, 920-921 (1960)
Phosphagens of marine animals	N. v. Thoai and J. Roche	90, 923-928 (1960)

ANTIBIOTICS - THEIR CHEMISTRY AND NON-MEDICAL USES

A collective volume, edited by H.S. Goldberg and published by D. Van Nostrand, Inc., Princeton, New Jersey.

Title	Author	Reference
The chemistry of antibiotics	P.P. Regna	58-173 (1959)

BIOCHEMICAL SOCIETY SYMPOSIA

These are the proceedings of the symposia organized by the Biochemical Society, London. Volumes 1, 2 and 4 to 13 were edited by R.T. Williams, volume 3 by R.T. Williams and R.L.M. Synge, volumes 14-17 by E.M. Crook; volume 18 by F. Clark and J.K. Grant, and volume 19 by J.K. Grant and W. Klyne. Published by the University Press, Cambridge.

Title	Author	Reference		
Relation of optical form to biological activity in the amino-acid-series. Symposium No. 1, London, 1947		1,	91 pp.	(1948)
The biochemical reactions of chemical warfare agents. Symposium No. 2, London, 1947		2,	73 pp.	(1948)
The chemical reactions of mustard gas in aqueous solution	A.G. Ogston	2,	2-7	(1948)
The action of mustard gas (β,β'-dichlorodiethyl sulphide) with proteins	J.C. Bournsnell	2,	8-15	(1948)
Partition chromatography. Symposium No. 3, London, 1948				
Application of partition chromatography to the study of protein structure	F. Sanger	3,	21-31	(1951)
Anthocyanins, flavones and other phenolic compounds	E.C. Bate-Smith	3,	62-71	(1951)
Biological oxidation of aromatic rings. Symposium No. 5, London, 1949		5,	96 pp.	(1950)
The oxidation of the aromatic ring by chemical means	R. Schoental	5,	3-14	(1950)
Biological transformations of starch and cellulose. Symposium No. 11, London, 1953		11,	84 pp.	(1953)
The chemistry and chemical degradation of cellulose	G.O. Aspinall	11,	42-48	(1953)
The biochemistry of vitamin B_{12}. Symposium No. 13, London, 1954		13,	123 pp.	(1955)
Isolation and chemistry of vitamin B_{12}	E.L. Smith	13,	3-16	(1955)
The structure of nucleic acids and their role in protein synthesis. Symposium No. 14, 1956		14,		(1957)
Recent views on the chemical structure of the polynucleotides	R. Markham	14,	6-12	(1957)
Metals and enzyme activity. Symposium No. 15, Leeds, 1956		15,	102 pp.	(1958)
Enzyme-metal substrates complexes as coordination compounds	L.E. Orgel	15,	8-20	(1958)

BIOCHEMICAL SOCIETY SYMPOSIA (Contd.)

The nature of metal-peptide complexes in aqueous solution and the relationship these have to proleolytic activity	B.R. Rabin	15,	21-47	(1958)
Gluthatione. Symposium, No. 17, London, 1958		17,	116 pp.	(1959)
Chemistry and biochemistry of glutathione	F.A. Isherwood	17,	3-16	(1959)
Steric aspects of the chemistry and biochemistry of natural products. Symposium No. 19, June, 1959		19,		(1960)
Stereochemical correlations	W. Klyne	19,	3-29	(1960)
Steric aspects of the biosynthesis of terpenes and steroids	D. Arigoni	19,	32-45	(1960)
Steric aspects of drug action	R.B. Badow	19,	46-66	(1960)
Cis-trans isomers of retinene in visual processes	G.A.J. Pitt and R.A. Morton	19,	67-89	(1960)

CAHIERS DE SYNTHÈSE ORGANIQUE

This is a collection of reviews, in French, on general and specific methods in organic synthesis, to be published in 13 volumes. Seven volumes had appeared by 1960, edited under the direction of L. Velluz, and published by Masson et Cie., Paris. The authors are J. Mathieu, A. Allais, J. Valls, and P. Poirier.

Title	Reference		
Principles of organic synthesis. Introduction to reaction mechanisms		450 pp.	(1957)
1. Attachment of a functional carbon to an aliphatic chain	1,	11-152	(1957)
2. Attachment of a functional carbon to an aromatic ring	1,	155-233	(1957)
3. Alkylation in the aliphatic series	2,	11-171	(1957)
4. Alkylation in the aromatic series	2,	175-270	(1957)
5. Arylation in the aromatic series	2,	273-299	(1957)
6. Condensations	3,	11-85	(1957)
7. Hydroxy-alkylation and amino-alkylation in the aliphatic series	3,	89-187	(1957)
8. Hydroxy-alkylation and amino-alkylation in the aromatic series	3,	191-239	(1957)
9. Acylation in the aliphatic series	4,	11-128	(1958)
10. Acylation in the aromatic series	4,	131-210	(1958)
11. Bifunctional condensation reactions	4,	213-234	(1958)
12. Removal of a functional carbon	5,	11-191	(1959)
13. Scission of carbon chains and opening of carbocyclic rings	5,	195-375	(1959)
14. Rearrangements of hydrocarbon structures	6,	11-205	(1960)
15. Migration of functions between carbon atoms	6,	209-313	(1960)
16. Migration of functions between heteroatoms and carbon atoms	6,	317-346	(1960)
17. Migration of carbon residues between heteroatoms	6,	349-392	(1960)

THE CARBOHYDRATES - CHEMISTRY, BIOCHEMISTRY AND PHYSIOLOGY

This is a collective volume, edited by W. Pigman and published by Academic Press, Inc., New York.

Title	Author	Reference	
Structure and stereochemistry of the monosaccharides	W. Pigman	1-76	(1957)
Occurrence, properties and synthesis of the monosaccharides	J.C. Sowden	77-137	(1957)
Esters	A. Thompson and M.L. Wolfrom	138-172	(1957)
Phosphate esters	W.Z. Hassid and C.E. Ballou	172-187	(1957)
Glycosides, simple acetals and thioacetals	M.L. Wolfrom and A. Thompson	183-240	(1957)
The polyols	R.L. Lohmar Jr.	241-298	(1957)
Acids and oxidation products	J.W. Green	299-366	(1957)
Ethers, anhydro sugars and unsaturated derivatives	J.C. Sowden	367-405	(1957)
Nitrogenous derivatives	W. Pigman	406-477	(1957)
Oligosaccharides	W.Z. Hassid and C.E. Ballou	478-535	(1957)
Naturally occurring glycosides and glycosidases	H. Baumann and W. Pigman	536-601	(1957)
The identification and quantitative determination of carbohydrates	G.R. Noggle	602-640	(1957)
Polysaccharides: general aspects and phyto- and microbial polysaccharides	R.L. Whistler and W.M. Corbett	641-708	(1957)
Animal polysaccharides and glycoproteins	W. Pigman and D. Platt	709-732	(1957)

THE CHEMICAL SOCIETY (LONDON)
SPECIAL PUBLICATIONS

Title	Author	Reference
The kinetics and mechanism of inorganic reactions Editor: K.W. Sykes. Symposium, London 1954		<u>1</u>, 1-84 (1954)
Peptide Chemistry. Symposium, London 1955 Editors: A.D. Jenkins and D.F. Elliott		
Deuterium exchange between peptides and water	K. Linderstrøm-lang	<u>2</u>, 1-24 (1955)
New aspects of the chemistry of polypeptide synthesis from N-carboxy-α-amino-acid anhydrides	D.G.H. Ballard and C.H. Bamford	<u>2</u>, 25-48 (1955)
The synthesis of cystine peptides with special reference to the synthesis of oxytocin	V. du Vigneaud	<u>2</u>, 49-70 (1955)
The use of carboxypeptidase for C-terminal group and sequence studies in polypeptide chains	J.I. Harris	<u>2</u>, 71-102 (1955)
The use of mixed anhydrides in peptide synthesis	G.W. Kenner	<u>2</u>, 103-115 (1955)
Recent work on naturally occurring nitrogen heterocyclic compounds. Symposium, Exeter, 1955		
Conessine	R.D. Haworth	<u>3</u>, 1-11 (1955)
Mitragyna alkaloids	J.D. Loudon	<u>3</u>, 12-18 (1955)
The alkaloids of gelsemium	T.S. Stevens	<u>3</u>, 19-27 (1955)
Some features of the chemistry of emetine	H.T. Openshaw	<u>3</u>, 28-35 (1955)
The structure and chemistry of emetamine	A.R. Battersby	<u>3</u>, 36-44 (1955)
Synthesis and biosynthesis in the indole alkaloid field	J. Harley-Mason	<u>3</u>, 45-50 (1955)
Intermediates in the biological synthesis of purine nucleotides	J. Baddiley	<u>3</u>, 51-59 (1955)
Interconversions and epimerizations of open and cyclic hydroxy-amino-acids. A contribution to the chemistry of the building stones of collagen	B. Witkop	<u>3</u>, 60-82 (1955)
Recent advances in the chemistry of colouring matters. Symposium, London, 1956.		
Steric effects in azo- and indigo dyes	W.R. Brode	<u>4</u>, 1-16 (1956)
Some aspects of cis-trans-isomerism in azo-dyes	E. Atherton and R.H. Peters	<u>4</u>, 17-27 (1956)
The synthesis of azoporphins and related macro-cycles	J.A. Elvidge	<u>4</u>, 28-46 (1956)
Synthetic carotenoids	O. Isler et. al.,	<u>4</u>, 47-63 (1956)
Modern theories of colour	M.J.S. Dewar	<u>4</u>, 64-87 (1956)

THE CHEMICAL SOCIETY (LONDON) (Contd.)

Antibiotics and mould metabolites. Symposium, Nottingham, 1956.

Fungal quinones	J.H. Birkinshaw	5,	1-15	(1956)
Synthesis of some fungal metabolites	D.H.R. Barton	5,	16-26	(1956)
Azaphilones, a general survey	A.D.C. Powell, A. Robertson and W.B. Whalley	5,	27-35	(1956)
The structure of purpurogenone	J.C. Roberts	5,	36-47	(1956)
Progress in the chemistry of oxytetracycline and related compounds	C.H. Conover	5,	48-81	(1956)
Actinomycin	A.W. Johnson	5,	82-96	(1956)
Chemistry of the cephalosporins	G.G.F. Newton and E.P. Abraham	5,	97-108	(1956)

Stability constants. Editors: J. Bjerrum, G. Schwarzenbach and L.G. Sillen

Part I: Organic Ligands. Editors: G. Anderegg and S.E. Rasmussen (1957)		6,	1-105 (1957)
Part II: Inorganic ligands. Editors: G. Berecki-Biedermann, L. Maltesen, S.E. Rasmussen and F.J.C. Rossotti		7,	1-131 (1958)

Phosphoric esters and related compounds. Symposium, Cambridge, 1957.

Studies of the solvolysis of some phosphate esters	F.H. Westheimer	8,	1-15	(1957)
The mechanics of hydrolysis of organic phosphates	C.A. Vernon	8,	17-32	(1957)
Hydrolysis of phosphoric esters and related compounds	G.S. Hartley	8,	33-45	(1957)
The Michaelis-Becker reaction with halogeno-ketones	B.A. Arbuzov	8,	47-59	(1957)
The structure and preparative applications of triaryl phosphite dihalides and related compounds	H.N. Rydon	8,	61-75	(1957)
Some aspects of the chemistry of phosphorus compounds derived from salicyclic acid	F.R. Atherton	8,	77-90	(1957)
Newer methods of polyphosphate synthesis	A. Todd	8,	91-102	(1957)
The synthesis of glycerol phosphates	E. Baer	8,	103-117	(1957)
Some reactions of polyol phosphates	J. Baddiley	8,	119-128	(1957)
The determination of nucleotide sequence in nucleic acids	A.S. Jones and M. Stacey	8,	129-137	(1957)
The dissociation and molecular structure of the nucleic acids	A.R. Peacocke	8,	139-164	(1957)
Physiological action of diidopropyl phosphorfluoridate	B.C. Saunders	8,	165-170	(1957)
Oxidative demethylation and hydrolysis of tetramethyl-phosphorodiamidic anhydride	E.Y. Spencer	8,	171-183	(1957)

Reactions of free radicals in the gas phase. Symposium, Cambridge, 1957.

The nature of free radicals	H.C. Longuet-Higgins	9,	5-16	(1957)
Termolecular free radical reactions	D.E. Hoare and A.D. Walsh	9,	17-33	(1957)

THE CHEMICAL SOCIETY (LONDON) (Contd.)

The study of radical reactions by competitive methods	J.H. Knox and A.F. Trotman-Dickenson	9,	35-47	(1957)
Thermal reactions involving free radicals	C. Hinshelwood	9,	49-63	(1957)
Peroxy-radicals and oxidation of hydrocarbons	C.E.H. Bawn	9,	65-80	(1957)
Studies of oxygen atoms at high temperatures	E.M. Bulewicz and T.M. Sugden	9,	81-96	(1957)
The chemistry of free alkoxyl radicals	R. Gray and A. Williams	9,	97-119	(1957)
Studies of the C10· radical by flash photolysis	F.H.C. Edgecombe, R.G.W. Norrish and B.A. Thrush	9,	121-137	(1957)
Free radicals and triplet states in aromatic vapours	G. Porter	9,	139-150	(1957)
The formation and reactions of free radicals in the high-energy irradiation of hydrocarbons in the gas phase	W.H.T. Davison	9,	151-166	(1957)
The mercury-photo sensitized reaction of hydrogen and oxygen at room temperature	R.H. Burgess and J.C. Robb	9,	167-186	(1957)
The isotopic exchange reactions between methyl radicals and methane	F.S. Dainton K.J. Ivin and F. Wilkinson	9,	187-195	(1957)
Some investigations of reaction mechanism in detonations and flames	W. Jost and H.G. Wagner	9,	197-206	(1957)
Propagation of flame in carbon monoxide-oxygen mixtures	J.E. Dove R. Goss and J.W. Linnett	9,	207-226	(1957)
Changes in the concentration of radicals before sensitized ignitions	P.G. Ashmore	9,	227-239	(1957)
Recent aspects of the inorganic chemistry of nitrogen. Symposium, Cambridge, 1957.		10,	1-136	(1957)
Tables of interatomic distances and configuration in molecules and ions. Editor: L.E. Sutton		11,	1-394	(1958)
Developments in aromatic chemistry. Symposium, Bristol, 1958				
Diphenylene and the cyclobutadiene problem	W. Baker and J.F.W. McOmie	12,	49-62	(1958)
Azulene and related substances	D.H. Reid	12,	69-81	(1958)
The fundamentals of conjugation in ring systems	C.A. Coulson	12,	85-106	(1958)
Benzyne as an intermediate in nucleophilic aromatic substitution reactions	J.D. Roberts	12,	115-128	(1958)
Applications of electron and nuclear resonance in chemistry. Chemical Society Symposia, Bristol, 1958. Special Publication No.12 Chemical Society, London (1958)				
Proton magnetic resonance in polyethylene and polymethylene	J.A.S. Smith	12,	199-209	(1958)

THE CHEMICAL SOCIETY (LONDON) (Contd.)

Title	Author	Reference
High-resolution proton magnetic resonance of organic compounds	J.A. Pople	12, 211-217 (1958)
Chemical applications of nuclear quadrupole spectroscopy	M.J.S. Dewar and E.A.C. Lucken	12, 223-233 (1958)
Recent applications of nuclear quadrupole resonance in structural and radiation chemistry	J. Duchesne	12, 235-244 (1958)
Recent work on the inorganic chemistry of sulphur. Edited by F.H. Pollard (1958)		12, 245-401 (1958)
International conference on co-ordination chemistry. Symposium, London, 1959		
New aspects of some organometallic complex compounds	K. Ziegler	13, 1-11 (1959)
The stability of metal complexes	H.M.N.H. Irving	13, 13-34 (1959)
Metal carbonyls and related compounds as catalytic intermediates in organic syntheses	H.W. Sternberg and I. Wender	13, 35-55 (1959)
Mechanisms of complex ion reactions: recent advances	H. Taube	13, 57-71 (1959)
Co-ordination compounds of unsaturated hydrocarbons with metals	E.O. Fischer	13, 73-92 (1959)
Metal-ligand bonds	L.E. Orgel	13, 93-102 (1959)
Complex acetylides of transition metals	R. Nast	13, 103-112 (1959)

CHEMISORPTION

These are the proceedings of a Symposium held at North Staffordshire, 1956, by the Chemical Society. Edited by W.E. Garnes and published by Butterworth Scientific Publications (London).

Title	Author	Reference
Chemisorption and valency	D.A. Dowden	3-16 (1957)
Chemisorption at room temperature on alumina and silica gel	J.J. Kipling and D.B. Peakall	59-67 (1957)
Protium-deuterium exchange between ethylene and γ-alumina	H. Kloosterziel	76-84 (1957)

CHEMISTRY OF CARBON COMPOUNDS

This is a comprehensive treatise of organic chemistry, in English, to be published in five volumes, each of them in several parts. Four volumes appeared between 1951 and 1960. Volumes 1 and 2A are devoted to Aliphatic compounds, volume 2B to Alicyclic compounds, volume 3 to Aromatic compounds and volume 4 to Heterocyclic compounds. Edited by E.H. Rodd; published by Elsevier Publishing Co., Amsterdam.

Title	Author	Reference	
The structure of carbon compounds -- historical	E.H. Rodd	1A, 2-17	(1951)
The classification and nomenclature of carbon compounds	E.H. Rodd	1A, 18-22	(1951)
Literature and documentation of organic chemistry	E.H. Rodd	1A, 23-24	(1951)
Quantitative analysis of carbon compounds and the determination of physical constants and molecular weights by micro and semimicro methods	R. Belcher	1A, 25-45	(1951)
The physical properties of carbon compounds	H.D. Springall	1A, 46-63	(1951)
Crystallography of carbon compounds	A.F. Wells	1A, 64-70	(1951)
The absorption of light by carbon compounds	E.A. Braude	1A, 71-98	(1951)
Modern physico-chemical views on acids and bases and their application to organic substances	H.D. Springall	1A, 99-106	(1951)
Stereochemistry of carbon compounds	E.E. Turner	1A, 107-156	(1951)
Mechanisms of reactions of carbon compounds	E.D. Hughes	1A, 157-194	(1951)
Free radicals and homolytic reactions	D.H. Hey and W.A. Waters	1A, 195-217	(1951)
The saturated or paraffin hydrocarbons. Alkanes	P.J. Garner and J.H. Beynon	1A, 221-248	(1951)
Unsaturated hydrocarbons	A.W. Johnson	1A, 249-273	(1951)
Halogen derivatives of the hydrocarbons	A.W. Johnson and J.G. Buchanan	1A, 274-284	(1951)
Monohydric alcohols; their ethers and esters	A.W. Johnson et al.	1A, 285-344	(1951)
Sulphur derivatives of the alcohol radicals	A.W. Johnson and I.R. Bick	1A, 345-356	(1951)
Nitrogen derivatives of the alcohol radicals	J. Walker	1A, 357-416	(1951)
Metal and metalloid compounds of the alkyl radicals	J. Chatt	1A, 417-458	(1951)
Aldehydes and ketones	A.W. Johnson et al.	1A, 459-536	(1951)
Monobasic carboxylic acids	A.W. Johnson, C.E. Dalgliesh and J. Walker	1A, 537-647	(1951)

CHEMISTRY OF CARBON COMPOUNDS (Contd.)

Dihydric alcohols or glycols and related compounds	A.W. Johnson, A.G. Long and C.E. Dalgliesh	1A,	648-701	(1951)
Hydroxy-aldehydes and ketones and related compounds: dicarbonyl compounds	A.W. Johnson et al.	1A,	702-731	(1951)
Hydroxy- and amino-monocarboxylic acids and related compounds	C.E. Dalgliesh, A.W. Johnson and L.J. Haynes	1B,	779-849	(1952)
Aldehydo- and keto-acids	C.E. Dalgliesh, A.W. Johnson and C. Buchanan	1B,	850-885	(1952)
Carbonic acid and its derivatives	I.D. Morton and E. Hoggarth	1B,	886-949	(1952)
Dicarboxylic acids	C.E. Dalgliesh, A.W. Johnson and C. Buchanan	1B,	950-1011	(1952)
Trihydric alcohols and their oxidation products (trihydric alcohols to triketones)	C.E. Dalgliesh, A.G. Long and G.J. Tyler	1B,	1012-1047	(1952)
Trihydric alcohols and their oxidation products (dihydroxy carboxylic acids to tricarboxylic acids)	C.E. Dalgliesh, A.W. Johnson, A.G. Long and C.J. Tyler	1B,	1048-1154	(1952)
Tetrahydric alcohols and their oxidation products	L.J. Haynes	1B,	1155-1196	(1952)
Pentahydric alcohols and their oxidation products	J.K.N. Jones	1B,	1197-1223	(1952)
Hexa- and poly-hydric alcohols and their oxidation products. Carbohydrates and related compounds	J.K.N. Jones	1B,	1224-1286	(1952)
Complex carbohydrates: oligosaccharides and polysaccharides	E.G.V. Percival	1B,	1287-1326	(1952)
Proteins	K. Bailey	1B,	1327-1357	(1952)
Enzymes	M. Stacey	1B,	1358-1391	(1952)
Introduction	R.A. Raphael	2A,	1-22	(1953)
Cyclopropane group	R.A. Raphael	2A,	23-45	(1953)
Cyclobutane group	R.A. Raphael	2A,	46-70	(1953)
Cyclopentane group	R.A. Raphael	2A,	71-123	(1953)
Cyclohexane group	R.A. Raphael	2A,	124-248	(1953)
Cycloheptane, cyclo-octane and macrocyclic groups	R.A. Raphael	2A,	249-288	(1953)
Polynuclear alicyclic compounds with separate ring systems and spiro compounds	R.A. Raphael	2A,	289-307	(1953)
Bridged ring systems	R.A. Raphael	2A,	335-351	(1953)
The carotenoid group	R.F. Hunter	2A,	352-390	(1953)
Open-chain and cyclic polymers derived from olefinic compounds; rubber and rubber-like compounds, natural and synthetic, and their derivatives	R.G.R. Bacon	2A,	391-436	(1953)
The terpenoids: acyclic and monocyclic monoterpenoids and related compounds	D.H.R. Barton and S.H. Harper	2B,	489-545	(1953)

CHEMISTRY OF CARBON COMPOUNDS (Contd.)

Title	Author(s)	Vol.	Pages	Year
Bicyclic monoterpenoids and related compounds	D.H.R. Barton and S.H. Harper	2B,	546-629	(1953)
The sesquiterpenoids	D.H.R. Barton	2B,	630-695	(1953)
The diterpenoids	D.H.R. Barton	2B,	696-725	(1953)
The triterpenoids	D.H.R. Barton	2B,	726-764	(1953)
Steroids : steroids and bile acids	C.W. Shoppee and E. Shoppee	2B,	765-875	(1953)
Steroids : sex hormones and adrenocortical hormones	C.W. Shoppee and E. Shoppee	2B,	876-982	(1953)
Steroids : cardiotonic glycosides and aglycones, toad poisons, steroid saponins and sapogenin	C.W. Shoppee and E. Shoppee	2B,	983-1049	(1953)
Introduction to aromatic compounds	C.K. Ingold	3A,	1-80	(1954)
Mononuclear hydrocarbons: benzene and its homologues	W.J. Hickinbottom	3A,	81-112	(1954)
Halogen-, nitro-, nitroso-, and hydroxylamino- derivatives of benzene and its homologues	W.J. Hickinbottom	3A,	113-157	(1954)
Aromatic amines derived from benzene and its homologues	W.J. Hickinbottom	3A,	158-229	(1954)
Sulphonic acids, sulphinic acids and sulphenyl compounds of the benzene series	W.J. Hickinbottom	3A,	230-248	(1954)
Nitrogen derivatives of anilines: nitrosamines, nitramines diazo-, azo-, azoxy- and hydrazo- compounds	Z.E. Jolles	3A,	249-380	(1954)
Aromatic metal and metalloid compounds	J. Chatt	3A,	381-412	(1954)
Nuclear hydroxy derivatives of benzene and its homologues. Phenols	W.J. Hickinbottom	3A,	413-486	(1954)
Aralkylamines, alcohols, aldehydes and ketones of the benzene series	W.J. Hickinbottom	3A,	487-540	(1954)
Monocarboxylic acids of the benzene series	W.J. Hickinbottom	3A,	541-601	(1954)
Quinones and related compounds of the benzene series	Z.E. Jolles	3B,	687-729	(1956)
Phenolic monohydric alcohols, monoaldehydes, monoketones and monocarboxylic acids	W.J. Hickinbottom and R.F. Garwood	3B,	730-815	(1956)
Dihydric and polyhydric alcohols and their oxidation products with functional groups in separate side chains	W.J. Hickinbottom and R.F. Garwood	3B,	816-869	(1956)
Phenyl derivatives of dihydric and polyhydric alcohols and their oxidation products	W.J. Hickinbottom, R.F. Garwood and M.F. Ansell	3B,	870-954	(1956)
Benzene derivatives with one or more unsaturated side chains	W.J. Hickinbottom and M.F. Ansell	3B,	955-1027	(1956)
The phenylbenzene group	W.J. Hickinbottom	3B,	1028-1053	(1956)
Di-, tri- and tetra- phenylmethanes	W.J. Hickinbottom	3B,	1054-1115	(1956)
Di- and poly- phenyl paraffins and their derivatives	S.H. Harper	3B,	1116-1220	(1956)
Monocyclic quasi-aromatic systems	G.L. Buchanan and R.A. Raphael	3B,	1221-1251	(1956)

CHEMISTRY OF CARBON COMPOUNDS (Contd.)

Title	Author(s)	Vol.	Pages	Year
Aromatic compounds with condensed nuclei : indene, naphthalene and other bicyclic compounds	E.H. Rodd and J. Van Alphen	3B,	1252-1445	(1956)
Aromatic compounds with condensed nuclei : fluorene, acenaphthene and polycyclic compounds	G.M. Badger and J.W. Cook	3B,	1446-1533	(1956)
Compounds with three- and four- membered heterocyclic rings	T.S. Stevens	4A,	10-27	(1957)
Compounds containing a five membered ring with one hetero-atom : nitrogen	T.S. Stevens	4A,	28-137	(1957)
Compounds containing a five membered ring with one hetero-atom : oxygen or sulphur	T.S. Stevens	4A,	138-243	(1957)
Compounds containing a five membered ring with two hetero-atoms : pyrazole and iminazole groups	J.D. Loudon	4A,	244-331	(1957)
Compounds containing a five membered ring with two hetero-atoms : dioxale and oxazole group	J.D. Loudon	4A,	332-438	(1957)
Compounds containing a five membered ring with more than two hetero-atoms	E. Hoggarth	4A,	439-487	(1957)
Compounds containing a six membered ring with one hetero atom, nitrogen	N. Campbell	4A,	488-713	(1957)
Compounds containing a six membered ring with one hetero atom, oxygen or sulphur	N. Campbell	4B,	809-1004	(1959)
Brazilin and haematozylin	R. Robinson	4B,	1005-1023	(1959)
Compounds containing two fused five or six membered heterocyclic rings each of one hetero atom	N. Campbell	4B,	1024-1052	(1959)
The cyanine and related dyes	G.W. Anderson	4B,	1053-1080	(1959)
The indigo group	T.S. Stevens	4B,	1081-1103	(1959)
The pyrrole pigments	T.S. Stevens	4B,	1104-1162	(1959)
Compounds containing unusual hetero atoms	I.G.M. Campbell and T.S. Stevens	4B,	1163-1200	(1959)
Compounds containing a six membered ring with two hetero atoms. The diazines	G.R. Ramage and J.K. Landqvist	4B,	1201-1389	(1959)
Compounds containing a six membered ring with two hetero atoms : oxazines, thiazines, dioxanes and their analogues	G.R. Ramage, E.H. Rodd and J.K. Landqvist	4C,	1465-1534	(1960)
Dyes derived from phenazine, phenoxazine and phenothiazine, and sulphur dyes	H.T. Howard and G.R. Ramage	4C,	1535-1558	(1960)
Compounds containing a six membered ring with more than two heteroatoms	E. Hoggarth	4C,	1559-1580	(1960)
Compounds having a seven membered or larger ring containing hetero atoms	P.M. Maitlis	4C,	1581-1634	(1960)
Picrines and related ring systems	G.A. Howard	4C,	1635-1706	(1960)
Nucleosides, nucleotides and nucleic acids	J. Baddiley	4C,	1707-1759	(1960)
Pteridines, alloxazines, flavins, vitamin B_2 and related compounds ; vitamin B_1 and related compounds	G.R. Ramage and T.S. Stevens	4C,	1760-1798	(1960)
Alkaloids : pyrrolidine, pyridine and piperidine, pyrrolizidine and tropane groups	A.R. Pinder	4C,	1799-1873	(1960)
Alkaloids of the quinoline and isoquinoline groups	A.R. Pinder	4C,	1874-1987	(1960)
Alkaloids of the lupinane, iminazole and quinazoline groups	A.R. Pinder	4C,	1988-2018	(1960)

CHEMISTRY OF CARBON COMPOUNDS (Contd.)

Alkaloids of the diterpene and steroid groups	A.R. Pinder	4C,	2019-2057 (1960)
Alkaloids of the morphine group	K.W. Bentley	4C,	2058-2087 (1960)
The indole alkaloids	G.F. Smith	4C,	2088-2119 (1960)
Erythrina alkaloids	A.R. Pinder	4C,	2120-2130 (1960)

CHEMISTRY OF COORDINATE COMPOUNDS

A symposium held in Rome, September 1957. Published by Pergamon Press, London.

New results on aromatic metal-carbonyls (in German)	E.O. Fisher	268-273 (1957)
On some aromatic molecular complexes of silver perchlorate (in Italian)	G. Peyronel, G. Belmondi and I. Vezzosi	577-581 (1957)

THE CHEMISTRY OF HETEROCYCLIC COMPOUNDS

This is a collection of review monographs covering the entire field of heterocyclic chemistry. A. Weissberger is consulting editor for the whole series, which is published by Interscience Publishers, Inc., New York.

Title	Author	Reference	
The heterocyclic derivatives of phosphorus, arsenic, antimony, bismuth, and silicon	F.G. Mann	1,	1-162 (1950)
Six-membered heterocyclic nitrogen compounds with four condensed rings	C.F.H. Allen (Editor, vols. 2-11)		
Azanaphthacenes	E.R. Webster	2,	3-56 (1951)
Azabenz(a)anthracenes	I.R. Crawford and E.R. Webster	2,	57-132 (1951)
Azabenzo(c)phenanthrenes	E.R. Webster	2,	133-150 (1951)
Azachrysenes and azatriphenylenes	I.R. Crawford	2,	151-200 (1951)
Azabenzanthrenes	C.F.H. Allen D.M. Burness and F.W. Spangler	2,	201-294 (1951)
Azapyrenes	E.R. Webster	2,	295-310 (1951)
Thiophene and its derivatives	H.D. Hartough F.P. Hochgesang and F.F. Blicke	3,	1-514 (1952)
Five-membered heterocyclic compounds with nitrogen and sulfur, or nitrogen, sulfur and oxygen (except thiazole)	L.L. Bambas	4,	1-378 (1952)
Condensed pyridazine and pyrazine rings (cinnolines, phthalazines, and quinoxalines)	J.C.E. Simpson	5,	1-366 (1953)
Imidazole and its derivatives. Part I.	K. Hofmann	6,	1-420 (1953)
Compounds with condensed thiophene rings	H.D. Hartough and S.L. Meisel	7,	1-500 (1954)
Heterocyclic compounds with indole and carbazole systems	W.C. Sumpter and F.M. Miller	8,	1-288 (1954)
Acridines	R.M. Acheson and L.E. Orgel	9,	1-389 (1956)
The 1,2,3- and 1,2,4-triazines, tetrazines and pentazines	J.G. Erickson P.F. Wiley and V.P. Wystrach	10,	1-261 (1956)
Phenazines	G.A. Swan and D.G.I. Felton	11,	1-693 (1957)

THE CHEMISTRY OF HETEROCYCLIC COMPOUNDS (Contd.)

Six-membered heterocyclic nitrogen compounds with three condensed rings	C.F.H. Allen (Editor, Vol. 12)		
Introduction and mechanisms	C.V. Wilson and G.A. Reynolds	12,	1-13 (1958)
Azanthracenes	C.V. Wilson	12,	14-164 (1958)
Azaphenanthrenes	I.R. Thirtle	12,	165-215 (1958)
4- and 5-Azaphenanthrenes	J.A. van Allan	12,	216-315 (1958)
Diazaphenanthrenes (except phenanthrolines)	J.R. Thirtle	12,	320-385 (1958)
1,10-, 7- and 4,7-Diazaphenanthrenes	B. Graham	12,	386-456 (1958)
Other polyazaphenanthrenes	J.R. Thirtle	12,	457-483 (1958)
Azabenzonaphthenes	J.H. Richmond	12,	484-550 (1958)
The ultraviolet absorption spectra of polycyclic heterocyclic aromatic compounds	G.M. Badger	12,	551-566 (1958)
s-Triazines and derivatives	E.M. Smolin and L. Rapoport	13,	1-644 (1959)
Pyridine and its derivatives	E. Klingsberg (Editor, Vol. 14)		
Properties and reactions of pyridine and its hydrogenated derivatives	R.A. Barnes	14, I,	1-97 (1960)
Synthetic and natural sources of the pyridine ring	F. Brody and P.R. Ruby	14, I,	99-589 (1960)

CHEMISTRY OF MICROBIAL PRODUCTS. (THE SQUIBB LECTURES)

This is an annual collection of lectures held at Rutgers, the State University of New Jersey, and published by John Wiley and Sons, New York.

Title	Author	Reference
Topics in microbial chemistry	F.M. Strong	157 pp. (1958)
Chemical transformations by microorganisms	F.H. Stodola	124 pp. (1958)

THE CHEMISTRY OF NATURAL PRODUCTS

This is a collection of review monographs on the chemistry of natural products. K.W. Bentley is editor of the series, which is published by Interscience Publishers, New York.

Title	Author	Reference
The alkaloids	K.W. Bentley	$\underline{1}$, 1-237 (1957)
Mono and sesquiterpenoids	P. de Mayo	$\underline{2}$, 1-320 (1959)
The higher terpenoids	P. de Mayo	$\underline{3}$, 1-239 (1959)
The natural pigments	K.W. Bentley	$\underline{4}$, 1-306 (1960)
The carbohydrates	S.F. Dyke	$\underline{5}$, 1-240 (1960)

THE CHEMISTRY OF PENICILLIN

Report on a collaborative investigation compiled under the auspices of the National Academy of Sciences, Washington, D.C. Editorial Board: H.T. Clarke, J.R. Johnson and Sir R. Robinson. Published by Princeton University Press, Princeton, New Jersey.

Title	Author	Reference	
Brief history of the chemical study of penicillin	H.T. Clarke J.R. Johnson and R. Robinson	3-9	(1949)
The earlier investigations relating to 2-pentenyl penicillin	E.P. Abraham et.al.,	10-37	(1949)
The chemistry of n-amylpenicillin up to December 1943	A.H. Cook and I.M. Heilbron	38-51	(1949)
Status of the research on the structure of benzyl-penicillin in December 1943)	R.L. Peck and K. Folkers	52-75	(1949)
Isolation and characterization of the various penicillins	O. Wintersteiner et.al.,	76-105	(1949)
Penillic acids and penicillamines	A.H. Cook	106-143	(1949)
Review of certain investigations on the structure of benzylpenicillin during 1944-1945	R.L. Peck and K. Folkers	144-206	(1949)
Some further inactivation and degradation reactions (of penicillins)	O. Wintersteiner et.al.,	207-242	(1949)
Desthiobenzylpenicillin and other hydrogenolysis products of benzylpenicillin	E. Kaczka and K. Folkers	243-268	(1949)
The thiocyanate derivative of benzylpenicillin methyl ester	V. du Vigneaud and D.B. Melville	269-309	(1949)
The X-ray crystallographic investigation of the structure of penicillin	D. Crowfoot et.al.,	310-366	(1949)
Identification and crystallography of penicillins and related compounds by X-ray diffraction methods	G.L. Clark et.al.,	367-381	(1949)
Infra-red spectroscopic studies on the structure of penicillin	H.W. Thompson et.al.,	382-414	(1949)
Other physical methods in the analysis of penicillin	R.B. Woodward A. Neuberger and N.R. Tenner	415-439	(1949)
The constitution of penicillins	J.R. Johnson R.B. Woodward and R. Robinson	440-454	(1949)
Penicillamine, its analogs and homologs	H.M. Crooks	455-472	(1949)
Penilloaldehydes and penaldic acids	E.V. Brown	473-534	(1949)
The penilloic and penicilloic acids and their derivatives and analogs	R. Mozingo and K. Folkers	535-656	(1949)

THE CHEMISTRY OF PENICILLIN (Contd.)

Biosynthesis of penicillins	O.K. Behrens	657-679 (1949)
Chemical modifications of natural penicillins	R.D. Coghill F.H. Stodola and J.L. Wachtel	680-687 (1949)
Oxazoles and oxazolones	J.W. Cornforth	688-848 (1949)
Attempted synthesis of penicillins	W.E. Bachmann and M.W. Cronyn	849-891 (1949)
The condensation of oxazolones and D-penicillamine and the resultant antibiotic activity	V. DuVigneaud J.L. Wood and M.E. Wright	892-908 (1949)
Methylbenzylpseudopenicillinate	J.H. Hunter J.W. Himan and H.E. Carter	909-920 (1949)
Thiazolidines	A.H. Cook and I.M. Heilbron	921-972 (1949)
The chemistry of β-lactones	S.A. Ballard D.S. Melstrom and C.W. Smith	973-1003 (1949)
Synthetic benzylpenicillin	V. DuVigneaud et. al.,	1018-1024 (1949)

THE CHEMISTRY OF PETROLEUM HYDROCARBONS

These are collective volumes edited by B.T. Brooks, C.E. Boord, S.S. Kurtz Jr. and L. Schmerling, and published by Reinhold Publishing Corporation, New York.

Title	Author	Reference
Hydrocarbons in natural gases	D.T. McRoberts	1, 1-4 (1954)
Hydrocarbons in gasolines, kerosenes, gas oils and lubricating oils	A.N. Sachanen	1, 5-36 (1954)
Composition of petroleum waxes	B.T. Brooks	1, 37-47 (1954)
Separation of aromatics by selective absorption	A.E. Hirschler	1, 155-196 (1954)
Separation of paraffins by urea and thiourea	R.L. McLaughlin	1, 241-274 (1954)
Physical properties and hydrocarbon structure	S.S. Kurtz Jr.	1, 275-331 (1954)
Ultraviolet spectra of hydrocarbons	W. Priestley and B.F. Dudenbostle	1, 333-350 (1954)
Molecular structure and spectroscopic data	E.J. Rosenbaum	1, 351-374 (1954)
Analytical applications of infrared and Raman spectroscopy	H.M. Tenney	1, 375-403 (1954)
Mass spectroscopy of hydrocarbons	W.S. Young	1, 405-434 (1954)
Preparation of pure paraffins and olefins	B.T. Brooks	1, 485-522 (1954)
Syntheses of low molecular weight alicyclic hydrocarbons	J.M. Derfer	1, 523-578 (1954)
Syntheses of low molecular weight aromatic hydrocarbons	J.M. Derfer	1, 579-599 (1954)
Syntheses of high molecular weight hydrocarbons	R.W. Schiessler and R.L. McLaughlin	1, 601-630 (1954)
The Fischer-Tropsch process	H.H. Storch	1, 631-646 (1954)
Mechanisms for the thermal decomposition of hydrocarbons	E.W.R. Steacie and S. Bywater	2, 1-25 (1955)
Acetylene by the pyrolysis of light hydrocarbons	L. Krames and J. Happel	2, 71-111 (1955)
Pyrolytic reactions of aromatic hydrocarbons	C.R. Kinney	2, 113-136 (1955)
Theory of catalytic cracking	B.S. Greenfelder	2, 137-164 (1955)
Aromatization, hydroforming and platforming	V. Haensel	2, 189-219 (1955)
Catalytic dehydrogenation	K. Kearby	2, 221-246 (1955)
Mechanisms of the reactions of non-benzenoid hydrocarbons	L. Schmerling	2, 247-275 (1955)
General theory of hydrocarbon oxidation	B. Lewis and G. von Elbe	2, 277-308 (1955)

THE CHEMISTRY OF PETROLEUM HYDROCARBONS (Contd.)

Low-temperature oxidation of paraffin hydrocarbons; oxidation of paraffin wax	W.E. Vaughan and F.F. Rust	2, 309-323 (1955)
Olefin autoxidation	R.H. Rosenwald	2, 325-355 (1955)
The partial oxidation of the simple paraffinic hydrocarbons	N.C. Robertson	2, 365-397 (1955)
Special oxidation reactions of unsaturated hydrocarbons	N.A. Milas	2, 399-436 (1955)
Oxidation of o-xylene to phthalic anhydride	J.E. Levine	3, 1-7 (1955)
Isomerization of saturated hydrocarbons	H. Pines and J.M. Mavity	3, 9-58 (1955)
Chlorination of paraffins and cycloparaffins	E.T. McBee and H.E. Ungnade	3, 59-71 (1955)
Fluorination and properties of fluoro derivatives of paraffins and cycloparaffins	E.T. McBee and O.R. Pierce	3, 73-84 (1955)
Nitration of paraffins and cycloparaffins	B.T. Brooks	3, 85-96 (1955)
Special chemical reactions of paraffins and cycloparaffins	B.T. Brooks	3, 97-114 (1955)
Isomerization of olefins	B.T. Brooks	3, 115-127 (1955)
Vinyl polymerization	C. Walling	3, 129-194 (1955)
Polyethylene	E.L. Kropa and P.B. Stickney	3, 195-206 (1955)
Diels-Alder condensations and related reactions	C. Walling	3, 207-219 (1955)
The chemistry of natural and synthetic rubbers	H.L. Fisher	3, 249-267 (1955)
Condensation of saturated halides with olefins	L. Schmerling	3, 269-281 (1955)
Catalytic hydrogenation of hydrocarbons	B.B. Corson	3, 283-325 (1955)
The oxo reaction	M. Orchin	3, 341-361 (1955)
Alkylation of saturated hydrocarbons	L. Schmerling	3, 363-408 (1955)
Special reactions of olefins	B.T. Brooks	3, 409-464 (1955)
Aromatic substitution theory and mechanism	H.C. Brown and K. Le R. Nelson	3, 465-578 (1955)
Sulfonation of aromatic hydrocarbons	E.E. Gilbert	3, 611-641 (1955)
Nitration of aromatic hydrocarbons	C.D. McKinney Jr.	3, 643-669 (1955)

CHOLESTEROL

A collective volume, edited by R.P. Cook and published by Academic Press Inc., New York.

Title	Author	Reference	
Chemistry of cholesterol	P. Blandon	15-115	(1958)
Conversion of cholesterol to steroid hormones	O. Hechter	309-348	(1958)

CIBA FOUNDATION COLLOQUIA ON ENDOCRINOLOGY

This is the collection of the proceedings of the annual symposia of the Ciba Foundation, held in London and devoted to Endocrinology. Published by Little, Brown and Co., Boston.

Title	Author	Reference		
Synthesis and metabolism of adrenocortical steroids	W. Klyne (Editor)	7,	pp.	(1953)
The chemistry of lanosterol	D.H.R. Barton	7,	27-33	(1953)
The ergosterol route to adrenal cortical hormones	H.B. Henbest	7,	39-43	(1953)
Investigations on the synthesis of 11-ketosteroids	H. Heusser	7,	46-54	(1953)
Partial synthesis of $\Delta^{9(11)}$-anhydrocorticosterone acetate	R. Casanova, A. Ruff and C.W. Shoppee	7,	59-60	(1953)
Cortisone and 11-epi-17-hydroxycorticosterone diacetate from sarmentogenin	A. Lardon and T. Reichstein	7,	65-72	(1953)
Synthesis of 11-oxygenated steroids from steroidal sapogenins	C. Djerassi and G. Rosenkranz	7,	79-90	(1953)
11-oxygenated steroids from ergosterol-D-acetate 22:23-dibromide	F.S. Spring et al.	7,	96-101	(1953)
Introduction of the 11-keto function in the steroids	J.M. Constantin and L.H. Sarett	7,	104-106	(1953)
The characterization of trisubstituted steroidal olefins by infra-red spectroscopy	H. Hirschmann	7,	110-123	(1953)
Some aspects of the stereochemistry of C-20	W. Klyne	7,	127-137	(1953)
The chemical action of X-rays on some steroids in aqueous systems	J. Weiss	7,	142-157	(1953)
Internal secretion of the pancreas	G.E.W. Wolstenholme and C.M. O'Connor (Editors)	9,	292 pp.	(1956)
Fractionation of insulin	E. Fredericq	9,	89-103	(1956)
The chemical structure of insulin	F. Sanger	9,	110-119	(1956)
A concept of the three-dimensional structure of insulin	D.F. Waugh	9,	122-132	(1956)
Chemical and biological characteristics of glucagon	O.K. Behrens, A. Staub, M.A. Root and W.W. Bromer	9,	167-174	(1956)

CIBA FOUNDATION SYMPOSIA

This is a collection of the proceedings of the symposia organized by The Ciba Foundation, London, and published by Little, Brown and Company, Boston.

Title	Author	Reference	
The chemical structure of proteins	G.E.W. Wolstenholme and M.P. Cameron (Editors)	222 pp.	(1953)
The importance and use of suitable fractionation procedures for structural studies with proteins	L.C. Craig	4-12	(1953)
Chromatographic purification of ribonuclease and lysozyme	W.H. Stein	17-27	(1953)
The partition chromatography of proteins, with particular reference to insulin and glucagon	R.R. Porter	31-39	(1953)
Peptides of ordinary tissues	R.L.M. Synge	43-53	(1953)
On the terminal residues of chymotrypsinogen, chymotripsins, trypsinogen and trypsin	P. Desnuelle and M. Rovery	58-67	(1953)
Identification and estimation of the amide and C-terminal residues in insulin by reduction of the ester with lithium borohydride	A.C. Chibnall and M.W. Rees	70-81	(1953)
Identification of C-end groups in proteins by reduction with lithium aluminium hydride	C. Fromageot and M. Jutisz	82-95	(1953)
Selective cleavage of peptides	P. Edman	98-101	(1953)
Phenylisothiocyanate as a reagent for the identification of the terminal amino-acids	H. Fraenkel-Conrat	102-107	(1953)
Specificity of certain peptidases and their use in the study of peptide and protein structure	E.L. Smith	109-125	(1953)
Acyl migration in the study of protein structure	D.F. Elliott	129-137	(1953)
Degradation of peptides from the amino end	F. Turba	142-145	(1953)
Degradation of peptides from the carboxyl end	T. Wieland	146-148	(1953)
Protamines and nucleoprotamines	K. Felix	151-161	(1953)
Fractionation of pepsin-catalysed hydrolysates of crystalbumin	P. Boulanger and G. Biserte	165-182	(1953)
Some experiments on the chromatographic separation and identification of peptides in partial hydrolysates of gelatin	W.A. Schroeder	184-192	(1953)
Electron optical and chemical studies on the structure of collagen	W. Grassmann	195-210	(1953)
Chemistry and biology of pteridines	G.E.W. Wolstenholme and M.P. Cameron (Editors)	425 pp.	(1954)

CIBA FOUNDATION SYMPOSIA (Contd.)

Ring-opening reactions of pteridines	E.C. Taylor Jr.	2-34	(1954)
The alkylation of pteridines	H.C.S. Wood	35-42	(1954)
The reduction and reoxidation of some 8-substituted pteridines	G.B. Elion	49-58	(1954)
The monosubstituted pteridines	D.J. Brown	62-71	(1954)
Some aspects of the ultraviolet absorption spectra of the pteridines	S.F. Mason	74-91	(1954)
The use of o-aminonitroso compounds in the synthesis of pteridines and some analogous ring systems	G.M. Timmis D.G.I. Felton T.S. Osdene	93-100	(1954)
Recent developments in pteridine synthesis	E.C. Taylor Jr. et.al.,	104-120	(1954)
Chromatographic and electrophoretic studies of pteridines	M. Polonovski H. Jérome and P. Gonnard	124-132	(1954)
The constitution of urothione	R. Tschesche	135-139	(1954)
The pteridines of drosophila melanogaster	H.S. Forrest and H.K. Mitchell	143-153	(1954)
The constitution of fluorescyanine	F. Korte	159-164	(1954)
New observations on fluorescyanine B	M. Polonovski et.al.,	165-169	(1954)
Sulphonamide derivatives of pteridines	M.J. Fahrenbach et.al.,	173-179	(1954)
Some dipyrimidopyrazines (pyrimidopteridines)	E.A. Falco and G.H. Hitchings	183-192	(1954)
Structural studies on pyrimidopteridines. The structure of "bis-alloxazine" and "diuracilpyridazine"	E.C. Taylor Jr. C.K. Cain and H.M. Loux	193-201	(1954)
Some unresolved problems	A. Albert	204-216	(1954)
Porphyrin biosynthesis and metabolism	G.E.W. Wolstenholme and E.C.P. Millar (Editors)	308 pp.	(1955)
The synthesis of uroporphyrins II and IV	S.F. MacDonald and K.H. Michl	285-291	(1955)
Paper electrophoresis	G.E.W. Wolstenholme and E.C.P. Millar (Editors)	224 pp.	(1956)
General methods of paper electrophoresis	W. Grassmann	2-21	(1956)
High voltage paper electrophoresis	B. Kickhöfen	206-208	(1956)
The chemistry and biology of purines	G.E.W. Wolstenholme and C.M. O'Connor (Editors)	327 pp.	(1957)
Synthesis and properties of purines of potential biological interest	A. Bendich A. Giner-Sorolla and J.J. Fox	3-15	(1957)
Some synthetic studies on purines and related heterocycles	C. Taylor et.al.,	20-32	(1957)

CIBA FOUNDATION SYMPOSIA (Contd.)

Title	Author	Pages	Year
Some new N-methyl purines	G.B. Elion	39-49	(1957)
The structure of the hydroxypurines investigated by O- and N-methylation	D.J. Brown	50-54	(1957)
The spectra and structure of the monohydroxypurines and other potentially tautomeric purines	S.F. Mason	60-71	(1957)
The 8-position in purines. The chemical and biological transformation of purines into pteridines	A. Albert	97-103	(1957)
Stereochemistry of nucleoside synthesis	B.R. Baker	120-129	(1957)
Synthetic chemical investigations related to the metabolism of purines	G.M. Dimmis, I. Cooke and R.S.L. Spickett	134-141	(1957)
The chemistry of new purines in the B_{12} series of vitamins	E.L. Smith	160-168	(1957)
Chemical and biological behaviors of 9 β-D-ribofuranosylpurine	G.B. Brown, M.P. Gordon, D.I. Magrath and A. Hampton	192-200	(1957)
Drug resistance in micro organisms	G.E.W. Wolstenholme and C.M. O'Connor (Editors)	352 pp.	(1957)
The reactions of the mutagenic alkylating agents with proteins and nucleic acids	P. Alexander, J.F. Cousens and K.A. Stacey	294-	(1957)
Chemistry and biology of mucopolysaccharides	G.E.W. Wolstenholme and M. O'Connor (Editors)	323 pp.	(1958)
General chemistry of the mucopolysaccharides	M. Stacey	4-16	(1958)
Physicochemical studies on hyaluronic acids	B.S. Blumberg and A.G. Ogston	22-37	(1958)
Immunochemical approaches to polysaccharide and mucopolysaccharide structure	E.A. Kabat	42-60	(1958)
Biosynthesis of mucopolysaccharides: the uridine nucleotides of group A streptococci	A. Dorfman and J.A. Cifonelli	64-81	(1958)
Sulphated galactosamine-containing mucopolysaccharides	R.W. Jeanloz, P.J. Stoffyn and M. Trémège	85-90	(1958)
Mucopolysaccharides of gram-negative bacteria: newer chemical and biological aspects	O. Westphal et.al.,	187-196	(1958)
Blood group active substances of plant origin	G.F. Springer	216-229	(1958)
Mucopolysaccharides of epithelial mucus	L. Odin	234-244	(1958)
Glycoproteins of plasma	R.J. Winzler	245-263	(1958)
Colloidal properties of urinary mucopolysaccharides	N.F. Maclagan and A.J. Anderson	268-282	(1958)
Neuraminic acid	E. Klenk	296-302	(1958)

CIBA FOUNDATION SYMPOSIA (Contd.)

Amino acids and peptides with antimetabolic activity	G.E.W. Wolstenholme and C.M. O'Connor (Editors)	286 pp.	(1958)
The stereochemistry of naturally occurring β-amino acids	K. Balenović	5-16	(1958)
Some aspects of azaserine, 6-diazo-5-oxo-L-norleucine and β-2-thienylalanine	H.C. Reilly	62-74	(1958)
Amino acid and peptide derivatives with potential antitumour properties	J.A. Stock	89-103	(1958)
Recent developments in actinomycin chemistry	A.W. Johnson	123-134	(1958)
The chemistry of etamycin	J.C. Sheehan, H.G. Zachau and W.B. Lawson	149-152	(1958)
The aminoacyl insertion reaction and peptide chemistry	M. Brenner	157-166	(1958)
Synthesis of cyclic polypeptides	R. Schwyzer	171-181	(1958)
Disulphide crosslinking in cysteine peptides	H.N. Rydon	192-201	(1958)
Structure and function of some sulphur-containing peptides	E.P. Abraham and G.G.F. Newton	205-223	(1958)
Bacitracin	L.C. Craig, W. Konigsberg and R.J. Hill	226-243	(1958)
Oxidative formation of biologically active compounds	A.J. Birch and H. Smith	247-257	(1958)
Biosynthesis of terpenes and sterols	G.E.W. Wolstenholme and C.M. O'Connor (Editors)	311 pp.	(1959)
Biogenesis and transformations of squalene	K. Bloch	4-16	(1959)
Discovery and elucidation of mevalonic acid	K. Folkers et. al.,	20-43	(1959)
The enzymic synthesis of branched-chain acids	M.J. Coon et. al.,	62-72	(1959)
The mechanism of a rearrangement occurring during biosynthesis of cholesterol. (The cyclization of squalene to lanosterol).	J.W. Cornforth et. al.,	119-132	(1959)
Semi-, mono-, sesqui-, and tri-terpenes as cholesterol precursors	O. Isler et. al.,	135-146	(1959)
Bile acids: formation and metabolism	S. Bergström	185-203	(1959)
Some aspects of acid-catalyzed cyclizations of terpenoid polyenes	A. Eschenmoser et. al.,	217-227	(1959)

LES COLLOQUES DU CENTRE NATIONAL DE LA RECHERCHE SCIENTIFIQUE

These are the proceedings of the international symposia organized by the C.N.R.S. and published both as part of a French Scientific Journal and as an independent collection by the C.N.R.S.   All articles are in French.

Title	Author	Reference		
High polymers (held at Strasbourg, 1946) (also published in J.Chim.Phys. 44, 1-154, 1947)		2,		(1947)
Molecular spectra (held in Paris, 1947) (also published in J.Chim.Phys. 45, 1-114, 1948)		3,		(1947)
Isotopic exchange and molecular structure (held in Paris, 1948). (Also published in J.Chim.Phys. 45, 141-250 (1948).		5,		(1948)
The diffusion of light and the Raman effect (held in Bordeaux, 1948). (Also published in J.Chim.Phys. 46, 1-138 (1949)		7,	145 pp.	(1948)
Polarization of matter (held in Paris, 1949) (Also published in Bull.Soc.Chim.France 1949, D336-D538)		17,	172 pp.	(1949)
Magnetochemical research on chelates and other compounds with an hydrogen bond	P. Rumpf and M. Séguin	17,	35-38	(1949)
Determination of the structure of some biphenyls by their dipole moments	A. Lumbroso	17,	56-61	(1949)
On the applicability of electric dipole measurements to the solution of problems in structural chemistry (in English)	M.L.E. Sutton	17,	81-87	(1949)
Geometric configuration and dipole moments of conjugated hydrocarbons	G. Berthier and B. Pulman	17,	90-98	(1949)
Diamagnetism of isomerides (in English)	W.R. Angus	17,	116-120	(1949)
The chemical bond (Paris, 1949) (also published in J.Chim.Phys. 46, 187-312, 407-437, 497-542, and 675-713, (1949)		18,	238 pp.	(1949)
Comparison of the methods of calculating the molecular wave functions	R. Daudel et.al.,	18,	1-10	(1949)
Localized and non-localized bonds	C.A. Coulson	18,	11-24	(1949)
Main characteristics of the electronic structure of several conjugated organic systems	A. Pulman and B. Pulman	18,	25-36	(1949)
Experimental proofs of hyperconjugation	M. Polanyi	18,	37-45	(1949)
The dipole moments of some semi-ionic compounds	R.W. Hill and L.E. Sutton	18,	46-50	(1949)
The index of free valence	R. Daudel et.al.,	18,	51-63	(1949)

LES COLLOQUES DU CENTRE NATIONAL DE LA RECHERCHE SCIENTIFIQUE (Contd.)

The van der Waals-London energies	H.B.G. Casimir	18,	126-129	(1949)
Absorption energies and heterogenous catalysis	E. Cremer	18,	130-138	(1949)
Hydrogen bonds. Electrostatic theory of some phenomena	E. Bauer	18,	139-143	(1949)
The energies associated with the hydrogen bond	J.A.A. Ketelaar	18,	144-147	(1949)
The thermal properties of the hydrogen bond in crystals	A.R. Ubbelohde	18,	148-156	(1949)
Adsorption and heterogeneous catalysis (also published in J.Chim.Phys. 47, 67-172, 221-311, 437-522 (1950)		19,	281 pp.	(1950)
Combustion of carbon (held in Nancy, 1949) (also published in J.Chim.Phys. 47, 315-378, 525-585 (1950)		20,	127 pp.	(1950)
Fiftieth anniversary of the discovery of radium (held in Paris, 1950)		29,	106 pp.	(1951)
The decomposition of fatty acids by alpha particles (in English)	L. Whitehead C. Goodman and I.A. Breger	29,	24-28	(1951)
Effect of ring on radiation chemistry of alkyl substituted benzenes (in English)	M. Burton S. Gordon and R.R. Hentz	29,	30-34	(1951)
Effect of X-rays on aqueous solutions of indole (in English)	C.B. Allsopp and J. Wilson	29,	35-37	(1951)
A study of the action of neutrons on organic halides (in English)	C.H. Collie and P.F.D. Shaw	29,	38-41	(1951)
The free radical produced by ionizing radiations in aqueous medium	J. Weiss	29,	55-57	(1951)
Molecular rearrangements and the Walden inversion. Held at Montpellier, 1950. (Also published in Bull.Soc.Chim.France 1951, C1-C144)		30,	152 pp.	(1951)
The allylic rearrangement. General aspects and attempted theoretical interpretation.	C. Prévost	30,	9-16	(1951)
The role of the organo-magnesium compounds in the allylic rearrangement	A. Kirrmann	30,	17-21	(1951)
Use of the allylic rearrangement for the preparation of carbonyl compounds	M. Julia	30,	21-25	(1951)
Reaction mechanism and the Walden inversion (in English)	E.D. Hughes	30,	25-29	(1951)
Steric rearrangements of the α,α'-dimethylcyclohexanones and the cyclohexanols	R. Cornubert et.al.,	30,	29-36	(1951)
Rearrangements of pinene under the influence of catalysts or of heat	G. DuPont and R. Dulou	30,	37-41	(1951)
The structure of the magnesium derivative of the pinene hydrochloride and the camphane carboxylic acids	G. Vavon et.al.,	30,	43-47	(1951)

LES COLLOQUES DU CENTRE NATIONAL DE LA RECHERCHE SCIENTIFIQUE (Contd.)

Anionotropy, and the Wagner rearrangement (in English)	E.D. Hughes	30,	47-51	(1951)
The expansion of carbon rings by the transposition reactions	B. Tchoubar	30,	52-57	(1951)
Recent progress in the interpretation of the intramolecular rearrangements	I. Elphimoff-Felkin and B. Tchoubar	30,	57-62	(1951)
Neighboring groups in displacements and rearrangements (in English)	S. Winstein	30,	63-68	(1951)
Rearrangements of halogenated ketones	G. Richard	30,	69-72	(1951)
Uses of optically active compounds in the study of the mechanism of organic reactions (in English)	J. Kenyon	30,	72-78	(1951)
A review of the π-complex theory (in English)	M.J.S. Dewar	30,	79-87	(1951)
Substitution reactions in the cyclohexanes with or without participation of neighboring groups	M. Mousseron and R. Jacquier	30,	88-93	(1951)
Acid catalyzed reactions of hydrocarbons (in English)	M.J.S. Dewar	30,	94-96	(1951)
The reactions of molecular transposition in the allylic series	M. Mousseron R. Jacquier and J. Jullien	30,	97-107	(1951)
Stereochemical factors in carbonium ion reactions (in English)	P.D. Bartlett	30,	108-113	(1951)
Rearrangements of certain derivatives of the gem-diphenylindanes	C. Dufraisse and M. Vaillant	30,	114-116	(1951)
Molecular rearrangement of some hydrofuranes and hydropyranes	R. Paul	30,	117-123	(1951)
Molecular rearrangements of dihydrofuranes	H. Normant	30,	123-127	(1951)
The i-steroid rearrangement (in English)	C.W. Shoppee	30,	128-131	(1951)
The reactivity of silver perchlorate in some organic reactions	G. Cauquil and H. Barbera	30,	132-135	(1951)
The rearrangement of phosphorous esters into phosphonic esters	P. Rumpf	30,	136-139	(1951)
Use of quantum mechanics and of radioactivity in the study of reaction mechanisms	N.P. Buu-Hoï et.al.,	30,	140-145	(1951)
Reduction of ketones	J. Wiemann	30,	145-148	(1951)
Rearrangements of organic sulfur compounds	D. Libermann	30,	149-152	(1951)
Hydroxycarbonylation (held at Strasbourg, 1952 and also published in Bull.Soc.Chim.France 1953, C1-C62)		56,	64 pp.	(1953)
Study of the hydration of aldehydes by spectrophotometry	C. Bloch and P. Rumpf	56,	8-11	(1953)
Condensation of aliphatic esters by branched organomagnesium halides	Y. Maroni-Barnaud and J.E. Dubois	56,	27-31	(1953)

LES COLLOQUES DU CENTRE NATIONAL DE LA RECHERCHE SCIENTIFIQUE (Contd.)

Reaction and condensations of aldehydes and ketones with the α-keto acids	P. Cordier	56,	37-40	(1953)
The chloromethylation of diphenylmethane	C. Maquin and H. Gault	56,	45-49	(1953)
A method of bromomethylation	F. Krausz	56,	51-52	(1953)
The reversibility of aminoalkylation	H. Larramona and B. Tchoubar	56,	53-58	(1953)
The condensation of aromatic aldehydes with esters and salts of glycine	I. Elphimoff-Felkin, H. Felkin and Z. Welvart	56,	58-62	(1953)
Some general aspects of macromolecular science. Strasbourg, 1954		57,	160 pp.	(1955)
Development of macromolecular chemistry	H. Staudinger	57,	10-21	(1955)
Dynamic study of the formation of high polymers	H.W. Melville	57,	22-32	(1955)
Structure and properties of plastomers	G. Champetier	57,	45-67	(1955)
Synthetic rubbers	G. Natta	57,	69-86	(1955)
Interactions between electrolytes	A. Katchalsky and P. Spitnik	57,	103-125	(1955)
Nucleic acid as a polyelectrolyte	J.A.V. Butler	57,	145-159	(1955)
The oxygen containing heterocycles (held at Lyon, 1955)	C. Mentzes (Editor)	69,	392 pp.	(1957)
Structure and properties of the 1,2-epoxides. Recent advances	M. Mousseron	69,	9-19	(1957)
Furane and pyrane derivatives as starting materials for organic synthesis	R. Paul	69,	21-47	(1957)
Research on the 2,2,5,5-tetramethyl tetrahydrofuranes	G. Sandris and G. Ourisson	69,	49-51	(1957)
The hydroxylation of flavanones in the 3-position and its importance for the biogenesis of the anthocyanins	T.R. Seshadri	69,	71-82	(1957)
Reactions of the hydroxy-3-flavones with alkalies	J. Gripenberg	69,	85-96	(1957)
Research in benzil chemistry. The stereochemical configuration of the diastereomeric 5,5'-dinitro-hydrosalicyloins	H. Moureau, P. Chovin and R. Sabourin	69,	99-107	(1957)
Recent advances in the chemistry of cumarones and related compounds	N.P. Buu-Hoï	69,	111-118	(1957)
The mechanism of the synthesis of α-naphthyl-3-hydroxy-4-coumarin	C. Beaudet, F. Henaux and A. Ville	69,	123-128	(1957)
Natural and synthetic reduced derivatives of the flavones	F.E. King	69,	135-138	(1957)
The "sclerothiorine"	W.B. Whalley	69,	141-145	(1957)
The oxidizability of phlorizin by oxygen and by hydrogen peroxide	J. Lavollay, G. Neumann and G. Lehongre	69,	147-156	(1957)
The oxygen containing rings of the sapogenins and of the sterolalkaloids	C. Sannié and H. Lapin	69,	159-176	(1957)
The chloromethylation of β-ethylenic alcohols and of β-arylalcohols. Formation of pyrans and isochromans	J. Cologne and P. Boisdé	69,	177-196	(1957)

LES COLLOQUES DU CENTRE NATIONAL DE LA RECHERCHE SCIENTIFIQUE (Contd.)

The isochromans	P. Maitte	69,	197-206 (1957)
A critical discussion of the synthetic methods for synthesis of benzopyrone rings	C. Mentzer	69,	207-226 (1957)
Flavone glycosides of the leaves of Calystegia Japonica and Calystegia Hederacea	S. Hattori and M. Shimokoriyama	69,	227-228 (1957)
The flavonic constituents of the conifers	H. Erdtman	69,	229-245 (1957)
The flavonic constituents of the dahlias	T. Swain and G. Nordstrom	69,	249-268 (1957)
Synthesis of α-pyrones	H.S. Dreiding	69,	269-276 (1957)
The chemistry of aurones	T.A. Geissman, J.B. Harborne and M.K. Seikel	69,	277-286 (1957)
The chemistry of some ethylenic lactones isolated from higher plants	H. Schmid	69,	303-318 (1957)
The structure of the calophyllolid extracted from the seeds of Calophyllum inopyllum	J. Polonsky	69,	319-328 (1957)
The $\Delta\epsilon$-method and its application to flavones and related compounds	G. Aulin-Erdtman	69,	329-340 (1957)
Study of the infra-red absorption of some hydroxy-flavones	L. Henry and D. Molho	69,	341-354 (1957)
Degradations of flavones and related compounds	D. Molho	69,	355-377 (1957)
Some stereochemical problems. Symposium held in Montpellier, 1959. Published in Bull. Soc. Chim. France 1307-1463 (1960). This symposium was not available as a separate publication (July 1961)			1307-1463 (1960)
Configurations and dipole moments of some ethers and esters (in German)	B.A. Arbusow		1311-1315 (1960)
Syntheses related to mycoseric acid (in French)	L. Ahlquist et al.		1316-1319 (1960)
Determination of the configuration of endo-exo isomers of bicyclo-(1,2,2)-heptane derivatives (in German)	S. Beckmann		1319-1322 (1960)
The conformation of medium sized rings (in French)	G. Chiurdoglu, T. Doehard and B. Tursch		1322-1326 (1960)
Orientation in the substitution of α-ethylenic ketones during carbanionic reactions (in French)	J.M. Conia and A. Le Craz		1327-1330 (1960)
Rearrangements of axial alkylcyclohexanols to sodium alkoxides under the influence of a small quantity of oxygen (in French)	B. Alexandre, R. Cornubert, Y. Fagnoni and W. Kondrachoff		1332-1337 (1960)
Stereochemistry in polycyclic systems (in English)	W.G. Dauben		1338-1342 (1960)
Stereochemistry of the formation of diastereoisomeric secondary alcohols (in French)	Y. Gault and H. Felkin		1342-1347 (1960)
Use of symetrical alicyclic 1,1-dienyls in synthesis of polycyclic compounds (in English)	D. Ginsburg		1348-1350 (1960)
Stereochemistry of bicyclo-(3.3.0)-octane (in French)	R. Granger, P. Nau and J. Nau		1350-1355 (1960)

LES COLLOQUES DU CENTRE NATIONAL DE LA RECHERCHE SCIENTIFIQUE (Contd.)

Title	Author(s)	Pages
Problems of stereochemistry in photochemical reactions in the anthracene series (in English)	F.D. Greene	1356-1359 (1960)
The stereochemistry of fragmentation reactions (in English)	C.A. Grob	1360-1364 (1960)
Directing effects of near and remote groups in the addition of reagents to double bonds (in English)	H.B. Henbest et al.	1365-1368 (1960)
Contribution to conformational analysis (in German)	W. Hückel	1369-1372 (1960)
Polar and steric effects in elimination reactions (in English)	D.V. Banthorpe and E.D. Hughes	1373-1376 (1960)
The bicyclo-(4,1,0)-heptanes and bicyclo-(3,1,0)-hexanes (in French)	P. Besinet et al.	1377-1380 (1960)
Homoallylic rearrangements. Stereochemical studies (in French)	M. Julia et al.	1381-1385 (1960)
Quantitative studies in reactivity. VII. β-chloro-alcohols; stereochemical aspects (in French)	H. Bodot et al.	1386-1395 (1960)
Optical rotatory dispersion in structural and stereochemical studies (in English)	W. Klyne	1396-1405 (1960)
Reaction conformations of substituted cyclohexenic acids (in French)	V.F. Koutchérov, V.M. Andreev and N.Y. Grigorieva	1406-1410 (1960)
Stereochemistry of the oxidation of Δ^4-octalincarboxylic acids (in French)	V.F. Koutchérov and G.M. Ségal	1410-1417 (1960)
The derivatives of 9,10 octalin (in French)	M. Mousseron, M. Mousseron and M. Granier	1418-1423 (1960)
Vinyl magnesium derivatives possessing a homocyclic ring (in French)	H. Normant and P. Maitte	1424-1428 (1960)
Study of the 1,3 interactions (in French)	J.F. Biellmann et al.	1429-1430 (1960)
Cis- and trans- hydroxy-2-cyclopentanecarboxylic acids (in French)	J. Pascual and J. Viñas	1430-1433 (1960)
Some newer developments in the chemistry of medium sized rings (in English)	V. Prelog	1433-1437 (1960)
Some recent studies on macrocyclic stereochemistry (in English)	J. Sicher et al.	1438-1442 (1960)
Steric implications of certain enolization and ketonization mechanisms (in French)	M. Charpentier et al.	1443-1449 (1960)
Stereochemistry of the bornylic and fenchylic rearrangements in the pinene series (in French)	N.A. Abraham and M. Vilkas	1450-1453 (1960)
Stereochemical problems in two series of heterogeneous reactions (in French)	J. Wiemann	1454-1459 (1960)
Formation of A-nor-steroids by dehalogenation with magnesium (in French)	F. Winternitz and A.C. de Paulet	1460-1462 (1960)

CONFERENCE ON HYPERCONJUGATION

These are the proceedings of a symposium on Hyperconjugation held in June 1958 at Bloomington, Indiana, with V.J. Shiner Jr. and E. Campaigne as co-chairman. Published by Pergamon Press, New York. These proceedings were also published as numbers 2 and 3 of Tetrahedron, volume 5, (1959).

Title	Author	Page
The thermochemical evidence for hyperconjugation	R.B. Turner	1-8
Possible effect of hyperconjugation on solvolysis of benzyhdral chlorides and spectra of related compounds	W.R. Moore et.al.,	9-15
Role of solvent in alkyl substituent effects	W.H. Schubert et.al.,	16-23
Evaluation of resonance effects on reactivity by application of the linear inductive energy relationship - IV. Hyperconjugation effects of p-alkyl groups	R.W. Taft, Jr. and I.C. Lewis	24-46
Experimental and theoretical evaluations of the Baker-Nathan effect	M.M. Kreevoy	47-56
A simple molecular orbital treatment of hyperconjugation	A. Streitwieser, Jr. and P.M. Nair	57-73
Bond lengths and hyperconjugation	L.E. Sutton	74-82
A re-evaluation of conjugation and hyperconjugation: the effects of changes in hybridisation on carbon bonds	M.J.S. Dewar and H.N. Schmeising	83-95
Conjugation and hyperconjugation: a survey with emphasis on isovalent hyperconjugation	R.S. Mulliken	96-117
Hyperconjugation in aromatic cation complexes	D.A. McCaulay and A.P. Lien	118-125
An assessment of some experimental approaches to NH and OH hyperconjugation	P.B.D. de la Mare	126-134
Substituent effects on hyperconjugation: evaluation of hyperconjugation energy for groups of the type $.CH_2X$	J.W. Baker	135-142
Some thoughts on the Baker-Nathan order	E. Berliner	143-150
Isotope effects and hyperconjugation	E.S. Lewis	151-156
Secondary hydrogen isotope effect in a gas-phase equilibrium	P. Love R.W. Taft, Jr. and T. Wartik	157-158
Deuterium isotope effects and hyperconjugation	V.J. Shiner, Jr.	159-168

CONTRIBUTION TO THE STUDY OF MOLECULAR STRUCTURE

This is a collective volume in memory of Professor Victor Henri, published in Liège, 1947-1948, by Maison Desoer.

Title	Author	Reference
The raman spectra of some fluoromethanes (in French)	M.L. Delwaulle and F. François	119-124 (1947-1948)
Analysis of the near ultraviolet absorption spectra of some trisubstituted benzenes (in English)	H. Sponer, M.B. Hall and M.J. Stallcup	211-228 (1947-1948)

CURARE AND CURARE-LIKE AGENTS

These are the proceedings of an international symposium held in Rio de Janeiro, 1957. Edited by D. Bovet, F. Bovet-Nitti and G.B. Marini-Bettòlo, and published by Pergamon Press, Inc., New York.

Title	Author	Reference
Alkaloids of calabash-curare and strychnos barks (in English)	P. Karrer	125-136 (1959)
Chemistry of the chondodendron alkaloids (in English)	O. Wintersteiner	153-162 (1959)
The curarizing alkaloids of erythrina species (in English)	V. Deulofeu	163-169 (1959)
Relation between chemical structure and pharmacodynamic activity of some synthetic curare-like agents (in French)	D. Bovet	252-282 (1959)
Synthesis and study of some curares and anticurares (in French)	R. Hazard, J. Cheymol, P. Chabrier and F. Bourillet	319-326 (1959)

CURRENT TRENDS IN HETEROCYCLIC CHEMISTRY

These are the proceedings of a symposium, held at Canberra, in September, 1957. Edited by A. Albert, G.M. Badger and C.W. Shoppee. Published by Academic Press, New York (1958).

Reactions of ethyl diazoacetate with heterocyclic systems	G.M. Badger and B.J. Christie	1-5
The reaction with benzoyl peroxide, with heterocyclic compounds	K.H. Pausacker	8-10
Factors influencing electrophilic substitution in nitrogen heterocycles	R.D. Brown	13-16
Addition to double-bonds in N-heteroaromatic six-membered rings	A. Albert	20-24
Physico-chemical studies on solubilized porphyrins	J.N. Phillips	30-37
Stereochemistry of catechins and related flavan derivatives	J.W. Clark-Lewis	40-49
Quantitative studies of tautomerism in heterocyclic mercaptans	A. Albert and G.B. Barlin	51-53
The effect of heteroelements in modifying some cyclizations: Part I: polycyclic aromatic compounds from the diene synthesis	W. Davies and Q.N. Porter	56-58
Part II: benzofuran derivatives formed by cyclization of ω-aryloxyacetophenones	W. Davies and S. Middleton	58-61
The possible formation of thiazoline and thiazolidine rings in peptides and proteins	J.M. Swan	65-72
The linear naphthiminazoles	D.J. Brown	75-79
Synthetic routes to mono-substituted phenanthridines	W.H.F. Sasse	82-90
A novel type of naturally-occurring quaternary base	J.R. Price	92-98
Hernandine - a new aporphine alkaloid from Hernandia bivalis Benth	R. Greenhalgh and F.N. Lahey	100-101
Some alkaloids of Australian Crotalaria species	C.C.J. Culvenor	103-109
Quinolizidine alkaloids	W.D. Crow	111-119
Syntheses of pyrimidine nucleosides	G. Shaw	122-128
Spectrum and bond-type in metalloporphyrins	J.E. Falk and R.S. Nyholm	130-138
Hydropteridines and their biological role	R.L. Blakley	140-147
Biotransformation products of ^{14}C-labelled codeine and morphine	T.K. Adler	151-154
The reactivity of some pyridine derivatives in enzyme systems	M.R. Atkinson	158-164

DETERMINATION OF ORGANIC STRUCTURES BY PHYSICAL METHODS

This is a collective volume, edited by E.A. Braude and F.C. Nachod and published by Academic Press Inc., New York.

Title	Author	Reference	
Phase properties of small molecules	H.F. Herbrandson and F.C. Nachod	3-23	(1955)
Equilibrium and dynamic properties of large molecules	P. Johnson	25-70	(1955)
Optical rotation	W. Klyne	73-130	(1955)
Ultraviolet and visible light	E.A. Braude	131-193	(1955)
Infrared light absorption	R.C. Gore	195-230	(1955)
Raman spectra	F.F. Cleveland	231-258	(1955)
Magnetic susceptibilities	C.A. Hutchison Jr.	259-321	(1955)
Surface films	E. Stenhagen	325-371	(1955)
Dipole moments	L.E. Sutton	373-425	(1955)
Electron diffraction	J. Karle and I.L. Karle	427-461	(1955)
X-ray diffraction	J.M. Robertson	463-502	(1955)
Microwave spectroscopy	E.B. Wilson Jr. and D.R. Lide Jr.	503-524	(1955)
Thermodynamic properties	J.G. Aston	525-566	(1955)
Dissociation constants	H.C. Brown D.H. McDaniel and O. Hafliger	567-662	(1955)
Reaction kinetics	E.A. Braude and L.M. Jackman	663-725	(1955)
Wave-mechanic theory	C.A. Coulson	727-757	(1955)

FARADAY SOCIETY - DISCUSSIONS

These are the proceedings of the General Discussions (Symposia) organized by the Faraday Society whose content is directly related to Organic Chemistry. Published by Gurney and Jackson, London, The Aberdeen University Press, Aberdeen.

Title	Author	Reference
The labile molecule		$\underline{2}$, 1-404 (1947)
The theory of the structure of free radicals	C.A. Coulson	$\underline{2}$, 9-18 (1947)
The properties of bonds involving carbon	A.D. Walsh	$\underline{2}$, 18-25 (1947)
The electronic structure of some free radicals	A. Pullman	$\underline{2}$, 26-35 (1947)
p-Quinodimethane and its diradical	C.A. Coulson et.al.,	$\underline{2}$, 36-38 (1947)
The resonance energy of the benzyl radical	M. Szwarc	$\underline{2}$, 39-46 (1947)
Some remarks on the $CH_2{=}\langle\rangle{=}CH_2$ molecule	M. Szwarc	$\underline{2}$, 46-49 (1947)
Calculated heats of formation of some π-complexes	M.J.S. Dewar	$\underline{2}$, 50-54 (1947)
Difficulties in the application of molecular orbital theory to mesomeric ions	C.A. Coulson	$\underline{2}$, 54-78 (1947)
Elementary reactions involving the lower paraffins	E.W.R. Steacie D. de B. Darwent and W.R. Trost	$\underline{2}$, 80-87 (1947)
Relative reaction rates of chlorine atoms with primary, secondary and tertiary hydrogen atoms in hydrocarbons	H. Steiner and H.R. Watson	$\underline{2}$, 88-97 (1947)
The structure of methylene	R.G.W. Norrish and G. Porter	$\underline{2}$, 97-104 (1947)
The reaction of free alkyl radicals in the gas phase	C.E.H. Bawn and C.F.H. Tipper	$\underline{2}$, 104-111 (1947)
Labile molecules in the kinetics of hydrocarbon reactions	C.F. Cullis et.al.,	$\underline{2}$, 111-132 (1947)
A. Electron-Transfer Reactions. The mechanism of oxidation of alcohols with Fenton's reagent	J.H. Merz and W.A. Waters	$\underline{2}$, 179-188 (1947)
On the nature of the "active" oxalic acid	J. Weiss	$\underline{2}$, 188-196 (1947)
B. Hydrocarbons in solution. The photolysis and photo-oxidation of organic iodides in the liquid state	E. Olaerts and J.C. Jungers	$\underline{2}$, 222-228 (1947)
A. Reactions of radicals and monomers. (a) Initiation. N-Nitrosoacylarylamines as catalysts in addition polymerisation	D.H. Hey and G.S. Misra	$\underline{2}$, 279-285 (1947)

FARADAY SOCIETY - DISCUSSIONS (Contd.)

(b) Propagation. Copolymerisation: the effects of structure on the reactions of ethylenic bonds with free radicals	F.R. Mayo F.M. Lewis and C. Walling	2, 285-295 (1947)
The effect of substitution on the reactivity of the styrene double bond towards free-radical attack: the nature of the "alternating effect" in copolymerisation	C. Walling and F.R. Mayo	2, 295-303 (1947)
The influence of structure on the relative reactivity of free radicals in polymerisation systems	C.C. Price	2, 304-309 (1947)
The reactivity of free radicals in polymerisation reactions	K. Nozaki	2, 337-342 (1947)
Structural aspect of lipo-protein association	D.G. Dervichian	6, 7-21 (1949)
The combination of fatty acid anions with proteins	J.M. Luck	6, 44-52 (1949)
Fully swollen alginate gels as permutites: kinetics of calcium-sodium ion exchange	J.L. Mongar and A. Wassermann	6, 118-123 (1949)
The chromatography of gases and vapours	C.S.G. Phillips	7, 241-248 (1949)
Chromatography of petroleum hydrocarbons	W.M. Smit	7, 248-255 (1949)
Chromatographic fractionation of black oils	A.S.C. Lawrence and D. Barby	7, 255-258 (1949)
Chromatography of the carboxylic acids	H.G. Cassidy and F.H. Max Nestler	7, 259-264 (1949)
Chromatographic analysis of fatty oils	K.A. Williams	7, 264-267 (1949)
The application of partition chromatography to the separation of the sugars and their derivatives	E.L. Hirst and J.K.N. Jones	7, 268-274 (1949)
The chromatography of proteins. The effect of salt concentration and pH on the adsorption of proteins to silica gel	C.C. Shepard and A. Tiselius	7, 275-285 (1949)
The application of chromatography to amino acids and peptides	T.S.G. Jones	7, 285-296 (1949)
Separation of bases and amino acids by displacement chromatography on ion-exchange columns	S.M. Partridge	7, 296-305 (1949)
Partition chromatography of the tertiary amine salts of the penicillins	T. Leigh	7, 311-316 (1949)
High molecular polymers separation	S. Claesson	7, 321-332 (1949)
Fifth Spiers Memorial Lecture. Catalysis: Retrospect and prospect	H.S. Taylor	8, 9-18 (1950)
The activated complex in heterogeneous catalysis	K.J. Laidler	8, 47-54 (1950)
Hydrogenation catalysts	O. Beeck	8, 118-128 (1950)
The mechanism of the catalytic hydrogenation of ethylene	G.H. Twigg	8, 152-159 (1950)
Alloy catalysts in dehydrogenation	G.-M. Schwab	8, 166-171 (1950)

FARADAY SOCIETY - DISCUSSIONS (Contd.)

Title	Author(s)	Vol., pages (year)
The mechanism of the catalytic cracking of unsymmetrical diarylethanes	D.R. May et.al.,	8, 290-307 (1950)
The low excited states of simple aromatic hydrocarbons	D.P. Craig	9, 5-14 (1950)
Applications of the electronic spectra of pyridine homologues to quantitative analysis and to the measurement of dissociation constants	E.F.G. Herington	9, 26-34 (1950)
The ultra-violet absorption spectra of fluorinated toluenes	W.T. Cave and H.W. Thompson	9, 35-46 (1950)
Natural hypsochromic shifts	Mme. A. Pullman and B. Pullman	9, 46-52 (1950)
The absorption spectra of some substituted benzenes and naphthalenes in the vacuum ultra-violet	V.J. Hammond et.al.,	9, 53-60 (1950)
The absorption spectroscopy of substances of short life	G. Porter	9, 60-82 (1950)
Infra-red absorption spectra of twelve substituted benzene derivatives from 15 to 40 microns	E.K. Plyler	9, 100-108 (1950)
Evidence of chain folding in polypeptides and proteins	A. Elliott and E.J. Ambrose	9, 246-251 (1950)
Some problems in the interpretation of the infra-red spectra of large molecules	G.B.B.M. Sutherland	9, 274-281 (1950)
Polymer types and specific absorptions in the ultra-violet by hydrogen-bridged amides and alcohols with application to the protein structure problem	G.A. Anslow	9, 299-334 (1950)
The ultra-violet absorption spectra of the aromatic amino acids in proteins and related compounds	G.H. Beaven E.R. Holiday and E.M. Jope	9, 406-417 (1950)
Observations of proteins in polarized ultra-violet light	M.F. Perutz M. Jope and R. Barer	9, 423-427 (1950)
A survey of the principles determining the structure and properties of molecules. Part I - The factors responsible for molecular shape and bond energies	Sir J. Lennard-Jones and J.A. Pople	10, 9-18 (1951)
Estimates of average bond energies and resonance energies of hydrocarbons	G. Glockler	10, 26-35 (1951)
Ionization and dissociation by electronic impact. The ionization potentials and energies of formation of *sec.*-propyl and *tert.*-butyl radicals. Some limitations on the method	D.P. Stevenson	10, 35-45 (1951)
Behaviour of paraffin hydrocarbons on electron impact. Synthesis and mass spectra of some deuterated paraffin hydrocarbons	D.O. Schissler S.O. Thompson and J. Turkevich	10, 46-53 (1951)
The ionization and dissociation of molecules by electron impact	C.A. McDowell and J.W. Warren	10, 53-65 (1951)
Potential energies for rotation about single bonds	K.S. Pitzer	10, 66-73 (1951)
The present status of the problem of hindered rotation in hydrocarbons and related compounds	J.G. Aston	10, 73-79 (1951)

FARADAY SOCIETY - DISCUSSIONS (Contd.)

Restricted rotation in ethane	L.J. Oosterhoff	10,	79-87	(1951)
The isomers of cyclohexane	P. Hazebroek and L.J. Oosterhoff	10,	87-93	(1951)
Molecular configuration and hydrocarbon reactivity	A.R. Ubbelohde and J.C. McCoubrey	10,	94-128	(1951)
The thermal decomposition of hydrocarbons	F.J. Stubbs and C.N. Hinshelwood	10,	129-136	(1951)
The reaction of methyl radicals with hydrogen	R.D. Anderson S. Davison and M. Burton	10,	136-143	(1951)
The thermal stability and reactivity of hydrocarbon radicals	M. Scwarc	10,	143-154	(1951)
The kinetics of the interaction of trichloromethyl radicals with cyclohexene	H.W. Melville J.C. Robb and R.C. Tutton	10,	154-163	(1951)
Structural factors governing the reactivities of -methylenic groups towards active free radicals	E.C. Kooyman	10,	163-174	(1951)
Ethane-ethylene and propane-propylene equilibria	G.B. Kistiakowsky and A.G. Nickle	10,	175-187	(1951)
The pyrolysis of dibenzyl	C. Horrex and S.E. Miles	10,	187-197	(1951)
Kinetics of diene reactions at high temperatures	D. Rowley and H. Steiner	10,	198-213	(1951)
The reactions of radicals from acetone with oxygen	F.B. Marcotte and W.A. Noyes Jr.	10,	236-241	(1951)
Reactions of free radicals associated with low temperature oxidation of paraffins	E.R. Bell et.al.,	10,	242-249	(1951)
The influence of substituents on the oxidation of hydrocarbons	C.N. Hinshelwood	10,	266-268	(1951)
Some properties of organic peroxides	A.C. Egerton W. Emte and G.J. Minkoff	10,	278-282	(1951)
Tables of the heats of formation and ionization potentials of hydrocarbon radicals	M. Szwarc	10,	336-338	(1951)
Radiation chemistry		12,	9-318	(1952)
Radiation chemistry of pure organic compounds: benzene and benzene-d_6	S. Gordon and M. Burton	12,	88-98	(1952)
The radiolysis of some organic liquids	A. Prévost-Bernas, et.al.,	12,	98-132	(1952)
Some aspects of the radiation chemistry of organic solutes	G. Stein	12,	227-234	(1952)
Radiation chemistry of organic solutions	W. Minder and H. Heydrich	12,	305-318	(1952)

FARADAY SOCIETY - DISCUSSIONS (Contd.)

Title	Authors	Vol.	Pages	Year
The physical chemistry of proteins		13,	3-287	(1953)
The molecular shapes of certain proteins and some of their interactions with other substances	J.T. Edsall	13,	9-28	(1953)
Zone electrophoresis in filter paper and other media	A. Tiselius	13,	29-33	(1953)
Polarization of the fluorescence of labelled protein molecules	G. Weber	13,	33-39	(1953)
The application of solubility measurements to the study of complex protein solutions and to the isolation of individual proteins	J.S. Falconer, D.J. Jenden and D.B. Taylor	13,	40-50	(1952)
Aggregation of globular proteins	L. Pauling	13,	170-176	(1952)
Protein interactions with organic molecules	I.M. Klotz and J. Ayers	13,	189-196	(1952)
Complexes of heparin and proteins	E. Gorter and L. Nanninga	13,	205-217	(1952)
Conjugated proteins	M. Stacey	13,	245-251	(1952)
The reactivity of free radicals		14,	3-256	(1953)
The reactions of hydrogen atoms with hydrocarbons	B. de B. Darwent and R. Roberts	14,	55-63	(1953)
The mechanism of biacetyl photolysis	F.E. Blacet and W.E. Bell	14,	70-76	(1953)
The reactions of radicals from diethyl ketone with oxygen. Part I.	A. Finkelstein and W.A. Noyes Jr.	14,	76-84	(1953)
The photolysis of trifluoromethyl iodide	J.R. Dacey	14,	84-88	(1953)
Photochemistry of anthracene. Part I. The photo-oxidation of anthracenes in solution	E.J. Bowen	14,	143-146	(1953)
Photochemistry of anthracene. Part II. The photochemical reaction of anthracene with carbon tetrachloride	E.J. Bowen and K.K. Rohatgi	14,	146-150	(1953)
The kinetics of the addition of bromotrichloromethane to unsaturated compounds. Part I. Cyclohexene and vinyl acetate	H.W. Melville, J.C. Robb and R.C. Tutton	14,	150-160	(1953)
The oxidation of benzene by hydrogen peroxide and iron salts	J.H. Baxendale and J. Magee	14,	160-169	(1953)
Kinetics of the reactions between cumene hydroperoxide and polyethylene polyamines in aqueous solution	R.J. Orr and H.L. Williams	14,	170-181	(1953)
Hydroperoxide decomposition in relation to the initiation of radical chain reactions	L. Bateman (Mrs.) Hilda Hughes and A.L. Morris	14,	190-199	(1953)
The instability of large free radicals	F.S. Dainton and K.J. Ivin	14,	199-207	(1953)
Partial rate factors for homolytic aromatic substitution	D.H. Hey and G.H. Williams	14,	216-221	(1953)
Liquid phase reactions between free radicals and aldehydes	K.E.J. Barrett and W.A. Waters	14,	221-256	(1953)

FARADAY SOCIETY - DISCUSSIONS (Contd.)

Title	Author	Reference
The physical chemistry of dyeing and tanning		16, 3-251 (1954)
Atomic models. Part 3. Some stereochemical problems in dyeing	C. Robinson	16, 125-132 (1954)
The selective absorption of optical antipodes by wool	W. Bradley, R.A. Brindley, G.C. Easty	16, 152-158 (1954)
The dyeing of synthetic polypeptides	C.H. Bamford et.al.,	16, 222-251 (1954)

L. FARKAS MEMORIAL VOLUME

This is a collection of articles in memoriam to L. Farkas. Edited by A. Farkas and E.P. Wigner and published by the Research Council of Israel, Jerusalem.

Title	Author	Reference
Fast reactions of atomic hydrogen	H.W. Melville and J.C. Robb	124-143 (1952)
The catalytic dehydrogenation and condensation of aliphatic alcohols: reaction mechanism	V.I. Komarewsky, W.J. Zimmerschied and J.R. Coley	181-187 (1952)
The mechanism of isomerization of methylcyclopentane	H. Pines	241-256 (1952)

FERMENTE VITAMINE HORMONE

This is a comprehensive collection, in German. Edited by R. Ammon and W. Dirscherl and published by G. Thieme Verlag, Stuttgart.

Title	Author	Reference		
Insulin	W. Dirscherl	_2_,	19-60	(1960)
Thyroid hormones	I. Abelin	_2_,	77-144	(1960)
The hormones of the parathyroid	F. Holtz and W. Ponsold	_2_,	145-159	(1960)
The sexual hormones	W. Dirscherl	_2_,	163-175	(1960)
The estrogens	W. Dirscherl	_2_,	176-259	(1960)
Progesterone	W. Dirscherl	_2_,	260-304	(1960)
Relaxin	R. Ammon	_2_,	305-307	(1960)
Androgens	W. Dirscherl	_2_,	308-372	(1960)
The hormones of the suprarenal medula	P. Holtz	_2_,	396-449	(1960)
The chemistry of the hormones of the suprarenal cortex	Ch. Tamm	_2_,	476-524	(1960)
The hormones of the anterior lobe of the hypophysis	H.E. Voss	_2_,	525-663	(1960)
Melanocito-stimulating hormones	H.E. Voss	_2_,	664-679	(1960)
Oxytocin and vasopressin	H. Nowakowski	_2_,	680-694	(1960)
Hormones of the digestive tract	R. Ammon	_2_,	695-701	(1960)
Hormones of the thymus	J. Comsa	_2_,	702-710	(1960)
Tissue hormones	P. Holtz	_2_,	711-801	(1960)
Hormones of invertebrates	G. Koller	_2_,	814-868	(1960)
Phytohormones	R. Pohl	_2_,	869-887	(1960)

FESTSCHRIFT ARTHUR STOLL

This is a volume of review articles in the field of natural products directly connected with the work of Professor A. Stoll. Publisher: Birkhäuser, Basel (1957). The articles are in several languages.

Title	Author	Reference	
The scientific work of Arthur Stoll (in German)	Cl. Schöpf	1-34	(1957)
The nature and mode of action of oxidation enzymes (in English)	H. Theorell	35-47	(1957)
Triphenylphosphinemethylene derivatives as olefin forming reagents and as acids in synthesis of natural products (in German)	G. Wittig	48-58	(1957)
Some experiments with ultrasonic waves (in English)	L. Zechmeister and E.F. Magoon	59-63	(1957)
The photochemical study of the reaction of simple alkyl radicals with oxygen (in English)	W.A. Noyes, Jr.	64-71	(1957)
Recent advances in the chemistry of pyrrolizidene alkaloids (in English)	R. Adams and M. Gianturco	72-97	(1957)
The radial method in paper chromatography and paper electrophoresis. Its use in the separation of natural substances (in Italian)	S. Berlingozzi	98-116	(1957)
Some biogenetic aspects of phenol oxidation (in English)	D.H.R. Barton and T. Cohen	117-143	(1957)
Phenoldehydrogenation as a biosynthetic reaction (in English)	H. Erdtman and C.A. Wachtmeister	144-165	(1957)
Some aspects of the chemistry of jervine and veratramine (in English)	O. Wintersteiner	166-176	(1957)
New synthesis of peptides (in German)	S. Goldschmidt	177-182	(1957)
Conjugated dienes (in French)	Ch. Prévost	183-198	(1957)
The chemistry of catechins and flavans (in German)	K. Freudenberg	199-202	(1957)
The chemistry of the hop resin acids (in English)	I. Heilbron	203-210	(1957)
Hydroxylysine (in English)	D.D. Van Slyke	211-219	(1957)
The synthesis of isoquinolines by use of ethylenic aromatic dienes (in German)	M. Lora-Tamayo and R. Madroñero	220-226	(1957)
Ozonization and ozonolyses of aromatic and heterocyclic compounds; relative reactivities of the ring systems (in German)	J.P. Wibaut	227-256	(1957)
Contribution to the study of the Brazilian strychnos alkaloids (in French)	G.B. Marini-Bettòlo	257-280	(1957)
Proofs of purity of solanaceous alkaloids by paper chromatography (in German)	J. Büchi and H. Schumacher	281-293	(1957)
The constitution of dihydropyridine compounds and their importance to clarifying the structure of dihydrocodehydrase (in German)	P. Karrer	294-304	(1957)

FESTSCHRIFT ARTHUR STOLL (Contd.)

The nature of the peptide bond (in English)	S.I. Mizushima and T. Shimanouchi	305-317	(1957)
Naturally occurring quinonoid anhydro bases (in English)	T.R. Seshadri	318-329	(1957)
Cactus triterpenes (in English)	C. Djerassi	330-352	(1957)
Naturally occurring anthraquinone derivatives (in English)	K. Venkataraman	360-375	(1957)
Remarks on the characterization of the C-terminal amino-acids by reduction to amino-alcohols (in French)	Cl. Fromageot	376-383	(1957)
Chemical constitution and synthesis of the "cord factor", toxic lipid of Mycobacterium tuberculosis (in French)	E. Lederer	384-394	(1957)
Modern methods of synthesis of glycerides and related compounds (in German)	P.E. Verkade	395-418	(1957)
Synthetic researches in the vitamin-D series (in German)	H.H. Inhoffen	419-433	(1957)
The effect of aqueous alkali hydroxides on o-quinol acetates (in German)	F. Wessely et. al.,	434-443	(1957)
The tropism of the mimosas and their hormones (in German)	G. Hesse B. Banerjee and H. Schildknecht	444-456	(1957)
The chemistry of ajmaline (in English)	R. Robinson	457-467	(1957)
Peptide synthesis via acetylenic ethers (in German)	J. Farens	468-473	(1957)
Synthetic methods for the obtention of two series of heterocyclic compounds with variable number of atoms (in French)	R. Delaby and R. Damiens	474-478	(1957)
Alloocimene and neo-alloocimene (in German)	K. Alder	479-488	(1957)
Chemical carcinogenesis (in English)	L.F. Fieser	489-498	(1957)
Biogenetic aspects of certain indole alkaloids (in French)	M.-M. Janot	499-507	(1957)
Recent advances in the synthesis of nucleotide coenzymes (in English)	A. Todd	508-516	(1957)
Cyclooctadecane-1,10-bis-(trimethylammonium iodide), a synthetic product with the ring size and effects of D-tubocurarin (in German)	A. Lüttringhaus L. Kerp and H. Preugschas	517-523	(1957)
The structure and biogenesis of the macrolides, a new class of natural products (in English)	R.B. Woodward	524-544	(1957)
The constitution of the so-called "composit-cumulene I" from scentless Mayweed (Matricaria inodora L.) (in English)	P. Christensen and N.A. Sorensen	545-550	(1957)
Research on the inactivation of yeast saccharasases (in German)	K. Myrbäck	551-564	(1957)
Concerning new amino acids and other physiologically significant nitrogen compounds in higher plants (in German)	A.I. Virtanen	565-581	(1957)
Poisons of the green deadly amanita mushroom (Amanita phaloides) (in German)	T. Wieland	582-596	(1957)

FESTSCHRIFT ARTHUR STOLL (Contd.)

Title	Author(s)	Pages	Year
The probability of errors in the process of synthesis of protein molecules (in English)	L. Pauling	597-602	(1957)
Fifty years of catalase research; chemical results and biological problems (in German)	H. von Euler	603-619	(1957)
Synthesis of bicyclic natural products with oxygen bridges (in German)	G.O. Schenck and K. Ziegler	620-636	(1957)
Synthesis in the purine and pyrimidine series (in German)	H. Bredereck	637-660	(1957)
Concerning the possibilities of producing gutta-percha in Spain (in French)	C. González Gómez, F. Gallego y Gómez and A. Swiatopolk-Mirski	661-681	(1957)
Stereochemical and electronic considerations in the synthesis and biogenesis of tropane alkaloids (in German)	G. Fodor	682-700	(1957)
Synthesis of naphthacenes meso-disubstituted in the peri position. Mechanism of cyclization of benzylnaphthoketimines to naphthacenes. Dihydronaphthacenic oxazines (in French)	C. Dufraisse and H.V. de Pradenne	701-704	(1957)
Chemical mechanisms of CO_2-assimilation and the Willstaeter-Stoll theory (in German)	O. Warburg	705-710	(1957)
Some aspects of research work on biochemical separation methods at the Institute of Biochemistry, Uppsala (in English)	A. Tiselius	711-714	(1957)
Glycosides from seeds of Erysimum helveticum (Jaquin). (in German)	W. Nagata, Ch. Tamm and T. Reichstein	715-727	(1957)
The aromatic erythrena alkaloids (in German)	V. Prelog	728-745	(1957)
The chemistry of natural tropolones and related troponoids (in English)	T. Nozoe	746-783	(1957)
Concerning the formation and transformations of monophosphate esters (in French)	E. Cherbuliez	784-794	(1957)
Configurational relations of synthetic plant-growth substances (in German)	A. Fredga	795-805	(1957)
The effect of certain demulcents on the taste nerve endings (in English)	G. Liljestrand and Y. Zotterman	806-813	(1957)
Position of alkaloids in total metabolism with special reference to the differentiation of plant organs (in German)	K. Mothes	814-823	(1957)
Amino sugars (in German)	R. Kuhn et.al.,	824-849	(1957)
Surface layers of the sea urchin egg and their role in fertilization (in English)	J. Runnström	850-868	(1957)
Ommochromes, a class of natural phenoxazone dyestuffs (in German)	A. Butenandt	869-885	(1957)
Solvolyses of compounds of the $\Delta^{1,9}$-10-hydroxy methyl-octalines (in German)	J.W. Rowe et.al.,	886-898	(1957)
Preparation and properties of the o-formamino-benzoylacetic acids and the o-aminobenzoylacetic acids; two types of cellular products of tryptophanes and heteroaurins (in German)	C. Schöpf et.al.,	899-911	(1957)

FLUORINE CHEMISTRY

This is a collective volume, in English. Edited by J.H. Simons and published by Academic Press Inc. New York.

Title	Author	Reference
The action of elementary fluorine on organic compounds	L.A. Bigelow	<u>1</u>, 373-399 (1950)
Fluorocarbons and their production	J.H. Simons	<u>1</u>, 401-422 (1950)
Fluorocarbons - their properties and wartime development	T.J. Brice	<u>1</u>, 423-462 (1950)
Fluorocarbon derivatives	W.H. Pearlson	<u>1</u>, 463-522 (1950)
Aliphatic chlorofluoro compounds	J.D. Park	<u>1</u>, 523-552 (1950)
Organic compounds containing fluorine	P. Tarront	<u>2</u>, 213-320 (1950)
Metallic compounds containing fluorocarbon radicals and organometallic compounds containing fluorine	H.J. Eméleus	<u>2</u>, 321-332 (1950)
Fluorocarbon chemistry	T.J. Brice	<u>2</u>, 333-448 (1950)
The infrared spectra of fluorocarbons and related compounds	D.G. Wieblen	<u>2</u>, 449-503 (1950)

FORMATION AND TRAPPING OF FREE RADICALS

This is a collective volume, edited by A.M. Bass and H.P. Broida, and published by Academic Press, New York.

Title	Author	Reference	
History of radical trapping	F.O. Rice	1-14	(1960)
Radical formation and trapping from the gas phase	B.A. Thrush	15-45	(1960)
Radical formation and trapping in the solid phase	G.C. Pimentel	69-115	(1960)
Optical spectroscopy of trapped radicals	D.A. Ramsay	169-211	(1960)
Electron spin resonance studies of trapped radicals	C.K. Jen	213-255	(1960)
Chemical and physical studies of trapped radicals	J.W. Edwards	257-299	(1960)
Free radical trapping. Theoretical aspects	J.L. Jackson	327-346	(1960)
Trapped radicals in high polymer systems	H. Morawetz	363-386	(1960)
Trapped radicals in radiation damage	R.S. Alger	411-437	(1960)
Trapped radicals in biological processes	C.H. Bamford and A.D. Jenkins	439-474	(1960)
Chemical utilization of trapped radicals	D.E. Carr	475-500	(1960)

FRONTIERS IN CHEMISTRY

This is a collection of lectures delivered at Western Reserve University between 1942 and 1949 on the recent progress in certain fields of Chemistry. They were edited by R.E. Burk and O. Grummitt, and published by Interscience Publishers, Inc., New York. This series was discontinued in 1950.

Title	Author	Reference
The chemistry of large molecules		<u>1</u>, 308 pp. (1943)
The mechanism of polyreactions	H. Mark	<u>1</u>, 1-31 (1943)
The investigation of high polymers with x-rays	H. Mark	<u>1</u>, 33-71 (1943)
Organic chemistry of vinyl polymers	C.S. Marvel	<u>1</u>, 219-241 (1943)
Chemistry of cellulose and cellulose derivatives	E. Ott	<u>1</u>, 243-308 (1943)
The chemical background for engine research		<u>2</u>, 291 pp. (1943)
Advances in nuclear chemistry and theoretical organic chemistry		<u>3</u>, 161 pp. (1945)
Applications of isotopes in catalytic reactions at surfaces	H.S. Taylor	<u>3</u>, 19-42 (1945)
Resonance and organic chemistry	L.G.S. Brooker	<u>3</u>, 63-136 (1945)
The hydrogen bond and its significance to chemistry	W.H. Rodebush	<u>3</u>, 137-161 (1945)
Major instruments of science and their applications to chemistry		<u>4</u>, 147 pp. (1945)
Chemical architecture		<u>5</u>, 197 pp. (1948)
Applications of molecular geometry in the field of reaction mechanism	H.S. Taylor	<u>5</u>, 1-22 (1948)
Dipole moment, resonance and molecular structure	C.P. Smyth	<u>5</u>, 23-51 (1948)
Structure of coordination compounds	W.C. Fernelius	<u>5</u>, 53-100 (1948)
High molecular weight organic compounds		<u>6</u>, 324 pp. (1949)
The nature of elastomers	H.L. Fisher	<u>6</u>, 113-144 (1949)
Aspects of the structure and reactions of proteins	J.T. Edsall	<u>6</u>, 145-209 (1949)
Condensation polymerization and constitution of condensation polymers	P.J. Flory	<u>6</u>, 211-282 (1949)
Physical and chemical structure of phenoplasts	T.S. Carswell	<u>6</u>, 283-324 (1949)
Recent advances in analytical chemistry		<u>7</u>, 203 pp. (1949)
Inorganic analysis with organic reagents	J.H. Yoe	<u>7</u>, 31-47 (1949)
Fractionation, analysis, and purification of hydrocarbons	F.D. Rossini	<u>7</u>, 157-182 (1949)
Frontiers in colloid chemistry		<u>8</u>, 154 pp. (1950)

HETEROCYCLIC COMPOUNDS

This is a collection of review articles on heterocyclic compounds, in English. Edited by R.C. Elderfield and published by John Wiley and Sons, Inc. New York.

Title	Author	Reference
Ethylene and trimethylene oxides	S. Winstein and R.B. Henderson	1, 1-60 (1950)
Ethylenimine	J.S. Fruton	1, 61-78 (1950)
Derivatives of azete	S.A. Ballard and D.S. Melstrom	1, 79-118 (1950)
Furan	R.C. Elderfield and T.N. Dodd, Jr.	1, 119-207 (1950)
The chemistry of thiophene	F.F. Blicke	1, 208-276 (1950)
The chemistry of pyrrole and its derivatives	A.H. Corwin	1, 277-342 (1950)
Monocyclic prans, pyrones, thiapyrans, and thiapyrones	J. Fried	1, 343-396 (1950)
The chemistry of the pyridines	H.S. Mosher	1, 397-616 (1950)
Piperidines and partially hydrogenated pyridines	H.S. Mosher	1, 617-676 (1960)
Benzofuran and its derivatives	R.C. Elderfield and V.B. Meyer	2, 1-67 (1951)
Isobenzofuran, phthalan, and phthalide	R.C. Elderfield	2, 68-122 (1951)
Dibenzofuran (diphenylene oxide)	W.E. Parham	2, 123-144 (1951)
Thionaphthene	D.K. Fukushima	2, 145-163 (1951)
Dibenzothiophene	D.K. Fukushima	2, 164-172 (1951)
Coumarins	S. Wawzonek	2, 173-216 (1951)
Isocoumarins	S. Wawzonek	2, 217-228 (1951)
Chromones, flavones, and isoflavones	S. Wawzonek	2, 229-276 (1951)
Chromenols, chromenes, and benzopyrylium salts: the enthocyanins	S. Wawzonek	2, 277-342 (1951)
Chromamones, flavanones, chromanols, and flavanols: catechin, brazilin, and hematoxylin	S. Wawzonek	2, 343-392 (1951)
Chromans	S. Wawzonek	2, 393-418 (1951)
Xanthones, xanthenes, xanthydrols and xanthylium salts	S. Wawzonek	2, 419-500 (1951)
Fluorans, fluoresceins, and rhodamines	S. Wawzonek	2, 501-532 (1951)
Thiochromans and related compounds	D.S. Tarbell	2, 533-550 (1951)
The chemistry of indoles	P.L. Julian, E.W. Meyer and H.C. Printy	3, 1-274 (1952)

HETEROCYCLIC COMPOUNDS (Contd.)

Isoindole	R.C. Elderfield and T.N. Dodd, Jr.	3, 275-290 (1952)
The chemistry of carbazole	W. Freudenberg	3, 291-341 (1952)
Pyrindine, quinandine, and related compounds	R.C. Elderfield and E.T. Losin	3, 342-360 (1952)
Bicyclic systems with a nitrogen atom common to both rings	H.R. Ing	3, 361-430 (1952)
The chemistry of quinoline	R.C. Elderfield	4, 1-343 (1952)
Isoquinoline	W.J. Gensler	4, 344-490 (1952)
The acridines	A. Albert	4, 491-563 (1952)
Phenanthridine	L.P. Walls	4, 564-624 (1952)
Benzoquinolines	L.P. Walls	4, 625-662 (1952)
1,3-Dioxolane and derivatives	R.C. Elderfield and F.W. Short	5, 1-44 (1957)
Pyrazoles and related compounds	T.L. Jacobs	5, 45-161 (1957)
Indazoles	R.C. Elderfield	5, 162-193 (1957)
Imidazoles and condensed imidazoles	E.S. Schipper and A.R. Day	5, 194-297 (1957)
Oxazole and its derivatives	J.W. Cornforth	5, 298-417 (1957)
Benzoxazoles and related systems	J.W. Cornforth	5, 418-451 (1957)
Isoxazoles	R.A. Barnes	5, 452-483 (1957)
Thiazoles and benzothiazoles	J.M. Sprague and A.H. Land	5, 484-722 (1957)
The chemistry of the monocyclic dioxanes	C.B. Kremer and L.K. Rochen	6, 1-58 (1957)
Benzodioxanes	R.C. Elderfield	6, 59-74 (1957)
Sulfur analogs of the dioxanes	R.C. Elderfield	6, 75-100 (1957)
Pyridazines	T.L. Jacobs	6, 101-135 (1957)
Cinnolines and related compounds	T.L. Jacobs	6, 136-185 (1957)
Phthalazine and its derivatives	R.C. Elderfield and S.L. Wythe	6, 186-233 (1957)
Pyrimidine and its derivatives	G.W. Kenner and A. Todd	6, 234-323 (1957)
The chemistry of quinazoline	T.A. Williamson	6, 324-376 (1957)
The pyrazines and piperazines	Y.T. Pratt	6, 377-454 (1957)
The quinoxalines	Y.T. Pratt	6, 455-495 (1957)

HETEROCYCLIC COMPOUNDS (Contd.)

The monocyclic oxazines	N.H. Cromwell	6, 496-563 (1957)
The benzoxazines	R.C. Elderfield W.H. Todd and S. Gerber	6, 564-600 (1957)
Thiazines and benzothiazines	R.C. Elderfield and E.E. Harris	6, 601-623 (1957)
Phenazines, phenoxazines, and phenothiazines	D.E. Pearson	6, 624-726 (1957)

HIGH POLYMERS

This is a series of reviews and monographs on the chemistry, physics and technology of high polymeric substances. Of those volumes (e.g., 4, 5) which have had a second edition, the latter one has been indexed. The present editorial board is composed of H. Mark, C.S. Marvel, H.W. Melville and G.S. Whitby. Published by Interscience Publishers, Inc., New York.

Title	Author	Reference	
Collected papers of Wallace Hume Carothers on high polymeric substances	H. Mark and G.S. Whitby	1,	3-432 (1940)
Physical chemistry of high polymeric systems	H. Mark	2,	1-334 (1940)
High polymeric reactions. Their theory and practice	H. Mark and R. Raff	3,	3-436 (1941)
Natural and synthetic high polymers	K.H. Meyer	4,	1-833 (1950)
Cellulose and cellulose derivatives Vol. 5 is in three parts: Part I, pp. 7-509 (1954); Part 2, 511-1055 (1954); Part III 1057-1483 (1955)	E. Ott H.M. Spurlin and M.W. Grafflin (Editors)	5,	Part I 1-509 (1954)
Chemical nature of cellulose and its derivatives	C.B. Purves	5,	29-215 (1954)
Structure and properties of cellulose fibers	H. Mark	5,	217-441 (1954)
Properties of substances associated with cellulose in nature	H.F. Lewis and G.J. Ritter	5,	443-509 (1954)
Derivatives of cellulose	H.M. Spurlin	5,	673-1055 (1954)
Mechanical behavior of high polymers	T. Alfrey Jr.	6,	1-570 (1948)
Phenoplasts	T.S. Carswell	7,	1-253 (1947)
Copolymerization	T. Alfrey Jr. J.J. Bohrer and H. Mark	8,	1-252 (1952)
Emulsion polymerization	F.A. Bovey et.al.,	9,	1-414 (1955)
Polymer processes	C.E. Schildknecht	10,	1-878 (1956)
Introduction to free radical polymerization	J.H. Baxendale	10,	1-30 (1956)
Ionic polymerizations	G.E. Schildknecht	10,	199-234 (1956)
Polyamides and polyesters	D.G. Bannerman and E.E. Magat	10,	235-294 (1956)
Condensation with formaldehyde	T.J. Suen	10,	295-350 (1956)
Cellulose and cellulose derivatives	B.G. Ránby and S.A. Rydholm	10,	351-428 (1956)
Epoxy resins	S.S. Stivala	10,	429-474 (1956)

HIGH POLYMERS (Contd.)

Title	Author(s)	Citation
Polysulfide polymers	E.M. Fettes and J.S. Jorczak	10, 475-498 (1956)
New adhesives	W.J. Powers	10, 499-524 (1956)
Polyethylene	R.A.V. Raff and J.B. Allison	11, 1-522 (1956)
Analytical chemistry of polymers. Analysis of monomers and polymeric materials - plastics, resins, rubbers and fibers	G.M. Kline (Editor)	12, 1-628 (1959)
Acrylic plastics	E.L. Stanley	12, 1-16 (1959)
Alkyds	J.R. Jones Jr.	12, 17-48 (1959)
Amino resins	P.R. Averell	12, 49-95 (1959)
Cellulose derivatives	P.H. Ericksen and B.F. Brown	12, 97-122 (1959)
Epoxy resins	R.E. Burge Jr. and B.P. Geyer	12, 123-164 (1959)
Ethylene and fluoroethylene polymers	R.R. Voter	12, 165-196 (1959)
Furan resins	L.H. Brown	12, 197-219 (1959)
Natural resins	C.M. Ferri	12, 221-238 (1959)
Phenolic resins	H.E. Riley	12, 239-271 (1959)
Polyamides	H.J. Frey and J.R. Knox	12, 273-293 (1959)
Polyesters	E.E. Parker	12, 295-307 (1959)
Proteins	H.K. Salzberg and D. Fergus	12, 309-342 (1959)
Rubbers (elastomers)	W.P. Tyler	12, 343-360 (1959)
Silicones	J.A. McHard	12, 361-397 (1959)
Styrene monomers and polymers	E.N. Luce	12, 399-448 (1959)
Vinyl polymers and copolymers	C.J. Kennett	12, 449-488 (1959)
Ion exchange resins	S. Fisher and R. Kunin	12, 489-530 (1959)
Plastisizers	C.A. Dentz and R.S. Clark	12, 531-556 (1959)
Synthetic and natural fibers	M.L. Staples	12, 557-597 (1959)

HYDROGEN BONDING

These are the proceedings of the symposium on "Hydrogen Bonding" held in Ljubljana, 1957. Edited by D. Hadži and H.W. Thompson, published by Pergamon Press, London.

Title	Author	Reference
Contribution to the study of aromatic molecules considered as proton-acceptors (in French)	M.L. Josien and G. Sourisseau	129-137 (1959)
Infra-red spectroscopic study of intra- and inter-molecular hydrogen bonding in methyl ureas (in German)	H.J. Becher	139-142 (1959)
On hydrogen bonds between nitro and hydroxy or amino groups (in English)	T. Urbański	143-146 (1959)
The tunnelling of the protons as a cause of the splitting of hydroxyl stretching bonds (in English)	R. Blinc and D. Hadži	147-153 (1959)
Infra-red studies of hydrogen bonding in methanol, ethanol and t-butanol (in English)	E.D. Becker	155-162 (1959)
Determination by infra-red spectroscopy of some molecular complexes of pyrrol and phenol (in French)	N. Fuson, P. Pineau and M.L. Josien	169-175 (1959)
Infra-red studies of solvent interaction with secondary amines (in English)	R.E. Dodd and G.W. Stephenson	177-182 (1959)
Effect of hydrogen bond formation on the electronic spectra of phenolic substances (in English)	A. Burawoy	259-276 (1959)
Hydrogen bridges in spiro (4,4) nonanediols (in English)	Th. Bürer and H.H. Günthard	301-305 (1959)
The hydrogen bonds and the structure of naphthazarin (1,4-dihydroxy-5,8-naphthoquinone) (in English)	R. Blinc, D. Hadži and E. Pirkmajer	333-338 (1959)
The influence of hydrogen bonding on tantomerism in diazoaminobenzenes (in English)	V.C. Farmer, R.L. Hardie and R.H. Thompson	475-482 (1959)

INTERNATIONAL CONGRESSES OF BIOCHEMISTRY

These are the collection of conferences and reports presented at the International Congresses of Biochemistry, and published by various publishers.

Title	Author	Reference
Second international congress of biochemistry, held in Paris, 1952. Published as a supplement to the "Bulletin de la Societe de Chimie Biologique" 35, 1953 by Masson et Cie., Paris.		
The initial steps in the enzymatic degradation of proteins by enzymes (in French)	K. Linderstrøm-Lang	100-116 (1953)
Third international congress of biochemistry, held in Brussels, 1955. Edited by C. Liebecq, published by Academic Press, New York.		
The isolation and proof of structure of the vasopressins and the synthesis of octapeptide amides with pressor antidiuretic activity	V. duVigneaud	49-54 (1956)
Chemistry and biochemistry of antimetabolites related to the purines	G.H. Hitchings and G.B. Elion	55-61 (1956)
The chemistry of mucopolysaccharides	R.W. Jeanloz	65-72 (1956)
On the mode of combination of carbohydrates with amino acid grouping in mucopolysaccharides and mucoproteins	H. Masamune	72-77 (1956)
The chemistry of the ribonucleic acids	R. Markham	144-150 (1956)
Fourth international congress of biochemistry, held in Vienna, 1958. The whole collection was edited in 15 volumes by O. Hoffman-Ostenhof, and published by Pergamon Press, New York. Individual editors were responsible for each of the symposia.		
Carbohydrate chemistry of substances of biological interest	M.L. Wolfrom (Editor)	1, 206 pp. (1959)
Hemicelluloses	R.C. Whistler and J.L. Sanella	1-14 (1959)
Seaweed polysaccharides	C. Araki	15-30 (1959)
Plant gums	E.L. Hirst	31-51 (1959)
Carbohydrates of nucleic acids	M. Stacey	107-122 (1959)
The sugars of cardioactive glycosides (in German)	T. Reichstein	124-139 (1959)
The non reductive oligosaccharides containing galactose (in French)	J.E. Courtois	140-159 (1959)
Phenyl hydrazones and related sugar derivatives (in German)	L. Mester	160-180 (1959)

INTERNATIONAL CONGRESSES OF BIOCHEMISTRY (Contd.)

Biochemistry of wood	K. Kratzl G. Billek (Editors)	2,	285 pp.	(1959)
Conifer chemistry and taxonomy of conifers	H. Erdtman	2,	1-	(1959)
Quinoid structures and benzyl alcohol groups in the chemistry and biochemistry of lignin (in German)	E. Adler	2,	137-	(1959)
Isolation and determination of active fractions (phenylpropanes) of lignin after incorporation of labelled products. (In German)	G. Billek	2,	207-	(1959)
Plant steroids and related substances	E. Mosettig (Editor)	4,	296 pp.	(1959)
Plant steroids and related substances	C. Djerassi	4,	1-20	(1959)
C_{21}-steroids of the plant kingdom	R. Tschesche	4,	21-27	(1959)
Synthesis of all trans-squalene	J. W. Cornforth R.H. Cornforth and K.K. Mathew	4,	59-60	(1959)
Hydroxylation of steroids in position 9. (in German)	A. Schubert	4,	120-122	(1959)

INTERNATIONAL CONGRESSES OF PURE AND APPLIED CHEMISTRY

These include the main congress lecture and lectures delivered in the individual sections. Published in June 1955 as a supplement to "Experientia", by Verlag Birkhäuser, Basel.

Title	Author	Reference	
Fourteenth international congress of pure and applied chemistry, held in Zurich, 1955. Supplement No. 2			
Oxytocin, the principal oxytocic hormone of the posterior pituitary gland: its isolation, structure and synthesis (in English)	V. Du Vigneaud	9-26	(1955)
Photo-oxidation (in French)	C. Dufraisse	27-48	(1955)
Double reactivity and tautomerism (in French)	N.A. Nesmeyanov	49-68	(1955)
Developments in the theory of steric hindrance (in English)	C.K. Ingold	69-85	(1955)
New developments in the diene-synthesis (in German)	K. Alder	86-118	(1955)
Some recent progress in conformational analysis (in English)	D.H.R. Barton	121-136	(1955)
Some recent aspects of carbonium ion behavior (in English)	S. Winstein	137-155	(1955)
The chemistry of heartwood constituents of conifers and their taxonomic importance (in English)	H. Erdtman	156-180	(1955)
Comparative study of some lyso-proteins belonging to the group of the lysozymes (in French)	C. Fromageot	181-193	(1955)
Natural compounds as a starting point for the synthesis of drugs (in English)	P. Pratesi	194-212	(1955)
The total synthesis of strychnine (in English)	R.B. Woodward	213-228	(1955)
Some recent developments in the chemistry of photographic sensitizing dyes (in English)	L.G.S. Brooker	229-257	(1955)
Synthesis following possible paths of biogenesis (in English)	R.T. Seshadri	258-273	(1955)
Aluminum in organic chemistry (in German)	K. Ziegler	274-287	(1955)
Fifteenth international conference of pure and applied chemistry. Supplement No. 5, held at Lisbon, 1956		240 pp.	(1956)
Gas liquid chromatography (in English)	A.J.P. Martin		(1956)
Development, present state, and prospects of organic spot test analysis (in English)	F. Feigl		(1956)
Organic complexing agents (in German)	G.S. Schwarzenbach		(1956)
Sixteenth international conference of pure and applied chemistry. Supplement No. 7 to Experientia, held in Paris, 1957		355 pp.	(1957)
Stereospecific catalysis and stereoisomeric polymers. Preparation of fibers, plastics and new elastomers (in French)	G. Natta	21-59	(1957)
Research on transannular eliminations and substitutions with the aid of isotopes (in German)	V. Prelog	261-274	(1957)

INTERNATIONAL CONGRESSES OF PURE AND APPLIED CHEMISTRY (Contd.)

The initiation of organic chain reactions (in English)	P.D. Bartlett	275-290	(1957)
Complex formation and reactivity in metallorganic chemistry (in German)	G. Wittig	291-305	(1957)
Chemistry of natural tropolone and allied compounds (in English)	T. Nozoe	306-327	(1957)
Structure of some delphinium alkaloids (in French)	L. Marion	328-342	(1957)
Electronic photoreactions of organic dyes (in French)	A. Terenin	343-355	(1957)

Seventeenth international congress of pure and applied chemistry. Held at München, 1959. Published by Butterworths, London, and Verlag Chemie, GMBH, Weinheim/Bergstrs.

Mechanism of the formation of the metal-carbon bond. Some aspects of the reactivity of organometallics of heavy metals (in German)	A. Reutow	1, 11-39	(1960)
Compounds of fluorocarbon radicals with metals and non-metals (in English)	H.J. Emeléus	1, 82-94	(1960)
Aspects of the chemistry of carbonyls, cyanides and olefin complexes (in English)	G. Wilkinson	1, 127-135	(1960)
From structure to synthesis of organometallic compounds (in English)	E.G. Rochow	1, 136-144	(1960)
The reactions of alkali metal hydrides and borohydrides with Lewis acids of boron and aluminium (in English)	H.C. Brown	1, 167-182	(1960)
New natural dyes, their biogenesis and physiological significance (in German)	A. Butenandt	2, 11-31	(1960)
The biosynthesis and structure of tyrosine melanin (in English)	J. Harley-Mason	2, 35-39	(1960)
Aspects of the biosynthesis of pteridines (in English)	H.S. Forrest	2, 40-51	(1960)
The biogenesis of carotenoids in plants (in German)	E.C. Grob	2, 52-72	(1960)
The biosynthesis of flavonoids and anthocyanins (in English)	A.J. Birch	2, 73-84	(1960)
The biogenesis of porphyrin (in English)	A. Neuberger	2, 85-98	(1960)
Synthesis of peptides with hormonal activity (in German)	R. Schwyzer	2, 130-142	(1960)
Cyclic peptides with antibiotic action (in English)	J.C. Sheehan	2, 143-149	(1960)
Peptide regions of identical structure in proteins (in English)	F. Šorm	2, 150-162	(1960)

INTERNATIONAL SYMPOSIUM ON MACROMOLECULAR CHEMISTRY

These are the proceedings of the symposium held in Prague, September 1957, and published by Pergamon Press, London, 1957. Also published as supplement No. 2 to "Tetrahedron".

Title	Author	Reference
Biological polymers (in English)	P. Doty	5-27 (1957)
Progress in the field of high polymers (in English)	H. Mark	28-34 (1957)
Chemical rearrangements in synthetic polymers (in German)	W. Kern	126-140 (1957)
Mechanism and kinetics of the polymerization of α-olefins (in French)	G. Natta, F. Danusso and I. Pasquon	191-218 (1957)
Cationic polymerization (in English)	D.C. Pepper	219-227 (1957)
The polymerization reaction as a tool in the study of kinetics of free radical reactions (in German)	G.V. Schulz	228-249 (1957)
Mechanism and kinetics of chain degradation (in English)	R. Simha	250-263 (1957)
Metallo-organic compounds from the viewpoint of macromolecular synthesis (in German)	K. Ziegler	295-306 (1957)

ION EXCHANGERS IN ORGANIC CHEMISTRY AND BIOCHEMISTRY

This is a collective volume, edited by C. Calmon and T.R.E. Kressman, published by Interscience Publishers, Inc., New York.

Title	Author	Reference
Separation of amino acids	P.B. Hamilton	255-298 (1957)
Separation of peptides	W.A. Schroeder	299-317 (1957)
Chromatography of proteins and nucleic acids	H.A. Sober and E.A. Peterson	318-344 (1957)
Nucleic acid derivatives	W.E. Cohn	345-359 (1957)
Chromatographic investigations of non-steroid hormones	I.D. Raake and C.H. Li	360-376 (1957)
Separation of carbohydrates	J.X. Khym, L.P. Zill and W.E. Cohn	392-417 (1957)
Isolation and purification of antibiotics	J.L. Wachtel and E.T. Stiller	502-519 (1957)
Vitamins	D.J. Hennessy	520-532 (1957)
Alkaloids	L. Saunders	533-547 (1957)
Ion exchangers in organic chemistry	H.F. Walton	640-657 (1957)
Ion exchangers as catalysts	M.J. Astle	658-687 (1957)

A LABORATORY MANUAL OF ANALYTICAL METHODS OF PROTEIN CHEMISTRY (INCLUDING POLYPEPTIDES)

This is a collection of review articles on experimental methods and results in the field of protein chemistry, edited by P. Alexander and R.J. Block and published by Pergamon Press, New York.

Title	Author	Reference
Separation of proteins	S. Keller and R.J. Block	<u>1</u>, 1-30 (1960)
Isolation of biologically active proteins	K. Okunuki	<u>1</u>, 31-64 (1960)
Fractionation of proteins by absorption and ion exchange	S. Keller and R.J. Block	<u>1</u>, 65-87 (1960)
A variable gradient device for chromatography	E.A. Peterson and H.A. Sober	<u>1</u>, 88-102 (1960)
Fractionation and characterization by dialysis	L.C. Craig	<u>1</u>, 103-119 (1960)
Multi-membrane electrodecantation	A. Polson	<u>1</u>, 161-191 (1960)
Zonal density gradient electrophoresis	H. Svensson	<u>1</u>, 193-244 (1960)
Amino acid analysis of protein hydrolysates	R.J. Block	<u>2</u>, 1-57 (1960)
The estimation of side-chain groups in the intact protein	L.G.D. Hamilton	<u>2</u>, 59-100 (1960)
Deuterium and ^{18}O exchange	A.A. Heidt G. Johansen and K. Linderstrøm-Lang	<u>2</u>, 101-130 (1960)
Dye-binding methods	R.M. Rosenberg	<u>2</u>, 131-168 (1960)
Electrophoresis of proteins in liquid media	B.S. Magdoff	<u>2</u>, 169-214 (1960)
Paper electrophoresis	C. Wunderly	<u>2</u>, 215-230 (1960)
The technique of immuno-electrophoresis in agar gel	C. Wunderly	<u>2</u>, 231-243 (1960)
Optical rotation	A. Todd	<u>2</u>, 245-283 (1960)
Infra-red spectra	R.D.B. Fraser	<u>2</u>, 285-351 (1960)
Analytical information from titration curves	A.W. Kenchington	<u>2</u>, 353-388 (1960)
X-ray diffraction	H. Zahn and H. Dietrich	<u>2</u>, 389-420 (1960)
Methods of sequence analysis in proteins	J.I. Harris and V.M. Ingram	<u>2</u>, 421-499 (1960)

MATTHEWS' TEXTILE FIBERS

This is a collective volume, edited by H.R. Manesberger in its sixth edition; published by J. Wiley and Sons, Inc., New York.

Title	Author	Reference
Cellulose; sources, constitution and chemical properties	P.C. Shere	53-101 (1954)
Wool; chemical nature and properties	W.V. Bergen	612-675 (1954)

MEDICINAL CHEMISTRY

This is a series of reviews prepared under the auspices of the division of Medicinal Chemistry of the American Chemical Society. Volume 1 was edited by C.M. Suter, Volume 2 by F.F. Blicke and C.M. Suter, and volumes 3 and 4 by F.F. Blicke and R.H. Cox. Published by John Wiley and Sons, Inc., New York.

Title	Author	Reference
Antithyroid compounds	G.W. Anderson	1, 2-150 (1951)
Antispasmodics. Derivatives of carboxylic acids	R.R. Burtner	1, 151-220 (1951)
Antibiotics from plants	C.J. Cavallito	1, 221-279 (1951)
Benzoates and substituted benzoates as local anaesthetics	T.P. Carney	1, 280-389 (1951)
Analgesics: Part A. Aralkylamines	E.J. Fellows and G.E. Ullyot	1, 390-437 (1951)
Analgesics: Part B. Partial structures related to morphine	J. Lee	1, 438-466 (1951)
Some chemical aspects of the cardiac glycosides	A. Stoll	2, 1-24 (1956)
Supplement to some chemical aspects of the cardiac glycosides	T.L. Johnson	2, 24-33 (1956)
Synthetic estrogens	J.A. Hogg and J. Korman	2, 34-217 (1956)
Analgesics. Arylpiperidine derivatives	C.M. Suter	2, 218-233 (1956)
β-Haloethylamine adrenergic blocking agents; chemistry and structure-activity relationships	G.E. Ullyot and J.F. Kerwin	2, 234-308 (1956)
Methadone and related analgesics	T.P. Carney	3, 1-41 (1956)
Quarternary ammonium germicides	P.L. de Benneville	3, 42-174 (1956)
Non-mercurial diuretics	V. Papesch and E.F. Schroeder	3, 175-237 (1956)
Synthetic analogs of physostigmine	A. Stempel and J.A. Aeschlimann	3, 238-340 (1956)
Barbituric acid hypnotics	W.J. Doran	4, 1-325 (1959)

METHODEN DER ORGANISCHEN CHEMIE

(Houben-Weyl) Fourth Edition, edited by E. Müller and published by G. Thieme, Verlag, Stuttgart, Germany.

This well-known work, initiated by T. Weyl and continued by G. Houben (second and third editions, 1921 and 1925) is now in its fourth greatly enlarged edition. In the listing below, the articles on general methods in volume 1 are not cited by separate titles, although they are contributed by various authors. This entire series is an indispensable compendium, and volumes continue to appear in it to complete the predetermined plan.

Title	Author	Reference
General laboratory methods		1/1 3-960 (1958)
General laboratory methods		1/2 3-761 (1959)
Carcinogenic substances		1/2 934-942 (1959)
Purification of organic products		1/2 769-868 (1959)
Organic elemental analysis	H. Roth	2, 9-248 (1953)
Determination of organic functions	H. Roth et. al.,	2, 249-710 (1953)
Gas analysis	H. Kienitz	2, 715-782 (1953)
Determination of physical constants	H. Kienitz	2, 783-825 (1953)
Thermal analysis and determination of complexes	H. Rheinboldt	2, 827-865 (1953)
Chromatographic analysis	T. Wieland and F. Turba	2, 867-910 (1953)
Thermodynamic methods	W. Luck	3/1 3-98 (1955)
Kinetic determinations	R. Huisgen	3/1 99-162 (1955)
Density, solubility and vapor pressure determinations	H. Kienitz	3/1 163-326 (1955)
Molecular weight determinations	H. Rast	3/1 327-370 (1955)
Molecular weight determinations of macromolecules	G.V. Schulz et. al.,	3/1 371-448 (1955)
Surface tension	K.L. Wolf and R. Wolff	3/1 449-480 (1955)
Calorimetry	F. Becker and A. Magnus	3/1 481-544 (1955)
Use of atomic models to determine and study molecular structure	G. Briegleb	3/1 545-572 (1955)
Mass spectroscopy	L. Jenckel and E. Dörnenburg	3/1 693-752 (1955)
Use of radioactive isotopes	H. Götte	3/1 753-838 (1955)
Use of non-radioactive isotopes	H. Hoyer	3/1 839-895 (1955)
Conductivity	E. Asmus	3/11 3-20 (1955)

METHODEN DER ORGANISCHEN CHEMIE (Contd.)

pH determinations	K. Cruse and U. Fritze	3/11	21-100	(1955)
Potentiometry	E. Abrahamczik	3/11	135-206	(1955)
Electrophoresis	H.J. Antweiler	3/11	207-255	(1955)
Electrochemical potential of organic compounds	M.v. Stackelberg	3/11	255-294	(1955)
Determination of the dielectric properties	O. Fuchs and F. Würstlin	3/11	351-406	(1955)
Refractometry and polarimetry	E. Asmus	3/11	407-442	(1955)
Fluorescence and phosphorescence	T. Förster	3/11	443-476	(1955)
X-ray analysis	W. Kast	3/11	541-592	(1955)
Absorption spectroscopy in the visible and the ultraviolet	M. Pestemer and D. Brück	3/11	593-764	(1955)
Raman spectroscopy	J. Goubeau	3/11	765-794	(1955)
Infra-red spectroscopy	H. Hoyer	3/11	795-900	(1955)
Micro-wave spectroscopy	R. Honerjäger	3/11	901-916	(1955)
Magnetochemical methods	E. Müller	3/11	917-982	(1955)
Ultrasounds	W. Schaaffs	3/11	982-1000	(1955)
Acid-base catalysis	H. Henecka	4/11	1-59	(1955)
Catalysis on complex cations and anions	G. Hesse	4/11	61-136	(1955)
Methods for the preparation of catalysts and mixed catalysts	K. Wimmer	4/11	137-240	(1955)
Practice of heterogeneous catalytic reactions	G. Schiller and H. Kroper	4/11	241-433	(1955)
General methods for carrying out chemical reactions	H. Koch	4/11	435-455	(1955)
Electrochemical reactions	F. Müller	4/11	457-503	(1955)
Methods for preparing optically-active compounds from inactive material	W. Theilacker	4/11	505-538	(1955)
Preparation of isotopically-labelled organic compounds	F. Weygand and H. Simon	4/11	539-728	(1955)
Methods for preparing and reacting large ring systems	K. Ziegler	4/11	729-822	(1955)
Preparation of bromo compounds	A. Roedig	5/IV	13-515	(1960)
Preparation of iodo compounds	A. Roedig	5/IV	517-677	(1960)
Reaction and transformations of chloro, bromo and iodo compounds	N. Kreutzkamp H. Meerwein and R. Stroh	5/IV	679-775	(1960)
Oxygen compounds II: aldehydes	O. Bayer	7/1	1-556	(1954)
Oxygen compounds III: peroxides	R. Criegee	_8_	1-74	(1952)
Derivatives of carbonic acids	S. Peterson and H.S. Piepenbrink	_8_	75-245	(1952)

METHODEN DER ORGANISCHEN CHEMIE (Contd.)

Title	Author	Vol.	Pages	Year
Nitriles and isonitriles (including fulminic acid)	P. Kurtz	8,	247-359	(1952)
Carbonic acids and decarboxylation	H. Henecka and E. Ott	8,	359-501	(1952)
Carbonic acid esters	H. Henecka	8,	503-646	(1952)
Functional N-derivatives of the carboxyl group	H. Henecka and P. Kurtz	8,	647-713	(1952)

Volume 9: Sulfur, selenium and tellurium compounds

Title	Author	Vol.	Pages	Year
Mercaptans and thiophenols	A. Schöberl and A. Wagner	9,	3-48	(1955)
Alkyl hydrogen polysulfides	H. Böhme	9,	49-54	(1955)
Disulfides, polysulfides and thioethers	A. Schöberl and A. Wagner	9,	55-148	(1955)
Ethylene sulfides	A. Schönberg	9,	149-170	(1955)
Sulfonium compounds	J. Goerdeler	9,	171-194	(1955)
Mercaptals and mercaptols	A. Schöberl and A. Wagner	9,	125-206	(1955)
Sulfoxides and sulfenamides	A. Schöberl and A. Wagner	9,	207-222	(1955)
Sulfones and sulfoximines	A. Schöberl and A. Wagner	9,	222-262	(1955)
Sulfenic acid and sulfenic acid derivatives	A. Schöberl and A. Wagner	9,	263-284	(1955)
Aliphatic sulfinic acid	M. Quaedvlieg	9,	285-298	(1955)
Aromatic sulfinic acid	F. Mott	9,	299-342	(1955)
Aliphatic sulfonic acid and their derivatives	M. Quaedvlieg	9,	343-406	(1955)
Sulfo chlorination according to C.F. Reed	H. Eckoldt	9,	407-408	(1955)
Aromatic sulfonic acids, anhydrides, halides, esters and functional N-derivatives	S. Muth	9,	429-682	(1955)
Thiol sulfones and thiol sulfinic acid esters, thiol aldehydes, thiol ketones, thiol acids and their derivatives	A. Schöberl and A. Wagner	9,	83-772	(1955)
Sulfur-containing carbonic acid derivatives	M. Bögemann et.al.,	9,	773-916	(1955)
Preparation and reactions of selenium and tellurium compounds	H. Rheinboldt	9,	917-1210	(1955)
Nomenclature of sulfur compounds	A. Wagner	9,	1211-1216	(1955)
Nitrogen compounds. II. Direct introduction of the amino group	F. Möller	11/1	9-23	(1957)
Amination by displacement reaction	G. Spielberger et.al.,	11/1	24-266	(1957)
Amination by addition reactions	F. Möller	11/1	267-340	(1957)
Amination by reduction	F. Schröter and F. Möller	11/1	341-730	(1957)

METHODEN DER ORGANISCHEN CHEMIE (Contd.)

Amination by condensation	R. Schröter	11/1	731-804	(1957)
Amination by reaction of organometallic compounds	R. Schröter	11/1	804-825	(1957)
Amination by rearrangement reaction	F. Möller	11/1	826-925	(1957)
Amination by scission	F. Möller	11/1	926-993	(1957)
Amination by special methods	F. Möller	11/1	994-1004	(1957)
Preparation of amino compounds from other amines by preservation of the amino group	G. Pieper	11/1	1005-1025	(1957)
Preparative separation of primary, secondary and tertiary amines	R. Schröter	11/1	1026-1033	(1957)
Properties and manipulation of ammonia	F. Möller	11/1	1034-1038	(1957)
The reactions of amines	H. Freytag et.al.,	11/11	1-222	(1958)
1,2-1,3-alkyleneimines	H. Bestian	11/11	223-268	(1958)
Amino acids and their derivatives	T. Wieland et.al.,	11/11	269-510	(1958)
Lactams	H. Schnell J. Nentwig and T. Wieland	11/11	511-586	(1958)
Quaternary ammonium compounds	J. Goerdeler	11/11	587-640	(1958)
Nitrogen sulfur compounds	A. Dorlars	11/11	641-752	(1958)

MICROCHEMISTRY: INTERNATIONAL SYMPOSIUM

These are the proceedings of the International Symposium on Microchemistry, held at Birmingham in 1958 and published by Pergamon Press, London (1960).

Title	Author	Reference
Specific and selective organic reagents	F.J. Welcher	6-21 (1960)
Forty years of quantitative organic microanalysis	H. Lieb	73-85 (1960)
Organic functional group analysis - the alkoxyl determination	W.I. Stephen	163-170 (1960)
Chromatography of the larger molecules	T.S.G. Jones	243-247 (1960)
Current trends in infrared structural determinations	L.J. Bellamy and R.L. Williams	369-372 (1960)

MODERN COORDINATION CHEMISTRY. PRINCIPLES AND METHODS

Edited by J. Lewis and R.G. Wilkins and published by Interscience Publishers Inc., New York.

Title	Author	Reference
The isomerism of complex compounds	R.G. Wilkins and M.J.G. Williams	174-228 (1960)
The infra-red spectra of transitional metal complexes	F.A. Cotton	301-399 (1960)

MOLECULAR STRUCTURE AND ORGANOLEPTIC QUALITY

These are the proceedings of a Symposium held at Geneva, May 1957, by the Society of Chemical Industry, London. Published by the Society as S.C.I. Monograph No. 1.

Title	Author	Page
Facts old and new concerning relationship between molecular structure and odour	M. Stoll	1-11
The relationship between the stereochemistry and odourous properties of organic substances	Y.-R. Naves	38-51
Structure and odour	M.G.J. Beets	54-90

NON-BENZENOID AROMATIC COMPOUNDS

This is a collective volume, edited by D. Ginsburg and published by Interscience Publishers Inc., New York.

Title	Author	Reference
Aromaticity	D.P. Craig	1-42 (1959)
Cyclobutadiene and related compounds	W. Baker and J.F.W. McOmie	43-105 (1959)
Compounds derived from cyclopentadiene	P.L. Pauson	107-140 (1959)
Pentalene and heptalene	E.D. Bergmann	141-169 (1959)
Azulenes	E. Heilbronner	171-276 (1959)
Pathways to azulenes	W. Keller-Schierlein and E. Heilbronner	277-337 (1959)
Tropones and tropolones	T. Nozoe	339-463 (1959)
Cyclooctatetraene	R.A. Raphael	465-476 (1959)
Cyclopolyolefins	W. Baker and J.F.W. McOmie	477-490 (1959)

NMR AND EPR SPECTROSCOPY

These are the proceedings of the third annual workshop held at Palo Alto, 1959. Published by Pergamon Press, New York.

Title	Author	Reference
High resolution NMR as a structure determining tool	J.N. Shoolery	100-121 (1960)
High resolution NMR as an analytical tool	J.N. Shoolery	122-139 (1960)
Chemical applications of EPR	L.H. Piette	207-223 (1960)
Photochemical studies with EPR	L.H. Piette	241-251 (1960)

NUCLEIC ACIDS

This is a collection of review articles on the chemistry and biochemistry of nucleic acids, edited by E. Chargaff and J.N. Davidson, published by Academic Press, Inc., New York.

Title	Author	Reference
Chemistry of ribose and desoxyribose	W.G. Overend and M. Stacey	1, 9-80 (1955)
Chemistry of purines and pyrimidines	A. Bendich	1, 81-136 (1955)
Chemistry of nucleosides and nucleotides	J. Baddiley	1, 137-190 (1955)
Isolation and composition of the desoxypentose nucleic acids and of the corresponding nucleoproteins	E. Chargaff	1, 307-372 (1955)
Isolation and composition of the pentose nucleic acids and of the corresponding nucleoproteins	B. Magasanik	1, 373-408 (1955)
Evidence on the nature of the chemical bond in nucleic acids	D.M. Brown and A.R. Todd	1, 409-446 (1955)
Deoxyribonucleic acids as macromolecules	C.L. Sadron	3, 1-38 (1960)
Photochemistry of nucleic acids and their constituents	D. Shugar	3, 39-104 (1960)
Chemical and enzymic synthesis of polynucleotides	H.G. Khorana	3, 105-146 (1960)
Chemistry of nucleic acids of microorganisms	A.N. Belozersky and A.S. Spirin	3, 147-186 (1960)

ORGANIC CHEMISTRY. AN ADVANCED TREATISE

This is a collection of reviews on the general aspects of organic chemistry, initiated and edited by H. Gilman. Volumes I and II, which first appeared in 1938, were revised in a second edition (1943). The earlier volumes are not indexed below. Volumes III and IV appeared in 1953. Published by John Wiley and Sons Inc., New York.

Title	Author	Reference
The reactions of aliphatic hydrocarbons	G. Egloff	1, 1-64 (1943)
Alicyclic compounds and the theory of strain	R.C. Fuson	1, 65-116 (1943)
Theory of the structure and reactions of aromatic compounds	L.F. Fieser	1, 117-213 (1943)
Stereoisomerism	R.L. Shriner, R. Adams and C.S. Marvel	1, 214-488 (1943)
Organometallic compounds	H. Gilman	1, 489-580 (1943)
Free radicals	W.E. Bachmann	1, 581-630 (1943)
Unsaturation and conjugation	C.F.H. Allen and A.H. Blatt	1, 631-700 (1943)
Synthetic polymers	C.S. Marvel and E.C. Horning	1, 701-778 (1943)
Catalytic hydrogenation and hydrogenolysis	H. Adkins and R.L. Shriner	1, 779-834 (1943)
Organic sulfur compounds	R. Connor	1, 835-943 (1943)
Aliphatic fluorides	A.L. Henne	1, 944-964 (1943)
Molecular rearrangements	E.S. Wallis	1, 965-1031 (1943)
Comparison of chemical reactivity	H. Adkins	1, 1032-1077 (1943)
Natural amino acids	H.T. Clarke	2, 1079-1165 (1943)
Alkaloids	L. Small	2, 1166-1258 (1943)
The chemistry of the porphyrins	A.H. Corwin	2, 1259-1292 (1943)
Chlorophyll	C.C. Steele	2, 1293-1314 (1943)
The anthocyanins and the flavones	K.P. Link	2, 1315-1340 (1943)
The steroids	W.H. Strain	2, 1341-1531 (1943)
Carbohydrates I	M.L. Wolfrom	2, 1532-1604 (1943)
Carbohydrates II	A.L. Raymond	2, 1605-1663 (1943)
Carbohydrates III - cellulose	E. Heuser	2, 1664-1719 (1943)
Constitution and physical properties of organic compounds	J.A. Leermakers and A. Weissberger	2, 1720-1805 (1943)
The redistribution reaction	G. Calingaert and H.A. Beatty	2, 1806-1820 (1943)

ORGANIC CHEMISTRY. AN ADVANCED TREATISE (Contd.)

Modern electronic concepts of valence	J.R. Johnson	2, 1821-1942	(1943)
The significance of resonance to the nature of the chemical bond and the structure of molecules	L. Pauling	2, 1943-1983	(1943)
The study of organic reaction mechanisms	P.D. Bartlett	3, 1-121	(1953)
Applications of infrared and ultraviolet spectra to organic chemistry	F.A. Miller	3, 122-177	(1953)
Lipids	J.C. Cowan and H.E. Carter	3, 178-242	(1953)
Organic dyes	H.W. Grimmel	3, 243-391	(1953)
Some aspects of chemotherapy	H.R. Ing	3, 392-532	(1953)
Antibiotics	L.C. Cheney	3, 533-580	(1953)
The terpenes	R.H. Eastman and C.R. Noller	4, 581-722	(1953)
Heterocyclic chemistry	R.H. Wiley	4, 723-900	(1953)
Starch	W.Z. Hassid	4, 901-950	(1953)
Chemistry of explosives	G.F. Wright	4, 951-1000	(1953)
Reactions of organic gases under pressure	W.E. Hanford and D.E. Sargent	4, 1001-1119	(1953)
Oxidation processes	W.A. Waters	4, 1120-1245	(1953)

ORGANOMETALLIC CHEMISTRY

This is a collective volume, of the ACS monograph series (N° 147) edited by H. Zeiss, published by Reinhold Publ. Corp., New York.

Carbon-metal bonding	J.W. Richardson	1-35	(1960)
Benzyne chemistry	R. Huisgen	36-87	(1960)
Vinylmetallics	H.D. Kaesz and F.G.A. Stone	88-149	(1960)
Organoboranes	H.C. Brown	150-193	(1960)
Organo-aluminium compounds	K. Ziegler	194-269	(1960)
Organo-silyl metallic chemistry	H. Gilman and H.J.S. Winkler	270-345	(1960)
Cyclopentadienyl metal compounds	P.L. Pauson	346-379	(1960)
Arene complexes of the transition metals	H. Zeiss	380-425	(1960)
Transition metals and aryls	G.E. Coates and F. Glockling	426-467	(1960)
Metalcarbonyls and related compounds	J. Chatt, P.L. Pauson and L.M. Venanzi	468-528	(1960)

THE ORIGIN OF LIFE ON EARTH

These are the proceedings of an International symposium held in Moscow, 1957. Edited in the English-French-German edition for the International Union of Biochemistry by F. Clark and R.L.M. Synge. Published by Pergamon Press, London, (1959).

Title	Author	Reference
Formation of organic compounds on the primitive earth	S.L. Miller	123-135 (1959)
Photosynthesis in the far ultraviolet	A.N. Terenin	136-139 (1959)
The reactions involved in the formation of compounds which precede the synthesis of protoplasm and other materials of biological importance	K. Bahadur	140-150 (1959)
The original formation of amino acids under the influence of ultraviolet rays and electric discharges	T.E. Pavlovskaya, and A.G. Pasynskii	151-157 (1959)
Absolute asymmetric synthesis and asymmetric catalysis	E.J. Klabunovskii	158-168 (1959)
On the origin of the fore-protein	S. Akabori	189-196 (1959)
Similarities in structure among proteins (in German)	F. Šorm	231-240 (1959)
The continuity of proteins (in German)	K. Felix	241-255 (1959)

PERSPECTIVES IN ORGANIC CHEMISTRY

These are a series of review articles, dedicated to Sir Robert Robinson and edited by Sir Alexander Todd. Published by Interscience Publishers, Inc. New York (1956).

Title	Author	Page
The nature of theory of resonance	L. Pauling	1-8
Reaction mechanisms	P.D. Bartlett	9-27
The development of the concept of aromaticity	W. Baker	28-67
Stereochemistry	D.H.R. Barton	68-95
Importance of many membered ring compounds for theoretical organic chemistry (in German)	V. Prelog	96-133
Biosynthetic theories in organic chemistry	A.J. Birch	134-154
Synthesis	R.B. Woodward	155-184
New developments in organometallic synthesis	K. Ziegler	185-213
Carbohydrates	E.L. Hirst	214-244
Nucleic acids	A. Todd	245-264
Importance of theoretical organic chemistry in terpene chemistry (in German)	L. Ruzicka	265-314
Steroids	C.W. Shoppee	315-346
Alkaloids	E. Schlitter	347-370
Isotopes in organic chemistry	J.W. Cornforth	371-391
Microorganisms in organic chemistry	K. Folkers	392-429
Chemotherapy	J. Walker	430-452
Organic chemistry and conifer taxonomy	H. Erdtman	453-494
Organic chemistry and genetics (in German)	A. Butenandt	495-518

THE PETER C. REILLY LECTURES IN CHEMISTRY

These are a series of lectures presented at the University of Notre Dame, Indiana, and published by the University.

Title	Author	Reference
Internal rotation, with reference to the structure of high polymers and especially of proteins	S.I. Mizushima	5, 1-37 (1952)
Some aspects of steroid stereochemistry	C.W. Shoppee	6, 1-30 (1953)
Acetylene chemistry	E.R.H. Jones	8, 1-32 (1954)
Reactions of free radicals in solution	D.H. Hey	9, 1-30 (1954)
Oxidation of benzene by hydrogen peroxide	J.H. Baxendale	10, 1-17 (1955)
The uses of nuclides in the determination of organic reaction mechanisms	L.C.S. Melander	11, 1-96 (1955)

PHOTOCHEMISTRY IN THE LIQUID AND SOLID STATES

These are the proceedings of a symposium held at Dedham, 1957, edited by L.J. Heidt, R.S. Livingston, E. Rabinovitch and F. Daniels; published by J. Wiley and Sons, Inc., New York and London.

Title	Author	Reference
Photochemical production of some organic compounds under possible primitive earth conditions	W. Groth	21-24 (1960)
Studies of the photo-initiated addition of mercaptans to olefins. General comments on the kinetics of mercaptan addition reaction to olefins, including cis-trans forms	C. Sivertz	25-33 (1960)
The sensitized fluorescence of β-naphthylamine. A study in transfer of electronic energy	J.T. Dubois	62-68 (1960)

PHYSICAL CHEMISTRY OF THE HYDROCARBONS

These are collective volumes edited by A. Farkas, and published by Academic Press Inc., New York.

Title	Author	Reference		
The chemical bond in hydrocarbon molecules	G.W. Wheland	1,	1-53	(1950)
The molecular structure of hydrocarbons as determined by spectroscopy and electron and X-ray diffraction	M.H. Jellinek	1,	55-81	(1950)
Mass spectroscopy in hydrocarbon analysis	J.J. Mitchell	1,	83-112	(1950)
Optical properties of hydrocarbons; infrared absorption, Raman and ultraviolet absorption spectroscopy	N.D. Coggeshall	1,	113-166	(1950)
Optical methods of hydrocarbon analysis	N.D. Coggeshall	1,	167-214	(1950)
Electrical properties of hydrocarbons	A. Gemant	1,	215-240	(1950)
Solvent extraction of hydrocarbons. Solubility relations between liquid hydrocarbons and other liquids	A.W. Francis	1,	241-313	(1950)
Solid-liquid equilibria of hydrocarbons	M.R. Cines	1,	315-362	(1950)
Chemical thermodynamic equilibria among hydrocarbons	F.D. Rossini	1,	363-434	(1950)
Density and refractive index of hydrocarbons	S.S. Kurtz Jr. and A. Sankin	2,	1-80	(1953)
Surface tension and parachor of hydrocarbons	O.R. Quayle and S.S. Kurtz Jr.	2,	81-98	(1953)
Heat capacity of hydrocarbons	J.G. Aston and S.V.R. Mastrangelo	2,	99-130	(1953)
Critical behavior of hydrocarbons	R.H. Olds	2,	131-152	(1953)
Optical activity of hydrocarbons	R.L. Burwell Jr.	2,	153-185	(1953)
Mechanisms of some hydrocarbon reactions	R.C. Hansford	2,	187-318	(1953)
Separation and purification of hydrocarbons by selective adsorption	A.J. Juhola	2,	319-389	(1953)

RADIOACTIVITY APPLIED TO CHEMISTRY

This is a collective volume, edited by A.C. Wahl and
N.A. Bonner and published by J. Wiley and Sons, New York.

Title	Author	Reference
Isotopic exchenge reactions	O.E. Myers and R.S. Prestwood	6-43 (1951)
Radioactivity applied to chemical kinetics	C.E. Crompton	44-53 (1951)
Radioactivity applied to structural chemistry	V.J. Zinnenbom	54-61 (1951)
Chemical phenomena accompanying nuclear reactions (hot-atom chemistry)	J.W. Barnes, W.H. Burgus and J.A. Miskel	244-283 (1951)

RADIOBIOLOGY SYMPOSIUM

These are the proceedings of the symposium held at Liège in
August-September 1954, published in French and English.
The editors are Z.M. Bacq and P. Alexander, published by
Academic Press Inc., New York.

Title	Author	Reference
Action of ionizing radiation on lipids (in French)	A. Chevallier and C. Burg	1-25 (1955)
Physico-chemical methods of protection against ionizing radiation (in English)	P. Alexander and A. Charbesby	49-59 (1955)

RECENT PROGRESS IN HORMONE RESEARCH

These are the proceedings of the Laurentian Hormone Conference, an annual conference on hormone research. Edited by G. Pincus and published by Academic Press, Inc. New York.

Title	Author	Reference		
Steroids derived from the bile acids: 3,9-epoxy-11-cholenic acid, an intermediate in the partial synthesis of dehydrocorticosterone	E. C. Kendall	1,	65-81	(1947)
Some advances in the partial synthesis of adrenal cortical steroids	T. F. Gallagher	1,	83-98	(1947)
The characterization of sterol hormones by ultraviolet and infrared spectroscopy	R. N. Jones	2,	3-29	(1948)
The identification and quantitative microdetermination of estrogens by ultraviolet absorption spectrophotometry	H. B. Friedgood and J. B. Garst	2,	31-78	(1948)
The metabolism of androgens	R. I. Dorfman	2,	179-206	(1948)
On the relation of activity to constitution in the sexogens, with special reference to the doisynolic acids	K. Miescher	3,	47-69	(1948)
Steroid excretion in health and disease: I. Chemical aspects	S. Lieberman and K. Dobriner	3,	71-101	(1948)
The biological synthesis of cholesterol	K. Bloch	6,	111-129	(1951)
Studies with isotopic steroid hormones	T. F. Gallagher et.al.,	6,	131-157	(1951)
Sterols XIII: chemistry of the adrenal cortex steroids	P. L. Julian	6,	195-214	(1951)
The nature and the biogenesis of the adrenal secretory product	O. Hechter et.al.,	6,	215-246	(1951)
Chemistry of corticotrophin	E. B. Astwood M. S. Raben and R. W. Payne	7,	1-57	(1952)
Synthesis of 11-oxygenated steroids from plant sources	G. Rosenkranz et.al.,	8,	1-25	(1953)
The preparation and chemistry of crystalline insulin	R. G. Romans	10,	241-263	(1954)
The chemistry of the corticotrophins	E. E. Hays and W. F. White	10,	265-291	(1954)
The use of microorganisms in the synthesis of steroid hormones and hormone analogues	J. Fried et.al.,	11,	149-181	(1955)
Recent progress in methods of isolation, chemistry and physiology of aldosterone	S. A. Simpson and J. F. Tait	11,	183-219	(1955)
The chemistry and biological activities of 16-hydroxylated steroids	S. Bernstein	14,	1-27	(1958)
Structural and hormonal activity of some new steroids	V. A. Drill and B. Riegel	14,	29-67	(1958)
Molecular structure of steroids and phenanthrene derivatives related to growth of transplanted mammary tumors	C. Huggins K. Mainzer and G. Briziarelli	14,	77-93	(1958)

THE ROGER ADAMS SYMPOSIUM

This is a collection of papers presented in honor of Professor Roger Adams at a symposium at the University of Illinois, September 1954. Published by John Wiley and Sons, Inc., New York.

Title	Author	Reference	
Steric effects in dyes	W.R. Brode	8-59	(1955)
The structure of gliotoxin - a sulfur containing antibiotic substance	J.R. Johnson	60-90	(1955)
The structure of nepetalic acid	S.M. McElvain	91-102	(1955)
Chemistry of flavylium salts	R.L. Shriner	103-124	(1955)
Some chemical studies on viruses	W.M. Stanley	125-140	(1955)

THE ROYAL INSTITUTE OF CHEMISTRY OF GREAT BRITAIN AND IRELAND

Lectures, Monographs and Reports

These are a collection of individual articles published by the Institute

Title	Author	Reference		
Anaesthetics	H.B. Nisbet	3-30	(No.3)	(1949)
The hydrogen bond in chemistry	L. Hunter	3-13	(No.1)	(1950)
Spectroscopic evidence for the hydrogen bond	W.C. Price	14-20	(No.1)	(1950)
Dipole interaction and the hydrogen bond	A.R. Martin	21-29	(No.1)	(1950)
Modern methods of organic solvent manufacture	J.L. Edgar	3-21	(No.2)	(1950)
The synthesis of purine nucleotides	J. Baddiley	3-17	(No.3)	(1950)
The synthesis of some natural products by the use of acetylenic precursors	R.A. Raphael	18-30	(No.3)	(1950)
Studies in the chemotherapy of tuberculosis	V.C. Barry	3-10	(No.2)	(1952)
The chemistry and toxicology of organic fluorine and phosphorus compounds	B.C. Saunders	3-17	(No.1)	(1953)
Plant growth substances	R.L. Wain	1-16	(No.2)	(1953)
A physical approach to terpenoid structures	J.M. Robertson	1-21	(No.6)	(1954)
Ionisation in organic chemistry	E.D. Hughes	1-24	(No.1)	(1955)
Chemistry, biochemistry and isotopic tracer technique	G. Popjak	1-59	(No.2)	(1955)
Fluorocarbon derivatives	R.N. Haszeldine	1-49	(No.1)	(1956)
Biological synthesis of carbohydrates	M. Stacey	1-18	(No.2)	(1956)
Furfural from agricultural sources. Production and chemistry	A.P. Dunlop	1-17	(No.4)	(1956)
Peroxidase. Action and use in organic synthesis	B.C. Saunders	1-27	(No.1)	(1957)
Hydrazine and its derivatives	R.A. Reed	1-49	(No.5)	(1957)
Recent progress in the chemistry of dyes and pigments	W. Bradley	1-92	(No.5)	(1958)
Recent developments in inorganic and organic analytical chemistry	T.S. West	1-41	(No.1)	(1959)
Structural analysis of polysaccharides	D.J. Manners	1-39	(No.2)	(1959)
Chemical mechanisms in the induction of cancer	A. Haddow	1-20	(No.4)	(1959)
Sugar and its industrial applications	L.F. Wiggins	1-44	(No.5)	(1960)

STERIC COURSE OF MICROBIOLOGICAL REACTIONS

This is the second of the Ciba Foundation studies, edited by G.E.W. Wolstenholme and C.M. O'Connor, published by J.A. Churchill Ltd., London.

Title	Author	Reference
The steric course of microbiological reactions. A historical review	F.W. Westheimer	3-9 (1959)
Mechanism of hydrogen transfer with pyridine nucleotides	K. Wallenfels	10-33 (1959)
The steric mechanisms involved in the reactions of lactic acid	N.O. Kaplan	37-52 (1959)
The steric and molecular specificity of steroid dehydrogenases	P. Talalay and N.R. Levy	53-74 (1959)
The steric course of some microbiological and enzymic reductions of ketones	V. Prelog	79-90 (1959)

STERIC EFFECTS IN CONJUGATED SYSTEMS

These are the proceedings of a symposium held at Hull, July 1958. Edited by G.W. Gray, and published by Butterworths Scientific Publications, London.

Title	Author	Page
Configuration and steric effects in conjugated systems	E.E. Turner	1-7
The dependence of electronic energy levels upon deformation in aromatic hydrocarbons	C.A. Coulson	8-19
The study of steric effects in substituted diphenyls by ultraviolet absorption spectroscopy	G.H. Beaven	22-33
Steric effects in basic di- and tri-phenylmethane dyes	C.C. Barker	34-45
The effect of non-coplanarity on the light absorption of cyanine dyes	M.J.S. Dewar	46-51
The classification of steric effects in ultraviolet absorption spectra	W.F. Forbes	62-71
Absorption spectra of conjugated carbonyl compounds	E.S. Waight and R.L. Erskine	73-80
Electronic spectra and chemical data	B.M. Wepster	82-92
Steric and electronic effects in the solvolysis of substituted phenyldimethylcarbinyl chlorides - electrophilic substituent constants	H.C. Brown	100-111
Steric effects in nucleophilic aromatic substitution	N.B. Chapman	119-129
A Hammett-type equation for the effects of *ortho*-substituents	A.C. Farthing and B. Nam	131-139
Dipole moment evidence regarding steric effects in aromatic molecules	J.W. Smith	141-148
Steric effects in the interaction between protons and aromatic hydrocarbons	G. Dallinga P.J. Smit and E.L. Mackor	150-157
Steric effects on the mesomorphism of mono- and di-benzylideneaminodiphenyls	G.W. Gray	160-169
The study of steric effects in alkyldiphenyls by vapour-phase chromatography	E.A. Johnson	174-181

STERIC EFFECTS IN ORGANIC CHEMISTRY

This is a collective volume, edited by M.S. Newman, and published by John Wiley and Sons, New York.

Title	Author	Reference
Conformational analysis	W.G. Dauben and K.S. Pitzer	1-60 (1956)
Substitution at saturated carbon atoms	E.L. Eliel	61-163 (1956)
Steric effects in aromatic substitutions	G.S. Hammond and M.F. Hawthorne	164-200 (1956)
Additions to unsaturated functions	M.S. Newman	201-248 (1956)
Intramolecular rearrangements	D.J. Cram	249-303 (1956)
Olefin forming elimination reactions	D.J. Cram	304-348 (1956)
Cleavage reactions of the carbon-carbon bond	H.H. Wasserman	349-393 (1956)
Steric effects among the common organometallic compounds	G.F. Wright	394-424 (1956)
Steric effects on equilibrated systems	G.S. Hammond	425-470 (1956)
Molecular complexes and molecular asymmetry	M.S. Newman	471-478 (1956)
Steric effects on certain physical properties	L.L. Ingraham	479-522 (1956)
Calculation of the magnitude of steric effects	F.H. Westheimer	523-555 (1956)
Separation of polar, steric and resonance effects in reactivity	R.W. Taft, Jr.	556-676 (1956)

SYMPOSIA ON COMPARATIVE BIOLOGY

This is a collection of symposia of the Kaiser Foundation Research Institute; published by Academic Press, New York.

Title	Author	Reference
Comparative biochemistry of photoreactive systems	M.B. Allen (editor)	
Recent studies of chlorophyll chemistry	A.J. Holt and H.V. Morley	169-179 (1960)
Chemical studies of phycoerythrins and phycocyanins	C.O. Heocha	181-203 (1960)
The biosynthesis of protochlorophyll	L. Bogorad	227-256 (1960)
Protochlorophyll transformations	J.H.C. Smith	257-275 (1960)

A SYMPOSIUM ON MOLECULAR BIOLOGY

These are the proceedings of a series of lectures and a symposium held at the University of Chicago in 1956/1957. Edited by R.E. Zirkle and published by the University of Chicago Press, Chicago, Illinois.

Title	Author	Reference
Some principles of molecular biology	K. Felix	1-15 (1959)
Current ideas of the structure of desoxyribonucleic acid	R.L. Sinsheimer	16-30 (1959)
Enzyme models	J.H. Wang	137-151 (1959)

SYMPOSIUM ON PROTEIN STRUCTURE

These are the proceedings of a symposium organized by the International Union of Pure and applied chemistry, Paris 1957. Edited by A. Neuberger, published by Methuen and Co., Ltd., London and John Wiley and Sons, Inc., New York.

Title	Author	Reference	
Deuterium exchange and protein structure	K. Linderstrøm-Lang	23-34	(1958)

THE STRATEGY OF CHEMOTHERAPY

These are the proceedings of the eighth symposium of the Society for General Microbiology, London, April 1958. Edited by S.T. Cowan and E. Rowatt, published by The University Press, Cambridge.

Title	Author	Reference	
Metal binding agents in chemotherapy: the activation of metals by chelation	A. Albert	112-138	(1958)
The designing of antimetabolites	D.W. Woolley	139-162	(1958)
Lethal synthesis	R. Markham	163-177	(1958)

TECHNIQUE OF ORGANIC CHEMISTRY

This is a comprehensive treatise covering all the techniques used in Organic Chemistry. The first edition, in 1946, was limited to "Physical Methods in Organic Chemistry", which is now volume 1 of the series. A second edition of volume 1 appeared in 1950, together with the first editions of volumes 2 to 10. Later editions of some of these volumes have appeared since. A. Weissberger is the general editor for the entire series, which is published, in English, by Interscience Publishers, Inc., New York.

Title	Author	Reference	
Physical methods of organic chemistry (third edition)		**1**,	(1959-1960)
Automatic control	J.M. Sturtevant	**1/1**, 1-33	(1959)
Automatic recording	D.R. Simonsen	**1/1**, 35-70	(1959)
Weighing	A.H. Corwin	**1/1**, 71-130	(1959)
Determination of density	N. Bauer and S.Z. Lewin	**1/1**, 131-190	(1959)
Determination of particle size and molecular weight	G.L. Beyer	**1/1**, 191-257	(1959)
Temperature measurement	J.M. Sturtevant	**1/1**, 259-285	(1959)
Determination of melting and freezing points	E.L. Skau, J.C. Arthur, Jr. and H. Wakeman	**1/1**, 287-355	(1959)
Determination of boiling and condensation temperatures	W. Swietoslawski and J.R. Anderson	**1/1**, 357-399	(1959)
Determination of vapor pressure	G.W. Thomson	**1/1**, 401-522	(1959)
Calorimetry	J.M. Sturtevant	**1/1**, 523-654	(1959)
Determination of solubility	W.J. Mader, R.D. Vold and M.J. Vold	**1/1**, 655-688	(1959)
Determination of viscosity	J.F. Swindells, R. Ullman and H. Mark	**1/1**, 689-726	(1959)
Determination of properties of insoluble monolayers at mobile interfaces	A.E. Alexander	**1/1**, 727-755	(1959)
Determination of surface and interfacial tension	W.D. Harkins and A.E. Alexander	**1/1**, 757-814	(1959)
Determination of osmotic pressure	R.H. Wagner and L.D. Moore, Jr.	**1/1**, 815-894	(1959)
Determination of diffusivity	A.L. Geddes and R.B. Pontius	**1/2**, 895-1005	(1960)
Determinations with the ultracentrifuge	J.B. Nichols and G.D. Bailey	**1/2**, 1007-1137	(1960)

TECHNIQUE OF ORGANIC CHEMISTRY (Contd.)

Refractometry	N. Bauer, K. Fajans and S.W. Lewin	1/2,	1139-1281 (1960)
Determination of crystal morphology	M.A. Peacock, J.D.H. Donnay and G. Donnay	1/2,	1283-1316 (1960)
Crystallochemical analysis	J.D.H. Donnay and G. Donnay	1/2,	1317-1346 (1960)
Light microscopy	E.E. Jelley	1/2,	1347-1473 (1960)
Microspectroscopy	E.R. Blout	1/2,	1475-1519 (1960)
X-ray microscopy	W.C. Nixon	1/2,	1521-1559 (1960)
Electron microscopy	F.A. Hamm	1/2,	1561-1639 (1960)
X-ray crystallography	W.N. Lipscomb	1/2,	1641-1738 (1960)
Electron diffraction by gases	L.O. Brockway	1/2,	1739-1762 (1960)
Neutron diffraction	J.M. Hastings and L.M. Corliss	1/2,	1763-1797 (1960)
Spectroscopy and spectrophotometry in the visible and ultraviolet	W. West	1/3,	1799-1958 (1960)
Infra-red spectroscopy	D.H. Anderson, N.B. Woodall and W. West	1/3,	1959-2019 (1960)
Calorimetry and photometric analysis	W. West	1/3,	2021-2061 (1960)
Determination of fluorescence and phosphorescence	N. Wotherspoon and G. Oster	1/3,	2063-2105 (1960)
Light scattering	G. Oster	1/3,	2107-2145 (1960)
Polarimetry	W. Heller and D.D. Fitts	1/3,	2147-2333 (1960)
Optical rotatory dispersion	W. Klyne and A.C. Parker	1/3,	2335-2385 (1960)
Streaming birefringence	H.A. Scheraga and R. Signer	1/3,	2387-2457 (1960)
The Kerr effect	C.G. Le Fèvre and R.J.W. Le Fèvre	1/3,	2459-2496 (1960)
Determination of the Faraday effect	C.E. Waring and R.L. Custer	1/3,	2497-2552 (1960)
Measurement of dielectric constant and loss	J.G. Powles and C.P. Smyth	1/3,	2553-2597 (1960)
Determination of dipole moments	C.P. Smyth	1/3,	2599-2634 (1960)
Microwave spectroscopy	B.P. Dailey	1/4,	2635-2662 (1960)
Nuclear magnetic resonance	H.S. Gutowsky	1/4,	2663-2799 (1960)
Paramagnetic resonance absorption	G.K. Fraenkel	1/4,	2801-2872 (1960)
Determination of magnetic susceptibility	P.W. Selwood	1/4,	2873-2913 (1960)
Potentiometry	C. Tanford and S. Wawzonek	1/4,	2915-3009 (1960)
Conductometry	T. Shedlovsky	1/4,	3011-3048 (1960)
Determination of transference numbers	M. Spiro	1/4,	3049-3111 (1960)

TECHNIQUE OF ORGANIC CHEMISTRY (Contd.)

Electrophoresis	D.H. Moore	<u>1/4</u>,	3113-3153 (1960)
Polarography	O.H. Muller	<u>1/4</u>,	3155-3279 (1960)
Controlled-potential electrolysis	L. Meites	<u>1/4</u>,	3281-3333 (1960)
Determination of radioactivity	B.M. Tolbert and W.E. Siri	<u>1/4</u>,	3335-3448 (1960)
Mass spectrometry	D.W. Stewart	<u>1/4</u>,	3449-3539 (1960)
Catalytic, photochemical and electrolytic reactions (second edition)		<u>2</u>,	523 pp. (1956)
Catalytic reactions	V.I. Komarewsky, C.H. Riesz and F.L. Morritz	<u>2</u>,	1-255 (1956)
Photochemical reactions	C.R. Masson, V. Boekelheide and W.A. Noyes, Jr.	<u>2</u>,	257-384 (1956)
Electrolytic reactions	S. Swann, Jr.	<u>2</u>,	385-523 (1956)
Separation and purification (second edition)		<u>3</u>,	(1956-1957)
Thermal diffusion of organic liquids	A.L. Jones	<u>3/1</u>,	2-37 (1956)
Barrier separations	K. Kammermeyer	<u>3/1</u>,	37-64 (1956)
Dialysis and electrodialysis	R.E. Stauffer	<u>3/1</u>,	65-119 (1956)
Zone electrophoresis	E. MacWilliam	<u>3/1</u>,	119-148 (1956)
Laboratory extraction and countercurrent distribution	L.C. Craig, D. Craig and E.G. Scheibel	<u>3/1</u>,	149-393 (1956)
Crystallization and recrystallization	R.S. Tipson	<u>3/1</u>,	395-562 (1956)
Centrifuging	C.M. Ambler and F.W. Keith, Jr.	<u>3/1</u>,	563-606 (1956)
Filtration	A.B. Cummins and F.B. Hutto, Jr.	<u>3/1</u>,	607-786 (1956)
Solvent removal, evaporation and drying	G. Broughton	<u>3/1</u>,	787-839 (1956)
Selection of materials for the construction of equipment (second edition)	R.F. Eisenberg and P.R. Kraybill	<u>3/2</u>,	1-49 (1957)
Heating and cooling	R.S. Egly	<u>3/2</u>,	51-182 (1957)
Grinding, screening and classifying	J.W. Axelson and W.C. Streib	<u>3/2</u>,	183-234 (1957)
Mixing	J.H. Rushton and M.P. Hofmann	<u>3/2</u>,	235-282 (1957)
Operations with gases	G.H. Miller	<u>3/2</u>,	283-374 (1957)
Distillation		<u>4</u>,	645 pp. (1951)
Theory	A. Rose and E. Rose	<u>4</u>,	1-174 (1951)
Ordinary fractional distillation. Part 1. Apparatus	A.L. Glasebrook and F.E. Williams	<u>4</u>,	175-294 (1951)

TECHNIQUE OF ORGANIC CHEMISTRY (Contd.)

Ordinary fractional distillation. Part 2. Procedure	F.E. Williams	4,	295-316 (1951)
Extractive and azeotropic distillation	C.S. Carlson	4,	317-387 (1951)
Distillation of liquefied gases and low-boiling liquids	A. Rose and E. Rose	4,	389-461 (1951)
Distillation under moderate vaccum	J.R. Bowman and R.S. Tipson	4,	463-494 (1951)
Distillation under high vaccum. Part 1. Distillation	E.S. Perry	4,	495-539 (1951)
Distillation under high vacuum. Part 2. The vacuum system	J.C. Hecker	4,	540-602 (1951)
Sublimation	R.S. Tipson	4,	603-645 (1951)
Adsorption and chromatography	H.G. Cassidy	5,	1-327 (1951)
Micro and semimicro methods	N.D. Cheronis, A.R. Ronzio and T.S. Ma	6,	1-582 (1954)
Organic solvents (physical properties and methods of purification) (second edition)	A. Weissberger, E.S. Proskauer, J.A. Riddick and E.E. Toops, Jr.	7,	1-529 (1955)
Investigation of rates and mechanisms of reactions	S.L. Friess and A. Weissberger (Editors)	8,	750 pp. (1953)
General theory of rate processes	R. Livingston	8,	1-36 (1953)
Fundamental operations and measurements in obtaining rate data	R. Livingston	8,	37-68 (1953)
Special experimental methods for determination of rate data. Part 1. Use of tagged atoms, groups and isotopes in reaction rate studies	P.R. O'Connor	8,	69-99 (1953)
Special experimental methods for determination of rate data. Part 2. Competing reactions	T.S. Lee	8,	100-130 (1953)
Special experimental methods for determination of rate data. Part 3. Measurement of instantaneous reaction rates in stirred constant-flow reactions	E. Grunwald	8,	130-133 (1953)
Special experimental methods for determination of rate data. Part 4. Determination of the concentration of active intermediates in reactions	G.M. Burnett and H.W. Melville	8,	133-168 (1953)
Evaluation and interpretation of rate data	R. Livingston	8,	169-230 (1953)
Homogeneous gas phase reactions	W.D. Walters	8,	231-301 (1953)
Reactions in the liquid phase. Part 1. General methods of study	J.E. Leffler and E. Grunwald	8,	303-335 (1953)
Reactions in the liquid phase. Part 2. Specific experimental techniques	B.K. Morse and S.I. Friess	8,	335-420 (1953)
Homogeneous catalysis in solution	T.H. James	8,	421-439 (1953)
Polymerization and polymer reactions	W.J. Priest	8,	441-534 (1953)
Biological reactions. Part 1. Measurement and general theory	F.M. Huennekens	8,	535-627 (1953)
Biological reactions. Part 2. Reaction kinetics of enzyme-substrate compounds	B. Chance	8,	627-667 (1953)
Rapid reactions. Part 1. General principles of measurement of velocity of rapid reactions in solution	F.J.W. Roughton	8,	669-690 (1953)

TECHNIQUE OF ORGANIC CHEMISTRY (Contd.)

Rapid reactions. Part 2. Accelerated and stopped flow methods using spectrophotometric measurements	B. Chance	8,	690-710 (1953)
Rapid reactions. Part 3. The thermal measurement of rapid reactions in solution	F.J.W. Roughton	8,	710-729 (1953)
Rapid reactions. Part 4. Quenching, electrometric and other rapid reaction techniques	F.J.W. Roughton	8,	730-738 (1953)
Chemical applications of spectroscopy	W. West (Editor)	9,	770 pp. (1956)
Introductory survey of molecular spectra	W. West	9,	1-70 (1956)
Microwave and radiofrequency spectroscopy	W. Gordy	9,	71-185 (1956)
Theory of infra-red and Raman spectra	A.B.F. Duncan	9,	187-245 (1956)
The application of infra-red and Raman spectrometry to the elucidation of molecular structure	R.N. Jones and C. Sandorfy	9,	247-580 (1956)
Electronic spectra in the visible and ultraviolet. Part 1. Theory of electronic spectra	A.B.F. Duncan	9,	581-629 (1956)
Electronic spectra in the visible and ultraviolet. Part 2. Applications	F.A. Matsen	9,	629-706 (1956)
Fluorescence and phosphorescence	W. West	9,	707-758 (1956)
Fundamentals of chromatography	H.G. Cassidy	10,	1-427 (1957)

THEORETICAL ORGANIC CHEMISTRY

These are the proceedings of the Kekulé Centennial Symposium, held September 1958, under the auspices of the International Union of Pure and Applied Chemistry. Published by Butterworths Scientific Publications, London (1959).

Title	Author	Page
August Kekulé	P.E. Verkade (Introduction 9-17)	
Kekulé and the chemical bond	L. Pauling	1-8
The ground state of some -electron systems	H.C. Longuet-Higgins	9-19
Aromatic character	D.P. Craig	20-34
Tropylium and related molecules	W. von E. Doering	35-48
Molecular geometry and steric deformation	C.A. Coulson	49-66
Stabilization energies and strain energies from heats of hydrogenation	R.B. Turner	67-83
Nucleophilic octahedral substitution	C.K. Ingold	84-102
Hydrolysis of diaryliodonium salts	M.C. Caserio, D.L. Glusker and J.D. Roberts	103-113
Fragmentation in solvolysis reactions	C.A. Grob	114-126
Some recent progress in conformational analysis	D.H.R. Barton	127-143
Nucleophilic substitution, at unsaturated centres	J.F. Bunnett	144-157
Recent developments in the elimination mechanism of nucleophilic aromatic substitution	R. Huisgen	158-175
Polar factors in the decomposition of unsymmetrical iodonium salts (in German)	O.A. Reutow	176-178
Aromatic rearrangements	M.J.S. Dewar	179-208
Nitration	E.D. Hughes	209-218
Some recent studies of reactivity and orientation in aromatic halogen substitution	P.B.D. de la Mare	219-229
Quasi-heterolytic reactions in the gas phase	A. Maccoll	230-249
Homolytic substitution reactions in the naphthalene series	D.H. Hey	250-261
The behaviour of radicals in addition and abstraction reactions	M. Szwarc and J.H. Binks	262-290

TRAITÉ DE CHIMIE ORGANIQUE

This is a collection of comprehensive review articles, in French. The bibliographies are complete to periods ranging from 1935 to 1950. The collection was first published in 1935 and republished after 1945 and the last volumes were published in 1954. Volumes 1 to 5 were edited by V. Grignard, volumes 6 onward were edited by V. Grignard, G. Dupont and R. Locquin. The publisher is Masson et Cie., Paris. This collection is also known as the "Grignard" after the name of its major editor.

Title	Author	Reference
Organic analysis	H. Pariselle	$\underline{1}$, 1-80 (1947)
Liquid crystals	Ch. Mauquin	$\underline{1}$, 81-119 (1947)
Distillation	M. Legat	$\underline{1}$, 121-267 (1947)
Organic colloids	P. Barry	$\underline{1}$, 269-362 (1947)
Defined compounds and pure products	J. Timmermans	$\underline{1}$, 363-385 (1947)
Determination of the molecular structure	G. Dupont	$\underline{1}$, 387-400 (1947)
Establishment of formula	R. Locquin	$\underline{1}$, 401-832 (1947)
Representation of chemical structures	M. Delepine	$\underline{1}$, 833-1071 (1947)
Nomenclature	V. Grignard	$\underline{1}$, 1073-1108 (1947)
Optical properties of organic compounds	E. Darmois	$\underline{2}$, 1-58 (1948)
Structure of molecules and absorption spectra. Spectra in the ultraviolet and in the visible	P. Ramart-Lucas	$\underline{2}$, 59-142 (1948)
Spectra in the infrared	J. Lecomte	$\underline{2}$, 143-293 (1948)
Fluorescence spectra	A. Andaut	$\underline{2}$, 295-349 (1948)
Applications of X-rays to the study of organic compounds	Ch. Mauguin	$\underline{2}$, 351-432 (1948)
Raman effect (application of Raman spectroscopy to organic chemistry)	M. Bourguel and L. Piaux	$\underline{2}$, 433-478 (1948)
Dielectric properties and chemical structure	P. Pascal	$\underline{2}$, 479-513 (1948)
Magnetic properties and chemical structure	P. Pascal	$\underline{2}$, 515-573 (1948)
Parachor and chemical structure	P. Pascal	$\underline{2}$, 575-593 (1948)
Organoleptic properties and chemical structure	J. Martinet	$\underline{2}$, 595-728 (1948)
Reaction mechanisms	M. Aumeras	$\underline{2}$, 729-760 (1948)
Organic free radicals	P. Pascal	$\underline{2}$, 761-808 (1948)
Intramolecular rearrangements	A. Kirrmann	$\underline{2}$, 809-850 (1948)
Steric hindrance	G. Vavon	$\underline{2}$, 851-940 (1948)
Catalysis in organic chemistry	E. Carrière and H. Bonnet	$\underline{2}$, 941-1145 (1948)

TRAITÉ DE CHIMIE ORGANIQUE (Contd.)

Catalysis of autooxidation: antioxidants and prooxidants	C. Dufraisse	2,	1147-1196	(1948)
Saturated aliphatic hydrocarbons	V. Grignard and J. Doeuvre	3,	1-76	(1948)
Unsaturated aliphatic hydrocarbons	R. Lespiau	3,	77-189	(1948)
Industries derived from acetylene	J. Lichtenberger	3,	191-246	(1948)
Halogenated derivatives of aliphatic hydrocarbons	F. Swarts	3,	247-394	(1948)
Nitro-nitrohalogenated-nitroso-nitrosohalogenated or nitroso-nitro derivatives of aliphatic hydrocarbons	J. Doeuvre	3,	395-416	(1948)
Industrial aspects of chlorinated derivatives of aliphatic hydrocarbons	J. Lichtenberger	3,	417-468	(1948)
General properties and functional correlations of cyclic hydrocarbons	G. Dupont	3,	469-475	(1948)
Theory of strains and stereochemistry of alicyclic groups	L. Ruzicka	3,	477-496	(1948)
Cyclanes and cyclenes	L. Palfray	3,	497-686	(1948)
Monocyclic terpenes	G. Dupont	3,	687-710	(1948)
Halogenated derivatives of cyclic hydrocarbons	F. Swarts	3,	711-732	(1948)
Nitro or nitroso derivatives of cyclanes and cyclenes	J. Doeuvre	3,	733-736	(1948)
The benzenoid ring	L. Bert	4,	1-38	(1948)
Benzenoid hydrocarbons, generalities and special descriptions	C. Duval	4,	39-140	(1948)
Halogenated derivatives of benzenoid hydrocarbons	F. Swarts	4,	141-179	(1948)
Sulfinic, sulfenic, selenic, sulfonic and selenonic acids and derivatives. Sulfones	Cl. Duval	4,	181-229	(1948)
Nitro-, nitro-halogenated, nitroso-halogenated, or nitrosonitro derivatives of aromatic hydrocarbons	J. Doeuvre	4,	231-273	(1948)
Nitrosulfinic, nitrosulfonic, nitrohalogenated and halogenosulfonic derivatives of aromatic hydrocarbons	Cl. Duval	4,	275-295	(1948)
Hydrocarbons of various non-condensed benzene rings (biphenyls and polyphenylbenzenes)	P. Amagat	4,	297-345	(1948)
Di-, tri- and polyphenyl derivatives of methane and ethane	L. Piaux	4,	347-479	(1948)
Polyarylpropanes and higher homologues	R. Heilmann	4,	481-496	(1948)
Unsaturated polyaryl hydrocarbons	R. Heilmann	4,	497-535	(1948)
Arylcyclanes derived from cyclopropane, cyclobutane and cyclopentane	R. Heilmann	4,	537-553	(1948)
Benzenoid hydrocarbon rings united directly by aliphatic chains	R. Heilmann	4,	555-561	(1948)
Industrial aspects of the chlorinated derivatives of aromatic hydrocarbons	J. Lichtenberger	4,	563-575	(1948)

TRAITÉ DE CHIMIE ORGANIQUE (Contd.)

Chemical studies of petroleum	G. Hugel	4,	577-626 (1948)
Industries derived from solid combustion agents	P. Baud	4,	627-786 (1948)
Metals in organic chemistry	Ch. Courtot	5,	1-606 (1949)
Alcohols	C. Prévost	5,	607-763 (1949)
Formation of alcohols by biochemical routes	C. Fromageot	5,	765-821 (1949)
The synthetic methanol industry	J. Lichtenberger	5,	823-839 (1949)
The ethyl alcohol industry	P. Baud	5,	841-975 (1949)
Ethers and esters of mineral acids	J.B. Senderens	5,	877-1023 (1949)
Glycols	M. Tiffeneau	6,	1-261 (1948)
Epoxides	M. Tiffeneau	6,	262-380 (1948)
Thiols and derivatives	R. Délaby	6,	381-545 (1948)
Higher polyvalent alcohols (higher polyols)	Ch. Prévost	6,	547-634 (1948)
Industrial aspects of glycols and some of their derivatives	J. Amiel	6,	635-642 (1948)
Industrial aspects of nitroglycerine	P. Pascal	6,	643-652 (1948)
Phenols	G. Laude	6,	651-925 (1948)
Nitro and nitroso derivatives of phenols	A. Seyewetz	6,	927-968 (1948)
Organic photographic developing agents	A. Seyewetz	6,	969-996 (1948)
Industrial aspects of phenols and some of their derivatives	P. Baud	6,	997-1029 (1948)
Sulfur, selenium or tellurium analogs of alcohols and phenols	G. Laude	6,	1031-1140 (1948)
Aldehydes	P. Cordier	7,	1-179 (1950)
Aliphatic aldehydes	J A. Gautier and P. Piganiol	7,	181-309 (1950)
Alicyclic aldehydes	P. Séguin	7,	183-331 (1950)
Aromatic aldehydes	P. Séguin	7,	332-507 (1950)
Unsaturated aldehydes	M.M. Janot and R. Dolique	7,	509-669 (1950)
Ketones	R. Lombard	7,	671-838 (1950)
Saturated ketones	Ch. Paquot	7,	839-1060 (1950)
Ethylenic ketones	R. Dulou	7,	1061-1258 (1950)
Acetylenic ketones	J. Germain	7,	1259-1296 (1950)
Enols	R. Lombard	7,	1297-1322 (1950)
Polyketones	H. Moureu and P. Chovin	7,	1323-1477 (1950)
Quinones	H. Pariselle and A. Hieulle	8,	1-46 (1947)
Ketenes	M. Sommelet and I. Marszak	8,	47-92 (1947)

TRAITÉ DE CHIMIE ORGANIQUE (Contd.)

Topic	Author(s)	Vol.	Pages (Year)
Hydroxy aldehydes and hydroxy ketones (non-sugars)	R. Dolique	8,	93-223 (1947)
Oses and holosides	V. Hasenfratz and M. Frèrejacque	8,	225-346 (1947)
General properties of the heterosides	H. Herissey and J. Rabaté	8,	347-616 (1947)
Starch	M. Schoen	8,	617-688 (1947)
Study of starch by X-rays	G. Champetier and R. Sutra	8,	689-696 (1947)
Cellulose	J. Duclaux and G. Champetier	8,	697-862 (1947)
Lichenin	G. Champetier	8,	863-867 (1947)
Artificial silks	M. Battegay	8,	869-890 (1947)
Industrial aspects of starch products	P. Baud	8,	891-1019 (1947)
Industry of the carbonization of wood	J. Lichtenberger	8,	1021-1087 (1947)
Phenolic aldehydes	J. Amiel	8,	1089-1162 (1947)
Phenolic ketones	J. Amiel	8,	1163-1197 (1947)
Cellulose	J. Duclaux and G. Champetier	8,	1199-1210 (1947)
Monoacids	R. Truchet	9,	1-92 (1948) 145-687
Esters	J.B. Senderens and J. Aboulenc	9,	93-143 (1948)
Industrial aspects of acetic acid and related products	J. Lichtenberger	9,	689-800 (1948)
Diacids	F. Salmon-Legagneur	10,	1-443 (1947)
Polyacids	F. Salmon-Legagneur	10,	445-630 (1947)
Fatty substances	R. Padova	10,	631-710 (1947)
Acidic derivatives with sulfur and selenium	H.J. Goudet	10,	711-774 (1947)
Hydroxy acids	M. Montagne	11,	1-495 (1945)
β-Olides	M. Sommelet and I. Marszak	11,	497-527 (1945)
Phenolic acids	P. Weill and R. Duckert	11,	531-1075 (1945)
Alcohols with phenolic and acidic functions	H.J. Goudet	11,	1075-1147 (1945)
Aldehyde acids	H. Gault	11,	1149-1233 (1945)
Ketonic acids	H. Gault and L. Piaux	11,	1235-1456 (1945)
Industrial aspects of some acids	P. Baud	11,	1457-1491 (1945)
Nomenclature of heteroatomic chains of complex acyclic compounds	R. Rambaud	11,	1493-1500 (1945)

TRAITÉ DE CHIMIE ORGANIQUE (Contd.)

Topic	Author	Vol., Pages	Year
Amines	M. Cramer	12, 1-392	(1941)
Amino-alcohols	E. Fourneau	12, 393-635	(1941)
Aminophenols	M. Lesbre	12, 637-690	(1941)
Amino-aldehydes and aminoketones	M. Lesbre	12, 691-725	(1941)
Amino acids	A. Morel	13, 1-323	(1941)
Amides, thioamides and imides	P. Amagat	13, 325-521	(1941)
Imines and imino-ethers	P. Amagat	13, 523-652	(1941)
Nitriles	P. Bruylants	13, 653-774	(1941)
Cyano compounds	P. Brun	13, 775-846	(1941)
Carbylamines and amidines	P. Bruylants	13, 847-919	(1941)
Nitrogen derivatives of carbonic acid	A. Guillaumin	14, 1-398	(1949)
Organic arsenic compounds	C. Courtot	14, 399-504	(1949)
Organic phosphorus compounds	C. Courtot	14, 505-552	(1949)
Organic derivatives of silicon	F.S. Kipping and J. Doeuvre	14, 553-570	(1949)
Diazonium and azo compounds. Aliphatic diazo compounds	A. Guillemonat	15, 1-81	(1948)
Aromatic diazo compounds	A. Gislon	15, 83-255	(1948)
Azo compounds. Aliphatic and mixed azo derivatives	A. Guillemonat	15, 258-269	(1948)
Aromatic azo derivatives	A. Gislon	15, 271-382	(1948)
Aliphatic triazenes, tetrazenes and pentazenes	A. Guillemonat	15, 383-392	(1948)
Aromatic triazenes	A. Gislon	15, 393-418	(1948)
Aliphatic azoxy compounds	A. Guillemonat	15, 419-420	(1948)
Aromatic azoxy compounds	A. Gislon	15, 421-457	(1948)
Hydrazines	M. Lesbré	15, 459-596	(1948)
Hydroxylamines	M. Lesbré	15, 597-655	(1948)
Oximes	P. Lauzent and P. Montheard	15, 657-696	(1948)
Amidoximes	N.P. Buu-Hoï and P. Cagniant	15, 697-714	(1948)
Azides	N.P. Buu-Hoï and P. Cagniant	15, 715-791	(1948)
Complex cyclic compounds	G. Dupont	16, 1-165 341-360	(1949)
Functional derivatives of the norcamphane group	R. Cornubert	16, 167-340 361-368	(1949)
Sesquiterpenes	R. Cornubert and P. Arziani	16, 369-465	(1949)

TRAITÉ DE CHIMIE ORGANIQUE (Contd.)

Essential oils	Y. R. Naves	16,	467-546 (1949)
Natural resins	G. Dupont	16,	547-649 (1949)
Artificial resins	A. Champetier	16,	651-839 (1949)
Sterols and bile-acids	J. Javillier	16,	841-985 (1949)
Natural products derived from sterols	J. Sivadgian	16,	987-1085 (1949)
Naphthalene and derivatives	J. Bougault and E. Chattelain	17,	1-189 (1949)
Naphthalenic aldehydes and hydroxy-ketones	J. Lichtenberger	17,	191-289 (1949)
Naphthoic acids	J. Lichtenberger and T. Paulus	17,	291-384 (1949)
Naphthylamines	R. Perrot	17,	385-497 (1949)
Aminonaphthols	J. Martinet	17,	499-543 (1949)
Naphthoquinones	J. Martinet	17,	547-649 (1949)
Hydrogenation products of naphthalene	L. Palfray	17,	651-760 (1949)
Complex homogeneous ring-systems with a naphthalenic and a benzene oronaphthalene ring (not fused)	L. Palfray	17,	761-809 (1949)
Benzocyclanes	L. Palfray	17,	811-982 (1949)
Anthracene and derivatives	E. Cattelain	17,	987-1133 (1949)
Antraquinones	H. Wahl	17,	1135-1218 (1949)
Amino and amino-hydroxy-anthraquinones	E. Cattelain	17,	1219-1239 (1949)
Naphtacene and rubrene	A. Willemart	17,	1241-1298 (1949)
Photo-oxides of "acenes"	A. Étienne	17,	1299-1332 (1949)
Phenanthrene and retene	R. Trubaut and A. Godfrin	17,	1333-1506 (1949)
Pyrene, chrysene and picene	R. Trubaut and A. Godfrin	17,	1507-1536 (1949)
Polycondensed aromatic rings	N. Lozac'h	17,	1537-1655 (1949) 1683-1786
Fluorene	C. Courtot	17,	1657-1682 (1949)
Spirans	J. Boeseken	17,	1787-1830 (1949)
Nomenclature of heterocyclic rings	V. Grignard and R. Rambaud	18,	1-14 (1945)
Properties of heterocyclic compounds	R. Rambaud	18,	15-35 (1945)
General properties of oxygen-containing heterocyclic compounds	R. Rambaud	18,	36-48 (1945)
Five-membered heterocycles containing oxygen	R. Dolique	18,	49-51 (1945)
Hexatomic heterocycles containing oxygen. Pyranes	R. Paul	18,	317-439 (1945)
Pyrane compounds with several condensed rings	P. Karrer	18,	441-541 (1945)

TRAITE DE CHIMIE ORGANIQUE (Contd.)

Tri- or tetra-atomic heterocycles with a sulfur	J. Décombe	18,	543-602 (1945)
Pentatomic heterocycles with a selenium atom	J. Décombe	18,	603-630 (1945)
Tri- or tetra-atomic heterocycles with a nitrogen atom	J. Décombe	18,	634-641 (1945)
Pyrrole and its derivatives	B. Oddo	19,	1-199 (1942)
Tetrapyrrole pigments	A. Kirrmann	19,	201-251 (1942)
Complex pyrrole rings	B. Oddo	19,	268-462 (1942)
Indigo and indigo dyes	J. Martinet	19,	463-685 (1942)
Some observations on heterocyclic compounds	A.E. Tchitchibabine	20,	1-32 (1953)
Hexatomic heterocycles with an atom of nitrogen pyridine, piperidine and derivatives	A.E. Tchitchibabine	20,	33-375 (1953)
Condensed systems derived from pyridine	C. Paquot	20,	377-621 (1953)
Condensed pyridine systems with 4, 5, 6 to 11 rings	J. Doeuvre	20,	623-678 (1953)
Heterocycles of more than six links with an atom of nitrogen	S. David	20,	679-705 (1953)
Pentatomic heterocycles. Pyrazole group	M. Julia	20,	707-847 (1953)
The imidazoles (-pyrazole, glyoxaline etc.)	A. Lespagnol	20,	849-956 (1953)
Hexatomic heterocycles with two nitrogen atoms. Pyridazines	A. Étienne	20,	957-1175 (1953)
Pyrimidines	M. Cramer	20,	1179-1357 (1953)
Hexatomic heterocycles with two atoms of nitrogen (diazines). Rings of the paradiazine or pyrazine systems	R. Paul	21,	1-307 (1953)
Heterocycles of more than six atoms with two hetero nitrogens	P. Jullien	21,	309-325 (1953)
Heterocycles with oxygen and nitrogen	P. Jullien	21,	327-437 (1953)
Heterocycles with two hetero-atoms (nitrogen and sulfur	R. Rambaud	21,	439-627 (1953)
Heterocycles with three hetero-atoms (trioxanes and trithianes, dioxathianes and oxadithianes)	A. Étienne	21,	637-674 (1953)
Pentatomic heterocycles with three atoms of nitrogen (triazoles)	A. Étienne	21,	675-837 (1953)
Symmetric triazoles (S-triazoles or 1, 2, 4-triazoles)	A. Étienne	21,	839-966 (1953)
Hexatomic heterocycles with three atoms of nitrogen (triazines)	J. Doeuvre	21,	967-980 (1953)
Pentatomic heterocycles with an atom of oxygen and two atoms of nitrogen (furadiazoles or furodiazoles)	J. Doeuvre	21,	981-1004 (1953)
Hexatomic heterocycles with three hetero-atoms (oxygen and nitrogen)	J. Doeuvre	21,	1005-1010 (1953)
Hexatomic heterocycles with three hetero-atoms (sulfur or selenium and nitrogen) (thialdines and thiadiazines)	J. Doeuvre	21,	1057-1064 (1953)

TRAITÉ DE CHIMIE ORGANIQUE (Contd.)

Heterocycles with four hetero-atoms	J. Doeuvre	21,	1065-1100 (1953)
Heterocycles containing metalloidal hetero-atoms or metallic hetero-atoms other than oxygen, sulfur (or selenium) or nitrogen	J. Doeuvre	21,	1103-1104 (1953)
General methods of industrial organic chemistry	G. Dupont	22,	1-65 (1953)
Large-scale syntheses of modern organic chemistry	H. Guinot	22,	67-204 (1953)
Dyes	H. Wahl	22,	205-473 (1953)
Tanning agents and tanning	L. Meunier	22,	475-513 (1953)
Synthetic high polymers. Plastics, textiles, elastomers	G. Champetier	22,	515-761 (1953)
Chemistry of natural rubber	J. LeBras	22,	763-832 (1953)
Soaps and related products	F. Lachampt and R. Perron	22,	833-1005 (1953)
Perfumes	L.-M. Labaune	22,	1007-1068 (1953)
The fermentation industries	P. Heitzmann	22,	1069-1112 (1953)
Chemotherapy	J. Tréfouel and T.J. Tréfouel	22,	1113-1250 (1953)
Compounds with condensed pyrimidine rings	M. Cramer	23,	1 A - 86 A (1954)

ÜBER STERINE, GALLENSÄURE UND VERWANDTE NATURSTOFFE

This is a collective volume on sterols, bile-acids and related natural products, in German, edited by H. Lettré and R. Tschesche, published by Enke Verlag, Stuttgart.

Title	Author	Reference
Sterols and bile-acids	H. Lettré	1, 1-168 (1954)
Vitamin D and irradiation products of the antirachitic provitamins	H. Lettré	1, 169-207 (1954)
The neutral saponins (spirostano glycosides)	R. Tschesche	1, 208-246 (1954)
The sterol alkaloids	H. Fernholz	1, 247-286 (1954)
The heart venoms	R. Tschesche	1, 287-431 (1954)
The androgens	H. Heusser and H. Jahnke	2, 1-113 (1959)
The estrogens	H. Jahnke	2, 114-181 (1959)
The pregnanes without C-11 oxygen	F. Blohmeyer	2, 182-352 (1959)
Steroids with an oxygenated function at C-11	J. Ecks	2, 353-587 (1959)
Aldosterone	A. Wettstein	2, 588-617 (1959)
Constellation-analysis of the steroid skeleton	D.H.R. Bartom	2, 618-636 (1959)
Aromatization of the A ring of steroids	H.H. Inhoffen	2, 637-654 (1959)
Total synthesis of vitamin D_3	K. Irmscher	2, 655-668 (1959)

VISTAS IN FREE-RADICAL CHEMISTRY

This is a collection of reviews in memoriam to Morris S. Kharasch. Edited by W.A. Waters and published by Pergamon Press, New York (1959).

Title	Author	Page
The significance of the work of M.S. Kharasch in the development of free-radical chemistry	W.A. Waters and F.R. Mayo	1-5
The published researches of M.S. Kharasch		6-16
Reprints of selected papers by M.S. Kharasch		17-138
The discovery of the peroxide effect	F.R. Mayo	139-142
The contributions of M.S. Kharasch to polymer chemistry	C. Walling	143-150
Some trends in the study of free-radical reactions in solution	W.A. Waters	151-161
The chemistry of free radicals in the gas phase	K.O. Kutschke and E.W.R. Steacie	162-195
Homolytic aliphatic substitutions	H.C. Brown	196-208
Homolytic aromatic substitution	D.H. Hey	209-223
Some new chain reactions induced by acyl peroxides	G.A. Rasuwajew	224-234
Electrophilic addition to 1:1:1-trichloropropene	A.N. Nesmeyanov et. al.,	235-241
The reaction of benzyl ethers with free tert.-butoxy radicals	R.L. Huang and S.S. Si-Hoe	242-251

ADDENDUM

The entries below give only the references and the name of the editor. The individual titles of contributions and names of authors within each symposia are not, however, listed.

Title	Editors	Reference
The chemistry of amino-acids and proteins (2nd. edition)	C. L. A. Schmidt	Thomas, Baltimore (1944) 1290 pp.
The chemistry and physiology of the hormones	F. R. Moulton	American Association for the Advancement of Science (1944) 243 pp.
Glycerol	C. S. Miner and N. N. Dalton	Reinhold, New York (1953) 460 pp.
Glycols	G. O. Curme and F. Johnston	Reinhold, New York (1953) 389 pp.
Joint symposium on the nomenclature of hydrocarbons	ACS Symposium	Am. Chemical Soc. (1949) 132 pp.
Moderne Methoden der Pflanzenchemie (Modern methods of plant chemistry)	K. Paech and M. V. Tracey	Springer, Berlin (1955-
Nature and structure of collagen	I. Randall	Butterworths, London (1953) 269 pp.
Organic reagents for metals (5th. ed.)	W. C. Johnson	Chadwell Heath, Essex (1955) 360 pp.
Polymer degradation mechanisms	NBS Symposium	Natl. Bureau of Standards (1953) 150 pp.
Polypeptides which stimulate plain muscle	J. H. Gaddum	Livingstone, Edinburgh (1955) 140 pp.
The proteins	H. Neurath and K. Bailey	Academic, New York (1954-5) 849 pp.
Preparation and measurement of isotopic tracers	D. Wright, A. O. C. Nier and S. P. Reimann	Edwards, Ann Arbor (1946) 108 pp.
Les proteines (The proteins)	No editor listed	R. Stoops, Bruxelles (1953) 350 pp.
Survey of the chemical literature dealing with fluorine containing organic compounds	A. Roe, E. C. Markham, and R. W. Boost	Univ. North Carolina Press (1943) 403 pp.
Silicones	S. Fordham	G. Newnes, London (1960) 252 pp.
Some conjugated proteines	W. H. Cole	Rutgers Univ. Press (1953) 73 pp.
Symposium on chemical concepts of psychosis	M. Rinkel and H. C. B. Denber	McDowell-Obolensky, New York (1958) 400 pp.
Symposium on steroid hormones	E. S. Gordon	Univ. Wisconsin Press (1950) 396 pp.
Vapor phase chromatography	D. H. Desty and C. L. A. Harbourn	Academic, New York (1956) 436 pp.
Industrial gums; polysaccharides and their derivatives	R. L. Whistler	Academic, New York (1959) 766 pp.
Wood chemistry (2d. edition)	L. E. Wise	Reinhold, New York (1952)

PART III
MONOGRAPHS ON ORGANIC CHEMISTRY
1940-1960
Pages 236-254

Title	Author	Publisher
Vitamine, Hormone, Fermente (Vitamins, Hormones and enzymes)	R. Abderhalden	Schwabe, Basel (1956) 250 pp.
Biology of some peptide and steroid antibiotics	E. P. Abraham	Wiley, New York (1957) 96 pp.
Electrophoresis of proteins and the chemistry of cell surfaces	H. A. Abramson L.S. Moyer and M.H. Gorin	Reinhold, New York (1942) 341 pp.
An introduction to the chemistry of heterocyclic compounds	R.M. Acheson	Interscience, New York (1960) 342 pp.
The physics and chemistry of surfaces (3rd edition)	N.K. Adam	Oxford Univ. Press, London (1941) 436 pp.
The acridines. Their preparation, physical, chemical and biological properties and uses	A. Albert	Arnold, London (1951) 381 pp.
Heterocyclic chemistry; an introduction	A. Albert	Athlone, London (1959) 424 pp.
Principles of ionic organic reactions	E.R. Alexander	Wiley, New York (1950) 318 pp.
Organic electrode processes	M.J. Allen	Reinhold, New York (1958) 174 pp.
The chemistry and pharmacy of vegetable drugs	N.L. Allport	Chemical, Brooklyn (1944) 252 pp.
Molecules and crystals in organic chemistry	A.E. von Arkel	Interscience, New York (1956) 270 pp.
Problems in theoretical organic chemistry (Priestley lectures)	F.G. Arndt	Pennsylvania State Univ. Press (1954) 57 pp.
Chemie und Technologie der Paraffin-Kohlenwasserstoffe (Chemistry and technology of parafin hydrocarbons)	F. Asinger	Akademie, Berlin (1956) 719 pp.
The chemistry of petrochemicals	M.J. Astle	Reinhold, New York (1956) 267 pp.
Physico-chimie des combustibles liquides et des lubrifiants (hydrocarbures) (Physical chemistry of liquid combustion and lubrifying agents (hydrocarbons)	M. Aubert	J. and R. Sennac, Paris (1951) 842 pp.
The chemistry of hydrazine	L.F. Audrieth and B. Ackerson	Wiley, New York (1951) 244 pp.
Hormones and horticulture; the use of special chemicals in the control of plant growth	G.S. Avery, Jr., E.B. Johnson, R.M. Addoms and B.F. Thomson	McGraw-Hill, New York (1947) 326 pp.
The structure and reactions of the aromatic compounds	G.M. Badger	University, Cambridge (Eng.) (1954) 456 pp.
Melting and solidification of fats	A.E. Bailey	Interscience, New York (1950) 357 pp.
Hyperconjugation	J.W. Baker	Clarendon, Oxford (1952) 158 pp.
Electronic theories of organic chemistry	J.W. Baker	Oxford Univ. Press, London (1958) 224 pp.
Photosynthesis	E.C.C. Baly	Methuen, London (1940) 248 pp.

MONOGRAPHS (Contd.)

Title	Author(s)	Publisher
The kinetics of vinyl polymerization by radical mechanisms	C.H. Bamford, W.G. Barb, A.D. Jenkins and P.F. Onyon	Butterworths, London (1958) 318 pp.
Mechanism of organic chemical reactions	E. de B. Barnett	Blackie, London (1956) 289 pp.
Modern rubber chemistry (2d edition)	H. Barron	Hutchinson's, London, New York (1947) 502 pp.
The proton in chemistry	R.P. Bell	Methuen, London (1959) 223 pp.
The infra-red spectra of complex molecules (2d edition)	L.J. Bellamy	Methuen, London Wiley, New York (1958) 425 pp.
The foundations of chemical kinetics	S.W. Benson	McGraw-Hill, New York (1960) 703 pp.
The chemistry of the morphine alkaloids	K.W. Bentley	Oxford Univ. Press, London (1954) 433 pp.
Isomerism and isomerization of organic compounds	E.D. Bergmann	Interscience, New York (1948) 138 pp.
The chemistry of acetylene and related compounds	E.D. Bergmann	Interscience, New York (1948) 108 pp.
Catalysis, inorganic and organic	S. Berkman, J.C. Morrell and G. Egloff	Reinhold, New York (1940) 1130 pp.
The pentaerythritols	E. Berlow, R.H. Barth and J.E. Snow	Reinhold, New York (1958) 317 pp.
Methods of synthesis in organic chemistry (2d edition)	J.H. Billman and E.S. Cleland	Edwards, Ann Arbor (1951) 229 pp.
Chromatography of sugars and related substances	W.W. Binkley and M.L. Wolfrom	Sugar Research Foundation, New York (1948) 33 pp.
Metal ammine formation in aqueous solution; theory of the reversible step reactions	J. Bjerrum	Haase, Copenhagen (1941) 208 pp.
The amino acid composition of proteins and foods; analytical methods and results (2d edition)	R.J. Block and D. Bolling	Thomas, Springfield (1951) 576 pp.
Amino acid handbook; methods and results of protein analysis	R.J. Block, K.W. Weiss and H.J. Almquist	Thomas, Springfield (1956) 386 pp.
Methyl glucoside; preparation, physical constants, derivatives	G.N. Bollenback	Academic, New York (1958) 183 pp.
Carotene; its determination in biological materials	V.H. Booth	Heffer, Cambridge (Eng.) (1957) 119 pp.
Styrene; its polymers, copolymers and derivatives	R.H. Boundy, R.F. Boyer and S.M. Stoesser	Reinhold, New York (1952) 1304 pp.
Röntgenographisch-analytische chemie (Chemical analysis by X-Rays)	E. Brandenberger	Birkhäuser, Basel (1945) 287 pp.

The chemistry of lignin	F.E. Brauns	Academic, New York (1952) 808 pp.
The chemistry of the nonbenzenoid hydrocarbons (2d edition)	B.T. Brooks	Reinhold, New York (1950) 615 pp.
An introduction to electronic theories of organic chemistry	G.I. Brown	Longmans, Green & Co., London (1958) 209 pp.
Separation and identification of organic compounds (2d edition)	C. Buchanan, A. Kent, J.D. Loudon, I.M. McAlpine, J. Robertson, T.S. Stevens, F.R. Storrie and S.H. Tucker	Univ. of London Press, (1950) 23 pp.
Bacterial polysaccharides; their chemical and immunological aspects	M. Burger	Thomas, Springfield (1950) 272 pp.
Tracer applications for the study of organic reactions	J.G. Burr, Jr.	Interscience, New York (1957) 291 pp.
Sulphated oils and allied products; their chemistry and analysis	D. Burton and G.F. Robertshaw	Chemical, New York (1940) 163 pp.
Ion exchangers in organic and biochemistry	C. Calmon and T.R.E. Kressman	Interscience, New York (1957) 761 pp.
Oxosteroids	B. Camber	Lewis, London (1960) 79 pp.
Isotopic carbon: techniques in its measurement and chemical manipulation	M. Calvin, C. Heidelberger, I.C. Reid, B.M. Tolbert and P.F. Yankwich	Wiley, New York (1949) 376 pp.
Organic sequestering agents	S. Chaberek and A.E. Martell	Wiley, New York (1959) 618 pp.
Aspects of the organic chemistry of sulphur	F. Challenger	Butterworths, London (1959) 253 pp.
Derives cellulosiques (2d edition) (Derivatives of cellulose)	G. Champetier	Dunod, Paris (1954) 270 pp.
Aromatische Kohlenwasserstoffe; polycyclische systeme (2d edition) (Aromatic hydrocarbons; polycyclic systems)	E. Clar	Springer, Berlin (1952) 481 pp.
Hydrazine	C.C. Clark	Mathieson Chemical Corp., Baltimore (1953) 133 pp.
Quantitative methods of organic microanalysis	S.J. Clark	Butterworths, London (1956) 253 pp.
Oxidation-reduction potentials of organic systems	W.M. Clark	Williams & Wilkins, Baltimore Baillière, Tindall & Co., London (1960) 584 pp.
Physical and azeotropic data; hydrocarbons and sulphur compounds boiling below 200°C	G. Claxton	National Benzole and Allied Products, Cambridge (1958) 146 pp.
Organo-metallic compounds	G.E. Coates	Methuen, London (1956) 197 pp.

MONOGRAPHS (Contd.)

Proteins, amino acids and peptides as ions and dipolar ions	E.J. Cohn and J.T. Edsall	Reinhold, New York (1943) 686 pp.
Acetylene and carbon monoxide chemistry	J.W. Copenhaver and M.H. Bigelow	Reinhold, New York (1949) 357 pp.
Einschlussverbindungen (inclusion compounds)	F. Cramer	Springer, Berlin (1954) 115 pp.
Chain reactions	F.S. Dainton	Methuen, London (1956) 183 pp.
The biochemistry of the nucleic acids (2d edition)	J.N. Davidson	Methuen, London Wiley, New York (1953) 200 pp.
Bestimmung des Molekulargewichts von Polyamiden (Determination of the molecular weight of polyamides)	W.N. Dawydoff	VEB Technik, Berlin (1954) 98 pp.
Electronic mechanisms of organic reactions	A.R. Day	American Book Co., New York (1950) 314 pp.
An outline of organic reactions	E.F. Degering	Ypsilanti, Michigan (1945) 752 pp.
Aromatic substitution; nitration and halogenation	P.B.D. de la Mare and J.H. Ridd	Academic, New York (1959) 252 pp.
Fluorescent chemicals and their applications	J. De Ment and H.C. Dake	Chemical, Brooklyn (1942) 240 pp.
Fluorochemistry	J. De Ment	Chemical, Brooklyn (1945) 796 pp.
Chemical insect attractants and repellents	V.G. Dethier	Blackiston, Philadelphia (1947) 289 pp.
The lipids, their chemistry and biochemistry (Volume 1: Chemistry)	H.J. Deuel	Interscience, New York (1951) 983 pp.
The electronic theory of organic chemistry	M.J.S. Dewar	Clarendon, Oxford (1949) 324 pp.
Optical rotatory dispersion	C. Djerassi	McGraw-Hill, New York (1960) 293 pp.
The chemistry and technology of naphtalene compounds	N. Donaldson	Arnold, London (1958) 512 pp.
The methods of cellulose chemistry	C. Dorée	Chapman and Hall, London (1947) 543 pp.
Le nitrile hydroxy-crotonique (The hydroxy-crotonic nitrile)	A. Dormael	Palais des Académies, Bruxelles (1945) 34 pp.
Physical constants of the principal hydrocarbons (4th edition)	M.P. Doss	Texas Co., New York (1943) 215 pp.
Properties of the principal fats, fatty oils, waxes, fatty acids and their salts	M.P. Doss	Texas Co., New York (1952) 244 pp.
Biological polymers (Priestley lectures)	P. Doty	Pennsylvania State Univ. Press, (1955) 62 pp.
Progres recents en chimie organique (Recent progress in organic chemistry)	R. Dulou and L. Peyron	Presses documentaires, Paris (1952) 395 pp.
The furans	A.P. Dunlop and F.N. Peters	Reinhold, New York (1953) 867 pp.

Anatomie und Chemie des Holzes (Anatomy and chemistry of wood)	J. Durat	Fachbuch, Leipzig (1953) 116 pp.
A new notation and enumeration system for organic compounds (2d edition)	G.M. Dyson	Longmans, Green & Co., London, New York (1949) 138 pp.
Organosilicon compounds	C. Eaborn	Butterworths, London (1960) 530 pp.
Chlorophyll in 1953	W.H. Eddy	Strong Cobb & Co., (1953) 60 pp.
Organische peroxyde (Organic peroxides)	W. Eggersgluss	Chemie, Weinheim (1951) 86 pp.
Isomerization of pure hydrocarbons	G. Egloff, G. Hulla and V.I. Komarewsky	Reinhold, New York (1942) 499 pp.
Alkylation of alkanes	G. Egloff and G. Hulla	Reinhold, New York (1948)
Colchicine in agriculture, medicine, biology and chemistry	O.J. Eigsti and P. Dustin	Iowa State College Press (1955) 470 pp.
Chemismus und Konstitution (Chemistry and structure)	B. Eistert	Enke, Stuttgart (1948)
The chemical action of ultraviolet rays	C. Ellis, A.A. Wells and F.F. Heyroth	Reinhold, New York (1941) 961 pp.
Grundriss der Kohlenhydratchemie (Carbohydrate chemistry)	H. Elsner	Parey, Berlin (1941) 216 pp. Edwards, Ann Arbor (1945) 216 pp.
Chemie und Biochemie der Reduktone und Reduktonate (Chemistry and biochemistry; reductones and reductonates)	H. von Euler-Chelpin, B. Eistert and H. Hasselquist	Enke, Stuttgart (1957) 344 pp.
Oxidation of carbohydrates; keturonic acids; salt catalysis	M.R. Everett and F. Sheppard	Univ. of Oklahoma Press (1944) 111 pp.
The chemistry of drugs (3rd. edition)	N. Evers	Interscience, New York (1959) 416 pp.
Encyclopedia of hydrocarbon compounds	J.F. Faraday	Chemical, Brooklyn (1946)
Electron structures of organic molecules	L.N. Ferguson	Prentice-Hall, New York (1952) 335 pp.
Handbook of hydrocarbons	S.W. Ferris	Academic, New York (1955) 324 pp.
Steroids (4th edition)	L.F. Fieser and M. Fieser	Reinhold, New York (1959) 945 pp.
Triäthanolamin und andere Alkanolamine (4th edition) (Triethanolamine and other alkylamines)	E.J. Fischer, C. Luttgen and H. Mollering	Chemie und Technik, Heidelberg (1953) 338 pp.
Die Chemie des Pyrrols (The chemistry of pyrrole)	H. Fischer and H. Orth	(1934-1940)
Maleic anhydride derivatives; reactions of the double bond	L.H. Flett and W.H. Gardner	Wiley, New York (1952) 269 pp.
Principles of polymer chemistry	P.J. Flory	Cornell Univ. Press, Ithaca (1953) 672 pp.
Fluoreszenz organischer Verbindungen (Fluorescence of organic compounds)	T. Forster	Vandenhoeck, Gottingen

MONOGRAPHS (Contd.)

Title	Author(s)	Publisher
Chemical activities of fungi	J.W. Foster	Academic, New York (1949) 648 pp.
Ultraviolet spectra of aromatic compounds	R.A. Friedel and M. Orchin	Wiley, New York (1951) 52 pp.
Holzöl und ähnlich trocknende Öle (Wood oils and related drying oils)	F. Fritz	Pansegrau, Berlin (1951) 258 pp.
Kinetics and mechanism. A study of homogeneous chemical reactions	A.A. Frost and R.G. Pearson	Wiley, New York (1958) 343 pp.
Optical activity and living matter	G.F. Gause	Biodynamica, Normandy (1941) 162 pp.
Reduction with complex metal hydrides	N.G. Gaylord	Interscience, New York (1956) 1046 pp.
Die ätherischen Öle (4th edition) (2 volumes) (The essential oils)	E. Gildemeister, F. Hoffman and W. Treibs	Akademie, Berlin (1956-1960) 902 pp.
An introduction to electronic absorption spectroscopy in organic chemistry (2d edition)	A.E. Gillam and E.S. Stern	Arnold, London (1958) 326 pp.
Organo-metallic and organo-metalloidal high-temperature lubricants and related materials	H. Gilman and R.D. Gorsich	Iowa State College Press (1955) 130 pp.
The chemistry of plant constituents (revised edition)	O. Gisvold and C.H. Rogers	Burgess, Minneapolis (1943) 484 pp.
Die Gerbstoffe und Gerbmittel (3rd edition) (The tannins and tanning agents)	H. Gnamm	Wissenschaftlicher, Stuttgart (1949) 570 pp.
The petroleum chemicals industry (2d edition)	R.F. Goldstein	Wiley, New York (1958) 458 pp.
Über das Molekulargewicht der Zellulose (The molecular weight of cellulose)	O.P. Golova and V.I. Ivanov	Akademie, Berlin (1953) 91 pp.
The comparative biochemistry of the carotenoids	T.W. Goodwin	Chapman and Hall, London (1952) 356 pp.
Mechanism and structure in organic chemistry	E.S. Gould	Holt, New York (1959) 790 pp.
Les isotopes lourds en biologie (The heavy isotopes in biology)	J. Govaerts	Masson, Paris (1947) 35 pp.
The chemistry of high polymer degradation processes	N. Grassie	Butterworths, London (1956) 335 pp.
Amino acids and proteins	D.M. Greenberg	Thomas, Springfield (1951), 950 pp.
Chemical pathways of metabolism	D.M. Greenberg	Academic, New York (1954)
Chemistry of the amino acids	J.P. Greenstein and M. Winnitz	Wiley, New York (196)
Amino acids and proteins; chemistry, pharmacology, clinical applications	J.Q. Griffith C.F. Krewson and J. Naghski	Mack, Easton, Pa. (1955) 275 pp.
The essential oils The essential oils (5 volumes)	E. Guenther, D. Althausen, F.S. Sterrett A.J. Haagen-Smit, E.E. Langenau and G. Urdang	Van Nostrand, Princeton, N.J. (1948-1952) 3172 pp.
Die biogenen Amine (The biogenic amines)	M. Guggenheim	S. Karger, Basel (1951) 619 pp.
The chemistry and reactivity of collagen	K.H. Gustavson	Academic, New York (1956) 342 pp.

The chemistry of tanning processes	K.H. Gustavson	Academic, New York (1956) 403 pp.
Polyisobutylen und Isobutylen Mischpolymerisate (Polyisobutylene and isobutylene mixed polymers)	H. Güterbock	Springer, Berlin (1959) 263 pp.
Tables of percentage composition of organic compounds	H. Gysel	Birkhauser, Basel (1951) 637 pp.
The chemistry of isobutyraldehyde and its derivatives	H.J. Hagemeyr and G.C. DeCroes	Tennessee Eastman Kingsport (1953) 94 pp.
Chemistry of wood	E. Hägglund	Academic, New York (1951) 631 pp.
Papierchromatography (Paper chromatography)	I.M. Hais and K. Macek	VEB-Fisher, Jena (1960) 1376 pp.
The technology and chemistry of alkaloids	F.E. Hamerslag	Van Nostrand, Toronto, New York (1950) 319 pp.
Physical organic chemistry. Reaction rates, equilibria and mechanisms	L.P. Hammett	McGraw-Hill, New York (1940) 404 pp.
Hanna's handbook of agricultural chemicals (2d edition)	L.W. Hanna	(1958) 489 pp.
Lipide chemistry	D.J. Hanahan	Academic, New York (1960) 330 pp.
Fluorine and its compounds	R.N. Haszeldine and A.G. Sharpe	Methuen, London Wiley, New York (1951) 153 pp.
The chemistry of petrochemical reactions	L.F. Hatch	Gulf, Houston (1955) 182 pp.
Anti-composition tables for carbon compounds (CH, CHO, CHS, and CHOS)	H.H. Hatt, T. Pearcey and A.Z. Szumer	University, Cambridge (Eng.) (1955) 191 pp.
Chemistry and biology of proteins	F. Haurowitz	Academic, New York (1950) 374 pp.
Silicic science	E.A. Hauser	Van Nostrand, Princeton (1955) 188 pp.
Handbuch der mikrochemischen Methoden (Manual of microchemical methods)	F. Hecht and K. Zacherl (editors)	Springer, Wien (1954)
Chemische Koordinationslehre (Coordination chemistry)	F. Hein	Hirzel, Zurich (1950) 683 pp.
Chemie der Beta-Dicarbonyl-Verbindungen (Chemistry of Beta-diketones)	H. Henecka	Springer, Berlin (1950) 409 pp.
The plant alkaloids (4th edition)	T.A. Henry	Churchill, London (1949) 804 pp.
Physics and chemistry of cellulose fibres	P.H. Hermans	Elsevier, New York (1949) 534 pp.
Introduction to theoretical organic chemistry	P.H. Hermans and R.E. Reeves	Elsevier, Amsterdam (1954) 505 pp.
Molecular spectra and molecular structure (2d edition)	G. Herzberg	Van Nostrand, New York (1950) 616 pp.

The chemistry of cellulose	E. Heuser	Wiley, New York Chapman and Hall, London (1944) 660 pp.
Die neueren Ergebnisse der Starkeforschung (Recent advances in starch chemistry)	K. Heyns	Vieweg, Braunschweig (1949) 148 pp.
An introduction to electronic theory of organic compounds	H.L. Heys	Harrap, London (1960) 236 pp.
Reactions of organic compounds (3rd edition)	W.J. Hickinbottom	Longmans and Green, London (1957) 608 pp.
The chemical constitution of natural fats (3rd edition)	T.P. Hilditch	Chapman and Hall, London (1956) 664 pp.
Photosynthesis	R. Hill and C.P. Whittingham	Methuen, London Wiley, New York (1955) 165 pp.
Physical organic chemistry	J. Hine	McGraw-Hill, New York (1956) 497 pp.
The chemical kinetics of the bacterial cell	C.N. Hinshelwood	Clarendon, Oxford (1946) 284 pp.
Recent progress in the chemistry of the carbohydrates especially in the United States	R.C. Hockett	Sugar Research Foundation, New York (1946) 20 pp.
Enzymologie (Enzymology)	O. Hoffmann-Ostenhof	Springer, Wien (1954) 772 pp.
Oxine and its derivatives (4 volumes)	R.G.W. Hollingshead	Butterworths, London (1954-1956) 1211 pp.
Recent advances in the chemistry of cellulose and starch	J. Honeyman	Heywood, London (1959) 358 pp.
Die polyamide (The polyamides)	H. Hopff, A. Müller and F. Wenger	Springer, Berlin (1954) 423 pp.
Fungicides and their action	J.G. Horsfall and D. Fairchild	Chronica botanica, Waltham (1945) 239 pp.
Die Pektine und ihre Verwendung (The pectins and their use)	B. Hottenroth	Oldenbourg, Munchen (1951) 210 pp.
Das Anthracen und die Anthrachinone (Anthracene and anthraquinones)	J. Houben and W. Fischer	Thieme, Leipzig (1929) 890 pp. Edwards, Ann Arbor (1944)
Vegetable gums and resins	F.N. Howes	Chronica botanica, Waltham (1949) 188 pp.
Theoretical principles of organic chemistry	W. Hückel	Elsevier, Amsterdam (1955) 1303 pp.
Collected papers	C.S. Hudson	Academic, New York (1946-1948) 1693 pp.
Chemie der phenolharze (Chemistry of the phenolic resins)	K. Hultzsch	Springer, Berlin (1950) 193 pp.
The preparation, properties, chemical behavior and identification of organic chlorine compounds	E.H. Huntress	Wiley, New York (1948) 1443 pp.
Chemie der Silikone (2d edition) (Chemistry of silicones)	A. Hunyar	VEB Technik, Berlin (1959) 343 pp.

MONOGRAPHS (Contd.)

A correlation of some physical properties of alkanes and alkenes	R.C. Huston	Michigan State College Press (1947) 96 pp.
Substitution at elements other than carbon	C.K. Ingold	Interscience, New York (1959) 60 pp.
Structure and mechanism in organic chemistry	C.K. Ingold	Cornell Univ. Press, Ithaca (1953) 828 pp.
Free radicals as studied by electron spin resonance	D.J.E. Ingram	Butterworths, London (1958) 274 pp.
Applications of nuclear magnetic resonance spectroscopy in organic chemistry	L.M. Jackman	Pergamon, New York (1959) 134 pp.
Synthetic analgenics. Diphenylpropylamines	P.A.J. Janssen	Pergamon, London (1960) 183 pp.
Estimation of thermodynamic properties of organic compounds	G.J. Janz	Academic, New York (1958) 211 pp.
The chemistry of organic medicinal products (3rd edition)	G.L. Jenkins and W.H. Hartung	Wiley, New York (1949) 745 pp.
Organic colloidals	B. Jirgensons	Elsevier, Amsterdam, New York (1958) 655 pp.
The chemistry of the acetylenic compounds. I. Acetylenic alcohols. II. Acetylenic acids	A.W. Johnson	Arnold, London (1946) 393 pp. (1950) 328 pp.
Vapor pressure of organic compounds	T.E. Jordan	Interscience, New York (1954) 266 pp.
Induced oxidation	W.P. Jorissen	Elsevier, Amsterdam. London, New York (1959) 208 pp.
Mecanismes electroniques en chimie organique (Electronic mechanisms in organic chemistry)	M. Julia	Gauthier-Villars, Paris (1959) 99 pp.
Organische Warmetrager fur hohe Temperaturen (Organic heat conductors at high temperature)	S.S. Kagan, A.W. Tschetschetkin and W.O. Fogel	VEB Technik, Berlin (1953) 167 pp.
Die Kohlenwasserstoff-Synthese nach Fischer-Tropsch (The hydrocarbon synthesis by the Fischer-Tropsch method)	F. Kainer	Springer, Berlin (1950) 322 pp.
Einfuhrung in die Elektrontheorie organischer Verbindungen (Introduction to the electronic theory of organic compounds)	G. Karagounis	Springer, Berlin (1959) 194 pp.
Les péroxydes organiques (Organic peroxides)	V. Karnojitzki	Hermann, Paris (1958) 142 pp.
Heterocyclic chemistry		
Carotinoide (Carotenoids)	P. Karrer and E. Jucker	Birkhäuser, Basel (1948) 388 pp. Elsevier, New York (1950) 384 pp.
Konstitution und vorkommen der organischen Pflanzenstoffe, exclusive Alkaloide (Structure and occurence of organic plant compounds, exclusive of alkaloids)	W. Karrer	Birkhäuser, Basel (1958) 1207 pp.

MONOGRAPHS (Contd.)

Title	Author(s)	Publisher
Bibliography for physical behavior of hydrocarbons under pressure and related phenomena	D. L. Katz and M. J. Rzasa	Edwards, Ann Arbor (1946) 306 pp.
Chemistry and industry of starch (2d edition)	R. W. E. Kerr	Academic, New York (1950) 719 pp.
The pectic substances	Z. I. Kertesz	Interscience, New York (1951) 628 pp.
Grignard reactions of nonmetallic substances	M. S. Kharasch and O. Reinmuth	Prentice-Hall, New York (1954) 1384 pp.
Literature review on selective hydrogenation of oils and fats	W. J. Kirkpatrick	International Nickel Co., Pittsburgh (1947) 11 pp.
Fats and oils. An outline of their chemistry and technology	H. G. Kirschenbauer	Reinhold, New York (1944) 154 pp.
Electrical properties of phtalocyanine; technical report	D. Kleitman	Purdue Univ. Press, Lafayette (1953) 66 pp.
Chemical constitution and antifungal action of sulphur compounds	H. L. Klöpping	(1951) 142 pp.
The chemistry of the steroids	W. Klyne	Methuen, London (1957) 215 pp.
Mikro-methoden zur Kennzeichnung organischer Stoffe und Stoffgemische (3rd edition) (Microchemical methods in organic chemistry)	L. Kofler, A. Kofler and M. Brandstatter	Chemie, Weinheim (1954) 608 pp.
Organophosphorus compounds	G. M. Kosolapoff	Wiley, New York (1950) 376 pp.
Polymerisationskinetik (Kinetics of polymerization)	L. Küchler	Springer, Berlin (1951) 287 pp.
Lecithin	R. Kunze and H. C. Buer	Rosenmeier, Berlin (1941) 166 pp. Edwards, Ann Arbor (1945) 166 pp.
Les derives chimiques du caoutchouc naturel (Chemical derivatives of natural rubber)	J. Le Bras, A. Delalande and J. Duclaux	Dunod, Paris (1950) 485 pp.
Organic derivatives of silicon and germanium; molecular motion in organosilanes and silicones	H. G. LeClair, J. C. Sternberg and E. G. Rochow	U.S. Department of Commerce, Washington, D.C. (1953) 143 pp.
Chromatographie en chimie organique et biologique (2 volumes) (Chromatography in organic and biological chemistry)	E. Lederer	Masson, Paris (1960) 1112 pp.
Dipole moments: their measurements and applications in chemistry (3rd edition)	R. J. W. LeFèvre	Wiley, New York (1953)
Epoxy resins. Their applications and technology	H. Lee and K. Neville	McGraw-Hill, New York (1957) 305 pp.
The reactive intermediates of organic chemistry	J. E. Leffler	Interscience, New York (1956) 275 pp.
Autoxidation of diethyl ether	G. O. Lindgren	Acta chirurgica Scandinavica, Stockholm (1946) 190 pp.

The petroleum acids and bases	H.L. Lochte and E.R. Littmann	Chemical, New York (1955) 368 pp.
Aliphatic fluorine compounds	A.M. Lovelace, D.A. Rausch and W. Postelnek	Reinhold, New York (1958) 270 pp.
The chemistry of synthetic dyes and pigments	H.A. Lubs	Reinhold, New York (1955) 702 pp.
Glyzerin und glyzerinähnliche Stoffe (2d edition) (Glycerin and related compounds)	C. Lüttgen	Chemie und Technik, Heidelberg (1955) 198 pp.
The characterization of organic compounds	S.M. McElvain	Macmillan, New York (1949) 282 pp.
The plant glycosides	R.J. McIlroy	Arnold, London (1951) 138 pp.
Die Pektine (The pectines)	H. Maase	Serger and Hempel, Braunschweig (1951) 415 pp.
The water-soluble gums	C.L. Mantell	Reinhol
The water-soluble gums	C.L. Mantell	Reinhold, New York (1947) 279 pp.
Fatty acids, their chemistry and physical properties	K.S. Markley	Interscience, New York (1947) 279 pp.
An introduction to the chemistry of cellulose (2d edition)	J.T. Marsh and F.C. Wood	Chapman and Hall, London (1942) 512 pp.
Chemistry of the metal chelate compounds	A.E. Martell and M. Calvin	Prentice-Hall, New York (1952) 613 pp.
The chemistry of phenolic resins	R.W. Martin	Wiley, New York (1956) 298 pp.
An introduction to the organic chemistry of high polymers	C.S. Marvel	Wiley, New York (1959) 82 pp.
Contribution a l'étude de la formation des systemes conjugues dans les corps gras (Conjugated systems in fats: contribution to the study of their formation)	R. Massoni	Institut des corps gras, Lons le Saunier (1952) 100 pp.
Constantes sélectionnées: Pouvoir rotatoire naturel (Selected constants: natural optical rotation)	J.P. Mathieu and A. Petit	Masson, Paris
Data book on hydrocarbons; applications to process engineering	J.B. Maxwell	Van Nostrand, New York (1950) 259 pp.
The chemistry of natural coloring matters	F. Mayer	Reinhold, New York (1943) 854 pp.
Phenolic resin chemistry	H.J.L. Megson	Butterworths, London (1958) 323 pp.
Biochemistry of the amino acids	A. Meister	Academic, New York (1957) 485 pp.
Organic reagents in inorganic analysis	I. Mellan	Blakiston, Philadelphia (1941) 682 pp.
Dictionnaire des huiles végétales (Dictionary of vegetable oils)	P.H. Mensier	Lechevalier, Paris (1957) 763 pp.
Organic insecticides; their chemistry and mode of action	R.L. Metcalf	Interscience, New York (1955) 392 pp.

Analyse und Konstitutionsermittlung organischer Verbindungen (6th edition) (Analysis and identification of structure of organic compounds)	H.J.L. Meyer	Edwards, Ann Arbor (1943) 886 pp.
Makromolekulare Chemie (2d edition) (macromolecular chemistry)	K.H. Meyer, H. Mark and A.J.A. van der Wyk	Geest and Portig, Leipzig (1950) 1023 pp.
Chemie der Zucker und Polysaccharide (2d edition) (Chemistry of sugars and polysaccharides)	F. Micheel and A. Klemer	Geest and Portig, Leipzig (1956) 512 pp.
Lithium aluminium hydride in organic chemistry	V.M. Mićović and M. Lj. Mihailović	Haucna Knjiga, Belgrad (1955) 193 pp.
The chemistry of organic cyanogen compounds	V. Migrdichian	Reinhold, New York (1947) 460 pp.
Cellulose nitrate	F.D. Miles	Oliver and Boyd, London Interscience, New York (1955) 422 pp.
The chemistry of plants	E.V. Miller	Reinhold, New York (1957) 174 pp.
Frozen free radicals	G.J. Minkoff	Interscience, New York (1960) 148 pp.
Structure of molecules and internal rotation	S.I. Mizushima	Academic, New York (1954) 244 pp.
Das Absorptionsspektrum der chemischen Bindung The absorption spectra of the chemical bond)	H. Mohler	Fischer, Jena (1943) 170 pp. Edwards, Ann Arbor (1946) 170 pp.
The chemical production of lactic acid from sugars	R. Montgomery	Sugar Research Foundation, New York (1949) 28 pp.
The chemistry of heterocyclic compounds	A.A. Morton	McGraw-Hill, New York, London (1946) 549 pp.
Levulinic acid as a source of heterocyclic compounds	A.A. Morton	Sugar Research Foundation, New York (1947) 28 pp.
Internationaler Kodex der aterschen Öle (International Kodex of ethereal oils)	A. Müller	Huthig, Heidelberg (1952) 244 pp.
Neuere Anschauungen der Organischen Chemie (New aspects of organic chemistry)	E. Müller	Springer, Berlin (1940) 391 pp. Edwards, Ann Arbor (1944) 391 pp.
DDT, das Insektizid Dichlordiphenyl-trichlorathan und seine Bedeutung (The insecticide dichlorodiphenyl-trichloroethane and its significance)	P. Müller et al.	Birkhauser, Basel (1955) 299 pp.
Aspects of the constitution of mineral oils	K. van Nes and H.A. van Westen	Elsevier, New York (1951) 484 pp.
Organic synthesis with isotopes. 2 vols. (2d. edition)	A. Murray and D.L. Williams	Interscience, New York (1958) 2254 pp.
Enzymatische Katalyze (Enzymatic catalysis)	K. Myrbäck	W. de Gruyter, Berlin (1953) 181 pp.
Enzyme chemistry	J.B. Neilands and P.K. Stumpf	Wiley, New York (1955) 315 pp.
Aspects of the constitution of mineral oils	K. van Nes and H.A. van Westen	Elsevier, New York (1951) 484 pp.

MONOGRAPHS (Contd.)

Title	Author(s)	Publisher
Plant growth-substance	H. Nicol	Chemical, Brooklyn (1941) 148 pp.
Micromethods of quantitative organic analysis (2d edition)	J.B. Niederl and V. Niederl	Wiley, New York (1942) 347 pp.
Chlorkautschuk und die übrigen Halogenverbindungen des Kautschuks (Chlorinated rubbers and other halogen derivatives of rubber)	A. Nielsen	Hirzel, Leipzig (1937) 123 pp. Edwards, Ann Arbor (1947) 123 pp.
Grundlagen der Stereochemie (Stereochemistry)	P. Niggli	Birkhauser, Basel (1945) 283 pp.
The chemistry of acetylene	J.A. Nieuwland and R.R. Vogt	Reinhold, New York (1945) 219 pp.
Die Chemie des Holzes (Chemistry of wood)	N.I. Nikitin	Akademie, Berlin (1955) 569 pp.
The sulfonamides and allied compounds	E.H. Northey	Reinhold, New York (1948) 576 pp.
A manual for coding organic compounds for use with a mechanized searching system	T.R. Norton and A. Opler	Dow, Pittsburg (1956) 55 pp.
A manual for programming computers for use with a mechanized system for searching organic compounds	A. Opler and T.R. Norton	Dow, Pittsburg (1956) 23 pp.
Aromatic cyclodehydrogenation	M. Orchin	U.S. Govt. Print. Office, Washington (1948) 40 pp.
Valency: Classical and modern	W.G. Palmer	Cambridge Univ. Press (1959) 244 pp.
The ring index	A.M. Patterson, L.T. Capell and D.F. Walker	American Chemical Society, Washington, D.C. (1960) 1425 pp.
Industrial fatty acids and their applications	E. Pattison	Reinhold, New York (1959) 230 pp.
The nature of the chamical bond and the structure of molecules and cuptals (3rd edition)	L. Pauling	Cornell Univ. Press, Ithaca (1960) 644 pp.
Principles and practice of gas chromatography	R.L. Pecsock	Chapman and Hall, London (1959) 226 pp.
Structural carbohydrate chemistry	E.G.V. Percival	Muller, London (1950) 246 pp.
Macromolécules (Macromolecules)	P. Piganiol	Dunod, Paris (1947) 275 pp.
Acetylene, homologs and derivatives	P. Piganiol	Mapleton, Brooklyn (1950) 356 pp.
The hydrogen bond	G.C. Pimentel and A.L. McClellan	Freeman, San Francisco (1960) 475 pp.
Cellulose chemistry	M. Plunguian	Chemical, New York (1943) 97 pp.
Preparation of humic acids	T.S. Polansky, C.R. Kinner and A.W. Ganger	Pennsylvania State College Press (1946) 68 pp.
High resolution nuclear magnetic resonance	J. Pople, W.G. Schneider and H.J. Bernstein	McGraw-Hill, New York (1959) 501 pp.

MONOGRAPHS (Contd.)

The chemistry of the aliphatic orthoesters	H.W. Post	Reinhold, New York (1943) 188 pp.
Silicones and other organic silicon compounds	H.W. Post	Reinhold, New York (1949) 230 pp.
The chemistry and physics of organic pigments	L.S. Pratt	Wiley, New York (1947) 359 pp.
Quantitative organische Mikroanalyse (Quantitative organic microanalysis)	F. Pregl	Springer, Wien (1958) 361 pp.
The molecular architecture of plant cell walls	R.D. Preston	Wiley, New York (1952) 211 pp.
Mechanisms of reactions at carbon-carbon double bonds	C.C. Price	Interscience, New York (1946) 120 pp.
Kartothek der thiazolverbindungen (Card catalog of thiazole compounds)	B. Prijs	Karger, New York, Basel
Fluorescence and phosphorescence	P. Pringsheim	Insterscience, New York (1949) 793 pp.
Organic reagents used in quantitative inorganic analysis	W. Prodinger	Elsevier, New York (1940) 203 pp.
Cancerisation par les substances chimiques (Production of cancer by chemical agents)	A. Pullman and B. Pullman	Masson, Paris (1955) 306 pp.
Les theories electroniques de la chimie organique (Electron theories in organic chemistry)	B. Pullman and A. Pullman	Masson, Paris (1952) 665 pp.
Starch and its derivatives	J.A. Radley	Chapman and Hall, London (1953)
Fatty acids and their derivatives	A.W. Ralston	Wiley, New York (1948) 986 pp.
Infra-red determination of organic structures	H.M. Randall	Van Nostrand, New York (1949) 239 pp.
Acetylenic compounds in organic synthesis	R.A. Raphael	Academic, New York (1955) 219 pp.
Organic chemistry; electronic theory and reaction mechanism	R.I. Reed and S.H. Tucker	Macmillan, London (1956) 108 pp.
Die Mannich-Reaktion (The Mannich reaction)	B. Reichert	Springer, Berlin (1959) 195 pp.
Excited states in chemistry and biology	C. Reid	Academic, New York (1957) 215 pp.
Organic chemistry of bivalent sulfur (2 volumes)	E.E. Reid	Chemical, New York (1958-1960) 1015 pp.
Electronic interpretations of organic chemistry (2d edition)	A.E. Remick	Wiley, New York (1949) 600 pp.
Free radicals	F.O. Rice	Catholic Univ. of America Press, Washington (1958) 278 pp.
Acetylene chemistry	J.W. Reppe	U.S. Dept. of Commerce, Washington, D.C. (1949) 209 pp.
Neue entwicklungen auf dem gebiete der Chemie des Acetylens und Kohlenoxyds (New developments in the chemistry of acetylene and carbon monoxide	J.W. Reppe	Springer, Berlin (1949) 184 pp.

Chemie und technik der acetylendruck reaktionen (Chemistry and technology of reactions of acetylene under pressure)	J.W. Reppe	Chemie, Weinheim (1951) 131 pp.
Monomeric acrylic esters	E.H. Riddle	Reinhold, New York (1954) 221 pp.
Alkylperoxyde und ozonide (Alkylperoxydes and ozonides)	A. Rieche	Edwards, Ann Arbor (1945) 172 pp.
The chemistry of the terpenes	A.R. Rinder	Wiley, New York (1960) 217 pp.
Nuclear magnetic resonance applications to organic chemistry	J.D. Roberts	McGraw-Hill, New York ((1959) 118 pp.
Organic crystals and molecules	J. Robertson	Cornell Univ. Press, Ithaca (1953) 340 pp.
Phenolic resins; their chemistry and technology	P. Robitschek and A. Lewin	Iliffe, London (1950) 261 pp.
The structural relations of natural products	R. Robinson	Clarendon Press, Oxford (1955) 150 pp.
An introduction to the chemistry of the silicones (2d edition)	E.G. Rochow	Wiley, New York (1951) 213 pp.
The chemistry of organometallic compounds	E.G. Rochow, D.T. Hurd and R.N. Lewis	Wiley, New York (1957) 344 pp.
Chemistry and physiology of the vitamins	H.R. Rosenberg	Interscience, New York (1942) 674 pp.
Selected values of physical and thermodynamic properties of hydrocarbons and related compounds	F.D. Rossini et al.	Carnegie, Pittsburgh (1953) 1050 pp.
Hydrocarbons from petroleum	F.D. Rossini, J. Mair and A.J. Streiff	Reinhold, New York (1953) 556 pp.
Organo-metallverbindungen (Organo-metallic compounds)	F. Runge	Edwards, Ann Arbor (1945) 738 pp.
The chemical constituents of petroleum	A.N. Sachanen	Reinhold, New York (1945) 451 pp.
Some properties of the lighter hydrocarbons, hydrogens sulfide and carbon dioxide	B.H. Sage and W.N. Lacey	American Petroleum Institute, New York (1955) 246 pp.
The chemistry of carbohydrates in relation to disease	W.T. Salter	Oxford Univ. Press, New York (1942) 304 pp.
Die neuere Entwicklung der Kolloidchemie der Starke (New developments in the colloido-chemistry of starch)	M. Samec and M. Blinc	Steinkopff, Dresden, Leipzig (1941) 543 pp.
Grundlagen der Chemie und chemischen Technologie des Holzes (Chemistry and chemical technology of wood)	W. Sandermann	Geest and Portig, Leipzig (1956) 498 pp.
Les spectres electroniques en chimie theorique (The electronic spectra in organic chemistry)	C. Sandorfy	Masson, Paris (1959) 230 pp.

MONOGRAPHS (Contd.)

Title	Author(s)	Publisher
Some aspects of the chemistry and toxic action of organic compounds containing phosphorus and fluorine	B.C. Saunders	Cambridge Univ. Press (1957) 231 pp.
The aromatic diazo-compounds and their technical application (2d edition)	K.H. Saunders	Arnold, London (1949) 442 pp.
Steroid chains as components of protein and carbon molecules	T. van Schelven	Kosmos, Amsterdam (1946) 62 pp.
The Lynn index; a bibliography of phytochemistry	J.W. Schermerhorn and M.W. Quimby	Mass. Coll. of Pharmacy, Boston (1957)
Die organischen Fluorverbindungen (Organic fluorine compounds)	G. Schiemann	Steinkopff, Darmstadt (1951) 221 pp.
Vinyl and related polymers	C.E. Schildknecht	Wiley, New York (1952) 723 pp.
Ins Innere von Kunststoffen, Kunstharzen und Kautschuken (Plastic materials, rubber and resins)	E.V. Schmid	Birkhauser, Basel (1949) 203 pp.
Propane et propylene (Propane and propylene)	P.M.E. Schmitz	Assoc. Franc. Tech. Petrol., Paris (1947) 89 pp.
Präparative organische photochemie (Preparative organic photochemistry)	A. Schönberg	Springer, Berlin (1958) 274 pp.
Chemische gasreaktionen (Reactions in the gas phase)	H.J. Schumacher	Steinkopff, Leipzig (1938) 487 pp. Edwards, Ann Arbor (1943) 487 pp.
Chemical constitution and biological activity	W.A. Sexton	Spon, London (1949) 412 pp.
Chemistry of the steroids	C.W. Shoppee	Butterworths, London (1958) 314 pp.
Quantitative organic analysis via functional groups	S. Siggia	Wiley, New York (1954) 227 pp.
The terpenes (5 volumes)	J.L. Simonsen, L.N. Owen, D.H.R. Barton and W.C.J. Ross	University, Cambridge (Eng.)
Vitamin B_{12}	E.L. Smith	Methuen, London (1960) 196 pp.
The chemistry of plant gums and mucilages and some related polysaccharides	F. Smith and R. Montgomery	Reinhold, New York (1959) 627 pp.
Phenanthroline and substituted phenanthroline indicators	G.F. Smith and F.P. Richter	Smith Chemical, Columbus (1944) 103 pp.
Analytical applications of periodic acid (H_5IO_6) and iodic acid (HIO_3) and their salts	G.F. Smith	Smith Chemical, Columbus (1950) 108 pp.
The sequestration of metals; theoretical considerations and practical applications	R.L. Smith	Chapman and Hall, London (1959) 251 pp.
The structural chemistry of proteins	H. Springall	Academic, New York (1954) 376 pp.

Chemical processing of wood	A.J. Stamm and E.E. Harris	Chemical, New York (1953) 595 pp.
Cellulose acetate plastics	V. Stannett	Temple, London (1950) 325 pp.
Gerbereichemie und Gerbereitechnologie (2d edition) (Chemistry and technology of tanning agents)	F. Stather	Akademie, Berlin (1951) 722 pp.
Organische Kolloidchemie (Organic colloid chemistry)	H. Staudinger	Wieweg, Braunschweig (1950) 308 pp.
Atomic and free radical reactions (2d edition)	E.W.R. Steacie	Reinhold, New York (1954) 901 pp.
Die Chemie des Thiophens (The chemistry of thiopene	G.W. Steinkopff	Steinkopff, Dresden (1941) 232 pp. Edwards, Ann Arbor (1944) 232 pp.
Rubber; natural and syntheitc	H.J. Stern	MacLaren, London (1954) 491 pp.
Recent advances in organic chemistry (2 volumes)	A.W. Stewart and H. Graham	Longmans Green, London, New York (1948) 829 pp.
Chloroplast pigments and chromatographic analysis	H.H. Strain	Pennsylvanie State Univ. Press (1958) 180 pp.
Chemistry and methods of enzymes (third edition)	J.B. Sumner and G.F. Somers	Academic, New York (1953) 462 pp.
Name reactions in organic chemistry	A.R. Surrey	Academic, New York (1954) 192 pp.
The organic chemistry of sulfur; tetracovalent sulfur compounds	C.M. Suter	Wiley, New York (1944) 858 pp.
Structure of molecules and the chemical bond	Y.K. Syrkin and M.E. Dyatkina	Butterworths, London (1950) 509 pp.
Chemistry of muscular contraction	A. Szent-Gyorgi	Academic, New York (1947) 150 pp.
The chemistry and technology of enzymes	H. Tauber	Wiley, New York (1949) 550 pp.
Les mécanismes reactionnels en chimie organique (The reaction mechanisms in organic chemistry)	B. Tchoubar	Dunod, Paris (1960) 221 pp.
Anhydrous aluminium chloride in organic chemistry	C.A. Thomas	Reinhold, New York (1941) 972 pp.
Naturally occurring quinones	R.H. Thomson	Butterworths, London (1957) 302 pp.
Physico-chemical constants of pure organic compounds	J. Timmermans	Elsevier, New York (1950) 694 pp.
Les constantes physiques des composés organiques cristallisés; essai de stoechiometrie (The physical constants of crystalline organic compounds)	J. Timmermans	Masson, Paris (1953) 556 pp.
Organic peroxides; their chemistry, decomposition and role in polymerization	A.V. Tobolsky and R.B. Mesrobian	Interscience, New York (1954) 197 pp.
Vitamins, coenzymes and nucleotides	A.R. Todd	Univ. of Notre Dame Press, (1949) 53 pp.

MONOGRAPHS (Contd.)

Boron fluoride and its compounds as catalysts in organic chemistry	A.V. Topchiev, S.V. Zavgorodnii and Ya.M. Paushkin	Pergamon, London, New York (1959) 326 pp.
Die Chemie der Pflanzenzellwand (The chemistry of the plant cell wall)	E. Treiber	Springer, Berlin (1957) 511 pp.
Das Holz als Rohstoff (Wood as raw material)	R. Trendelenburg and H. Mayer-Wegelin	Hanser, Munich (1955) 541 pp.
On the structure of the protein molecule	N. Troensegaard	Munksgaard, Copenhagen (1944) 126 pp.
A new orientation within protein chemistry	N. Troensegaard	Munksgaard, Copenhagen (1949) 139 pp.
Free radicals. An introduction	A.F. Trotman-Dickenson	Methuen, London (1959) 142 pp.
Wool wax -- chemistry and technology	E.V. Truter	Interscience, New York (1956) 368 pp.
An electronic outline of organic chemistry	S.H. Tucker	Univ. of London Press (1959) 478 pp.
Chromatographische Methoden in der Protein-Chemie (Chromatographic methods in protein chemistry)	F. Turba	Springer, Berlin (1954) 358 pp.
Porphyrins; their biological and chemical importance	A. Vannotti	Hilger and Watts, London (1954) 258 pp.
Phosphorus and its compounds (2 volumes)	J.R. Van Wazer	Interscience, New York (1958-1960) 370 pp.
The chemistry of synthetic dyes (2 volumes)	K. Venkataraman	Academic, New York (1952) 1442 pp.
Chemie und Technik der Vitamine (third edition) (Chemistry and technology of vitamins)	H. Vogel and H. Knobloch	F. Encke, Stuttgart (1950)
Formaldehyde (2d edition)	J.F. Walker	Reinhold, New York (1953) 575 pp.
Free radicals in solution	C. Walling	Wiley, New York (1957) 631 pp.
The chemistry of free radicals	W.A. Waters	Clarendon, Oxford (1946) 295 pp.
Physical aspects of organic chemistry (4th edition)	W.A. Waters	Van Nostrand, New York (1950) 539 pp.
Modern theories of organic chemistry	H.B. Watson	Clarendon, Oxford (1942) 267 pp.
Organic analytical reagents (4 volumes)	F.J. Welcher	Van Nostrand, New York (1947-1948) 2219 pp.
Uber Silikone (Silicones)	W. Weltzien and G. Hauschild	Westdeutscher, Koln (1955) 120 pp.
DDT, the synthetic insecticide	T.F. West and G.A. Campbell	Chapman and Hall, London (1946) 301 pp.
Resonance in organic chemistry (Revised edition)	G.W. Wheland	Wiley, New York (1955) 846 pp.
Polysaccharide chemistry	R.L. Whistler and C.L. Smart	Academic, New York (1953) 493 pp.
Industrial gums; polysaccharides and their derivatives	R.L. Whistler (Editor)	Academic, New York (1959) 766 pp.

Die chemische Affinität (Chemical affinity)	E. Wiberg	Gruyter, Berlin (1951) 254 pp.
Homolytic aromatic substitution	G.H. Williams	Pergamon, Oxford (1960) 133 pp.
Cyanogen compounds, their chemistry detection and estimation	H.E. Williams	Arnold, London (1948) 443 pp.
The biochemistry of B vitamins	R.J. Williams	Reinhold, New York (1950) 741 pp.
Molecular vibrations ; the theory of infra-red and Raman vibrational spectra	E.B. Wilson, J.C. Decius and P.C. Cross	McGraw-Hill, New York (1955) 388 pp.
The optical properties of organic compounds (2d. edition)	A.E. Winchell	Academic, New-York (1954) 487 pp.
A line-formula chemical notation	W.J. Wiswesser	Crowell, New York (1954) 149 pp.
The phosphatides	H. Wittcoff	Reinhold, New York (1951) 564 pp.
Gewinnung der höheren Fettsäuren durch Oxydation der Kohlenwasserstoffe (Obtention of higher fatty acids by oxidation of hydrocarbons)	F. Wittka	Barth, Leipzig (1940) 167 pp. Edwards, Ann Arbor (1945) 167 pp.
A study of antimetabolites	D.W. Woolley	Wiley, New York (1952) 269 pp.
New fibres from proteins	R.L. Wormell	Academic, New York (1954) 208 pp.
Handbook of magnesium-organic compounds	S.T. Yoffe and A.N. Nesmeyanov	Pergamon, London (1956)
Principles and practice of chromatography	L. Zechmeister and L. Cholnoky	Wiley, New York (1941) 362 pp.
Chemische Bestimmungsmethoden von Steroidhormonen (Chemical determination methods of steroid hormones)	W. Zimmermann	Springer, Berlin (1955) 119 pp.
Chemie der Azofarbstoffe (Chemistry of azo-dyes)	H. Zollinger	Birkhäuser, Basel (1958) 308 pp.

INDEXES

Author index 256-290

Subject index 291-341

Appendix 343-345

ABADIE, P. 33
ABDERHALDEN, R. 114, 236
ABEL, A.L. 58
ABELIN, I. 174
ABELSON, P.H. 69
ABOOD, L.G. 127
ABOULENC, J. 227
ABRAHAM, E.P. 78, 79, 137 148, 157, 236
ABRAHAM, N.A. 163
ABRAHAMCZIK, E. 197
ABRAMSON, H.A. 236
ABRAHAMS, S.C. 99
ACHESON, R.M. 145
ACKERMANN, H. 22
ACKERSON, B. 236
ADAM, N.K. 236
ADAMS, D.A.W. 58
ADAMS, J.T. 87
ADAMS, R. 17, 20, 37, 41, 52 101, 175, 203
ADAMS, R.M. 117
ADAMSON, D.W. 55
ADDINALL, C.R. 72
ADDOMS, R.M. 236
ADELSON, D.E. 43
ADKINS, H. 72, 87, 203
ADLER, E. 188
ADLER, T.K. 166, 189
AESCHLIMANN, J.A. 195
AGGARWOL, S.L. 51
AHLQUIST, L. 162
AIKEN, J.K. 57
AINEHAM, A.W. 50
AKABORI, S. 205
ALBERT, A. 67, 97, 107, 155 156, 166, 201, 217
ALBRIGHT, C.F. (see R.M. Washburn et al), 117
ALDER, K. 15, 67, 176
ALEXANDER, A.E. 118, 218
ALEXANDER, E.R. 236
ALEXANDER, P. 1, 156, 209
ALEXANDRE, B. 162
ALFIN-SLATER, R. 29
ALFREY, T. 31, 184

ALGER, R.S. 179
ALLAIS, A. 23, 134
ALLARD, S. 111
ALLEN, C.F.H. 45, 48, 52, 145, 146, 203
ALLEN, G. 98
ALLEN, M.B. 216
ALLEN, M.J. 77
ALLENDORFER, H. (see H. Meerwein et al), 21
ALLISON, J.B. 185
ALLPORT, N.L. 236
ALLSOPP, C.B. 159
ALMQUIST, H.J. 237
ALTHAUSER, D. 241
AMAGAT, P. 225, 228
AMBLER, C.M. 220
AMBROSE, E.J. 94, 170
AMES, G.R. 51, 52
AMIEL, J. 226, 227
AMMON, R. 174
AMUNDSEN, L.H. 72
ANANTAKRISHNAN, S.V. 44
ANBAR, M. 49
ANDAUT, A. 224
ANDERSON, A.J. 156
ANDERSON, A.R. 117
ANDERSON, D.H. 219
ANDERSON, E.C. 30
ANDERSON, G.W. 130, 143, 195
ANDERSON, J.R. 218
ANDERSON, J.S. 96
ANDERSON, L. 5
ANDERSON, P. 31
ANDERSON, R.C. (see F.S. Spring et al), 153
ANDERSON, R.D. 171
ANDRAC, M. (see C. Prevost et al), 38
ANDREEV, V.M. 163
ANDREWS, A.C. 44
ANDREWS, J.C. 27
ANDREWS, L.J. 49
ANFINSEN, C.B. 11
ANFT, B. 74
ANGYAL, S.J. 5, 87, 99, 107

ANNER, G. 65
ANSELL, M.F. 142
ANSLOW, G.A. 170
ANSON, F.C. 1
ANSON, M.L. 10
ANTONY, F. (see F. Wessely et al), 176
ANTWEILER, H.J. 197
APPLEQUIST, D.E. 49
APPLEZWEIG, N. 126
ARAKI, C. 187
ARBUSOW, B.A. 162 (sam
ARBUZOV, B.A. 137
ARCHER, S. 129
ARDIS, A. 72
ARENS, J.F. 9
ARIGONI, D. 65, 133 (see a] J.W. Rowe et al), 177
ARKEL, A.E. von 236
ARMITAGE, F. 56
ARNDT, F.G. 16, 83, 236
ARNOFF, S. 48
ARNOLD, H. 15, 22
ARNOLD, R.G. 50, 74
ARNOLD, R.T. (see W.R. Moore et al), 164
ARNOLD, R.T. 102
ARNOTT, S. 65
ARNSTEIN, H.R.V. 96
ARTHUR, J.C. 11, 218
ARUNDALE, E. 48
ARZIANI, P. 228
ASAHINA, Y. 66
ASH, A.B. 101
ASHFORD, W.R. 122
ASHMORE, P.G. 138
ASINGER, F. 22, 236
ASKER, W. 45
ASMUS, E. 196, 197
ASPINALL, G.O. 4, 5, 132
ASSELINEAU, C. (see L. Ahliquist et al), 162
ASSELINEAU, J. 35, 67 (se also L. Ahlquist et al), :
ASTBURY, W.T. 54, 89
ASTLE, M.J. 192, 236
ASTON, J.G. 167, 170, 208

ASTWOOD, A.B. 210
ATHERTON, E. 136
ATHERTON, F.R. 96, 137
ATKINSON, M.R. 166
ATLAS, S.M. 22, 24
AUBERT, M. 236
AUDRIETH, L.F. 43
AUGOOD, D.R. 51
AUGDAHL, E. (see R.N. Jones et al), 127
AUGUS, W.R. 34, 158
AULIN-ERDTMAN, G. 162
AULT, W.C. 58
AUMERAS, M. 224
AUSTERWEIL, G.V. 56
AVERELL, P.R. 185
AVERY, G.S. 236
AVISON, A.W.D. 56
AXELSON, J.W. 220
AYERS, J. 172

BACHMANN, W.E. 85, 149, 203
BACHRACH, A.L. 112
BACKER, H.J. 34, 37
BACON, R.G.R. 98, 141
BACQ, Z.M. 209
BADDELEY, G. 98
BADDENHAUSEN, H. 23
BADDILEY, J. 8, 29, 91, 136, 137, 143, 202, 212
BADGER, G.M. 1, 97, 108, 143, 146, 166
BADOW, R.D. 133
BAER, D.R. 88
BAER, E. 29, 44, 137
BAER, H.H. 70
BAGANZ, H. 23
BAHADUR, K. 205
BAIRD, W. 95
BAIER, W.E. 127
BAILAR, J.C. 101
BAILEY, A.E. 236
BAILEY, G.D. 218
BAILEY, K. 10, 29, 141

BAILEY, P.S. 51
BAINES, H. 55
BAKER, B.R. 156
BAKER, J.W. 164, 236
BAKER, W. 57, 63, 89, 91, 93, 99, 138, 201, 206 (see also E.P. Abraham et al), 148
BAKER, W.O. 72, 120, 127
BALANDIN, A.A. 6
BALENOVIĆ, K. 157
BALLARD, D.G.H. 136
BALLARD, S.A. 149, 181
BALLI, H. (see S. Hunig et ^{a}al), 22
BALLOU, C.E. 4, 135
BALTAZZI, E. 98
BALY, E.C.C. 236
BAMBAS, L.L. 145
BAMFORD, C.H. 136, 173, 179, 237
BANERJEE, B. 176
BANKS, C.K. 117, 120
BANN, B. 54
BANNERMAN, D.G. 184
BANTHORPE, D.V. 163
BARB, W.G. 237
BARBERA, H. 160
BARCLAY, B.M. 46
BARDONE-GAUDEMAR, F. (see C. Prevost et al), 38
BARER, R. 170
BARKEMEYER, H. 69
BARKER, C.C. 214
BARKER, G.R. 4
BARKER, S.A. 3
BARLIN, G.B. 166
BARLTROP, J.A. 99
BARNARD, A.J. 1
BARNARD, P.W.C. 57
BARNES, J.W. 209
BARNES, R.A. 146, 182
BARNETT, E. de B. 237
BARRETT, K.E.J. 172
BARRON, H. 237
BARRY, A.J. 117
BARRY, M.C. (see T.F. Gallagher et al), 210

BARRY, P. 224
BARRY, V.C. 212
BARSEL, N. 68
BARTH, R.H. 237
BARTLETT, P.D. 18, 73, 101, 160, 190, 204, 206
BARTON, D.H.R. 36, 55, 64, 90, 91, 93, 96, 98, 99, 102, 103, 137, 141, 142, 153, 175, 189, 206, 223, 232
BASS, A.M. 179
BASS, R.L. 58
BASSETT, I.M. 57,
BASSHAM, J.A. 74
BASTELL, F.E. 118
BATEMAN, L. 98, 172
BATESMITH, E.C. 132
BATTEGAY, M. 227
BATTERSBY, A.R. 100, 121, 136
BAUD, P. 226, 227
BAUER, E. 159
BAUER, N. 219
BAUER, S.H. 31
BAUMAN, W.C. 126
BAUMANN, F. 19
BAUMANN, H. 22, 135
BAUMANN, P. 58
BAUMGARTE, U. (see W. Theilacker et al), 21
BAVER, N. 218
BAWN, C.E.H. 58, 63, 90, 91, 138, 168
BAXENDALE, J.H. 172, 184, 207
BAXTER, J.G. 67
BAYER, O. 15, 16, 17, 22, 25, 197
BAYLISS, N.S. 97
BAYNE, S. 4
BEACHAM, H.H. 118
BEASLEY, J.K. 31
BEATTY, H.A. 118, 203
BEAUQUEJNE, L. 26
BEAUDET, C. 161
BEAVEN, G.H. 11, 170, 214
BECHER, H.J. 186
BECKE-GOEHRING, M. 9
BECKER, B. 66

BECKER, E. 81
BECKER, E.D. 186
BECKER, E.I. 48, 75
BECKER, F. 17, 196
BECKETT, A.H. 77, 78
BECKEY, H.D. 22
BECKMAN, L.J. 48
BECKMANN, S. 162
BEECK, O. 169
BEEKMANN, P. (see H. Meerwein et al), 21
BEÉLIK, A. 4
BEERMANN, C. 23
BEERTHUIS, R.K. 129
BEETS, M.G.J. 201
BEHNISCH, R. 16
BEHR, L.C. 87
BEHRENS, O.K. 113, 149, 153
BEHRINGER, H. 15
BELCHE, R. 140
BELL, D.J. 3, 28
BELL, E.R. 171
BELL, F. 110
BELL, P.H. 126
BELL, R.P. 6, 237
BELL, W.E. 166
BELLAMY, L.J. 57, 105, 200, 237
BELMONDI, G. 144
BELOZERSKY, A.N. 202
BELYAVSKY, A.B. (see A.N. Nesmeyanov et al), 233
BeMILLER, J.N. 5
BENCZE, W.L. 77
BENDER, M.L. 52
BENDICH, A. 155, 202
BENEDETTI-PICHLER, A.A. 80
BENKESER, R.A. 51, 116
BENNET, L.L. 47
BENSON, A.A. 74
BENSON, F.R. 46, 47
BENSON, S.W. 237
BENT, R.L. 73, 74
BENTLEY, K.W. 144, 147, 237
BENTLEY, R. 96
BENZ, F. 28

BERDNIKOVA, N.G. 105
BERGEL, F. 54, 55, 58, 78, 93, 96
BERGEN, W.V. 194
BERLAGE, F. (see P. Karrer et al), 22
BERGMAN, E.D. 88
BERGMAN, W. 131
BERGMANN, E. 33, 44, 60
BERGMANN, E.D. 49, 93, 201, 237
BERGMANN, F. 6
BERGMANN, W. 44, 95
BERGSTROM, F.C. 42
BERGSTROM, F.W. 41, 42, 45
BERGSTRÖM, S. 157
BERKMAN, S. 237
BERLIN, K.D. 52
BERLINER, E. 86, 164
BERLINGOZZI, S. 175
BERLOW, E. 237
BERNADER, K. (see P. Karrer et al), 22
BERNANOSE, A. 35, 36
BERNAUER, K. 69
BERNHARD, K. 114
BERNSTEIN, H.J. 128
BERNSTEIN, S. 210
BERSIN, T. 14
BERSOHN, R. 32
BERTHIER, G. 34, 158
BESINET, P. 163
BESSELL, C.J. 13
BEST, C.H. 112
BESTIAN, H. 23, 199
BESTMANN, H.J. 24
BETHELL, D. 99
BETTELHEIM-JEVONS, F.R. 11
BEVAN, E.A. 54
BEVAN, T.H. 95
BÉVILLARD, P. 36
BEVINGTON, J.C. 58, 97
BEYER, G.L. 218
BEYLER, R.E. 75
BEYNON, J.H. 119, 140
BICK, I.R. 140

BIDMEAD, D.S. 106
BIEBER, T.I. 57, 75
BIEDERMANN, W. 18
BIEL, J.H. 129
BIELLMANN, J.F. 163
BIEMANN, K. 62
BIENERT, B. 19
BIER, G. 18
BIER, M. 129
BIGELOW, H.E. 41
BIGELOW, L.A. 46, 178
BIGELOW, M.H. 239
BIGGS, B.S. 72
BILLEK, G. 188
BILLET, D. 34, 35
BILLIG, F.A. (see R.M. Washburn et al), 117
BILLMAN, J.H. 237
BILLMEYER, F.W. 31
BINKLEY, S.B. 44, 237
BINKLEY, W.W. 4
BINKS, J.H. 223
BINTE, H.J. 61
BIRCH, A.J. 96, 99, 107, 110, 157, 190, 206
BIRCH, S.F. 93
BIRKINSHAW, J.H. 78, 137
BIRKOFER, L. 15
BIRKOFER, N. (see T. Wieland et al), 199
BIRNBAUM, S.M. (see R.J. Koegel et al), 127
BISERTE, G. 35, 76, 154
BISSIER, J.R. 26
BJERRUM, J. 237
BJORKSTEN, J. 11
BLACET, F.E. 172
BLAIR, M.G. 4, 21
BLAKLEY, R.L. 166
BLANDON, P. 152, 201
BLATT, A.H. 41, 43, 85, 203
BLICKE, F.F. 85, 120, 145, 18
BLINC, R. 186
BLINN, R.C. 73
BLITZER, S.M. (see T.H. Pearson et al), 118

BLOCH, C. 160
BLOCH, E. 45
BLOCH, K. 113, 157, 210
BLOCK, R.J. 10, 46, 193, 237
BLOHM, H.W. 98
BLOEMENDAL, H. 76
BLOHMEYER, F. 232
BLOUT, E.R. 219
BLUESTEIN, B.A. 117
BLUMBERG, B.S. 156
BOBBITT, J.M. 4
BOCKEMÜLLER, W. 14
BODANSZKY, M. 103, 130
BODOT, H. 163
BOEKELHEIDE, V. 93, 103, 122, 220
BOELHOUWER, C. 6
BÖESEKEN, J. 3, 229
BÖGEMANN, M. 198
BOGERT, M.A. 47
BOGERT, M.T. 43
BOGORAD, L. 216
BOHLMANN, F. 16, 17, 19, 20, 70
BÖHME, H. 198
BOHRER, J.J. 184
BOISDÉ, P. 161
BOKHOVEN, C. 119
BOLLAND, J.L. 96
BOLLENBACK, G.N. 237
BOLLING, D. 237
BOND, G.C. 98
BONE, J.F. (see P.H. Bell et al), 126
BONNER, J. 73
BONNER, N.A. 209
BONNER, W.A. 3
BONNET, H. 224
BOOHER, L.E. 54
BOON, W.R. (see O. Wintersteiner et al), 148 (see also E.P. Abraham et al), 148
BOORD, C.E. 150
BOOTH, N. 56
BORISOV, A.E. 111

BORMAN, A. (see J. Fried et al), 210
BORROWS, E.T. 47
BORSOOK, H. 11
BOSCHAN, R. 50
BOTHNER-BY, A.A. 128
BOTHOREL, P. 36
BOUDART, M. 127
BOUGAULT, J. 229
BOULANGER, P. 35, 154
BOUNDY, R.H. 237
BOURGUEL, M. 224
BOURILLET, F. 165
BOURNE, E.J. 3, 29, 56, 57
BOURNSNELL, J.C. 132
BOURSEAUX, F. 22
BOUVENG, H.O. 5
BOVET, D. 26, 64, 165
BOVET-NITTI, F. 64, 165
BOVEY, F.A. 47, 184
BOWDEN, K. 79
BOWEN, E.J. 54, 172
BOWMAN, G.B. 43
BOWMAN, J.R. 221
BOYER, J.H. 49
BOYER, R.F. 237
BRADFIELD, A.E. 55
BRADLEY, D.C. 63, 92, 103, 105, 116
BRADLEY, W. 173, 212
BRADLOW, H.L. 73
BRADSHER, C.K. 46
BRADSTREET, R.B. 43
BRAGG, L. 57
BRANCONE, L.M. (see S. Kushner et al), 126
BRAND, E. 28
BRANDENBERGER, E. 237
BRANDT, W.W. 49
BRATTAIN, R.R. (see H.W. Thompson et al), 148
BRAUDE, E.A. 93, 94, 97, 110, 140, 167
BRAUNITZER, G. 20, 24
BRAUNS, F.E. 66, 238
BRAY, H.G. 2, 4
BREDERECK, H. 23, 177
BREGER, I.A. 159

BREGMAN, J.I. 126
BRENNER, M. 60, 157
BREWSTER, J.H. 87
BRIAN, P.W. 69
BRICAS, E. 11
BRICE, T.J. 178
BRIEGLEB, G. 17, 24, 70, 196
BRINDLEY, R.A. 173
BRINK, N.G. 99
BRIZIARELLI, G. 210
BROCKMANN, H. 14, 25, 68, 69, 130
BROCKMANN, H.H. 93
BROCKWAY, L.O. 31, 219
BRODE, W.R. 102, 136, 211
BRODY, F. 146
BROIDA, H.P. 127, 179
BROMER, W.W. 113, 153
BROOKER, L.G.S. 31, 47, 180, 189
BROOKS, B.T. 40, 150, 151, 238
BROSER, W. 18
BROSSMER, R. (see R. Kuhn et al), 25
BROTHERTON, T.K. 52
BROUGHTON, G. 220
BROWN, B. 51
BROWN, B.F. 185
BROWN, D.J. 107, 155, 156, 166
BROWN, D.M. 202
BROWN, E.V. 148
BROWN, G.B. 156
BROWN, G.I. 238
BROWN, H.C. 36, 75, 91, 101, 102, 151, 167, 190, 204, 214, 233,
BROWN, J.B. 7, 27, 28, 95
BROWN, L.H. 185
BROWN, R.D. 57, 97, 166
BROWN, T.L. 51
BROWN, W.G. 87
BROWNSTEIN, S. 52
BRÜCK, D. 197
BRÜCKNER, K. 67
BRUIN, P. 58
BRUN, P. 228
BRUNET, H. 33
BRUNET, V. 38
BRUSON, H.A. 86

BRUYLANTS, A. 38, 104
BRUYLANTS, P. 228
BUCHANAN, C. 238 (see also A.W. Johnson et al), 141
BUCHANAN, G.L. 142
BUCHANAN, J.G. 140
BUCHANAN, J.M. 30
BÜCHEL, K.H. 23
BÜCHI, J. 175
BUCK, J.S. 86
BUCKLES, R.E. 50, 51
BUDZIAREK, R. (see F.S. Spring et al), 153
BUER, H.C. 245
BUESS, C.M. 52
BUHLE, E.L. 73
BUIST, J.M. 59
BULEWICZ, E.M. 138
BU'LOCK, J.D. 99
BULL, B.A. 42
BULL, H.B. 8, 29
BULMAN, N. 67
BUNN, C.W. 58 (see also D. Crowfoot et al), 148
BUNNETT, J.F. 48, 99, 223
BUNTON, C.A. 56 (see also P.W.C. Barnard et al), 57
BURAWOY, A. 111, 186
BÜRER, T. 186
BURG, A.B. 24
BURG, C. 209
BURGE, R.E. 185
BURGER, A. 72, 74, 77, 122
BURGER, M. 238
BURGESS, R.H. 138
BURGUS, W.H. 209
BURK, R.E. 180
BURKHARD, C.A. 46
BURNESS, D.M. 145
BURNETT, G.M. 31, 49, 97, 221
BURR, G.O. 44
BURR, J.G. 238
BURTNER, R.R. 195
BURTON, D. 238
BURTON, H. 56, 97
BURTON, M. 159, 171
BURWELL, R.L. 49, 51, 208

BUTENANDT, A. 20, 24, 81, 82, 177, 190, 206
BUTLER, G.B. 52
BUTLER, J.A.V. 161
BUTLER, M.J. (see L.F. Audrieth et al), 43
BUTZ, L.W. 86
BUU-HOÏ, N.P. 102, 109, 160, 161, 228 (see also A. Lacassagne et al), 1
BYWATER, S. 150

CABLE, J.W. 50
CABRERA, B. 71
CADOGAN, J.I.G. 98
CADY, G.H. 9, 91
CAESAR, G.V. 5
CAGLIOTI, L. (see D. Arigoni et al), 65
CAGNIANT, P. 109, 228
CAHN, R.S. 65
CAIN, C.K. 155
CALDIN, E.F. 98
CALAM, C.T. (see E.P. Abraham et al), 148
CALDWELL, W.A. 105
CALINGAERT, G. 40, 203
CALLEN, J.E. 129
CALLOWAY, N.D. 42
CALMON, C. 192, 238
CALVERT, J.G. 31
CALVIN, M. 43, 73, 74, 91, 238, 246
CAMBER, B. 238
CAMERON, M.D. 73
CAMERON, M.P. 154
CAMPAIGNE, E.E. 46, 75
CAMPBEL, B.K. 44
CAMPBELL, D.H. 67
CAMPBELL, G.A. 253
CAMPBELL, I.G.M. 143
CAMPBELL, K.N. 44
CAMPBELL, N. 46, 63, 143
CAMPBELL, T.N. 48
CANBÄCK, C. 78
CANNAN, R.K. 29

CANNON, C.G. 57
CANTER, F.C. 49
CANTOR, S.M. 2, 3
CAPELL, L.T. 248
CAPON, B. 5
CAPPEL, N.O. 72
CARBON, J.A. (see E.C. Taylor et al), 155
CARDWELL, H.M.E. 56
CARLEY, D.R. (see T.H. Pearson et al), 118
CARLSON, C.S. 221
CARMACK, M. 86
CARNEY, T.P. 122, 195
CAROTHERS, W.H. 41
CARPENTER, D.C. 72
CARPENTER, F.H. (see V. DuVigneaud et al), 149
CARR, D.E. 179
CARR, E.P. 46
CARRINGTON, H.C. (see E Abraham et al and O. Wintersteiner et al), 148
CARRIÈRE, E. 224
CARSWELL, T.S. 180
CARTER, H.E. 86, 149, 204
CARTER, M.K. 73
CASANOVA, R. 153
CASERIO, M.C. 65, 223
CASIMIR, H.B.G. 159
CASON, J. 46, 86
CASSIDY, H.G. 169, 221, 222
CASY, A.F. 78
CATCH, J.R. 126
CATTELAIN, E. 109, 229
CAUQUIL, G. 160
CAVA, M.P. 38
CAVALIERI, L.F. 47
CAVALLITO, C.J. 195
CAVE, W.T. 170
CAWLEY, C.M. 105
CECIL, R. 12
CEFOLA, M. 80
CERNAK, E.S. (see R.M. burn et al), 117
CESCA, S. (see G. Natta et al), 22

CHABEREK, S. 238
CHABRIER, C. 165
CHABRIER, P. 34, 109
CHAIN, E. (see E.P. Abraham et al), 148
CHAIN, E.B. 28, 29, 63
CHALKLEY, L. 40
CHALLENGER, F. 45, 63, 238
CHAMBERLAIN, D.L. 117
CHAMLIN, G.R. 72
CHAMPETIER, A. 229
CHAMPETIER, G. 35, 36, 161, 227, 231, 238
CHANCE, B. 221, 222
CHANLEY, J.D. 68
CHAPMAN, N.B. 214
CHARBESBY, A. 209
CHARGAFF, E. 10, 202
CHARPENTIER, M. 163
CHATT, J. 48, 103, 140, 204
CHATTELAIN, E. 229
CHATTERJEE, A. 68
CHATTERJEE, A. (née Mookerjee) 67
CHAUCHARD, P. 109
CHEN, K.K. 122
CHENEY, L.C. 204
CHENICEK, A.G. 72
CHERBULIEZ, E. 177
CHERONIS, N.D. 74, 85, 221
CHEVALLIER, A. 209
CHEYMOL, J. 78, 109, 165
CHIANTA, M. 127
CHIBNALL, A.C. 154
CHILDS, A.P. 108
CHILDS, R. (see H.P. Schwarz et al), 127
CHIURDOGLU, G. 34, 162
CHIUSOLI, G.P. 23
CHOLNOKY, L. 254
CHOPIN, J. 35
CHOVIN, P. 37, 38, 161, 226
CHOW, B.F. 10
CHRISTENSEN, P. 176
CHRISTIE, B.J. 166
CHUOKE, R.L. 46

CIEREZKO, L.S. 131
CIFONELLI, J.A. 156
CILENTO, G. 52
CINES, M.R. 208
CLAESSON, S. 125, 169
CLAR, E. 15, 238
CLARK, C. 127
CLARK, C.C. 238
CLARK, C.W. 45
CLARK, F. 132, 205
CLARK, G.C. 148
CLARK, M. 40
CLARK, R.S. 185
CLARK, S.J. 238
CLARK, W.M. 238
CLARKE, H.T. 148, 203
CLARK-LEWIS, J.W. 51, 166
CLAUDE, A. 10
CLAXTON, G. 238
CLAYTON, J.H. 54
CLEGG, D.L. 126
CLELAND, E.S. 237
CLEMO, G.R. 91
CLEVELAND, F.F. 167
CLEVERDON, D. 57
CLIFFE, W.H. 58
COATES, G.E. 97, 204, 238
COBB, R.L. 50
COENEN, M. 16
COFFEY, S. 56, 58
COGGESHALL, N.D. 83, 208
COGHILL, R.D. 149 (see also O. Wintersteiner et al), 148
COHEN, A. 110
COHEN, T. 175
COHN, E.J. 239
COHN, W.E. 192
COLE, A.R.H. 107
COLE, R.D. 130
COLE, W.H. 234
COLEY, J.R. 6, 173
COLLIE, C.H. 159
COLLIN, J. 119
COLLINS, C.J. 100, 129
COLLINS, K.H. (see M.J. Fahrenbach et al), 155
COLLINSON, E. 50, 98

COLONGE, J. 34, 161
COLOWICK, S.P. 27
COMMERFORD, J.D. 117
COMPTON, J. 2
COMSA, J. 174
COMYNS, A.E. 52
CONANT, J.B. 40, 42
CONCHIE, J. 4
CONIA, J.M. 37, 162
CONN, G.K.T. 105
CONNAN, R.K. 125
CONNOR, R. 203
CONOVER, C.H. 137
CONROY, H. 9
CONSTANTIN, J.M. 153
CONWAY, A.C. (see J.H. Biel et al), 129
COOK, A.H. 66, 93, 96, 148, 149
COOK, J.W. 54, 93, 97, 121, 143
COOK, R.P. 152
COOKE, I. 156
COOKE, R.G. 108
COOKE, W.D. 83
COOKSON, R.C. 56, 98
COON, M.J. 157
COPE, A.C. 88
COPE, A.S. 101
COPENHAVER, J.W. 239
COPLEY, G.N. 54
COPPINGER, G.M. 48
CORBETT, W.M. 135
CORDIER, P. 161, 226
COREY, E.J. (see D. Arigoni et al), 65
COREY, R.B. 10, 29, 43, 67, 88
CORLISS, L.M. 219
CORNUBERT, R. 36, 159, 162, 228
CORNFORTH, J.W. 93, 107, 149, 157, 182, 188, 206
CORNFORTH, R.H. (see J.W. Cornforth et al), 157
CORSON, B.B. 151
CORUMBERT, R. 228
COTTON, F.A. 50, 92, 200
COTTRELL, T. 96
CORWIN, A.H. 181, 203, 218
COULSON, C.A. 1, 91, 138, 158, 167, 168, 214, 223 (see also N.P. Buu-Hoï et al), 109

COURTOIS, J. 32, 187
COURTOT, C. 226, 228, 229
COUSENS, J.F. 156
COWAN, J.C. 204
COWAN, S.T. 217
COWDREY, W.A. 97
COX, R.H. 195
CRABBE, P. 103
CRAIG, D. 220
CRAIG, D.P. 58, 107, 170, 201, 223
CRAIG, L.C. 27, 102, 122, 126, 130, 154, 157, 193, 220
CRAIG, L.E. 47, 48
CRAIG, P.N. 126
CRAIG, R. 28
CRAM, D.J. 31, 103, 215
CRAMER, F. 17, 19, 24, 239
CRAMER, F.D. 107
CRAMER, M. 228, 230, 231
CRAVEN, J.M. (see W.H. Schubert et al), 164
CRAWFORD, I.R. 145
CRAWFORD, V.A. 96
CRICK, F.H.C. 11
CRIEGEE, R. 14, 21, 70, 103, 197
CROFTS, P.C. 100
CROMBIE, L. 97
CROMPTON, C.E. 209
CROMWELL, N.H. 45, 103, 183
CRON, M.J. 129
CRONSHAW, C.J.T. 63
CRONYN, M.W. 149
CROOK, E.M. 132
CROOKS, H.M. 148
CROSS, A.D. 100
CROSS, P.C. 254
CROSSLE, N.S. (see H.B. Henbest et al), 163
CROUNSE, N.N. 86
CROW, W.D. 166
CROWFOOT, D. 28, 112, 148
CROWTHER, A.F. 79

CRUM, J.D. 5
CRUSE, K. 197
CULLIS, C.F. 51, 168
CULVENOR, C.C.J. 107, 166
CUMMINS, A.B. 220
CURME, G.O. 234
CURPHEY, E.G. 56
CURTIN, D.Y. 102
CUSTER, R.L. 219
CUTHBERT, J. 100
CSUROS, Z. 105
CZEKALLA, J. 24

DACEY, J.R. 172
DAHMLOS, J. 23
DAHN, H. 39, 60
DAINTON, F.S. 99, 138, 172, 239
DAKE, H.C. 239
DALE, E. 48
DALE, H. 55
DALGLIESH, C.E. (see A.W. Johnson et al), 140, 141
DAL NOGARE, S. 83, 84
DALL'ASTA, A. (see G. Natta et al), 22
DALLEMAGNE, M.J. 122
DALLINGA, G. 214
DALMA, G. 122
DALTON, N.N. 234
DAM, H. 8
DAMIENS, R. 176
DANACZKO, J. (see J.G. Tolpin et al), 73
DANE, E. 81
DANIEL, H. 23
DANIELS, F. 207
DANIELS, T.C. 27
DANNENBERG, H. 17
D'ANS, J. 18
DANUSSO, F. 191
DARBY, D. 169

DARKIS, F.R. 40
DARMOIS, E. 33, 224
DARMON, M. 36
DAUB, G.H. 87
DAUBEN, W.G. 162, 215
DAUBERT, B.F. 28, 44
DAUDEL, P. 35 (see also N.P. Buu-Hoi et al), 109
DAUDEL, R. 7, 158 (see also A. Lacassagne et al), 1 an N.P. Buu-Hoi et al), 109
DAVID, S. 230
DAVIDSON, D. 72
DAVIDSON, H.R. 73
DAVIDSON, J.N. 202, 239
DAVIE, A.W. (see S. Arnot et al), 65
DAVIES, A.G. 98
DAVIES, C.W. 55
DAVIES, D.A.L. 5
DAVIES, D.S. 97
DAVIES, W. 166
DAVIS, W. 46
DAVISON, S. 171
DAVISON, W.H.T. 58, 138
DAVYDOV, B.E. (see A.V. Topchiyev et al), 58
DAWSON, C.R. 10, 72, 102
DAWYDOFF, W.N. 239
DAY, A.R. 182, 239
DAY, B.F. 48
DAY, J.H. 49
DEAN, F.M. 67
DEAN, J.G. 118
DEASY, C.L. 44, 45, 72
de BENNEVILLE, P.L. 195
de BOER, J.H. 58
DECELLES, C. 73
DECIUS, J.C. 254
DECKER, F. 70
DECROES, G.C. 242
de DARWENT, D.B. 168, 17
DÉCOMBE, J. 230
DEDONDER, R. 35

DEGENER, E. 25
DEGERING, E.F. 239
DE HEER, J. 96
DEITZ, V.R. 4
DEKKER, E.E. (see M.J. Coon et al), 157
DÉLABY, R. 176, 226
DELALANDE, A. 245
de la MARE, P.B.D. 74, 94, 96, 164, 223, 239
del CAMPILLO, A. (see M.J. Coon et al), 157
DELÉPINE, M. 37, 224
DELFS, D. 25
DELHOSTE, J. (see H. Bodot et al), 163
DELWAULLE, M.L. 165
de MAYO, P. 9, 99, 147
De MENT, J. 239
DENBER, H.C.B. 234
DENIVELLE L. 33
DENO, M.C. 31, 52
DENT, S.G. (see L.G.S. Brooker et al), 47
DENTON, J.J. (see S. Kushner et al), 126
DENTZ, C.A. 185
de PAULET, A.C. 163
de PRADENNE, H.V. 177
DePUY, C.H. 52
DERFER, J.M. 150
DERMER, O.C. 41, 50
DERVICHIAN, D.G. 71, 169
DESNUELLE, P. 34, 95, 154
de SOUSA, J.B. 119
de STEVENS, G. 70
DESTY, D.H. 234
De TAR, D.F. 88
DETHIER, V.G. 239
DEUEL, H. 8, 29, 60
DEUEL, H.J. 28, 29, 239
DEUEL, V. 64
DEULOFEU, V. 3, 66, 165
DEV, S. (see D. Arigoni et al). 65
DEWAR, M.J.S. 93, 103, 105, 136, 139, 160, 164, 168, 214, 223, 239

De WOLFE, R.H. 50
DIAPER, D.G.M. 51
DIBELER, V.H. 84
DIEHL, H. 102
DIETRICH, H. 193
DIEUZEIDE, E. (see H. Bodot et al), 163
DIJKSTRA, G. (see R.K. Beerthuis et al), 129
DIMLER, R.J. 3
DIMMIS, G.M. 156
DIMROTH, K. 15, 24
DINER, S. 38
DIPPY, J.F.J. 43
DIRINGER, R. 30
DIRSCHERL, W. 174
DJERASSI, C. 37, 47, 87, 103, 113, 128, 153, 176, 188 (see also G. Rosenkranz et al), 210), 239
DOAK, G.O. 51
DOBRINER, K. 112, 210 (see also T.F. Gallagher et al), 210
DODD, R.E. 186
DODD, T.N. 181, 182
DODDS, E.C. 55, 78
DOEHARD, T. 162
DOERING, W. von E. 20, 223
DOISY, E.A. 44
DOJA, M.Q. 4
DOLE, M. 75
DOLIQUE, R. 226, 227, 229
DOMAGK, G. 82
DOMINGUEZ, X.A. 73
DOMSKY, I.I. 131
DONALDSON, N. 239
DONAMURA, L.G. 88
DONNAY, G. 219
DONNAY, J.D.H. 219
DORAN, W.J. 195
DOREE, C. 239
DORFMAN, A. 156
DORFMAN, L. 49
DORFMAN, L.M. 48
DORFMAN, R.I. 210
DORLARS, A. 199
DORMAEL, A. 239
DORNBUSH, A.C. (see P.H. Bell et al), 126

DÖRNENBURG, E. 196
DOSS, M.P. 239
DOSSOW, K. 18
DOTY, P. 191, 239
DOUDOROFF, M. 3
DOVE, J.E. 138
DOWDEN, D.A. 139
DRAKE, N.L. 85
DRAWERT, F. 24
DREIDING, A.S. 61
DREIDING, H.S. 162
DREISBACH, L. (see H.P. Schwarz et al), 127
DREUSCH, F.L. 70
DRILL, V.A. 210
DROSSLER, H.G. (see W. Theilacker et al), 21
DRUEY, J. 21, 77
Du BOIS, A.S. 86
DUBOIS, J.E. 37, 160
Du BOIS, J.T. 207
DUCHESNE, J. 139
DUCKERT, R. 227
DUCLAUX, J. 227, 245
DUDENBOSTLE, B.F. 150
DUFRAISSE, C. 160, 177, 189 225
DULL, M.P. (see G. Egloff et al), 41
DULOU, R. 159, 226, 239
DUNCAN, A.B.F. 46, 222
DUNITZ, J.D. 25, 105
DUNLOP, A.P. 212, 239
DUNLOP, D.M. 78
DUNLOP, E.C. 126
DUNN, G.E. 49
DUNN, M.S. 10, 27
DUNNING, W.J. 98
DUNWORTH, W.P. 6
Du PONT, G. 33, 37, 159, 224, 225, 228, 229, 231
DUQUENOIS, P. 26
DURAT, J. 240
DUSTIN, P. 240
DUTCHER, J.D. 28 (see also O. Wintersteiner et al), 148
DUTTON, H.J. 95

DUVAL, C. 225
DUVEEN, D. 109
du VIGNEAUD, V. 136, 148, 149, 187, 189
DUYCKAERTS, G. 13
DWYRER, F.P. 49
DYALL, L.K. 108
DYATKINA, M.E. 252
DYKE, S.F. 147
DYSON, G.M. 40, 56, 73, 105, 240

EABORN, C. 240
EARL, J.C. 105
EASTHAM, J.F. 100
EASTMAN, R.H. 204
EASTY, G.C. 173
EBERHARDT, G. 18
EBERSBERGER, J. 20
ECKHOLDT, H. 198
ECKS, J. 232
EDDY, N.B. 58
EDGAR, J.L. 212
EDGECOMBE, F.H.C. 138
EDMAN, P. 30, 130, 154
EDMISON, M.T. 50
EDSALL, J.T. 10, 27, 28, 70, 172, 180, 239
EDWARD, J.T. 57
EDWARDS, J.D. 52
EDWARDS, J.W. 179
EDWARDS, R.R. 30
EGERTON, A.C. 171
EGGE, H. (see R. Kuhn et al), 25
EGGERSGLUSS, W. 240
EGGERT, J. 64
EGLOFF, G. 40, 41, 42, 43, 45, 203, 237, 240
EGLY, R.S. 220
EICHENBERGER, E. (see O. Westphal et al), 156
EIGEN, I. 18
EIGEN, M. 32
EIGSTI, O.V. 240

EILINGSFELD, H. 25
EIRICH, F.R. 129
EISCH, J. 9, 51
EISENBERG, R.F. 220
EISTERT, B. 14
EITER, K. 25
ELBE, G. 150
ELDERFIELD, R.C. 2, 42, 102, 181, 182, 183
ELEK, A. 83
ELEY, D.D. 6, 106
ELIEL, E.L. 74, 75, 87, 215
ELION, G.B. 155, 156, 187
ELKIN, M. 112
ELLIOT, A. 12, 170
ELIOTT, D.F. 154
ELLIOTT, J.R. 50
ELLIOTT, M. 59
ELLIS, C. 240
ELLIS, G.P. 4, 5
ELMING, N. 9
ELMORE, D.T. (see A.W. Johnson et al), 140
ELPHIMOFF-FELKIN, I. 37, 160, 161
ELSNER, H. 240
ELVIDGE, J.A. 136
ELVING, P.J. 45, 83, 102
EMBLEM, H.G. 57
EMELÉUS, H.J. 9, 54, 56, 70, 89, 90, 102, 178, 190
EMERSON, W.S. 47, 86
EMERY, W.B. 56
EMTE, W. 171
ENGLAND, D.C. 87
ENGLISH, J.P. (see P.H. Bell et al), 126
ERDTMAN, H. 93, 105, 162, 175, 188, 189, 206
ERICKSEN, P.H. 185
ERICKSON, J.G. 145
ERNST, F. 23
ERREDE, L.A. 99
ERSKINE, R.L. 214
ESCHENMOSER, A. 157 (see also J. Schreiber et al), 23

ESMAY, D.L. 116
ÉTIENNE, A. 229, 230
EUCKEN, A. 81
EUGSTER, C.H. 9
EULER-CHELPIN, H. von 2
EULER, H. v. 14, 60, 177
EVANS, M.G. 96
EVANS, R.C. 54
EVANS, R.M. 100
EVANS, T.H. 2
EVANS, W.L. 3, 40, 44
EVERETT, M.R. 240
EVERING, B.L. 6
EVERS, E.C. 31
EVERS, N. 240
EWINS, A.J. 89
EYRING, H. 30, 31

FABIAN, J. 37
FAGNONI, Y. 162
FAHRENBACH, M.J. 155
FAIRBAIRN, J.W. 78
FAIRCHILD, D. 243
FAIRLEY, J.L. 75
FAJANS, K. 219
FALCO, E.A. 155
FALCONER, J.S. 172
FALK, J.E. 166
FANKUCHEN, I. 10, 124
FANTA, P.E. 45, 52
FARADAY, J.F. 240
FARDIG, O.B. (see M.J. Cron et al), 129
FARENS, J. 176
FARKAS, A. 173, 208
FARKAS, L. 124
FARMER, E.H. 118
FARMER, V.C. 186
FARQUHAR, B.S. 129
FARRAR, K.R. 91
FARRAR, W.V. 91
FARTHING, A.C. 91, 214
FAWCETT, F.S. 48
FEIGL, F. 105, 189
FEINSTEIN, L. 67

FELIX, D. (see A. Eschenmoser et al). 157
FELIX, K. 12, 154, 201, 205, 216
FELKIN, H. 37, 161, 162
FELLNER, I.J. 73
FELLOWS, C.E. (see P.H. Bell et al), 126
FELLOWS, E.J. 195
FELTON, D.G.I. 145, 155
FENTON, S.E. (see W.R. Moore et al), 164
FERGUS, S. 185
FERGUSON, L.N. 45, 47, 48, 74, 240
FERINGTON, T.E. 75
FERM, R.J. 49, 51
FERNELIUS, W.C. 41, 42, 43, 49, 180
FERNHOLZ, H. 232
FERRI, C.M. 185
FERRIER, R.J. 100
FERRINI, P.G. (see D. Arigoni et al), 65
FERRIS, S.W. 240
FESSLER, W.A. 48
FETTES, E.M. 185
FIELD, F.H. 111
FIERENS, P.J.C. 34
FIESER, L.F. 36, 64, 85, 101, 111, 176, 203, 240
FIESER, M. 64, 111, 240
FEWSTER, J.A. 4
FINDLAY, G.M. 78
FINEGOLD, H. 128
FINKELSTEIN, A. 172
FINN, S.R. 55
FISCHER, E.O. 9, 19, 139, 144
FISCHER, E.J. 240
FISCHER, F.G. 14, 81
FISCHER, H. 42, 81, 240
FISCHER, H.O.L. 21, 27, 29, 44
FISCHER, S.G. 70
FISCHER, W. 243
FISHER, H.L. 40, 151, 180

FISHER, S. 185
FITTS, D.D. 219
FLASHKA, H. 1
FLETCHER, H.G. 2, 3, 72, 103
FLETT, L.H. 240
FLEURY, P. 36
FLODIN, P. 13
FLOREY, H.W. (see E.P. Abraham et al), 148
FLOREY, K. 61
FLORY, P.J. 46, 180, 240
FODOR, G. 37, 122, 177
FOGEL, W.O. 244
FOLCH-PI, J. 28
FOLKERS, K. 87, 113, 148, 157, 206
FONTAINE, M. 32
FORBES, W.F. 214
FORDHAM, S. 234
FORDYCE, C.R. 2
FORREST, H.S. 155, 190
FÖRSTER, T. 82, 197, 240
FOSTER, A.B. 3, 4, 5, 99
FOSTER, D.J. (see R.A. Benkeser et al), 51
FOSTER, H. 84
FOSTER, J.W. 241
FOSS, O. 9
FOURNEAU, E. 26, 228
FOX, H.H. 73
FOX, J.J. 5, 103, 155
FOX, S.W. 10, 44
FRAENKEL, G. 113
FRAENKEL, G.K. 127, 219
FRAENKEL-CONRAT, H. 12, 27, 29, 154
FRAISSE, R. (see P. Besinet et al), 163
FRANCIS, A.W. 40, 47, 208
FRANÇOIS, F. 165
FRANK, C.E. 47
FRANKE, W. 19, 24
FRANKLIN, E.C. 41, 42
FRASER, R.D.B. 193
FRÉDÉRICQ, E. 153

FREDGA, A. 111, 177
FREEMAN, G.G. (see E.P. Abraham et al), 148
FREEDMAN, L.D. 51
FREEMAN, N.K. 127
FREIDLINA, R.K. 99 (see also A.N. Nesmeyanov et al), 233
FRENCH, D. 4, 10
FRÉREJACQUE, M. 227
FRESENIUS, P. 17
FREUDENBERG, K. 19, 20, 21, 38, 53, 65, 67, 68, 70, 111, 175
FREUDENBERG, W. 182
FREY, H.J. 185
FREYTAG, H. 199
FREY-WYSSLING, A. 66
FRIDENSON, A. 37
FRIED, J. 113, 181, 210
FRIEDEL, R.A. 241
FRIEDLANDER, G. 30
FRIEDMAN, H.L. 127
FRIEDMAN, S. 113
FRIES, D. (see E. Muller et al), 23
FRIESS, S.I. 221
FRITSCH, K.H. (see S. Hunig et al), 22
FRITZ, F. 241
FRITZ, H.P. 9
FRITZE, U. 197
FROMAGEOT, C. 11, 29, 154, 176, 189, 226
FROST, A.A. 241
FRUSH, H.L. 29
FRUTON, J.S. 10, 181
FUCHS, O. 197
FUKUSHIMA, D.K. 181 (see also T.F. Gallagher et al), 210
FULLER, C.S. 43, 72
FUNKE, W. 23
FURNESS, F.N. 124
FUSON, N. 186
FUSON, R.C. 40, 42, 85, 102, 203

GADDUM, J.H. 234
GAERTNER, R. 47
GALINOVSKY, F. 67
GALLAGHER, T.F. 210
GALLEGO y GÓMEZ, F. 177
GANGER, A.W. 248
GÄNSHEIMER, J. 21
GANSSER, C. 26
GARDNER, H.J. 107
GARDNER, W.H. 240
GARLAND, R.B. (see E.C. Taylor et al), 155
GARNER, P.J. 140
GARNES, W.E. 139
GARRETT, A.B. 102
GARST, J.B. 210
GARTEN, V.A. 108
GARWOOD, R.F. 142
GASCOIGNE, R.M. 98
GATES, M. 46
GAUDEMAR, M. (see C. Prevost et al), 38
GAUHE, A. (see R. Kuhn et al), 25
GAULT, H. 161, 227
GAULT, Y. 162
GAUSE, G.F. 241
GAUSS, W. 18, 21
GAUTIER, J.A. 36, 39, 109, 226
GAYLORD, N.G. 48, 241
GEDDES, A.L. 218
GEE, G. 96
GEISELER, G. 19
GEISSMAN, T.A. 52, 72, 73, 85, 162
GEMANT, A. 208
GENSLER, W.J. 51, 87, 182
GENT, W.L.G. 96
GEORGE, F.D. 50
GEORGE, P. 6
GERBER, S. 183
GERMAIN, J. 226
GERO, A. 74
GERRARD, W. 51, 52

GESCHKE, P. 17
GETZ, C.A. 42
GEY, K.F. (see O. Isler et al), 157
GEYDERIKH, M.A. (see A.V. Topchiyev et al), 58
GEYER, B.P. 185
GIACHETTI, E. 21
GIANNINI, U. (see G. Natta et al), 22
GIANTURCO, M. 20, 175
GIBBONS, G.C. 8
GIBSON, D.T. 41
GIDDINGS, J.C. 32
GILBERT, E.E. 72, 151
GILCH, H. 23
GILDEMEISTER, E. 241
GILFILLAN, J.L. (see K. Folkers et al), 157
GILKY, J.W. 117
GILLAM, A.E. 241
GILLESPIE, R.J. 96, 98
GILLIS, R.G. 74
GILMAN, H. 9, 41, 44, 49, 51, 52, 87, 88, 100, 116, 203, 204, 241
GINER-SOROLLA, A. 155
GINSBURG, D. 49, 88, 111, 162, 201
GIRARD, M. 26
GIRARD, P. 33
GIRWOOD, R.H. 7
GISLON, A. 228
GISVOLD, O. 241
GLASEBROOK, A.L. 220
GLASER, H. (see G. Spielberger et al), 198
GLASGOW, A.R. 101
GLAZIER, E.R. (see D. Arigoni et al), 65
GLENN, A.L. 98
GLOCKLER, G. 170
GLOCKLING, F. 204
GLOVER, J. 113
GLUECKAUF, E. 128

GLUSKER, D.L. 223
GNAMM, H. 241
GNICHTEL, H. 18
GODDU, R.F. 1
GODFRIN, A. 229
GOEHRING, H.L. 103
GOEHRING, M. 70
GOEPP, R.M. 3
GOERDELER, J. 198, 199
GOLD, H. 25
GOLD, V. 99
GOLDBERG, H.S. 131
GOLDSCHMIDT, S. 19, 20, 17
GOLDSMITH, H.A. 45
GOLDSTEIN, R.F. 241
GOLOVA, O.P. 241
GOMBERG, M. 40
GOMER, R. 48
GOMPPER, R. (see H. Bredereck et al), 23
GONNARD, P. 26 (see also M. Polonovski et al), 155
GONZÁLEZ GARCÍA, F. 4
GONZÁLEZ GÓMEZ, C. 177
GOODHUE, L.D. 44
GOODMAN, C. 159
GOODMAN, I. 5, 105
GOODMAN, M. 11, 130
GOODWIN, T.W. 29, 241
GORDON, E.S. 234
GORDON, M. 48, 130
GORDON, M.P. 156
GORDON, S. 159, 171
GORE, P.H. 49
GORE, R.C. 72, 126, 167
GORIN, M.H. 124, 236
GORSICH, R.D. 241
GORTER, E. 172
GOSS, R. 138
GOSTING, L.J. 11
GÖTTE, H. 23, 196
GOUBEAU, J. 82, 197
GOUDET, H.J. 227
GOULD, E.S. 241
GOUTAREL, R. 38

GOVAERTS, J. 241
GOVINDACHARI, T.R. 87
GOWENLOCK, B.G. 99
GRAFFLIN, M.W. 184
GRAHAM, B. 146
GRAHAM, H. 252
GRANGER, R. 162
GRANIER, M. 163
GRANT, J.K. 132
GRASSIE, N. 56, 58, 241
GRASSMANN, W. 68, 82, 154, 155
GRAUER, R. 61
GRAY, G.W. 214
GRAY, H. LeB. 40
GRAY, P. 52
GRAY, R. 138
GREEN, A.A. 27
GREEN, D.E. 109
GREEN, J.H.S. 106, 110
GREEN, J.W. 2, 135
GREEN, M.L.H. 24
GREENBERG, D.M. 10, 241
GREENE, F.D. 163
GREENE, R. 81
GREENFELDER, B.S. 150
GREENHALG, R. 166
GREENSPAN, J. 41
GREENSTEIN, J.P. 1, 10, 11, 27, 241 (see also R.J. Koegel et al), 127
GREENWOOD, C.T. 3
GREGORY, J.D. 126
GREWE, R. 15
GRIESBACH, H. 70
GRIFFITH, J.Q. 241
GRIGAT, E. (see S. Hunig et al), 22
GRIGNARD, V. 224, 225, 229
GRIGORIEVA, N.Y. 163
GRIMMEL, H.W. 204
GRIPENBERG, J. 161
GROB, C.A. 103, 163, 190, 223
GROSS, J. 113
GROSS, P.M. 124

GROSSE, A.V. 102
GROTH, W. 207
GROVE, J.F. 69
GRUMMITT, O. 72, 180
GRUNDMANN, C. 15
GRUNDY, J. 51
GRUNE, A. 61
GRUNTFEST, I.J. 129
GRUNWALD, E. 221
GSELL, O. 32
GUAYLE, R. 119
GUENTHER, E. 241
GUGGENHEIM, M. 241
GUILLAUMIN, J. 228
GUILLEMONAT, A. 33, 228
GUINOT, H. 231
GULLAND, J.M. 89
GUNNING, H.E. 74
GUNSTONE, F.D. 9, 93, 95, 97
GÜNTHARD, H.H. 186
GUNTHER, F.A. 73
GÜNZL, M. 24
GÜNZL, W. 24
GURD, F.R.N. 11
GUSTAFSON, R.L. 130
GUSTAVSON, K.H. 10, 241, 242
GUT, M. (see A. Eschenmoser et al), 157
GUTERBOCH, H. 242
GUTOWSKY, H.S. 128, 219
GUTSCHE, C.D. 88
GUTTENBERG, H. v. 82
GUY, J. 26
GUZMAN-BARRON, E.S. 127
GYARFAS, E.D. 49
GYERMEK, L. 79
GYSEL, H. 242
GYSIN, H. 18, 61

HAAGEN-SMIT, A.J. 66, 67, 241
HAAR, R.W.V. (see H. Diehl et al), 102
HABERLAND, H. 20

HADDOCK, N.H. 105
HADDOW, A. 1, 63, 212
HADŽI, D. 186
HAEGI, W. 36
HAENSEL, V. 6, 150
HAFLIGER, O. 167
HAFNER, K. 22
HAFNER, W. (see J. Smidt et al), 22
HAGEMAN, H.A. 87
HAGEMEYER, H.J. 242
HAGENBACH, R.E. 18
HAGGLUND, E. 242
HAHN, D.A. 41
HAHN, G. 24
HAHN, W. 20, 21
HAIS, I.M. 242
HAÏSSINSKY, M. 71
HALE, D.K. 13, 105
HALEBSKY, N. 124
HALL, M.B. 165
HALL, R.T. 83
HALLER, H.L. 41, 44, 72
HALPERN, J. 6
HALSALL, T.G. 67
HAMANN, K. 17, 23, 82
HAMER, F.M. 97
HAMERSLAG, F.E. 242
HAMILL, W.H. 31
HAMILTON, C.S. 85
HAMILTON, L.G.D. 193
HAMILTON, P.B. 192
HAMLIN, K.E. 88
HAMM, F.A. 219
HAMMETT, L.P. 242
HAMMOND, C.W. 83
HAMMOND, G.S. 31, 215
HAMMOND, V.J. 170
HAMMOND, W.T.C. 56
HAMPTON, A. 156
HANAHAN, D.J. 242
HANDRICK, G.R. 47
HANFORD, W.E. 86, 204
HANNA, L.W. 242
HANSCH, C. 49

HANSFORD, R.C. 195, 208
HAPPEL, J. 150
HARBOURN, C.L.A. 234
HARDIÉ, R.L. 186
HARDY, C.J. 76
HARDY, D.V.N. 63
HARINGTON, C.R. 89
HARKINS, W.D. 218
HARLEY-MASON, J. 136, 190
HARMAN, R.E. 99
HARPER, S.H. 141, 142
HARRIS, E.E. 3, 183, 252
HARRIS, G. 93
HARRIS, G.M. 107
HARRIS, J.I. 136, 193
HARRIS, M.M. 94, 96
HARRIS, R.S. 112
HARTECK, P. 81
HARTLEY, G.S. 137
HARTMAN, L. 51
HARTMAN, S.C. 30
HARTNELL, E.D. (see E.L. Buhle et al), 73
HARTOUGH, H.D. 73, 145
HARTUNG, W.H. 41, 87, 244
HARTWELL, J.L. 68
HARVEY, L. 57
HARVEY, W.E. (see A.W. Johnson et al), 140, 141
HARWOOD, H.J. 95
HASENFRATZ, V. 227
HASHIMOTO, Y. 131
HASKINS, J.F. 2
HASLAM, J.H. 118
HASLEWOOD, G.A.D. 131
HASS, H.B. 44, 101
HASSALL, C.H. 88, 93
HASSEL, O. 91, 98, 105
HASSID, W.Z. 3, 27, 135, 204
HASSELQUIST, H. 240
HASTINGS, A.B. 112
HASTINGS, J.M. 219
HASZELDINE, R.N. 18, 212, 242
HATCH, L.F. 129, 242
HATT, H.H. 56, 105, 107, 242
HATTORI, S. 162

HAUBRICH, H. 22
HAUROWITZ, F. 64, 242
HAUSCHILD, G. 253
HAUSER, C.R. 85, 87
HAUSER, E.A. 72, 242
HAUSER, K.H. 61
HAUSERMAN, F.B. 118
HAUSMAN, H. 72
HAUSSER, K.H. 20
HAWKINS, E.G.E. 97
HAWORTH, R.D. 89, 136
HAWORTH, W.N. 89, 90
HAWTHORNE, J.N. 57
HAWTHORNE, M.F. 215
HAYES, B.T. 58
HAYNES, L.J. 4, 100, 141
HAYS, E.E. 210
HAZARD, R. 78, 165
HAZEBROEK, P. 171
HEACOCK, R.A. 51
HEANEY, H. 99
HEARLE, J.W.S. 106
HEARON, W.M. 50
HECHT, F. 242
HECHTER, O. 152, 201, 210
HECKER, J.C. 221
HEDGES, E.S. 106, 117
HEFTMANN, E. 50
HEHRE, E.J. 4
HEIDELBERGER, L. 238
HEIDT, L.J. 207
HEILBRON, I.M. 27, 37, 63, 89, 90, 112, 148, 149, 175
HEILBRONNER, E. 201
HEILMAN, R. 225
HEIN, F. 242
HEINCKE, B. 21
HEINES, V. 75
HEITLER, W. 71
HEITZMANN, P. 231
HELBERGER, J.H. 15
HELDT, W.Z. 88
HELFERICH, B. 2, 3
HELLER, C.A. 49
HELLER, H. 78
HELLER, W. 219

HELLMANN, H. 16, 17, 20, 21
HEMS, B.A. 55, 58, 78
HENAUX, F. 161
HENBEST, H.B. 153, 163
HENDERSON, R.B. 181
HENDRICKS, S.B. 40
HENECKA, H. 25, 70, 197, 198
HENGLEIN, A. 22, 23, 24
HENNE, A.L. 85, 203
HENNESSY, D.J. 192
HENRI, V. 40
HENRICKSON, J.B. 122
HENRY, L. 162
HENRY, T.A. 242
HENSEKE, G. 61
HENTZ, R.R. 159
HEOCHA, C.V. 216
HERBRANDSON, H.F. 167
HERINGTON, E.F.G. 170
HERMAN, D.F. 117
HERMANS, P.H. 242
HERRIOTT, R.M. 10
HERRMAN, M. (see G. Eglo et al), 41
HERRMANN, H. (see S. Hun et al), 22
HERRMANN, W. 18
HERZ, J. (see J. Fried et al), 210
HERZBERG, G. 242
HESS, F.G. 41
HESSE, G. 16, 19, 176, 197
HEUSCHKEL, U. (see E. Muller et al), 23
HEUSER, E. 73, 203, 243
HEUSNER, A. 17, 22
HEUSSER, H. 66, 153, 232
HEWITT, L.F. 27
HEWITT, R.I. (see S. Kushn et al), 126
HEY, D.H. 43, 90, 93, 98, 140, 168, 172, 207, 223, 233
HEYDRICH, H. 171
HEYMANS, C. 122
HEYNS, K. 21, 82, 243
HEYROTH, F.F. 240

HEYROVSKÝ, J. 13
HEYS, H.L. 243
HIBBENS, J.H. 42
HIBBERT, H. 2, 27
HICKINBOTTOM, W.J. 142, 243
HIEBERT, E.N. 75
HIEULLE, A. 226
HIGUCHI, T. 83
HILDEBRAND, D. (see H. Zahn et al), 28
HILDITCH, T.P. 27, 29, 66, 90, 243
HILL, D.W. 42
HILL, R. 56, 243
HILL, R.J. 157
HILL, R.L. 30
HILL, R.W. 158
HILLENBRAND, E.F. 83
HILMER, H. 18
HIMAN, J.W. 149
HINDERT, M. 4
HINE, J. 31, 243
HINSHELWOOD, C.N. 90, 138, 171, 243
HIRS, C.H.W. 130
HIRSCHLAND, H.E. 117
HIRSCHLER, A.E. 150
HIRSCHMANN, H. 153
HIRST, E.L. 2, 63, 89, 90, 91, 105, 169, 187, 206
HITCHINGS, G.H. 155, 187
HOARE, D.E. 137
HOBBS, M.E. 124
HOCHGESANG, F.P. 145
HOCHSTRASSER, R.M. 100
HOCK, H. 21, 23
HOCKETT, R.C. 243
HODEL, E. 18
HODGE, J.E. 4
HODGKIN, D.C. 68
HODGSON, H.H. 46
HODSON, H.F. 100
HOELSCHER, H.E. 49
HOFF, D.R. (see E.C. Taylor et al), 155

HOFFMAN, F. 241
HOFFMAN, R.A. 85
HOFFMANN, H. 20
HOFMANN, K. 8, 102, 130, 145
HOFMANN, M.P. 220
HOFFMANN-OSTENHOF, O. 243
HOGG, J.A. 195
HOGGARTH, E. 141, 143
HOLBRO, T. 61
HOLDSWORTH, R.S. 46
HOLIDAY, E.R. 11, 170
HOLLAND, D.O. 47
HOLLEMAN, A.F. 40
HOLLEMAN, J.W. (see G. Biserte et al), 76
HOLLEMAN-DEHOVE, J. (see G. Biserte et al), 76
HOLLINGSHEAD, R.G.W. 243
HOLMAN, R.T. 65, 95
HOLMES, H.L. 86, 88, 121
HOLT, A.J. 216
HOLTZ, F. 174
HOLTZ, P. 174
HONERJÄGER, R. 197
HONEYMAN, J. 3, 4, 243
HOOK, D.E. 117
HOOPER, I.R. (see M.J. Cron et al), 129
HOPFF, H. 243
HOPFF, M. 38
HORLEIN, U. 25
HÖRMANN, H. 20
HORN, O. 57
HORNER, L. 20, 23
HORNING, E.C. 45, 203
HORNING, M.G. (see J.W. Cornforth et al), 157
HORREX, C. 171
HORSFALL, J.G. 243
HORTON, D. 5
HOSKINS, W.M. 28
HOSTETTLER, F. 64
HOTTENROTH, B. 243

HOUBEN, J. 243
HOUGH, L. 5
HOUSE, H.O. 88
HOWARD, H.T. 143
HOWARD, K.S. (see P.H. Bell et al), 126
HOWELL, C.F. (see E.C. Taylor et al), 155
HOWES, F.N. 243
HOYER, H. 196, 197
HUANG, R.L. 233
HUBBARD, R. 129
HUBER, G. 17
HÜCKEL, W. 14, 15, 81, 163, 243
HUDSON, B.E. 85
HUDSON, C.S. 2, 72, 243
HUENNEKENS, F.M. 8, 221
HUFF, J.W. (see K. Folkers et al), 157
HUGEL, G. 226
HUGGARD, A.J. 4
HUGGINS, C. 210
HUGGINS, M.L. 75
HUGHES, E.D. 90, 96, 97, 140, 159, 160, 163, 212
HUGHES, E.W. 31
HUGHES, G.K. 107
HUGHES, Mrs. H. 172
HUGHES, J.D. 223
HUGHES, N.A. 8
HUGHES, W.L. 29, 128
HUISGEN, R. 16, 19, 21, 23, 24, 196, 204, 223
HULLA, G. 45, 240 (see also G. Egloff et al), 42
HULTQUIST, M.E. (see M.J. Fahrenbach et al), 155
HULTZSCH, K. 16, 17, 243
HÜNIG, S. 22
HUNSBERGER, I.M. 74
HUNTER, J.H. 149
HUNTER, L. 54, 94, 105, 212
HUNTER, R.F. 54, 56, 141
HUNTRESS, E.H. 243

HUNYAR, A. 243
HURD, C.D. 28
HURD, R. 59
HURD, D.T. 250
HUSTON, R.C. 244
HUTCHINGS, B.L. 112
HUTCHISON, C.A. 167
HUTT, H.H. 57
HUTTO, F.B. 220
HUTTRER, C.P. 48, 64
HVIDT, A.A 193

IDE, W.S. 86
IDSON, B. 48
IHDE, A. 75
ING, H.R. 122, 182, 204
INGERSOLL, A.W. 85
INGHAM, R.K. 50, 52
INGOLD, C.K. 35, 41, 71, 90, 91, 97, 99, 142, 223, 244
INGRAHAM, L.L. 215
INGRAM, D.J.E. 13, 244
INGRAM, V.M. 193
INHOFFEN, H.H. 14, 15, 17, 25, 67, 68, 70, 71, 82, 93, 176, 232
IPATIEFF, V.N. 6, 33
IRMSCHER, K. 68, 232
IRVINE, J.C. 40
IRVING, H.M.N.H. 139
ISAACS, N.S. 52
ISBELL, H.S. 27, 29
ISELIN, B. (see R. Schwyzer et al), 25
ISLER, O. 20, 22, 60, 61, 113, 117, 136, 157
ISHERWOOD, F.A. 133
ISLIKER, H.C. 11
IVANOV, V.I. 241
IVIN, K.J. 99, 138, 172

JACKER, E. 61

JACKMAN, L.M. 9, 167, 244
JACKSON, E.L. 85
JACKSON, J.L. 179
JACKSON, K.E. 41, 42, 44
JACKSON, M.A. 42
JACKSON, W.R. (see H.B. Henbest et al), 163
JACOBS, T.L. 86, 182
JACOBSEN, R.P. (see O. Hechter et al), 210
JACOBSEN, M. 67
JACQUES, J. 34
JACQUES, R. (see R. Daudel et al), 158
JACQUIER, R. 34, 35, 160 (see also P. Besinet et al), 163
JAFFE, H.H. 49
JAHNKE, H. 232
JAIN, A.C. 98
JAMES, T.H. 221
JAMES, W.O. 78, 121
JANAK, J. 129
JANICAUD, J. 109
JANOT, M.M. 26, 121, 176, 226
JANSSEN, P.A.J. 244
JANZ, G.J. 98, 244
JARMAN, G.N. 118
JAVILLIER, J. 229
JAYME, G. 24
JEAN, M. (see R. Daudel et al), 158
JEANLOZ, R. 3, 5, 28, 35, 156, 187 (see also O. Hechter et al), 210
JEGER, O. 64, 66, 121, 123 (see also D. Arigoni et al), 65 and J.W. Rowe et al), 177
JELLEY, E.E. 219
JELLINEK, H.H.G. 107
JELLINEK, M.H. 208
JEN, C.K. 179
JENCEKOL, L. 196
JENDEN, D.J. 172

JENKINS, A.D. 179, 237
JENKINS, G.L. 244
JENNY, E.F. 65
JENSEN, H. 28
JERCHEL, D. 18, 22
JEROME, H. (see M. Polonc et al), 155
JESKEY, H. 51
JIRA, H. (see J. Smidt et al), 22
JIRGENSONS, B. 244
JOHANSEN, G. 193
JOHNSON, A.W. 63, 90, 107, 110, 113, 130, 137, 140, 141, 157, 244
JOHNSON, D.L. (see M.J. Cron et al), 129
JOHNSON, E.A. 214
JOHNSON, E.B. 236
JOHNSON, J.R. 85, 102, 148, 204, 211
JOHNSON, J.S. 32
JOHNSON, O.H. 48
JOHNSON, P. 167
JOHNSON, R.G. 50
JOHNSON, T. (see F.S. Spring et al), 153
JOHNSON, T.B. 41
JOHNSON, T.L. 195
JOHNSON, W.A. 55
JOHNSON, W.C. 234
JOHNSON, W.S. 85, 87, 101
JOHNSTON, F. 234
JOHNSTONE, R.A.W. 52
JOLIBOIS, P. 34
JOLLES, Z.E. 142
JOLLEY, J.E. 50
JONAS, J. (see J. Sicher et al), 163
JONES, A.L. 220
JONES, A.S. 137
JONES, B. 45
JONES, D.G. 96
JONES, E.K. 6
JONES, E.R.H. 27, 54, 67, 90, 91, 102, 207

JONES, H. 60
JONES, H.A. 44
JONES, J.I. 54
JONES, J.K.N. 2, 3, 29, 55, 141, 169
JONES, J.R. 185
JONES, N. 112
JONES, R.G. 49, 87
JONES, R.N. 44, 47, 127, 210, 222
JONES, T.S.G. 126, 169, 200
JONES, W.E. 112
JONES, W.N. 45
JONSEN, J. 5
JOPE, E.M. 170
JORCZAK, J.S. 185
JORDAN, D.O. 29
JORDAN, T.E. 244
JORDON, L.A. 58
JORDAN, P. 81
JORISSEN, W.P. 244
JOSIEN, M.L. 186
JOST, W. 81, 138
JUCKER, E. 18, 23, 244
JUHOLA, A.J. 208
JU-HWA-CHU, E. 55
JULIA, M. 159, 163, 230, 244
JULIA, S. (see M. Julia et al), 163
JULIAN, P.L. 181, 210
JULLIEN, J. 160 (see also M. Julia et al), 163
JULLIEN, P. 230
JUNGERS, J.C. 37, 168
JUNGNICKEL, J.L. 83
JUNKMANN, K. 114
JUTISZ, M. 29, 35, 154

KABASHNIK, M.I. 111
KABAT, E.A. 156
KACZKA, E. 148
KAESZ, H.D. 204
KAGAN, S.S. 244
KAHRS, K.H. 18
KAINER, F. 244

KAINRATH, K. 15
KALCKER, H.M. 28
KALIL, E.O. (see C.J. Marsel et al), 117
KAMM, O. 27
KAMMERER, H. 22
KAMMERMEYER, K. 220
KANDRACHOFF, W. 162
KAPLAN, N.O. 103, 213
KAPPELER, H. (see R. Schwyzer et al), 25
KARABINOS, J.V. 3, 4
KARAGOUNIS, G. 244
KARGIN, V.A. (see A.V. Topchiyev et al), 58
KARLE, I.L. 167
KARLE, J. 167
KARLSON, P. 82
KARNOJITZKI, V. 244
KARRER, P. 19, 22, 32, 33, 34, 37, 41, 55, 60, 63, 68, 78, 165, 175, 229, 244
KARRER, W. 244
KARY, R.M. 118
KASASIAN, L. 59
KAST, W. 197
KÄSTNER, D. 14
KATCHALSKI, E. 10, 11
KATCHALSKY, A. 161
KATRITZKY, A.R. 57, 99, 100
KATZ, D.L. 245
KAUFFMAN, G.B. 74
KAUFMAN, J.V.R. 52
KAUFMANN, H.P. 14
KAUTTER, C.T. 15
KAUZMANN, W. 11
KAY, H. 118
KAY, R.L. 31
KAYE, W.I. (see G.L. Clark et al), 148
KE, B. 84
KEARBY, K. 150
KEBARLE, P. 119
KEFFORD, J.F. 107
KEITH, F.W. 220
KELLER, R.A. 32

KELLER, R.N. 43
KELLER, S. 193
KELLER-SCHIERLEIN, W. 201
KELLIE, A.E. 13
KEMBALL, C. 6, 91
KENCHINGTON, A.W. 193
KENDALL, E.C. 210
KENDALL, J.O. 55
KENDE, A.S. 88
KENDREW, J.C. 11
KENNER, G.W. 11, 66, 91, 136, 182
KENNER, J. 54, 57, 111
KENNETT, C.J. 185
KENNEY, C.N. 58
KENT, A. 238
KENT, P.W. 2
KENYON, J. 98, 160
KEPPLER, J.G. (see R.K. Beerthius et al), 129
KERN, W. 19, 20, 23, 191
KERP, L. 176
KERR, R.W.E. 245
KERTESZ, Z.I. 245
KERWIN, J.F. 195
KETELAAR, J.A.A. 159
KEZDY, F. 104
KHARASCH, N. 46, 52, 74
KHARASCH, M.S. 40, 245
KHORANA, H.G. 49, 97, 202
KHYM, J.X. 192
KIBRICK, A. 125
KICKHOFEN, B. 155
KIENITZ, H. 24, 196
KILBY, B.A. 105
KILPATRICK, J.E. 46
KILPATRICK, M. 31
KIMMEL, J.R. 30
KINDLER, H. 25
KING, C.G. 44
KING, F.E. 56, 90, 161
KING, R.W. 52
KING, T.P. 130
KINNER, C.R. 248
KINNEY, C.R. 150
KINSEY, R.H. 83

KIPLING, J.J. 139
KIPPING, F.S. 228
KIRCHOF, W. 70
KIRK, E. 27
KIRK, P.L. 10
KIRKPATRICK, W.J. 245
KIRMSE, W. 23
KIRRMANN, A. 159, 224, 230
KIRSCHENBAUER, H.G. 245
KIRST, W. 18
KIRSTEN, W.J. 80
KISE, M.A. 48
KISTIAKOWSKY, G.B. 42, 171
KISTLER, S.S. 118, 120
KJAER, A. 69
KLARMANN, E. 40
KLEBE, J.F. 23
KLEINBERG, J. 46, 73
KLEITMAN, D. 245
KLEMER, A. 247
KLENK, E. 20, 156
KLESSE, P. (see R. Kuhn et al), 25
KLEVENS, H.B. 46
KLINE, G.M. 185
KLINGSBERG, E. 49, 146
KLOETZEL, M.C. 86
KLOOSTERZIEL, H. 139
KLOPPING, H.L. 245
KLOTZ, I.M. 47, 172
KLOTZ, J.R.M. 44
KLUMPP, T.G. 101
KLYNE, W. 9, 55, 56, 65, 94, 132, 133, 153, 163, 167, 219, 245
KNELL, M. 116
KNOBLOCH, H. 253
KNOX, J.H. 138
KNOX, J.R. 185
KOBE, K.A. 40, 49
KOBRICH, G. (see S. Hunig et al), 22
KOCH, F.C. 27
KOCH, H. 197
KOCH, H.P. 54
KOEGEL, R.J. 127
KOEHLER, J.O. 117

KOFLER, A. 245
KOFLER, L. 245
KÖGL, F. 64, 81
KOHLSCHÜTTER, H.W. 70
KOHN, M. 72
KOJER, H. (see J. Smidt et al), 22
KOLB, D.K. 95
KOLLER, G. 174
KOLTHOFF, I.M. 47, 83, 126 (see also F.A. Bovey et al), 184
KOMAREWSKY, V.I. 6, 173, 220, 240
KOMPPA, G. 53
KONIGSBER, W. 130, 157
KOOYMAN, E.C. 171
KOPAC, M.J. 126
KORMAN, J. 195
KORNBLUM, N. 85
KORNFELD, E.C. 103
KORTE, F. 17, 23, 69, 155
KORTIJM, G. 21
KOSOLAPOFF, G.M. 87, 245
KOST, V.N. (see A.N. Nesmeyanov et al), 233
KOUTCHÉROV, V.F. 163
KOWKABANY, G.N. 4
KRACHT, W. 20
KRAEMER, E.O. 118
KRAFT, R. 19
KRAMER, L. (see C.J. Marsel et al), 117
KRAMES, L. 150
KRATZL, K. 64, 188
KRAUCH, H. 20
KRAUS, C.A. 73
KRAUSS, H.L. 19
KRAUSS, M. 30
KRAUSZ, F. 161
KRAYBILL, P.R. 220
KRĆ, J. 84
KREEVOY, M.M. 164
KREMER, C.B. 72, 182
KREMS, I.J. 46
KRENTSEL, B.A. (see A.V. Topchiyev et al), 58

KRESSMAN, T.R.E. 192, 23
KREUTZKAMP, N. 197
KREWSON, C.F. 241
KRÖHNKE, F. 18
KROLL, H. 130
KROPA, E.L. 151
KROPER, H. 197
KROPF, A. 129
KROPF, H. 21, 23
KRUBER, O. 14
KRUEGER, H. 122
KRZIKALLA, R. (see H. Za et al), 20
KUCHLER, L. 82, 245
KÜHLE, E. 22
KUHN, H. 22, 60, 64, 65, 68,
KUHN, R. 18, 20, 21, 25, 32,
KUHN, W. 31
KUKSIS, A. 51
KULKA, M. 87, 122, 123
KULLMANN, R. 34
KUNA, M. 126
KUNERT, F. (see H. Meerwein et al), 21
KUNIN, R. 185
KUNTZE, H. 82
KUNZE, R. 245
KUPFER, G. 24
KUPIECKI, F.P. (see M.J. Coon et al), 157
KURTH, E.F. 46
KURTZ, P. 198
KURTZ, S.S. 150, 208
KURZER, F. 48, 50, 74
KUSHNER, S. (see P.H. Bell et al), 126
KUSTANOVICH, I.M. (see A.V. Topchiyev et al), 58
KUTEPOW, N. von 25
KUTSCHKE, K.O. 233

LABAUNE, L.M. 231
LABHART, H. 61
LACASSAGNE, A. 7
LACEY, R.N. 9
LACEY, W.N. 250

LACHAMPT, F. 231
LADBURY, J.W. 51
LAFORGE, F.B. 41
LAGOWSKI, J.J. 100
LAHEY, F.N. 166
LAIBLE, R.C. 51
LAIDLAW, R.A. 3
LAIDLER, K.J. 169
LAKER, D. 57
LALAND, S. 5
LAMBERTON, A.H. 97
LAMBERTON, J.A. 105
LA MER, V.K. 124
LAMLA, E. 81
LAMPE, F.W. 111
LAMPREY, H. 117
LAND, A.H. 182
LANDLER, Y. 36
LANDQUIST, J.K. 143
LANE, J.F. 86
LANGENAN, E.E. 241
LANGENBECK, W. 16, 81
LAPIN, H. 161
LAPPERT, M.F. 50, 51
LAPPORTE, S.J. 24
LARDON, A. 153
LARDY, H.A. 73
LAROCHE, M.J. 26
LARRAMONA, H. 161
LARSON, M.L. 118
LASSETTRE, E.N. 42
LATHROP, W.L. 47
LAUDE, G. 226
LAUER, W. (see H. Zahn et al), 20
LAUERER, D. 24
LAUTERBUR, B.C. 128
LAUTSCH, W. 18
LAUZENT, P. 228
LAVOLLAY, J. 161
LAW, H.D. 99
LAWRENCE, A.S.C. 169
LAWSON, D.D. 52
LAWSON, W.B. 157
LEA, C.H. 56
LEACH, S.J. 108

LEAKE, P.H. 50
LE BRAS, J. 231, 245
LEBRETON, P. 39
LE CLAIR, H.G. 245
LECOMTE, J. 33, 36, 38, 224
LE CRAZ, A. 162
LEDERER, E. 24, 35, 66, 67, 90, 176, 245
LEDERER, M. 76
LEE, H. 245
LEE, J. 195
LEE, T.S. 83, 126, 221
LEEPER, R.W. 49
LEERMAKERS, J.A. 203
LeFÈVRE, C.G. 107, 219
LeFÈVRE, R.J.W. 107, 219, 245
LEFFLER, J.E. 47, 221, 245
LEFFLER, M.T. 85
LEGAT, M. 224
LEGRAND, M. 37, 38
LEHNE, M. 109
LEHONGRE, G. 161
LEICESTER, H.M. 75
LEIGH, T. 169
LEIMGRUBER, W. (see J. Schreiber et al), 23
LEISTEN, J.A. 98
LELOIR, L.F. 66
LEMBERG, R. 67, 107
LEMIEUX, R.U. 2, 4
LEMPERT, C. 52
LENJI, L. 51
LENNARD-JONES, J. 170
LENNARTZ, T.A. 15
LEONARD, N.J. 45, 103, 121, 122
LERMANN, H.G. 61
LERNER, R.W. 117
LESBRÉ, M. 228
LESLIE, W.B. 44
LESPAGNOL, A. 26, 39, 230
LESPIEAU, R. 2, 225
LESTER, G.R. 119
LESTER SMITH, E. 78, 132, 156
LETORT, M. 71
LETSINGER, R.L. 21

LETTRÉ, H. 15, 17, 81, 232
LEVENE, P.A. 40
LEVENS, E. (see R.M. Washburn et al), 117
LEVI, I. 2
LEVINE, J.F. 151
LEVINE, R. 49
LEVINSON, B.L. (see G. Egloff et al), 41
LEVISALLES, J. 38
LEVY, H. (see O. Hechter et al), 210
LEVY, M. 29
LEVY, N. 96
LEVY, N.R. 213
LEVY, R. 35
LEVVY, G.A. 4
LEWIN, A. 250
LEWIN, S.W. 219
LEWIN, S.Z. 218
LEWIS, B. 150
LEWIS, E.S. 99, 164
LEWIS, F.M. 169
LEWIS, G.N. 43
LEWIS, H.F. 184
LEWIS, I.C. 164
LEWIS, J. 200
LEWIS, J.J. 79
LEWIS, R.N. 250
LEWIS, T.A. 56
LEWIS, W.R. 117
LI, C.H. 11, 28, 112, 192
LIBERMANN, D. 160
LICHTENBERGER, J. 225, 226, 227, 229
LIDE, D.R. 161
LIDDEL, U. 127
LIEB, H. 60, 200
LIEBER, E. 6, 43
LIEBERMAN, S. 210
LIEN, A.P. 164
LIEWALD, R.A. (see J.G. Tolpin et al), 73
LIGETT, W.B. 45
LIGGETT, R.W. 4
LILJESTRAND, G. 177

LINDBERG, B. 5
LINDEN, H. 18
LINDERSTRØM-LANG, K. 136, 187, 193, 217
LINDGREN, G.O. 245
LINDLAR, H. (see O. Isler et al), 136
LINDSAY, K.L. 117
LINDSEY, A.S. 51
LINDWALL, H.G. 44
LINK, K.P. 203
LINN, B.O. (see K. Folkers et al), 157
LINNETT, J.W. 138
LINSTEAD, R.P. 90
LIPSCOMB, W.N. 219
LISSITZKY, S. 35
LITTMANN, E.R. 44, 246
LIVINGSTON, R. 102, 103, 221
LIVINGSTON, R.L. 31
LIVINGSTON, R.S. 207
LLEWELLYN, D.R. 56 (see also P.W.C. Barnard et al), 57
LOCATELL, L. 50
LOCHINGER, W. (see R. Kuhn et al), 25
LOCHTE, H.L. 246
LOEWENTHAL, H.J.E. 111
LOFFLER, K. (see W. Pelz et al), 25
LOHMAR, R.L. 3, 135
LOMBARD, R. 226
LONG, A.G. 141
LONG, F.A. 51, 129
LONG, L. 43
LONGENECKER, H.E. 28, 44
LONGINESCU, G.G. 40
LONGSWORTH, L.G. 125
LONGUET-HIGGINS, H.C. 91, 137, 223
LOOFBOUROW, J.R. 112
LOQUIN, R. 34, 224
LORA-TAMAYO, M. 175
LORENZ, W. 22
LOSIN, E.T. 182

LOSSING, F.P. 119, 127
LOUDON, J.D. 97, 121, 136, 143, 238
LOUX, H.M. 155
LOVE, P. 164
LOVELACE, A.M. 246
LOVERN, J.A. 28
LÖW, I. 66
LÖWDIN, P.-O. 31
LOWE, A. 59
LOWRY, C.D. 41
LOWRY, T.M. 40
LOZAC'H, N. 103, 229
LUBS, H.A. 246
LUCAS, C.C. 112
LUCAS, F. 11
LUCE, E.N. 185
LUCK, J.M. 27, 169
LUCK, W. 23, 196
LUCKEN, E.A.C. 139
LUDER, W.F. 45
LUDERITZ, O. 25 (see also O. Westphal et al), 156
LUGG, J.W.H. 28
LUIJTEN, J.G.A. (see G.J.M. van der Kerk et al), 22
LUMBROSO, A. 158
LUMBROSO, M. 34
LUNDBERG, W.O. 95
LUNDGREN, H.P. 10, 11, 28
LUSCHER, M. 82
LUTHER, H. 21
LUTTGEN, C. 240, 246
LÜTTKE, W. 99
LÜTTRINGHAUS, A. 81, 176
LWOWSKY, W. 22
LYNN, J.W. 52
LYNN, R.E. 49
LYONS, L.E. 107
LYTHGOE, B. 91, 96

MA, T.S. 80, 221
MAASE, H. 246
MACCOLL, A. 96, 223
MACEK, K. 242
MACKLEN, E.D. 52
MACKOR, E.L. 214

MADER, W.J. 83, 218
MADROÑERO, R. 175
MAGASANIK, B. 202
MAGAT, E.E. 184
MAGAT, M. 36
MAGDOFF, B.S. 193
MAGEE, J. 172
MAGERLEIN, B.J. 86
MAGNUS, A. 196
MAGOON, E.F. 175
MAGRATH, D.I. 156
MAHER, G.G. 4
MAINZER, K. 210
MAIR, B.J. 101, 125
MAIR, J. (see F.D. Rossini et al), 250
MAITLIS, P.M. 143
MAITTE, P. 162, 163
MAKOVKY, A. 51
MALATESTA, L. 92
MALISOFF, W.M. 41
MALKIN, T. 95
MALLETTE, M.F. 10
MANCERA, O. (see G. Rosenkranz et al), 210
MANESBERGER, H.R. 194
MANN, F.G. 89, 93, 94, 145
MANNERS, D.J. 5
MANNERS, T.J. 212
MANSKE, R.H.F. 44, 87, 9, 121, 122, 123
MANTELL, C.L. 246
MAPSON, L.W. 113
MAQUIN, C. 161
MARCOTTE, F.B. 171
MARCUS, E. (see W.R. M et al), 164
MARCUS, R.A. 127
MARES, F. (see J. Sicher et al), 163
MARINI-BETTÒLO, G.B. 175
MARION, L. 36, 37, 121, 122, 190
MARK, H. 18, 22, 43, 105, 180, 184, 191, 218, 247
MARK, H.F. 24, 31, 58, 12

MARK, H.L. 102
MARKHAM, E.C. 234
MARKHAM, R. 132, 187, 201, 217
MARKLEY, K.S. 246
MARKS, E.M. 41
MARON, S.H. 124
MARONI-BARNAUD, Y. 160
MARRACK, J.R. 94
MARRIAN, G.F. 56, 112
MARRIAN, S.F. 47
MARSEL, C.J. 117
MARSH, C.A. 4
MARSH, J.T. 246
MARSHALK, C. 36
MARSHALL, W.L. (see A.B. Garrett et al), 102
MARSZAK, I. 226, 227
MARTELL, A.E. 130, 238, 246
MARTIN, A.J. 84
MARTIN, A.J.P. 10, 125
MARTIN, A.R. 212
MARTIN, E.L. 85
MARTIN, H. 61
MARTIN, M. (see N.P. Buu-Hoi et al), 109
MARTIN, R.W. 246
MARTINET, J. 224, 229, 230
MARTIN-SMITH, M. 77
MARVEL, C.S. 102, 180, 184, 203, 246
MARXER, A. 77
MASAMUNE, H. 187
MASON, S.F. 155, 156
MASSART, L. 114
MASSIE, S.P. 49
MASSON, C.R. 220
MASSONI, R. 246
MASTRANGELO, S.V.R. 208 (see also H.P. Schwarz et al), 127
MATHEW, K.K. 188
MATHIEU, J. 23, 24, 37, 134
MATHIEU, J.P. 246
MATHIS, F. 36
MATSEN, F.A. 46, 222
MATTIL, K.F. 29
MATTNER, S. 18

MAUQUIN, C. 224
MAVITY, J.M. 151
MAX NESTLER, F.H. 169
MAXWELL, J.B. 246
MAY, D.R. 170
MAYER, F. 246
MAYER, R. 19
MAYER, R.L. 64
MAYER, W. 19
MAYERLE, E.A. (see J.G. Tolpin et al), 73
MAYER-WEGELIN, H. 253
MAYNE, B.C. 32
MAYO, F.R. 43, 48, 75, 120, 169, 233
MAYOR, Y. 109
MAZZANTI, G. 111 (see also G. Natta et al), 22
MEADE, E.M. 95
MECKE, R. 19
MEDALIA, A.I. (see F.A. Bovey et al), 184
MEEHAN, E.H. (see F.A. Bovey et al), 184
MEERWEIN, H. 19, 21, 25, 197
MEGSON, H.J.L. 246
MEGSON, N.J.L. 54, 55
MEHLENBACHER, V.C. 83
MEHLTRETTER, C.L. 4
MEIER, J. (see A. Eschenmoser et al), 157
MEISEL, S.L. 145
MEISTER, A. 246
MEISTER, H. 24
MEITES, L. 220
MELANDER, L.C.S. 207
MELARA, A. (see D. Arigoni et al), 65 (see also J.W. Rowe et al), 177
MELLAN, I. 246
MELLER, A. 107
MELSTROM, D.S. 149, 181
MELVILLE, D.B. 112, 113, 148
MELVILLE, H.W. 49, 55, 58, 63, 89, 161, 166, 171, 173, 184, 221

MENDIOLA, L. 130
MENSIER, P.H. 246
MENTLER, C. 39
MENTZER, C. 162
MERIAN, E. 24, 61
MERRIMAN, P. 106
MERROW, R.T. 50
MERZ, J.H. 168
MESROBIAN, R.B. 31, 252
MESTER, L. 5, 187
METCALF, R.L. 246
METZES, C. 161
METZGER, H. (see E. Muller et al), 23
MEUNIER, L. 231
MEUNIER, P. 33, 67
MEYER, E. 82
MEYER, E.W. 181
MEYER, H. 16
MEYER, H.J.L. 247
MEYER, K. 10
MEYER, K.H. 8, 64, 118, 184, 247
MEYER, V.B. 181
MEYERHOF, W.E. 30
MEYERS, M.B. (see H.B. Henbest et al), 163
MICHAELIS, L. 10, 42, 124
MICHEEL, F. 81, 247
MICHEL, G. 39
MICHEL, R. 11, 35, 68
MICHELSON, A.M. 111
MICHL, H. 76
MICHL, K.H. 155
MICOVIC, V.M. 247
MIDDLETON, S. 166
MIES, F. 130
MIESCHER, K. 47, 64, 210
MIETZSCH, F. 16, 17, 18
MIGINIAC, L. (see C. Prevost et al), 38
MIGRDICHIAN, V. 247
MIHAILOVIC, M.L. 247
MIHALYI, E. 29
MIKESKA, L.A. 48
MIKUSCH, J.D.V. 16
MILAS, N.A. 41, 112, 151

275

MILDE, R.L. 118
MILES, F.D. 247
MILES, S.E. 171
MILLAR, E.C.P. 155
MILLAR, I.T. 99
MILLAR, J.R. 58
MILLEN, D.J. 96
MILLER, A.A. 129
MILLER, E.C. 1
MILLER, E.S. 44
MILLER, E.V. 247
MILLER, F.A. 204
MILLER, F.M. 145
MILLER, G.H. 220
MILLER, J. 107
MILLER, J.A. 1
MILLER, R.E. 3
MILLER, S.A. 51
MILLER, S.L. 205
MILLS, J.A. 4, 94, 107
MILLS, W.H. 89
MINDER, W. 171
MINER, C.S. 234
MINKOFF, G.J. 171, 247
MINTON, R.G. (see W.H. Schubert et al), 164
MIQUEL, J.F. 26
MIRO, P. (see H. Zahn et al), 20
MISKEL, J.A. 209
MISLOW, K. 22
MISRA, G.S. 168
MITCHELL, H.H. 112
MITCHELL, H.K. 155
MITCHELL, J. 83
MITCHELL, J.J. 208
MITTERMAIER, J. 14
MIZUSHIMA, S.I. 11, 31, 176, 207, 247
MOCK, G.V. 50
MOELWYN-HUGHES, E.A. 41
MOGEY, G.A. 79
MOHLER, H. 247
MOLHO, D. 162
MOLLER, E.F. 70
MÖLLER, F. 197 (see also G. Spielberger et al), 198 and H. Freytag et al), 199

MOLLERING, H. 240
MONCRIEFF, R.W. 74
MONDON, A. 17
MONGAR, J.L. 169
MONTAGUE, B.A. 83
MONTAGNE, M. 227
MONTAVON, M. 61 (see also O. Isler et al), 136
MONTGOMERY, R. 29, 247, 251
MONTHEARD, P. 228
MONTREUIL, J. 35
MONTREUIL, L. 32
MOORE, A.M. (see E.L. Buhle et al), 73
MOORE, D.H. 220
MOORE, L.D. 218
MOORE, M.L. 86
MOORE, S. 11, 125
MOORE, T.E. 44
MOORE, W.R. 164
MOORMEIR, L.F. 117
MORAWETZ, H. 179
MOREAU, R.C. 26
MOREHOUSE, E.L. 118
MOREL, A. 228
MORGAN, J.F. 85
MORGAN, J.W.W. 4
MORGAN, K.J. 99
MORGAN, S.O. 124
MORI, T. 4
MORLEY, H.V. 216
MORRELL, J.C. 43, 237
MORRIS, A.L. 172
MORRIS, H.E. 41
MORRISON, A.L. 96
MORRISON, G.O. 54
MORRISON, J.I. (see H. Diehl et al), 102
MORRITZ, F.L. 6, 220
MORSCHEL, H. 25 (see also H. Meerwein et al), 21
MORSE, B.K. 221
MORTON, A.A. 45, 247
MORTON, I.D. 141
MORTON, R.A. 54, 68, 78, 95, 133
MORTON, R.K. 108
MOSETTIG, E. 86, 87, 188

MOSHER, H.S. 181
MOTHES, K. 122, 177
MOTT, F. 198
MOUBACHER, R. 48
MOULTON, F.R. 234
MOUREAU, H. 161
MOUREU, H. 226
MOUSSERON, M. 37, 60, 160, 161, 163
MOWAT, J.H. 112, 125
MOWRY, D.T. 47
MOYER, L.S. 236
MOZINGO, R. 86, 148
MUHLETHALER, K. 66
MÜHLMANN, R. 22
MUKERJEE, S.K. 56
MÜLLER, A. 243, 247
MÜLLER, E. 16, 17, 23, 25, 70, 197, 247 (see also S.H. et al), 22
MÜLLER, O.H. 43, 124, 220
MÜLLER, P. 65, 247
MULLER, R. (see T. Wiel et al), 199
MULLER, R.H. 126
MULLIKEN, R.S. 111, 164
MUNCH, R.H. 103
MUNIER, R. 35
MUNIYAPPAN, T. 74
MURALT, A. v. 64
MURIE, R. (see H. Diehl et al), 102
MURPHY, A.M. 48
MURPHY, R.B. (see W.H. Schubert et al), 164
MURRAY, A. 247
MURRAY, G.R. 128
MURRAY, K.E. 95
MURRAY, W.J. 57
MUSGRAVE, W.K.R. 98
MUSSO, H. 20
MUSTAFA, A. 46, 47, 48, 4
MUTH, S. 198
MOTT, F. 198
MYERS, O.E. 209
MYERS, R.R. 128
MYRBÄCK, K. 176, 247

McALPINE, I.M. 238
McCALDIN, D.J. 52
McCALLUM, R.A. (see R.J. Koegel et al), 127
McCAULAY, D.A. 164
McCAWLEY, E.L. 122
McCLELLAN, A.L. 248
McCLOSKEY, C.M. 4
McCOUBREY, J.C. 97, 171
McCREW, F.C. 75
McCULLOUGH, J.P. 31
McDANIEL, D.H. 167
McDONALD, E.J. 2
McDOWELL, C.A. 170
McENTEE, H.R. 117
McELHINNEY, R.S. (see H.B. Henbest et al), 163
McELVAIN, S.M. 47, 86, 211, 246
McEWEN, W.E. 50, 51
McEWEN, W.L. (see S. Kushner et al), 126
McGEE, B.E. 80
McGILVRAY, O.I. 29
McGINTY, D.A. 128
McHARD, J.A. 185
McILROY, R.J. 246
McKAY, A.F. 48
McKAY, T.W. (see T.H. Pearson et al), 118
McKEEVER, C.H. 85
McKENNA, J. 98
McKINNEY, C.D. 151
McLAFFERTY, F.W. 119
McLAREN, A.D. 8
McLAUGHLIN, R.L. 150
McLEAN, M.J. 44
Mc L. MATHIESON, A. 107
McMEEKIN, T.L. 28
McNESBY, J.R. 49
McOMIE, J.F.W. 93, 138, 201
McPHEE, G.R. 12
McQUADE, A.J. 129
McQUILLIN, F.J. 58
McROBERTS, D.T. 150

NAAR-COLIN, C. 128
NABARRO, J.D.N. 78
NACHMIAS, G. 34
NACHOD, F.C. 167
NADOR, K. 79
NAGATA, W. 177
NAGHSKI, J. 241
NAIR, P.M. 164
NAKAMURA, M. 75
NAM, B. 214
NANNINGA, L. 172
NASON, A. 113
NAST, R. 23, 139
NATTA, G. 6, 20, 21, 22, 58, 111, 161, 191
NAU, J. 162
NAU, P. 162
NAVEZ, Y.R. 60, 61
NAVES, Y.R. 35, 36, 37, 201, 229
NEELY, W.B. 4, 5
NEHER, R. 32, 76
NEILANDS, J.B. 84, 247
NELLES, J. 14
NELSON, J.A. 50, 74
NELSON, P.F. 74
NENTWIG, J. 199
NERDEL, F. 17
NESMEYANOV, A.N. 33, 38, 111, 189, 233, 254
NETER, E. (see O. Westphal et al), 156
NEUBERG, C. 3
NEUBERGER, A. 10, 148, 190, 217
NEUHAUS, A. 15
NEUMANN, F.W. 45
NEUMANN, G. 161
NEUMANN, W. 18, 82
NEUNHOEFFER, O. 82
NEURATH, H. 27, 234
NEUVILLE, C. (see M. Julia et al), 163
NEVILLE, K. 245
NEWBOLD, G.T. (see F.S. Spring et al), 153

NEWMAN, M.S. 74, 86, 102, 215
NEWTH, F.H. 3, 4, 100
NEWTON, G.G.F. 79, 137, 157
NICHOLS, J.B. 218
NICHOLLS, B. (see H.B. Henbest et al), 163
NICHOLSON, A.J.C. 107
NICKERSON, R.F. 3
NICKLE, A.G. 171
NICKON, A. (see R.N. Jones et al), 127
NICOL, H. 248
NIEDERL, J.B. 248
NIEDERL, V. 248
NIEMANN, C. 66
NIEMANN, E. (see T. Wieland et al), 199
NIER, A.O.C. 234
NIEUWLAND, J.A. 248
NIELSEN, A. 248
NIGGLI, P. 248
NIGHTINGALE, D.V. 43, 46
NIKITIN, N.I. 248
NISBET, H.B. 212
NISIZAWA, K. 29
NIXON, W.C. 219
NOACK, K. 19
NOBIS, J.F. 117 (see also R.A. Benkeser et al), 51
NOGGLE, G.R. 135
NOLAND, W.E. 49
NOLL, W. 18
NOLLER, C.R. 28, 73, 204
NOLTES, J.G. (see G.J.M. van der Kerk et al), 22
NOMINE, G. 24
NORD, F.F. 6, 8, 40, 70
NORDSTROM, G. 162
NORMAN, A.G. 27
NORMANT, H. 9, 38, 39, 160, 163
NORRISH, R.G.W. 91, 138, 168
NORTHEY, E.H. 43, 120, 248
NORTON, J.A. 44
NORTON, T.R. 248
NOTHER, H. (see S. Hunig et al), 22

NOWAKOWSKI, H. 174
NOYES, W.A. 38, 50, 171, 175, 220
NOZAKI, K. 169
NOZOE, T. 68, 177, 190, 201
NUHFER, P.A. (see J.H. Biel et al), 129
NUKINA, S. 52
NURNBERG, H.W. 24
NYHOLM, R.S. 94, 166

O'CONNOR, C.M. 153, 155, 156, 157, 213
O'CONNOR, M. 156
O'CONNOR, P.R. 221
ODIN, L. 156
OEDIGER, H. 25
OELERT, H. 21
OETTE, K.H. (see S. Hunig et al), 22
OFFE, H.A. 15
OGSTON, A.G. 29, 132, 156
OKUNUKI, K. 193
OLAERTS, E. 168
OLDHAM, K.G. (see P.W.C. Barnard et al), 57
OLDS, R.H. 208
OLIVETO, E.P. 129
OLLIS, W.D. 57, 99
OLSON, E.J. 5
OLSZANSKI, E.B. (see J.G. Tolpin et al), 73
OMIETANSKI, G.M. 51
ONCLEY, J.L. 124
ONYON, P.F. 237
OOSTERHOFF, L.J. 171
OPENSHAW, H.T. 121, 122, 136
OPITZ, G. 20
OPLER, A. 248
ORCHIN, M. 6, 151, 241, 248
ORGEL, L.E. 132, 139, 145
ORLANS, E.S. 94
ORLOFF, H.D. 49
ORR, C.H. 129
ORR, R.J. 172
ORTEN, J.M. 103
ORTH, H. 17

ORTHNER, L. 16
OSBORN, M.J. 8
OSDENE, T.S. 155 (see also C. Taylor et al), 155
OSTER, G. 219
OTT, E. 55, 120, 180, 184, 198
OTT, W. 82
OURISSON, G. 111, 161
OVERBERGER, C.G. 103
OWEN, L.J. 70
OWEN, L.N. 63, 251
OXFORD, A.E. 28

PACAULT, A. 36, 109
PACSU, E. 2, 66
PADDOCK, N.L. 9, 57, 106
PADOVA, R. 227
PAECH, K. 234
PAGE, I.H. 127
PAGE, J.E. 57, 97
PAICE, E.S. 55
PAILER, M. 67
PAINE, C. 106
PAINTER, E.P. 43
PAKRASHI, S.C. 68
PALERMITI, F.M. (see M.J. Cron et al), 129
PALFRAY, L. 225, 229
PALLMAN, H. 60
PALMER, A.H. 125
PALMER, W.G. 248
PANOUSE, J.J. 36
PAPESCH, V. 195
PAPPO, R. 88
PAQUOT, C. 226, 230
PARHAM, W.E. 181
PARIS, R. 26
PARISELLE, H. 224, 226
PARK, J.D. 178
PARKER, A.C. 219
PARKER, A.J. 52
PARKER, E.E. 185
PARKER, L.F.J. 13
PARKER, R.E. 52
PARKES, M.W. 93
PARKS, G.S. 42
PARMERTER, S.M. 88

PARRISH, C.I. 42
PARTRIDGE, S.M. 55, 169
PARTRIDGE, W.S. 73
PASCAL, P. 224, 226
PASCUAL, J. 163
PASQUON, I. 21, 61, 191
PASYNSKII, E.J. 205
PATAKI, J. (see G. Rosenkr et al), 210
PATAT, F. 17, 22
PATRICK, C.R. 111
PATTERSON, A.M. 248
PATTISON, E. 248
PAUL, M.A. 51
PAUL, R. 17, 33, 36, 160, 161 229, 230
PAULING, L. 19, 55, 67, 102, 172, 177, 204, 206, 223, 248
PAULSEN, H. 21
PAULUS, T. 229
PAUNCZ, R. 111
PAUSACKER, K.H. 166
PAUSHKIN, Y.M. 253
PAUSON, P.L. 49, 91, 98, 110, 201, 204
PAVLOSKAYA, T.E. 205
PAWELLEK, F. (see H. Meerwein et al), 21
PAYNE, J.S. 129
PAYNE, R.W. 210
PEACOCK, M.A. 219
PEACOCKE, A.R. 137
PEAKALL, D.B. 139
PEAKER, F.W. 13, 31
PEARLEY, T. 242
PEARLSON, W.H. 178
PEARSON, D.E. 73, 183
PEARSON, R.G. 241
PEARSON, T.H. 118
PEAT, S. 2, 3, 67
PECK, R.L. 125, 148
PECSOCK, R.L. 248
PEDERSEN, K.O. 28
PEETERS, H. 7
PELTER, A. (see J.W. Cor et al), 157
PELZ, W. 25
PENFOLD, A. 57

PENTZ, C.A. 83
PEPPER, D.C. 98, 191
PEPPER, K.W. 54
PERCHERON, F. 26
PERCIVAL, E.G.V. 2, 3, 28, 96, 141, 248
PERILSTEIN, W.L. 117
PERLIN, A.S. 5
PERLMAN, D. 75 (see also J. Fried et al), 210
PERLMANN, G.E. 11, 30
PERRON, R. 229, 231
PERRY, E.S. 221
PERUTZ, M.F. 170
PESARD, M. (see J. Schreiber et al), 23
PESEZ, M. 38
PESTEMER, M. 19, 24, 197
PETERS, C.A. 72
PETERS, E.D. (see J.L. Jungnickel et al), 83
PETERS, F.N. 239
PETERS, R.H. 136
PETERSEN, E.M. 126
PETERSEN, S. 17, 18, 21, 25, 82, 126, 197 (see also M. Bogemann et al), 198
PETERSON, D.H. 105
PETERSON, E.A. 192, 193
PETERSON, H.J. 52
PETIT, A. 34, 246
PETROV, A.D. 37
PETROVA, R.G. (see A.N. Nesmeyanov et al), 233
PEYRON, L. 36, 239
PEYRONEL, G. 144
PFEFFER, K.H. 114
PFEIFFER, P. 14, 53
PFEIL, E. 17
PFIFFNER, J.J. 27
PFITZNER, H. 16, 22
PFLEIDERER, G. 8
PHADKE, R. 87
PHELISSE, J. 38
PHILIP, J.E. (see O. Wintersteiner et al), 148
PHILIPSBORN, W.V. (see P. Karrer et al), 22

PHILLIPS, C.S.G. 169
PHILLIPS, J.N. 108, 166
PHILLIPS, J.P. 50
PHILLIPS, M. 40, 41
PHILLIPS, R.R. 88
PHILLIPS, W.D. 128
PIAUX, L. 224, 227
PICARD, J.P. 52
PIEPENBRINK, H.F. 17
PIEPENPRINK, H.S. 197
PIEPER, G. 199 (see also H. Freytag et al), 199
PIERCE, O.R. 151
PIETTE, L.H. 202
PIGANIOL, P. 33, 226, 248
PIGMAN, W.W. 2, 21, 29, 135
PILLON, D. 35
PIMENTEL, G.C. 179, 248
PINCUS, G. 29 (see also O. Hechter et al), 210
PINDER, A.R. 143, 144
PINEAU, P. 186
PINES, H. 6, 151, 173
PINNER, S.H. 54
PIPENBERG, K.J. (see G.L. Clark et al), 148
PIRKMAJER, E. 186
PIRSCH, J. 15
PISKUR, M.M. 28
PITT, G.A.J. 68, 95, 133
PITT-RIVERS, R. 113
PITZER, E.C. 120
PITZER, K.S. 46, 170, 215
PLATT, D. 135
PLATT, J.R. 31, 46
PLATTNER, A. 15
PLESCH, P.H. 105
PLETSCHER, A. (see O. Isler et al), 157
PLIMMER, J.R. 52, 100
PLOETZ, T. 15
PLUMMER, A.J. 18, 75
PLUNGUIAN, M. 248
PLYLER, E.K. 170
POHL, H.A. 124
POHL, R. 174
POIRIER, P. 37, 134

POLAK, L.S. (see A.V. Topchiyev et al), 58
POLANSKY, T.S. 248
POLANYI, M. 63, 158
POLGÁR, A. 83 (see also J.L. Jungnickel et al), 83
POLGLASE, W.J. 4
POLLARD, F.H. 76
POLONOVSKI, M. 155
POLONSKY, J. 37, 162
POLSON, A. 193
POMMER, H. 16, 25
PONSOLD, W. 174
PONTIUS, R.B. 218
POPJAK, G. 212 (see also J.W. Cornforth et al), 157
POPLE, J. 248
POPLE, J.A. 128, 139, 170
POPP, F.D. 51
PORAI-KOSHITS, B.A. 111
PORTER, G. 138, 168, 170
PORTER, G.B. 100
PORTER, J.B. 50
PORTER, Q.N. 166
PORTER, R.R. 154
POST, H.W. 249
POSTELNEK, W. 246
POSTERNAK, T. 32
POTATOV, V.M. 111
POTEMPA, S.J. 46
POWELL, A.D.C. 137
POWELL, H.M. 63, 90
POWELL, R.E. 31
POWELL, W.H. 101
POWERS, W.H. 120
POWERS, W.J. 185
POWLES, J.G. 219
POYNTER, W.G. 49
PRADHAM, S.K. (see D. Arigoni et al), 65
PRAILL, P.F.G. 56, 97
PRATT, L.S. 249
PRATT, Y.T. 182
PREECE, I.A. 93
PREGL, F. 249
PRELOG, V. 20, 21, 25, 36, 64, 65, 90, 93, 103, 121, 123, 163, 177, 206, 213

PRESTON, R.D. 249
PRESTWOOD, R.S. 209
PREUGSCHAS, H. 176
PRÉVOST, C. 38, 159, 175, 226
PRÉVOST-BERNAS, Mrs. A. 171
PRICE, C.C. 44, 75, 86, 101, 120, 125, 127, 169, 249
PRICE, D. 125
PRICE, J.R. 68, 103, 121, 166
PRICE, W.C. 32, 46, 212
PRIDDLE, J.E. 5
PRIEST, W.J. 221
PRIESTLEY, W. 150
PRIGOGINE, I. 7
PRIJS, B. 249
PRINCE, A.K. 130
PRINGSHEIM, P. 249
PRINS, D.A. 28
PRINTY, H.C. 181
PRITCHARD, H.O. 50
PRITCHETT, E.G.K. 55
PROBER, M. 50
PRODINGER, W. 249
PROSKAUER, E.S. 83, 221
PROSSER, T.J. 74
PRUETT, R.L. 118
PUCHER, G.W. 27
PULLMAN, A. 1, 249
PULLMAN, Mme, A. 1, 93, 158, 168, 170 (see also N.P. Buu-Hoi et al) 109
PULLMAN, B. 1, 34, 93, 158, 170, 249 (see also N.P. Buu-Hoi et al), 109
PURRMANN, R. 15, 66
PURNELL, J.H. 128
PURVES, C.B. 2, 184
PUSCHEL, W. (see W. Pelz et al), 25
PUTNAM, F.W. 10

QUADBECK, G. 20
QUAEDVLIEG, M. 198
QUAYLE, O.R. 49, 208

QUIMBY, M.W. 251
QUINKERT, G. 65

RAAKE, I.D. 192
RABATÉ, J. 227
RABEN, M.S. 210
RABIN, B.R. 133
RABINOVITCH, E. 207
RABJOHN, N. 86
RADLEY, J.A. 249
RAECKE, B. 21
RAFF, R.A.V. 184, 185
RALLS, J.W. 52
RALSTON, A.W. 249
RAMACHANDRAN, L.K. 12, 50
RAMAGE, G.R. 143
RAMART-LUCAS, P. 33, 244
RAMBAUD, R. 227, 229, 230
RAMSAY, D.A. 127, 179
RÁNBY, B.G. 184
RANDALL, H.M. 249 (see also H.W. Thompson et al), 148
RANDALL, I. 234
RAOUL, Y. 32
RAPHAEL, R.A. 9, 141, 142, 201, 212, 249
RAPOPORT, L. 146
RASMUSSEN, R.S. (see H.W. Thompson et al), 148
RAST, H. 196
RASUWAJEW, G.A. 233
RATHGEBER, P. (see H. Zahn et al), 20
RAUSCH, D.A. 246
RAUSCH, M.D. 74, 75
RAY, F.E. 43
RAY, R.L. (see T.H. Pearson et al), 118
RAYMOND, A.L. 2, 203
READ, J. 40
READ, W.J. 58
READQ, J. 78
RECOURT, J.H. (see R.K. Beerthuis et al), 129
REDFARN, C.A. 64
REDFIELD, R.R. 11

REDMON, B.C. 72
REED, L.J. 8
REED, R.A. 212
REED, R.I. 249
REES, A.L.G. 107
REES, M.W. 154
REESE, J.S. 41
REEVE, K.D. 107
REEVES, L.W. 128
REEVES, R.E. 3, 29, 242
REGNA, P.P. 55, 126, 131
REICH, H. 28, 29
REICHARD, S.M. 113
REICHERT, B. 249
REICHSTEIN, T. 17, 28, 60, 11, 153, 177, 187
REID, C. 249
REID, D.H. 138
REID, E.E. 249
REID, I.C. 238
REID, S.T. 77
REID, W.G. 55
REIDLINGER, A. (see C.J. Marsel et al), 117
REIFSCHNEIDER, W. 37
REILLEY, C.N. 1
REILLY, H.C. 157
REIMANN, S.P. 234
REINEKE, E.P. 126
REINMUTH, O. 74, 75, 245
REITSEMA, R.H. 47
REMICK, A.E. 101, 249
RENARD, S.H. 34
RENAULT, J. 36
REPORT, 38
REPPE, J.W. 249, 250
REPPE, W. 60, 64
RETI, L. 66, 121, 122
REUTOW, O.A. 24, 190, 223
REXROTH, E. (see H. Zahn et al), 20
REYERSON, L.H. 40
REYNOLDS, A.K. 122
REYNOLDS, D.D. 3
REYNOLDS, G.A. 146
REYNOLDS, W.B. 73
RHEINBOLDT, H. 196, 198

RHODES, D.N. 57
RIBKA, J. 22
RIBNER, A. 75
RICAUD, P. 38
RICE, F.O. 41, 42, 179, 249
RICE, J.B. 101
RICHARD, G. 160
RICHARDSON, J.W. 204
RICHMOND, J.H. 146
RICHTER, E. (see C. Taylor et al), 155
RICHTER, F. 22, 41, 82
RICHTER, F.P. 251
RICHTMYER, N.K. 2, 3
RIDD, J.H. 239
RIDDICK, J.A. 221
RIDDLE, E.H. 250
RIDEAL, E.K. 89, 90
REIBSOMER, J.L. 45, 49
RIECHE, A. 22, 250
RIED, W. 17
RIEDEL, O. 24
RIEGEL, B. 210
RIEMAN, W. 102
RIEMSCHNEIDER, R. 17
RIESZ, C.H. 220
RIEVESCHL, G. 43
RIDGE, D. 57
RIDGE, M.J. 107
RILEY, D. (see A.B. Garrett et al), 102
RILEY, E.F. 44
RILEY, H.E. 185
RINDER, A.R. 250
RINGOLD, H.J. (see G. Rosenkranz et al), 210
RINKEL, M. 234
RISI, J. 60
RISSE, K.H. 25
RISSER, W.C. (see O. Wintersteiner et al), 148
RITCHIE, E. 107
RITTEL, W. (see R. Schwyzer et al), 25
RITTER, G.J. 184
RITTER, H. 16

RIVIÈRE, H. 38 (see also M. Charpentier et al), 163
ROBB, J.C. 138, 171, 172, 173
ROBERTS, C.W. 58, 74
ROBERTS, G. (see R.N. Jones et al), 127
ROBERTS, I. 124
ROBERTS, J.C. 137
ROBERTS, J.D. 31, 49, 65, 74, 103, 138, 223, 250
ROBERTS, R. 166
ROBERTS, R.B. 130
ROBERTSHAW, G.F. 238
ROBERTSON, A. 137
ROBERTSON, J. 238, 250
ROBERTSON, J.M. 89, 212 (see also S. Arnott et al), 65
ROBERTSON, N.C. 151
ROBERTSON, W.W. 46
ROBINET, F.G. 37
ROBINSON, C. 178
ROBINSON, F.A. 54, 79
ROBINSON, F.M. (see K. Folkers et al), 157
ROBINSON, R. 20, 38, 58, 63, 74, 89, 90, 93, 143, 176, 250 (see also E.P. Abraham et al), 148
ROBINSON, R.E. 117
ROBITSCHEK, P. 250
ROCEK, J. (see J. Sicher et al), 163
ROCHE, J. 11, 68, 69, 131
ROCHEN, L.K. 182
ROCHOW, E.G. 46, 190, 245, 250
ROCKLAND, L.B. 10
RODD, E.H. 140, 143
RODD, E.M. 110
RODEBUSH, W.H. 46, 180
ROE, A. 86, 234
ROEBUCK, D.S.P. 55
ROEDIG, A. 197
ROGERS, C.A. 241
ROGERS, M.M. (see P.H. Bell et al), 126
ROGERS, M.T. 104

ROGERS_LOW, B.W. (see D. Crowfoot et al), 148
ROHDE, W. (see W. Theilacker et al), 21
ROHM, E. (see R. Kuhn et al), 25
ROHATGI, K.K. 172
ROLLEFSON, G.K. 31
ROMANCHEK, L. 127
ROMANS, R.G. 210
ROMO, J. (see G. Rosenkranz et al), 210
RONDESTVEDT, C.S. 88
RONZIO, A.R. 80, 221
ROOT, M.A. 153
RÖSCH, G. 19
ROSE, A. 220, 221
ROSE, B.A. 13
ROSE, E. 220, 221
ROSE, F.L. 63, 90
ROSE, J.D. 96
ROSENBAUM, E.J. 150
ROSENBERG, H. 74
ROSENBERG, H.R. 250
ROSENBERG, S.D. 52
ROSENBERG, R.M. 193
ROSENKRANZ, G. 67, 153, 210
ROSENWALD, R.H. 151
ROSS, R.B. 75
ROSS, W.C.J. 1, 127, 251
ROSSINI, F.D. 75, 101, 180, 208, 250
ROTH, H. 14, 196
ROTH, W.L. 31
ROUSSEL, P.A. 73
ROUGHTON, F.J.W. 221, 222
ROVAL, G. 109
ROVERY, M. 154
ROWATT, E. 217
ROWE, J.W. 177
ROWLEY, D. 171
RUBY, P.R. 146
RUDGE, A.J. 57
RUEGG, R. (see O. Isler et al), 136, 157
RUFF, A. 153
RUIGH, W.L. 28

281

RUMPF, P. 33, 109, 158, 160
RUNGE, F. 250
RUNNSTROM, J. 177
RUSHTON, J.H. 220
RUST, F.F. 151
RUSSELL, A. 42
RUSSELL, G.A. 75
RUSSELL, P.B. 57
RUTTINGER, R. (see J. Smidt et al), 22
RUZICKA, L. 42, 64, 91, 206, 225 (see also J.W. Rowe et al), 177
RYDHOLM, S.A. 184
RYDON, H.N. 137, 157
RYTINA, A.W. 86
RZASA, M.J. 245

SAAD, I.A. 129
SABOURIN, R. 161
SACHANEN, A.N. 150, 250
SADLER, P.W. 52
SADRON, C.L. 202
SAFRANSKI, L.W. 84
SAGE, B.H. 250
SAINES, G.S. 52
SALMON, A.J. 82
SALMON-LEGAGNEUR, F. 38, 227
SALTER, W.T. 250
SALZBERG, H.K. 185
SAMEC, M. 250
SAMUELS, L.T. 29, 112
SANDER, A. 15
SANDERMANN, W. 250
SANDERS, A.G. (see E.P. Abraham et al), 148
SANDERSON, P.M. 74
SANDIN, R.B. 44
SANDORFY, C. 222, 250 (see also R. Daudel et al), 158
SANDRIS, G. 161
SANDS, R.H. 128
SANELLA, J.L. 187

SANGER, F. 11, 29, 32, 58, 63, 132, 153
SANGSTER, A.W. 75
SANKIN, A. 208
SANNIÉ, C. 161
SARETT, L.H. 28, 75, 153
SARGENT, D.E. 204
SARGENT, L.J. 29
SARTEN, P. 16
SARTORI, M.F. 48
SASSE, W.H.F. 166
SATTLER, L. 2
SAUCY, G. (see O. Isler et al), 136, 157
SAUER, J. 23, 24
SAUER, J.C. 86
SAUER, R.O. 72
SAUNDERS, B.C. 137, 212, 251
SAUNDERS, J.H. 47
SAUNDERS, K.H. 251
SAUNDERS, L. 78, 192
SAUNDERS, M. 128
SAUTIÈRE, P. (see G. Biserte et al), 16
SAUVE, D.M. (see R.A. Benkeser et al), 51
SAVELL, W.L. 47
SAWYER, D.T. 130
SAXTON, J.E. 98, 122
SCARBOROUGH, E. 112
SCHAAD, R.E. 40, 41
SCHAAFFS, W. 197
SCHAAP, L.A. 6
SCHACH, T.J. 2
SCHAEFER, W. 22
SCHÄFER, F. 18
SCHAFER, K. 70
SCHÄFF, R. 18
SCHAFFNER, K. (see D. Arigoni et al), 65
SCHALLENBERGER, H. (see W. Pelz et al), 25
SCHAUMANN, O. 18
SCHEFFER, F. 82
SCHEIBE, G. 82

SCHEIBEL, E.G. 220
SCHEMJAKIN, M.M. 24
SCHENCK, G.O. 17, 21, 82, 177
SCHENKER, V. (see O. Hechter et al), 210
SCHERAGA, H.A. 130, 219
SCHERMERHORN, J.W. 25
SCHETTY, G. 22
SCHICKH, O. v. 16
SCHIFF, L.I. 30
SCHIELTZ, N.C. (see G.L. Clark et al), 148
SCHIEMANN, G. 251
SCHIERZ, E.R. 73
SCHIESSLER, R.W. 150
SCHILDKNECHT, C.E. 184
SCHILDKNECHT, H. 19, 17
SCHILLER, G. 197
SCHINDLER, O. 114
SCHINZ, H. 66
SCHIPPER, E.S. 182
SCHISSLER, D.O. 170
SCHLENK, F. 8
SCHLENK, H. 95
SCHLENK, W. 16, 70
SCHLESINGER, M.J. (see M.J. Coon et al), 157
SCHLITTLER, E. 18, 65, 20
SCHMEISING, H.N. 164
SCHMERLING, L. 6, 73, 15
SCHMID, E.V. 251
SCHMID, G. (see E. Muller et al), 23
SCHMID, H. 19, 61, 67, 162 also P. Karrer et al), 22
SCHMIDT, C.H. 19
SCHMIDT, C.L.A. 41
SCHMIDT, F. 17 (see also Zahn et al), 20
SCHMIDT, G. 27, 29, 73
SCHMIDT, G.H. 19
SCHMIDT, H. 16
SCHMIDT, L.H. 122
SCHMIDT, O. 41, 42, 53, 81
SCHMIDT, O.T. 19, 68

SCHMIDT, R.W. 131
SCHMITT, E.E. 130
SCHMITT, F.O. 10
SCHMITZ, H. (see M.J. Cron et al), 129
SCHMITZ, P.M.E. 251
SCHNEIDER, J.A. 18
SCHNEIDER, W.G. 128, 248
SCHNELL, H. 20, 199
SCHÖBERL, A. 16, 82, 198 (see also T. Wieland et al), 199
SCHOCH, T.J. 73
SCHOENTAL, R. 132
SCHOFIELD, K. 47, 97
SCHÖLLKOPF, U. 23, 24
SCHÖNBERG, A. 45, 46, 48, 198, 251
SCHÖNIGER, W. 1, 19
SCHÖPF, C. 20, 175, 177
SCHRADER, G. 16, 22
SCHRAMM, G. 14
SCHRECKER, A.W. 68
SCHREIBER, J. 23
SCHROEDER, D.C. 49
SCHROEDER, E.F. 195
SCHROEDER, W.A. 125, 154, 192
SCHRÖTER, F. 198 (see also G. Spielberger et al), 198
SCHRÖTER, R. 14, 199
SCHUBERT, A. 188
SCHUBERT, M. 16, 124
SCHUBERT, W.H. 164
SCHUBERT, W.J. 8
SCHUDEL, P. (see J. Schreiber et al), 23
SCHUH, H.G. v. (see H. Bredereck et al), 23
SCHULTZ, H.W. 28
SCHULTZ, O.E. (see M. Bogemann et al), 198
SCHULTZ, R.F. 117
SCHULZ, G.V. 23, 191, 196
SCHULZ, H. 16 (see also W. Theilacker et al), 21

SCHULTZ, R.C. 20
SCHUMACHER, H. 175
SCHUMACHER, H.J. 251
SCHUMACHER, M. 67
SCHUSTER, C. 70
SCHÜTZ, F. 16
SCHWAB, G.M. 19, 169
SCHWARZ, H.P. 127
SCHWYZER, R. 25, 30, 61, 103, 113, 157, 190
SCOTT, W.D. 55
SCWARC, M. 171
SEACIE, E.W.R. 91, 168
SEALOCK, R.R. (see H. Diehl et al), 102
SEARLE, H.T. 9
SEARLES, S. 52
SEDLMEIR, J. (see J. Smidt et al), 22
SEEBECK, E. 8
SEEFELDER, M. 25
SEEL, F. 16
SÉGAL, G.M. 163
SEGESSER, A. v. 60
SÉGRE, E. 30
SÉGUIN, M. 158
SÉGUIN, P. 226
SEIDEL, B. (see H. Zahn et al), 20
SEIKEL, M.K. 162
SEKERA, V.C. (see J.G. Tolpin et al), 73
SELA, M. 11
SELMAN, S. 100
SELWOOD, P.W. 72, 219
SELYE, H. 28
SEMENOV, N.N. 21
SEMENOW, D.A. 74
SEMENTSOF, A. 75
SENDERENS, J.B. 226, 227
SÉRIS, L. 109
SESHADRI, T.R. 56, 98, 107, 111, 161, 176
SESTAK, Z. 76
SETHNA, S.M. 45, 48, 87
SEXTON, W.A. 56, 79, 251
SEYDEL, R. 21
SEYEWETZ, A. 226

SEYFERTH, D. 50
SHAEFER, W.E. 83
SHAFIZADEH, F. 5
SHALIT, H. 6
SHAN, M.N. 45
SHAPIRO, B.L. 56
SHAPIRO, H. 118
SHAREFKIN, J.G. 75
SHARPE, A.G. 9, 242
SHAW, G. 166
SHAW, J.T.B. 11
SHAW, P.F.D. 159
SHAW, W.H.C. 13
SHCHUKINA, L.A. 99
SHEDLOVSKY, T. 125, 219
SHEEHAN, J.C. 88, 130, 157, 190
SHEIBLEY, F.E. 72
SHELINE, R.K. 50
SHEMYAKIN, M.M. 99
SHEPARD, C.C. 169
SHEPHERD, J.W. 117
SHEPHERD, R.G. (see P.H. Bell et al), 126
SHEPPARD, F. 240
SHEPPARD, N. 12, 61, 97
SHERE, P.C. 194
SHERMAN, W.R. (see E.C. Taylor et al), 155
SHERWOOD, P.W. 59
SHIMANOUCHI, T. 31, 176
SHIMOKORIYAMA, M. 162
SHINER, V.J. 129, 164
SHIRLEY, D.A. 87
SHIVER, H.E. 40
SHOOLERY, J.N. 202
SHOPPEE, C.W. 27, 29, 64, 112, 142, 153, 160, 166, 206, 207, 251
SHORLAND, F.B. 29
SHREVE, O.D. 84
SHRINER, R.L. 45, 85, 101, 203, 211
SHUGAR, D. 202
SHUNK, C.H. (see K. Folkers et al), 157
SHUYKIN, N.I. 105
SICHER, J. 163
SIDGWICK, N.V. 41, 42, 89

SIDMAN, J.W. 51
SIEBER, R. (see J. Smidt et al), 22
SIEDEL, W. 14, 15
SIEGEL, A. (see F. Wessely et al), 176
SIEMER, H. 67
SIFFORD, D.H. 131
SIGGIA, S. 251
SIGNER, R. 11, 82, 219
SI-HOE, S.S. 233
SIM, G.A. (see S. Arnott et al), 65
SIMES, J.J.H. 98
SIMHA, R. 191
SIMON, H. 23, 197
SIMON, W. 61
SIMONOFF, R. 87
SIMONS, J.H. 178
SIMONSEN, D.R. 218
SIMONSEN, J.L. 63, 251
SIMPSON, D.M. 97
SIMPSON, J.C.E. 145
SIMPSON, S.A. 210
SIMPSON, W.T. 31
SIMS, L.L. (see T.H. Pearson et al), 118
SINEX, F.M. 29
SINN, H. 22
SINSHEIMER, R.L. 201, 216
SIRI, W.E. 220
SISLER, H.H. 51 (see also L.F. Audrieth et al), 43
SISLER, H.S. 75
SIVADGIAN, J. 229
SIVERTZ, C. 207
SKAU, E.L. 218
SKEGGS, H.R. (see K. Folkers et al), 157
SKELL, P.S. 31
SKELLON, J.H. 56
SKINNER, H.A. 50
SKRIMSHIRE, G.E.H. 55
SLADE, R.E. 55
SLICHTER, C.P. 128
SLIM, J. 73
SLOCOMBE, R.J. 47

SLOTTA, K. 64, 68
SMALL, L. 203
SMALL, L.F. 29, 126
SMART, C.L. 253
SMETS, G. 18
SMIDT, J. 22
SMIT, P.J. 214
SMIT, W.M. 169
SMITH, C.E. 41, 43
SMITH, C.W. 149
SMITH, D.G. 58
SMITH, E.L. 30, 58, 154, 251
SMITH, F. 2, 3, 29, 251
SMITH, G.B.L. 43
SMITH, G.F. 42, 144, 251
SMITH, H. 99, 157
SMITH, J.A.B. 27
SMITH, J.A.S. 138
SMITH, J.C.B. 13
SMITH, J.F. 101
SMITH, J.H.C. 216
SMITH, J.M. (see M.J. Fahrenbach et al), 155
SMITH, J.W. 214
SMITH, L.I. 43, 85, 101
SMITH, M.J.H. 78
SMITH, P.A.S. 86, 88
SMITH, P.G. 57
SMITH, R.L. 251
SMITH, S.G. 11
SMITH, W. 55
SMITH, W.B. 13
SMITH, W.E. 117
SMITHIES, O. 12
SMOLIN, E.M. 146
SMYTH, C.P. 40, 124, 180, 219
SNELL, E.E. 113
SNOW, J.E. 237
SNYDER, H.R. 9
SOBER, H.A. 192, 193
SOBOTKA, H. 7, 42, 45, 68
SOLOWAY, S. 130
SOLL, H. (see M. Bogemann et al), 198
and T. Wieland et al), 199
and H. Freytag et al), 199

SOLMS, U. 60
SOLMSSEN, U.V. 45
SOLLNER, K. 126
SOLOMONS, I.A. 126
SOMERS, G.F. 252
SOMMELET, M. 226, 227
SONDHEIMER, F. 67 (see a G. Rosenkranz et al), 210
SONENBERG, M. 113
SONNTAG, N.O.V. 49
SORENSEN, N.A. 176
SORGE, G. 20
ŠORM, F. 103, 190, 205
SOSNOWSKY, G. 51
SOURISSEAU, B. 186
SOWDEN, J.C. 3, 4, 27, 29,
SPAETH, I. 17
SPANGLER, F.W. 145
SPEAKMAN, J.C. 94
SPECK, J.C. 5
SPENCER, E.Y. 137
SPENGLER, G. 21
SPERLING, W. 65
SPERON, E. 73
SPERRY, W.M. 28
SPICKETT, R.S.L. 156
SPIELBERGER, G. 198
SPIELMAN, M.A. 86
SPIELMAN, M.S. (see O. Wintersteiner et al), 148
SPIKES, J.D. 32
SPINDLER, M. 65
SPIRIN, A.S. 202
SPIRO, M. 219
SPITNIK, P. 161
SPOERRI, P.E. 86
SPONER, H. 46, 165
SPOOR, H. 24 (see also H. Zahn et al), 20
SPORRI, P.E. 46
SPRAGUE, J.M. 128, 182
SPRAGUE, R.H. (see L.G. Brooker et al), 47
SPRING, F.S. 90, 93, 103, 1!
SPRINGALL, H. 251
SPRINGALL, H.D. 99, 140
SPRINGER, G.F. 156
SPRINSON, D.B. 5

SPRUNG, M.M. 43
SPURLIN, H.M. 184
STAAB, H.A. 21
STACEY, K.A. 156
STACEY, M. 2, 3, 54, 57, 63, 90, 93, 110, 137, 141, 156, 172, 187, 202, 212
STACKELBERG, M. v. 197
STADLER, P. (see A. Eschenmoser et al), 157
STALLBERG-STENHAGEN, S. (see L. Ahlquist et al), 162
STALLCUP, M.J. 165
STALLMANN, O. 75
STAMM, A.J. 252
STANEK, J. 122, 123
STANLEY, E.L. 185
STANLEY, W.M. 211
STANNETT, V. 252
STAPLES, M.L. 185
STASCHEWSKI, D. 23
STATHER, F. 252
STAUB, A. 153
STAUDINGER, H. 61, 82, 114, 161, 252
STAUFFER, R.E. 220
STAVELY, N.E. (see O. Wintersteiner et al), 148
STEACIE, E.W.R. 43, 105, 125, 233, 252
STEELE, C.C. 42, 203
STEHLE, R.L. 112
STEIN, G. 14, 171
STEIN, H. 74
STEIN, R.A. 52
STEIN, W.H. 11, 125, 154
STEINBERG, D. 12, 29
STEINER, H. 168, 171
STEINHARDT, J. 28, 125
STEINKOPF, G.W. 252
STEMPEL, A. 195
STEMPEL, G.H. 73
STENHAGEN, E. 167
STEPHEN, W.I. 200
STEPHENS, R. 29
STEPHENSON, G.W. 186
STERN, E.S. 97, 122, 123, 241

STERN, H.J. 252
STERNBERG, H.W. 6, 139
STERNBERG, J.C. 245
STERNHELL, S. (see D. Arigoni et al), 65
STERRETT, F.S. 241
STETTER, H. 18, 19
STEVENS, B. 127
STEVENS, T.F. 143
STEVENS, T.S. 136, 238
STEVENSON, D.P. 170
STEVENSON, R. (see F.S. Spring et al), 153
STEWART, A.W. 252
STEWART, C.P. 7
STEWART, D.W. 220
STEWART, G.H. 32
STEWART, G.W. 40
STEWART, H.W. (see S. Kushner et al), 126
STEYERMARK, A. 80, 83
STICKNEY, P.B. 151
STILLE, J.K. 51
STILES, M. 130
STILLER, E.T. 192
STIVALA, S.S. 184
STOCK, J.A. 157
STOCKHAMMER, P. (see F. Wessely et al), 176
STOCKMAYER, W.H. 31, 120
STODOLA, F.H. 147, 149 (see also O. Wintersteiner et al), 148
STOESSER, S.M. 237
STOFFYN, P.J. 156
STOLL, A. 8, 18, 48, 58, 61, 64, 65, 66, 67, 70, 78, 195
STOLL, M. 60, 201
STONE, F.G.A. 204
STORA, G. 38
STORCH, H.H. 6, 150
STORK, G. 121, 122 (see also G. Rosenkranz et al), 210
STORRIE, F.R. 238
STÖTTER, H. 15
STRAIN, H.H. 252
STRAIN, W.H. 203

STRAND, C.J. 40
STREATFIELD, E.L. 56
STREIFF, A.J. (see F.D. Rossini et al), 250
STREITWIESER, A. 50, 129, 164
STROH, R. 20, 21, 197
STROHMEIER, W. 17
STRONG, F.M. 147
STRUVE, W.S. 85
STUBBS, F.J. 171
STUMPF, P.K. 247
STÜPEL, H. 60
STURTEVANT, J.M. 218
STUTZ, E. 8
SUBBAROW, Y. 112 (see also S. Kushner et al), 126 and P.H. Bell et al), 126
SUCKFÜLL, F. 22
SÜE, P. 71
SUEN, T.J. 184
SUFFERT, F. 81
SUGDEN, T.M. 138
SUGIHARA, J.M. 3, 28
SUMMERS, L. 49
SUMNER, J.B. 252
SUMPTER, W.C. 45, 145
SURREY, A.R. 252
SUTER, C.M. 43, 86, 195, 252
SUTHERLAND, G.B.B.M. 11, 170
SUTTON, L.E. 34, 89, 96

SUTTON, M.L.E. 158
SVANOE, H. 73
SVEDA, M. (see L.F. Audrieth et al), 43
SVENSSON, H. 10, 193
SVOBODA, J. (see J. Sicher et al), 163
SWAIN, C.G. 102
SWAIN, T. 162
SWALLOW, A.J. 50, 98
SWAMER, F.W. 87
SWAN, G.A. 145
SWAN, J.M. 166
SWANN, S. 220
SWARTS, F. 225
SWEET, A. (see A.B. Garrett et al), 102

SWEETING, O.J. 51
SWERN, D. 47, 87, 95
SWIATOPOLK-MIRSKI, A. 171, 177
SWIFT, E.H. 1
SWINDELLS, J.F. 218
SWIETOSLAWSKI, W. 218
SYMONS, M.C.R. 99
SYNGE, R.L.M. 10, 132, 154, 205
SYRKIN, Y.K. 252
SZWARC, M. 7, 97, 99, 168, 171, 223
SZENT-GYORGI, A. 252
SZUMER, A.Z. 242

TAMAYO, L. 32
TAMELEN, E.E.V. 68
TAMM, C. 61, 68, 174, 177
TANFORD, C. 219
TARBELL, D.S. 43, 48, 85, 181
TARRONT, P. 178
TAUBE, H. 30, 103, 139
TAUBER, H. 252
TAVEL, P. v. 11
TAYLOR, A.W.C. 96
TAYLOR, C. 155
TAYLOR, D.B. 172
TAYLOR, E.C. 9, 155
TAYLOR, H.A. 127
TAYLOR, H.S. 125, 169, 180
TAYLOR, W.I. 65
TCHITCHIBABINE, A.E. 230
TCHOUBAR, B. 36, 160, 161, 252 (see also M. Charpentier et al), 163
TEAGUE, R.S. 4
TEDDER, J.M. 50, 100
TEITELBAUM, P. 129
TELLER, E. 125
TEMPLETON, J.F. (see D. Arigoni et al), 65
TENEY, H.M. 150
TENNER, N.R. 148
TERENIN, A. 190
TERENIN, T.N. 205

TERTIAN, R. 109
THANNHAUSER, S.J. 27
THATER, F. (see W. Theilacker et al), 21
THAYER, S.A. 44
THEILACKER, W. 21, 24, 197
THEILIG, G. (see H. Bredereck et al), 23
THEOBALD, R.S. 5, 47
THEORELL, H. 175
THESING, J. 20
THEUWEN, H.J. 119
THIEL, M. 22
THIESSEN, G.W. 104
THIMANN, K.V. 112
THIRTLE, I.R. 146
THOAI, N. van 69, 131
THOMA, R.W. (see J. Fried et al), 210
THOMAS, C.A. 252
THOMAS, C.L. 43
THOMAS, H.C. 125
THOMAS, K. 22
THOMAS, S.L. 98
THOMPSON, A. 135
THOMPSON, A.W. 12
THOMPSON, E.O.P. 9
THOMPSON, H.W. 89, 148, 170
THOMPSON, R.H. 108, 186
THOMPSON, S.O. 170
THOMSON, B.F. 236
THOMSON, G.W. 218
THOMSON, R.H. 98, 252
THRUSH, B.A. 138, 179
THUILLIER, G. 38
THYAGARJAN, B.S. 49, 51
TIFFENEAU, M. 33, 109, 226
TILAK, B.D. 111
TIMMERMANS, J. 38, 224, 252
TIMMIS, G.M. 79, 155
TIPPER, C.F.H. 168
TIPSON, R.S. 2, 3, 220, 221
TISELIUS, A. 10, 11, 55, 82, 90, 169, 172, 177
TISHLEZ, M. 102

TOBINAGA, S. (see D. Arigoni et al), 65
TOBOLSKY, A.V. 252
TODD, A. 22, 57, 63, 110, 1. 176, 182, 193, 206
TODD, A.R. 17, 34, 57, 58, 64, 89, 90, 107, 202, 252
TODD, D. 86
TODD, M. 57
TODD, W.H. 183
TOENNIES, G. 27
TOLBERT, B.M. 220, 238
TOLKMITH, H. 129
TOOPS, E.E. 221
TOLPIN, J.G. 73
TOMITA, M. 67
TOPLEY, B. 55
TOPCHIYEV, A.V. 58, 253
TOUMA, A. (see A.B. Ga et al), 102
TOUSTER, O. 87 (see also Wintersteiner et al), 148
TRACEY, M.V. 108, 234
TRAILL, D. 55
TREIBER, E. 253
TRÉFOUEL, J. 26, 231
TRÉMÈGE, M. 156
TRENDELENBURG, R. 25
TRELOAR, L.R.G. 54
TREIBS, A. 16, 82
TREIBS, W. 70, 241
TRILLAT, J.J. 109
TRIPPETT, S. 9
TRISCHMANN, H. (see R. et al), 25
TRISTRAM, G.R. 10, 55
TROENSEGAARD, N. 253
TROST, W.R. 168
TROTMAN-DICKENSON, A 98, 138, 253
TROTTER, J. 111
TROTTER, W.R. 78
TRUBAUT, R. 227, 229
TRUCE, W.E. 48, 88
TRUCHET, R. 109
TRUMBULL, E.R. 88
TRUSCHEIT, E. 25
TRUTER, E.V. 97, 105, 25

TSCHAMPEL, D. (see R. Kuhn et al), 25
TSCHESCHE, R. 15, 66, 155, 188, 232
TSCHETSCHETKIN, A.W. 244
TSUIKI, S. 29
TSUTSUI, E.A. 52
TSUTSUI, M. 52
TUCKER, S.H. 48, 73, 238, 249, 253
TUPPY, H. 82
TURBA, F. 114, 154, 196, 253
TURNER, E.E. 96, 140, 214
TURNER, H.S. 98
TURNER-JONES, A. (see D. Crowfoot et al), 148
TURNER, R.B. 47, 121, 164, 223
TURNER, R.J. (see S. Kushner et al), 126
TURNEY, T.A. 52
TURKEVICH, J. 170
TURRIAN, H. 113
TURSCH, B. 162
TUTTON, R.C. 171, 172
TWIGG, G.H. 169
TWISS, S.B. 120
TWOMBLY, G.H. 112
TYLER, G.J. 141
TYLER, W.P. 185

UBBELOHDE, A.R. 54, 97, 159, 171
UEBERREITER, K. 20
UFFMANN, H. (see W. Theilacker et al), 21
UHLIG, F. 9, 18
UHLIG, H.H. 102
ULBRICHT, T.L.V. 100
ULLMAN, R. 218
ULLYOT, G.E. 195
UMBREIT, W.W. 28
UNGNADE, H.E. 46, 51, 151

URBAŃSKI, T. 105, 186
URBSCHAT, E. 18
URDANG, G. 241
URUSHIBARA, Y. 75

VAILLANT, M. 160
VAITEKUNAS, A. 70
VALLEE, B.L. 11
VALENTA, Z. 68
VALLS, J. 23, 37, 134
VAN ALPHENS, J. 143
VAN ALLAN, J.A. 146
VAN ARSDELL, P.M. (see G. Egloff et al), 42
van der KERK, G.J.M. 22
van ROSSEM, A. 55
VANDERWERF, C.A. 73
VANDERWYK, A.J.A. 64, 247
van DOLAH, R.W. 50
van NES, K. 247
VANNOTTI, A. 253
van SCHELVEN, T. 251
VAN SLYKE, D.D. 175
VAN WAZER, 253
van WESTEN, H.A. 247
VAN ZANDT, G. (see L.G.S. Brooker et al), 47
VASINGTON, F.D. 117
VAUGHAN, G. 57
VAUGHAN, L.H. 57, 58
VAUGHAN, M. 12
VAUGHAN, W.E. 74, 151
VAUGHAN, W.R. 47
VAVON, G. 159, 224
VEIBEL, S. 36
VELLUZ, L. 24, 26, 32, 33, 35, 134
VÈNE, J. 33, 35
VENAZI, L.M. 204
VENKATARAMAN, K. 68, 176, 253
VENTKATARAMAN, R. 44
VERBANC, J.J. 50, 74
VERKADE, P.E. 176, 223
VERNON, C.A. 137 (see also P.W.C. Barnard et al), 57

VERWEY, E.J.W. 118
VIALLEFONT, P. (see P. Besinet et al), 163
VICKERS, A.E.J. 105
VICKERY, H.B. 27, 41, 124
VILKAS, M. 163
VILLE, A. 161
VIÑAS, J. 163
VIRTANEN, A.I. 19, 176
VOGEL, E. 23, 70
VOGEL, H. 253
VOGEL, M. 74
VOGL, O. (see C. Taylor et al), 155
VOGT, R.R. 248
VOIGT, D. 34
VOLD, M.J. 218
VOLD, R.D. 218
VÖLKER, O. 69
VOLKER, T. 24
VOLLMANN, H. 19
VOSS, H.E. 174
VOTER, R.R. 185
VOTOCEK, E. 26
VROELANT, C. (see R. Daudel et al), 158

WACEK, A. v. 14, 64
WACHTEL, J.L. 149, 192 (see also O. Wintersteiner et al), 148
WACHTMEISTER, C.A. 175
WAGNER, A. 198 (see also T. Wieland et al), 199
WAGNER, H. 16
WAGNER, H.G. 138
WAGNER, R.H. 218
WAHL, A.C. 209
WAHL, H. 34, 35, 229, 231
WAHRHAFTIG, A.L. 30
WAIDELICH, E. (see E. Muller et al), 23
WAIGHT, E.S. 94, 214
WAILES, P.C. 107
WAIN, R.L. 212
WAITKINS, G.R. 45

WAKEMAN, H. 218
WALDEN, J.D. 119
WALDRON, J.D. 106
WALDRON, E.T. 129
WALKER, D.F. 248
WALKER, H.G. 48
WALKER, J. 206 (see also A.W. Johnson et al), 140
WALKER, J.F. 253
WALLENFELS, K. 213
WALLER, C.W. 125
WALLING, C. 43, 48, 127, 151, 169, 233, 253
WALLIS, E.S. 28, 86, 203
WALLS, L.P. 55
WALSH, A.D. 94, 137, 168
WALTER, W. 82
WALTERS, W.D. 221
WALTHERT, F. 26
WALTON, H.F. 192
WANG, J.H. 201, 216
WARBURG, O. 177
WARBURTON, W.K. 51, 98
WARD, A.G. 105
WARD, W.H. 11, 28
WARDLAW, W. 63, 91, 105
WARE, E. 48
WARING, C.E. 219
WARING, W. 48
WARNER, R.C. 28
WARREN, B.E. 124
WARREN, F.L. 68, 103
WARREN, J.W. 170
WARTH, A.H. 95
WARTIK, T. 164
WASHBURN, R.M. 117
WASSERMAN, D. 72
WASSERMAN, H.H. 215
WASSERMANN, A. 169
WATERMAN, H.I. 6
WATERS, K.L. 47
WATERS, W.A. 40, 43, 89, 99, 140, 168, 172, 204, 233, 253
WATKINS, T.I. 79
WATT, G.W. 42, 44, 48, 72
WATTERS, A.J. 105

WATSON, D.G. (see S. Arnott et al), 65
WATSON, H.B. 40, 253
WATSON, H.R. 168
WAUGH, D.F. 11, 153
WAUGH, J.S. 128
WAUGH, R.C. 117
WAUGH, T.D. 117
WAWZONEKS, S. 181, 219
WEBBER, J.M. 5
WEBER, G. 172
WEBSTER, B.M. 94
WEBSTER, E.R. 145
WEEDON, B.C.L. 9, 37, 93, 97
WEGER, E. 49
WEGLER, R. 16, 19, 22
WEGNER, E. 24
WEHRMEISTER, H.L. 46
WEIDINGER, H. 25
WEIDLICH, H.A. 15
WEIGLE, J. 64
WEILL, P. 227
WEINBRENNER, E. 17
WEINGES, K. 68, 111
WEINHEIMER, A.J. 131
WEISER, D. 21
WEISIGER, J.R. 83
WEISS, D.E. 108
WEISS, F.T. (see J.L. Jungnickel et al), 83
WEISS, J. 153, 159, 168
WEISS, K.W. 237
WEISSBERGER, A. 83, 145, 203, 218, 221
WEISSBURGER, E.K. 1
WEISSBURGER, J.H. 1
WEITZ, E. 18
WEITZEL, G. 20
WEIZMANN, A. 44
WELCHER, F.J. 200, 253
WELLS, A.F. 140
WELLS, J.H. 45
WELTI, D. 106
WELTZIEN, W. 253
WELVART, Z. 161
WEMPEN, I. 5

WENDER, L. 6, 139
WENDLAND, R.T. 72
WENGER, F. 243
WENKART, E. 65
WENZL, H.F.J. 60
WEPSTER, B.M. 214
WERKMAN, C.H. 8
WERLE, E. 15
WERNER, G. 68
WERNER, H. (see S. Hunig et al), 22
WERTZ, J.E. 50
WESSELY, F. 14, 110, 176
WEST, C.D. 112
WEST, G.B. 78
WEST, T.F. 54, 253
WEST, T.S. 212
WEST, W. 125, 219, 222
WESTHEIMER, F.H. 101, 1 137, 213, 215
WESTLAKE, H.E. 46
WESTON, A.W. 86, 88
WESTPHAL, O. 25, 156
WETTSTEIN, A. 28, 65, 232
WEYGAND, F. 18, 24, 70, 82, 197
WHALEY, W.M. 87
WHALLEY, M. 48
WHALLEY, W.B. 93, 137, 1
WHEATON, R.M. 126
WHEELER, D.H. 95
WHEELER, O.H. 52
WHEELER, T.S. 103, 110
WHELAN, W.J. 30
WHELAND, G.W. 124, 208,
WHELEN, M.S. 117
WHIFFEN, D.H. 32, 57
WHINFIELD, J.R. 63
WHISTLER, R.L. 2, 3, 5, 29 135, 187, 234, 253
WHITAKER, G.C. 117
WHITBY, G.S. 118, 184
WHITE, A. 27, 29, 112
WHITE, D.E. 107, 113
WHITE, E.G. 124
WHITE, F.L. (see L.G.S. Brooker et al), 47

WHITE, W.F. 210
WHITEHEAD, L. 159
WHITEHOUSE, M.W. 5
WHITTAKER, E.J.W. 55
WHITTIER, E.O. 40
WHITTINGHAM, D.J. (see
    R.N. Jones et al), 127
WHITTINGHAM, L.P. 243
WIBAUT, J.P. 34, 61, 64,
    93, 175
WIBERG, E. 81, 254
WIBERG, K.B. 50
WICKE, E. 82
WIEBEMANN, E. 70
WIEBLEN, D.G. 178
WIECHERT, K. 15
WIELAND, T. 8, 15, 16, 18,
    20, 23, 25, 66, 70, 154, 176,
    196, 199
WIEMANN, J. 160, 163
WIESNER, K. 68
WIESNER, L. 23
WIGGINS, L.F. 3, 55, 212
WIGNER, E.P. 173
WILCOX, P.E. 11
WILDMAN, W.C. 122
WILDS, A.L. 85
WILES, L.A. 50
WILEY, P.F. 145
WILEY, R.H. 45, 47, 87,
    204
WILKINS, R.G. 200
WILKINSON, F. 138
WILKINSON, G. 92, 190
WILKINSON, S. 126
WILLEMART, A. 33, 34,
    73, 109, 229
WILLEMS, J. 81
WILLERSINN, H. 19
WILLI, A. v. 61
WILLIAMS, A. 52, 138
WILLIAMS, A.F. 57
WILLIAMS, F.E. 220, 221
WILLIAMS, D.L. 247
WILLIAMS, G.H. 94, 51, 172,
    254
WILLIAMS, H.E. 254

WILLIAMS, H.L. 172
WILLIAMS, J.W. 40
WILLIAMS, K.A. 169
WILLIAMS, M.J.G. 200
WILLIAMS, R.B. 128
WILLIAMS, R.J. 8, 254
WILLIAMS, R.J.P. 50
WILLIAMS, R.L. 200
WILLIAMS, R.T. 110, 132
WILLIAMS, T.I. 63
WILLIAMSON, T.A. 182
WILSON, C.V. 88, 146
WILSON, E. 42 (see
    also G. Egloff et al),
    42
WILSON, E.B. 254
WILSON, H.N. 13
WILSON, J. 159
WILSON, P.J. 45
WILSON, R.A.L. (see H.B.
    Henbest et al), 163
WIMMER, K. 197
WINCHELL, A.E. 254
WINGLER, A. 16
WINITIZ, M. 241 (see also
    R.J. Koegel et al), 127
WINKELMANN, E.H. 23
WINKLER, H.J.S. 204
WINSTEIN, S. 160, 181
WINTERBOTTOM, R. (see
    P.H. Bell et al), 126
WINTERNITZ, F. 163
WINTERSTEIN, A. 25
WINTERSTEINER, O. 28, 102,
    148, 165, 175
WINZLER, R.J. 156
WISE, L.E. 234
WISELOGLE, F.Y. (see E.L.
    Buhle et al), 73
WISELOGLE, L.R. (see E.L.
    Buhle et al), 73
WISHNIA, A. 128
WISS, O. 113 (see also O.
    Isler et al), 113
WISWESSER, W.J. 254
WITKOP, B. 15, 36, 136
WITTE, K. (see E. Muller
    et al), 23

WITTCOFF, H. 254
WITTENBERG, D. 100
WITTIG, G. 14, 16, 18, 20,
    21, 65, 81, 175, 190
WITTKA, F. 254
WITTREICH, P.E. (see K.
    Folkers et al), 157
WITZEL, D. 20
WITZEL, H. 114
WIZINGER-AUST, R. 16
WOLF, A.P. 23, 30
WOLF, D.E. 113
WOLF, E. 87
WOLF, K.L. 196
WOLF, W. 19, 25
WOLFF, H. 70, 86
WOLFF, R. 196
WOLFROM, M.L. 2, 28, 103,
    135, 187, 203
WOOD, F.C. 246
WOOD, J.L. 86, 149
WOLSTENHOLME, G.E.W.
    153, 154, 155, 156, 157, 213
WOOD, H.C.S. 155
WOOD, W.S. 58
WOODALL, N.B. 219
WOODFORD, E.K. 59
WOODWARD, R.B. 19, 20, 24,
    64, 121, 148, 176, 206
WOOLLEY, D.W. 201, 217, 254
WOOSTER, C.B. 41, 72
WORKING, E.B. 44
WORMELL, R.L. 254
WOTHERSPOON, N. 219
WRAGG, W.R. 35
WREN, J.J. 76
WRIGHT, D. 234
WRIGHT, G.A. 52
WRIGHT, G.F. 41, 83, 127,
    204, 215
WRIGHT, J.B. 48
WRIGHT, L.D. 112
WRIGHT, M.E. 149
WUNDERLICH, K. (see H.
    Meerwein et al), 21
WUNDERLY, C. 193
WÜNSCH, E. 68

WURSCH, J. (see O. Isler et al), 157
WÜRSTLIN, F. 197
WUSTRACH, V.P. 145
WYLDE, J. (see H. Bodot et al), 163
WYMAN, G.M. 50
WYMAN, J. 10, 42
WYNBERG, H. 9, 52
WYTHE, S.L. 182

YAGI, K. 37
YALE, H.L. 44, 45, 77
YANKWICH, P.E. 30
YANKWICH, P.F. 238
YOE, J.H. 180
YOFFE, S.T. 254
YONKMAN, F.F. 75
YOUNG, W.G. 50, 73, 74, 102
YOUNG, W.S. 150
YPHANTIS, D.A. 130
YU, T.S. (see M. Julia et al), 163
YUAN, H.C. 41

ZACHAU, H.G. 157
ZACHERL, K. 242
ZACHRY, J.B. 117
ZAFFARONI, A. (see O. Hechter et al), 210
ZAHLER, R.E. 48
ZAHN, H. 19, 20, 62, 193
ZAJDELA, F. (see A. Lacassagne et al), 1
ZAKHARKIN, L.I. 99
(see also A.N. Nesmeyanov et al), 233
ZANDER, M. 24
ZAUGG, H.E. 88
ZAVGORODNII, S.V. 253
ZECHMEISTER, L. 32, 45, 64, 66, 68, 69, 112, 125, 175, 254
ZEILE, K. 19, 53

ZEISS, H.H. 47, 204
ZELLER, P. 113 (see also O. Isler et al), 136
ZEMPLÉN, G. 53
ZERWECK, W. 16
ZIECHMANN, W. 82
ZIEDEL, W. 53
ZIEGENBEIN, W. 24, 70
ZIEGLER, K. 16, 17, 20, 23, 24, 25, 36, 139, 177, 191, 197, 204, 206
ZIETZ, J.R. (see T.H. Pearson et al), 118
ZILBERSTEIN, G. 35
ZILL, L.P. 192
ZILLIKEN, F. 5
ZIMMER, C. (see J.G. Tolpin et al), 73
ZIMMERMANN, W. 254
ZIMMERSCHIED, W.J. 173
ZINNENBOM, V.J. 209
ZIRKLE, R.E. 216
ZITTLE, C.A. 8
ZOLLINGER, H.C. 21, 48, 60, 65, 254
ZOTTERMAN, Y. 177
ZUBER, H. 62
ZUFFANTI, S. 45, 72
ZUIDEMA, H.H. 45

Subject index

Absorption spectra (see spectra)
Acenaphthene, 143
Acenes, 36
    photo-oxides, 229
Acetaldehyde
    peroxide derivatives of, 18
    urea condensation products, 82
Acetals, 3, 83
Acetic acid, industrial, 227
Acetone, radicals from, 171
Acetoacetic aldehyde, 19
Acetoacetic ester condensation, 85
Acetylene, 59, 60, 64, 93, 150, 207, 225, 239, 248, 249, 250
Acetylene bond
    formation of, 24
    structure and reactivity of, 20
Acetylenes, 33, 86, 90, 99, 207, 212, 237, 244, 249
    natural, 99, 107
Acetylenic acids, 95
Acetylenic ethers and thioethers, 9, 176
Acetylenic ketones, 226
Acetylides, of transition metals, 23, 139
Acid-base catalysis, 6
Acids and bases, modern theories, 140
Acidity
    effect of ring size on, 57
Acids, 34, 72
Acids and bases, of petroleum, 246
Acid(s) (see also Fatty Acids)
    aconitic, 3
    aldehyde, 141, 227
    alkane dioic, 51
    amides, 23
    amino-hydroxy, 25
    anhydrides, 83
    angelic, 50
    carboxylic, 140
    chlorides, aliphatic, 49
    cyclopentanecarboxylic, 163
    degradation of, 50
    dehydroabietic
    dicarboxylic, 141
        aromatic, 21
    doisynolic, 47, 210
    enzymatic synthesis of, 157
    fatty, 246
    hydroxamic, 36
    industrial, 227
    keto, 141
    mycoseric, 162
    nonulasaminic, 5, 63
    polyfunctional, 227
    tartaric, 109
    terephthalic, 24, 59
    tetrahydrophthalic, 51
    tetronic, 100
    thioctic, 26
    tiglic, 50
    tricarboxylic, 21, 141
    unsaturated, fatty, 93
Aconitegarrya alkaloids, 68
Aconitum alkaloids, 122, 123
Acridine(s), 145, 182, 236
Acridine alkaloids, 121

Acroleins, 16
Acrylic plastics, 72, 185
Acrylic esters, 250
Acrylonitrile, 16
    polymerization of, 58
Actinides, coordination of, 52
Actinomycin(s), 25, 68, 69, 137, 157
Actinomycin D, 130
Acylation, 134
Acyl cyanides, 20
α-Acyl cycloalkanones, 57
N-Acyldihydroisoquinaldonitriles, 50
N-Acyldihydroquinaldonitriles, 50
Acyl-lactone rearrangement
    for preparation of heterocyclic systems, 23
Acyloins, 35, 86
Acyl migration, in study of protein structure, 154
Addition reactions, 14, 37, 166
    by radicals, 223
    of free radicals to olefins, 98
    of halogens to olefins, 96
    of hydrogen to carbon-carbon bonds, 44
    of urea, 16
    to multiple bonds, 24
    steric effects in, 215
1,3 Additions, 43
Additions, stereochemistry of, 163, 215
Addition polymerization, 99
Adhesives, 185
Adrenalin (epinephrine), 41, 78
    (see also hormones)
Adrenergic blocking agents, 195
Adrenochrome and related compounds, 51
Adrenocortical hormones, 11, 56, 65, 112, 153
Adsorption, 221
Adsorption analysis
    for polymers and decomposition products, 82
Agar gel, electrophoresis in, 193
Aggregation, of globular proteins, 172
Aglycones, 68, 142
    digitaloid, 66
Agricultural chemicals, 119
    handbook of, 242
Ajmaline, 20, 176
Alanine, 2-thienyl, 157
Albumin, 125
Alcian blue, 105
Alcohols, 141, 226 (see also polyols)
    alkylation with, 75
    amino, 228
    biochemical routes to, 226
    α-epoxy, 36
    hydrates, crystalline, 107
    hydrogen bonding in, 186
    manufacture of, 40
    monohydric, 140
    resolution of, 85
    synthesis of, 25
    trihydric, 141
Aldosterone, 210

Aldehydes, 140 (see also carbonyl compounds)
    amino, 228
    aromatic, 161
    auto-oxidation of, 16, 49
    condensation with glycine, 161
    condensation with α-keto acids, 161
    hydration of, 160
    Gatterman synthesis of, 88
    naphthalenic, 229
    oxidation by oxygen, 49
    photolysis, 107
    polymerization, 97
    preparation from carboxylic acids, 18, 87
    reactions with amines, 43
    reactions with free radicals, 172
    various types, 226

Aldonic acids, acylated nitriles of, 3

Aldosterone, 232

Algae, 89

Alginate gels, as permutites, 169

Alicyclic-aromatic isomerization, 45

Alicyclic hydrocarbons, 50
    conformational analysis of, 111
    polynuclear, 141

Aliphatic compounds (see also hydrocarbon, aliphatic and individual listings)
    acid chlorides, 49
    amides, hydrolysis of, 104
    diazo, 43
    electric moments and structures of, 40
    fluorides, 203
    higher, 15
    hydrocarbons, utilization of, 15
                mechanism of reactions of, 73
    introduction of sulfo groups, 15
    ketones, electronic transitions in, 46
             photo chemistry of, 46, 107
    nitrogen, 140
    reactions with free radicals, 100
    reactions with sulfur, 22
    substitution reactions of, 14
    syntheses via organometallics, 25
    synthesis from olefins, 25
    theory of strain in, 203

Alkali compounds
    amides, 41, 42, 49
    organic, 41
    stereochemistry of reactions of, 21

Alkali metals, 119

Alkaloids, 27, 35, 69, 93, 121-123, 147, 192, 203
    aconitegarrya, 68
    aconitum, 122, 123
    acridine, 121
    alkaloids and plants, 177
    amaryllidaceae alkaloids, 121, 122
    apocynacea, 38
    aporphine, 166
    aromatic erythrena, 177
    biogenesis of, 37, 65, 78, 136
    brazilian strychnos, 175
    cactus, 66
    calabash, 37
    calabash-curare, 69, 78, 100
    cevine, 64
    chondrodendrum, 165
    delphinium, 190
    diterpenoid, 123
    ephedra, 121
    ergot, 20, 48, 64, 67, 98, 103, 110
    erythrina, 20, 103, 121, 122, 144, 165
    garrya, 123
    gelsenium, 136
    indole, 15, 65, 93, 98, 136, 176
    ipecac, 67
    isoquinoline, 90
    labelled, 166
    lupin, 36, 67, 121, 122
    mitragyna, 136
    morphine group, 81, 97, 144, 166
    of Australian crotolaria, 166
    of calabash curare barks, 165
    of diterpene and steroid groups, 144
    of merispermaceae plants, 67
    of quinoline and isoquinoline groups, 143
    of steroid group, 66
    of strychnos barks, 165
    of the lupinane, iminazole and quinazoline group,
    of tobacco, 44
    of unknown structure, 122, 123
    pyrrolidine, pyridine, and piperidine, 143
    pyrrolizidine, 20, 68, 103, 143, 175
    pyridine, 121, 122
    quinolizidine, 166
    rauwolfia, 18, 67, 68, 79
    related to anthranilic acid, 68
    senecio, 17
    solanaceous, 175
    stereochemistry of, 56
    steroidal, 38, 66, 98
    sterol, 161
    structures of, 75
    strychnos, 16, 19, 37, 69, 100
    synthesis, physiological conditions, 107
    synthesis and drugs, 61
    tropane, 18, 61, 121, 122, 143, 177
    veratrum, 99, 102, 121, 123

Alkanes, 16, 45, 140, 244 (see hydrocarbons, aliphatic
    alkylation of, 240
    dioic acids, 51
    isomerization of, 6
    sulfoxidation of, 16

Alkenes (see also olefins), 140, 244
    oxymercuration of, 127
    polymerization of, mechanism, 6

Alkenylmagnesium halides, 9

Alkoxides, 41, 91

Alkoxides
    aluminum, 85
    metal, 92

Alkoxyl group, determination, 83

Alkoxy radicals, 52, 74, 138

Alkyl resins, 185

Alkyl aluminum compounds, 120

Alkylated alkanedioic acids, 51

Alkylating agents
    alkylation(s), 43, 45, 76, 240
    clinical and biological effects of, 127
    cytotoxic, 1
    effect on spectra, 46
    effect on ionization potentials, 46
    of aromatic amines, 20
    of aromatic hydrocarbons, 6, 47
    of paraffins, 6
    of phenols by olefins, 21
    of saturated hydrocarbons, 151
    reductive alkylation, 86
    with alcohols, 75

Alkyl aryl sulfonates as detergents, 60

Alkylation of alkanes, 240

Alkylbenzenes, 47, 225
    (see also hydrocarbons, aromatic)
    absorption intensities of, 46
    action of aluminum halides on, 43
    hydrogenation of, 105
    radiolysis of, 159

Alkylcyclohexanols, rearrangement of, 162
Alkyl derivatives, of transition metals, 103
Alkyldiphenyls, steric effects in, 214
Alkyl fluorophosphates, 105
Alkyl group, hyperconjugation of, 164
Alkyleneimines(1,2;1,3-), 199
Alkyl mercurials, 120
Alkyl methoxysilanes, as water repellants, 120
Alkyl peroxides, 250
Alkyl polymerizations, 51
Alkyl radicals, 74, 175
Alkylperoxy radicals, 74
Allergenic compounds, 64
Alliin, 8
Allocimene, 176
Allophanates, 48
Alloxazine(s), 143
    bis, 155
Allylic compounds, 50, 73, 102, 103, 160
"Alternating effect", in copolymerization, 169
Altroses, 2
Aluminum, 189
Aluminum alkoxides, reductions with, 85
Aluminum alkyls, 120
Aluminum chloride, 34, 252
Aluminum halides, action on alkylbenzenes, 43
Amadori rearrangement, 4
Amanita phaloides, poisons of, 176
Amaryllidaceae alkaloids, 121, 122
Amebicidal activity, 26
Amide chlorides, 25
Amides, 228
    analysis of, 83
    octapeptide, 187
Amidines, 45, 228
Amidomethylations, 21
Amidoximes, 228
Aminations, 15, 85, 198, 199
Amine oxidase inhibitors, 129
Amine oxides, 107
    pyrolysis of, 88
Amines, 35, 228
    analysis of, 83
    aralkyl as analgesics, 195
    aromatic, 142
    biogenic, 241
    by reductive alkylation, 86
    carbon-carbon alkylation with, 87
    primary, 199
    reactions with aldehydes, 43
    reactions with nitrous acid, 105
    secondary, 199
    secondary, hydrogen bonding interactions with solvents, 186
    tertiary, 199
    tertiary, configurations of, 37
    triethanol and other alkyl-, 240
Amino acid hydrolysates, 55
Amino acid mixtures, adsorption analysis of, 10

Amino acids, 27, 28, 29, 30, 35, 90, 130, 141, 199, 228, 234, 239, 241, 246
    (see also individual listings, proteins, peptides, etc.)
    activation, 8
    activated, in peptide synthesis, 130
    analysis, 55
    anhydrides, N-carboxy, 136
    antimetabolic activity of, 157
    and vitamins, 112
    aromatic, ultraviolet absorption spectra of, 170
    arrangement in proteins, 11
    as antitumor agents, 157
    biosynthesis of, 19
    bridge reactions in, 19
    chromatography of, 169
    complex formation with metallic cations, 11
    complex formation with carbohydrates, 63
    composition of proteins, 10
    configuration of, 40
    dinitrophenyl, chromatography of, 76
    handbook, 237
    history and discovery of, 41
    hydroxyamino-, 136
    infrared analysis of structure, 11
    in green plants, 19
    in proteins, 82
    iodinated, 68
    isolation of, 46
    mass spectroscopy of, 62
    natural, 20, 176, 203
    of plants, 176
    optical activity of, 11, 132
    origin of, on earth, 205
    partition chromatography of, 125
    poly- -, 10
    poly- -, synthesis and structure of, 11
    preparation and criteria of purity, 10
    racemic, resolution of, 11
    reactions with formaldehyde, 10
    separation of, 70, 192
    solid-state infrared absorption of
    stereochemistry of, 10
    Strecker degradation of, 48
    synthesis, 46, 55
    of sulfur containing, 16
    terminal, in peptides and proteins, 10
    X-ray studies of, 10
β-Amino acids, stereochemistry of, 157
Amino alcohols, 228
Amino aldehydes, 228
Amino alkylation, 161
Amino-aryl insertion reaction, 157
o-Aminoaryl thiols, 51
Aminoazobenzene, diazotized, 22
Aminoazo dyes, carcinogenic, 1
Aminochromes, 68
2-Amino-2-deoxysugars, tables of properties, 5
Amino group (see also amines, and individual listings)
    aromatic, replacement by hydrogen, 85
    hyperconjugation of, 164
Aminoguanidines, 43
Aminohydroxy acids, 25
Amino ketones, 45, 228
Aminomethylation, 20
Aminophenols, 228
Aminonaphthols, 229
Aminonaphthoquinones, 61
o-Aminonitroso compounds, for pteridine syntheses, 155
Amino sugars, 3, 5, 20, 70

Amphenone analogs, 77
Ammonia, liquid, 43, 72, 110, 199
Ammonium compounds, 199
   configuration of, 37
Ammonolysis, in liquid ammonia, 43
Ampholites, 125
Anaemia, 78
Analgesics, 78, 96, 212
   aralkylamines as, 195
   arylpiperidine-, 195
   morphine-like, 58
   narcotics and, 122
   natural and synthetic, 126
   physostigmine, 195
   related to methadone, 195
   related to morphine, 195
Analysis, changing aspects in, 13
   of organic compounds, 246, 247

Analysis
   advances in, 1, 13
   anticomposition tables, use in, 56
   based on reaction rates, 83, 126
   by enzymatic reactions, 84
   by NMR methods, 84
   by X-ray methods, 84
   coulometric, 83
   elemental, 80, 196, 224
   for active hydrogen, 83
   functional group, quantitative, 80
   inorganic, with organic reagents, 180
   ion exchange resins in, 78
   infrared spectroscopy in, 72
   mass spectroscopy in, 74
   microbiological metabolic, 70
   micro, quantitative, 249
   of acetals, 83
   of acid anhydrides, 83
   of alkoyl groups, 83
   of amides and amines, 83
   of amino acids, 55
   of carbonyl compounds, 83
   of carboxyl groups, 83
   of cyanogen compounds, 254
   of α-epoxy compounds, 83
   of esters, 83
   of gases, 196
   of hydrocarbons, special, 208
   of hydroxyl groups, 83
   of impurities by mass spectra, 119
   of nitro, nitroso and nitrate groups, 83
   of olefins, 83
   of organosulfur compounds, 83
   of penicillin, 148
   of peroxides, 84
   of polypeptides, and proteins, 10, 193
   of side-chain groups, in intact proteins, 193
   of steroid hormones, 254
   of synthetic resins, 84
   of volatile substances, 128
   phase-solubility analysis, 83
   photometric, 219
   qualitative, 80
   quantitative, 80, 140
   recent progress in (1958), 212
   refractometric, 72
   specific methods, 126
   structure analysis, methods, 81
   reaction rates and analysis, 83, 126
   use of anti-composition tables, 56
   with HIO_4 and HIO_3, 251

Androgens, 174, 210, 232

Anaemia, anti-pernicious substance of liver, 112

Anaesthetics, 212 (see also analgesics)
   benzoate derivatives as, 195
   local, 122
Angelic acids, 50
Angiotensin, 113
1,6-Anhydrohexofuranoses, 3
Anion exchange processes, 126
   (see also Ion Exchange)
Anionic chemistry, 18, 65
Anionotropy, 97, 160
Anthocyanidins, 65
Anthocyanins, 101, 132, 161, 181
Anthocyanins
   and flavones, 203
   biosynthesis, 190
Anthracene, 36
Anthracenes
   and anthraquinones, 243
   photo-oxidation of, 172
   photochemical reactions of, 163, 172
   ultraviolet spectra of, 47
Anthranilic acid
   alkaloids related to, 68
   discovery of, 72
Anthraquinone and various derivatives, 40, 176, 229
Anthraquinone-acridones, 52
Anthraquinone dyes, 56
Anti-, (see under parent name)
Antibiotics, 28, 29, 32, 55, 78, 79, 99, 131, 204
   actinomycetes, 68
   etamycin, 157
   from bacillus polymyxa, 126
   from plants, 195
   Kanamycin A, 129
   peptide biochemistry of, 236
   purification of, 192
   steroid, 236
   symposium on, 137
   terramycin, 78, 126
Antibodies, chemical nature of, 11, 67
Anticoagulants, 78
Anti-composition tables, for organic compounds, 56, 2
Antidiuretic activity, 187
Antiepileptic compounds, 78
Antifolic acid, in chemotherapy, 79
Antifungal compounds, containing sulfur, 245
Antigens, chemical nature of, 67
Antigoitrogens, 195
Antihistamine drugs, 18, 26, 48, 55, 64, 78
Antihypertensive agents, 75
Antimalarial drugs, 63
Antimalarials, 122
Antimetabolites, 254, 217,
   purine derivatives as, 187
Antimetabolic activity
   of amino acids, 157
   of peptides, 157
Antimicrobial research, 26
Antimony compounds
   chemotherapy of, 16
   heterocyclic derivatives, 93

Antioxidants, 54, 225
Antipurines, 79
Antirachitic vitamins, 25
Antispasmodics, 120, 195
Antithyroid compounds, 78, 195
Antitumor agents
    amino acids as, 157
    peptides as, 157
Antivitamins, 67
Apiose, 2
Apocynacea, 38
Apoferritin, 10
Aporphine alkaloids, 122, 166
Araliphatic compounds, reactions with sulfur, 22
Arene metal compounds, 92
Arines (arynes) (see also benzyne)
    aromatic substitution via, 23
Arndt-Eister synthesis, 85
Aromatic aldehydes, synthesis of, 45
Aromatic amidines, 126
Aromatic amines, alkylation of, 20
Aromatic amino acids, ultra-violet absorption spectra of, 170
Aromatic bond, 97
Aromatic-cation complexes, 164
Aromatic character, 110, 223
    and thermal stability, 24
    box-model theory of, 53
Aromatic chemistry, symposium (1958), 138
Aromatic cine substitution, 108
Aromatic compounds, 142, 236
    action of ozone on, 61
    bicyclic, 143
    condensation with formaldehyde, 16
    electrophilic substitution on, 70
    fluorescence of, 110
    from pyrilium salts, 24
    multi-ring, 229
    non-benzenoid, 89, 93, 201
    nucleophilic substitution in, 70, 107
    polycyclic, 75
    reactivity of, 61
    various derivatives, 142
Aromatic hydrocarbons
    constitution, reactivity and color, 15
    electronic spectra of, 107
    interactions with protons, 214
    liquid-phase alkylation of, 47
    low excited states of, 170
    nitration, 151
    syntheses, 150
    ultraviolet spectra of, 44, 241
Aromatic molecular complexes, electron donor-acceptor type, 49
Aromatic nuclei, radical substitution in, 50
Aromatic nucleophilic substitution, 48, 99
Aromatic rings, biological oxidation, 132
Aromatic substances, paper chromatography of, 20
Aromatic substitution, 40, 103, 134
    anionic, 102
    by free radicals, 74
    homolytic, 254
    homolytic, partial rate factors in, 172
    nucleophilic, via additive mechanism, 24
    nucleophilic, via arines, 23
    some aspects of, 110
    steric effects in, 214, 215
Aromatic systems
    as proton acceptors, 186
    monocyclic, quasi-, 142
    nucleophilic substitution in, 74
Aromatic triazenes, 48
Aromaticity
    in 7-membered rings, 90
    theory of, 203
Aromatics, separation in petroleum hydrocarbons, 150
Aromatization, 150
Arrow poisons, 15
Arsinic acids, 85
Arsenic compounds, 89, 121, 228
    developments in,
    heterocyclics, 93
Arsonic acids, 85
Artificial resins, 229 (see also plastics, polymers)
Arylation, homolytic aromatic, 51
Arylation reactions, 134
Aryl derivatives, of transition metals, 103
Arylhalosilanes, preparation, 120
Arylthiazathiolium salts, 51
Ascorbic acid, 113
Ascorbic acid analogs, 2
Association, molecular, 40, 42, 105
Asymmetry, 100
Atomic and free radical reactions, 252
Atoms
    action radii of molecules, 70
    physical chemical studies of, 71
Atropisomeric diaryl compounds, configurations of, 22
Aureomycin, 78
Aurones, 162
Automatic control, 218
Auto-oxidation, 41, 75, 225
    of aldehydes, 16
    of diethyl ether, 245
    of hydrocarbons, 21, 47
    of metallic compounds, mechanism, 23
    of olefins, 151
    of unsaturated compounds, catalysis of, 19
Autosynthesis, 90
Auxins, occurrence and action of, 82
Avogadro, (1776-1865), 110
Azabenz(a)anthracenes, 145
Azabenzanthrenes, 145
Azabenzo(c)phenanthrenes, 145
Azabenzonaphthenes, 146
Azachrysenes, 145
Azanaphthacenes, 145
Azanthracenes, 146
Azaphenanthrenes, 146
Azaphilones, 137
Azapyrenes, 145
Azatriphenylenes, 145

Azeotropic data, 119
Azete, derivatives of, 181
Azides, 49, 228
Azine derivatives, 145
Azlactones, 86
Azo compounds, 228
Azo couplings, kinetic isotope effects in, 21
Azo dyes, 136, 254
Azoles, ring opening of, 24
Azoporphins, 136
Azo phosphonic acid esters, 22
Azopyrazolones
    oxidative coupling of, 25
    ring splitting of, 25
Azoxy compounds, 41, 228
Azulene, 70, 157
Azulene, and related substances, 138
Azulene chemistry, 15, 16, 22, 48, 66, 201
Azulenes, pathways to, 201

Bacillus polymyxa, antibiotics derived from, 126
Bacitracin, 157
Bacteria, gram negative, polysaccharides from, 5
Bacterial cell, chemical kinetics of, 243
Bacterial lipids, 67
Bacterial nucleosides, 5
Bactericidal properties, of phenols, 43
Baeyer-Villiger oxidation, 88
Baker-Nathan effect, 46, 164
Barbituric acid, 73
Barks, composition of, 46
Barrier separations, 220
Bart reaction, 85
Bases, 72
    quaternary, natural, 166
    quinonoid, anhydro, 176
Béchamp reaction, 85
Beckmann rearrangement, 41, 45, 88
Beilstein's handbook, 22
Benzacridines, angular, as carcinogens, 1
Benzene, 225
Benzene(s)
    directive influences in, 40
    hydrogenation of, 105
    oxidation by H_2O_2, 172, 207
    substitution in, 44, 48
    trisubstituted, electronic transitions in near
        ultraviolet, 46
    ultraviolet spectra, 165, 170
Benzeneboronic acid, 120
Benzene derivatives, with unsaturated side chain, 142
Benzene hexachloride, 72
Benzhydril chloride, 164
Benzilic acid rearrangements, 100
Benzidine rearrangement, 89

Benzil, 161
Benzimidazoles, 3, 48
Benzoates, as local anaesthetics, 195
Benzocyclanes, <u>229</u>
Benzocyclobutadiene, 38
Benzocyclobutene, 38
Benzodioxanes, 182
Benzofuran, iso,-181
Benzofurans, 166, 181
Benzoins, 86
Benzopinacols, rearrangements, 73
Benzopyrone rings, 162
Benzopyrrylium salts, 42, 181
Benzoquinolines, 182
Benzoquinones, 86
Benzothiazines, 183
Benzothiazoles, 182
Benzoxazines, 183
Benzoxazole, 182
Benzoyl peroxide, reaction with heterocycles, 166
Benzyl ethers
    of sugars, 4
    reactions with t-butoxy radicals, <u>233</u>
Benzyl groups, hydrogenolysis of, 87
Benzyl radical, resonance energy of, 168
Benzylisoquinoline, alkaloids, 122, 123
Benzyne, 21, 65, 138, 204
Biacetyl, mechanism of photolysis, 172
Biaryls, Ullmann synthesis of, 45
    unsymmetrical; preparation, 85
Bicyclic aromatic compounds, 143
Bicyclic compounds, substitution in, 24
Bicycloheptanes, stereochemistry, 163
Bicyclohexanes, stereochemistry, 163
Bile acids, 42, 157, <u>229</u>, <u>232</u>
    relation to cancer, 17
    steroids from, 210
Bile-dyes, 14
Bile pigment, mechanism of formation, 107
Biochemical, routes to alcohols, <u>226</u>
Biochemistry, International Conferences on, 187
Bioflavonoids, 126, 127
Biogenic amines, formation and degradation of, 15
Biogenesis as a chemical model, 189
Biogenesis
    of flavonoids and anthocyanins, 190
    of pteridines, 190
    of tetracyclic triterpenes, 103
    of terpenoids, 64
Biological activity, and structure, 52, 55, <u>251</u>
Biological methylation, 45
Biological oxidation, of aromatic rings, 132
Biological polymers, 239
Biological processes, trapped radicals in, 179
Biologically-active agents, 58

Biologically-active proteins, 193
Biology, comparative (symposium on), 216
    impact of chemistry on, 107
Biosynthesis (see also biogenesis)
    of aminoacids, 19
    of anthocyanins, 190
    of aromatic compounds from D-glucose, 5
    of cholesterol, 210
    of flavonoids, 190
    of penicillins, 149
    of porphyrin, 155
Biosynthetic theories, 206
Biotin, 8, 55, 112
Biotin derivatives, 55
Biphenyls (see diphenyls)
Biradicalism, historical development of, 17
Bischler-Napieralski reaction, 87
Bismuth compounds, organic, 44
Bitter substances, of plants, 69
Biuret and related compounds, 50
Black oils, chromatographic fractionation of, 169
Bleaching rhodopsin, mechanism of, 129
Block polymers, 31
Blood dyes, metabolism, 53
Blood-group active substances, 156
Bodenstein, contributions to catalysis, 90
Boiling points, methods of estimation of, 73, 218
Bond, 158
    aromatic, 97
    chemical, 69
Bond dissociation energies, 97
    of hydrocarbons, 170
Bond energies, 75, 111
    factors responsible for, 170
Bond hybridization, in metal carbonyls, 50
Bond lengths, 111
    hyperconjugation and, 164
Bond properties, interpretation, 96
Bonds, 223
    metal ligands, 139
Borate, reactions of biological interest, 8
Borate esters, 120
Boric acid, use in carbohydrate structure determination, 3
Bornylic rearrangement, 163
Boron compounds, 50, 120
    analytical use of, 1
Boron fluoride
    as catalyst, 14
    catalyst in organic chemistry, 253
Boron hydride derivatives, 24
Boron trichloride, reactions of, 51
Boroxine, trimethoxy, 120
Brazilin, 38, 143, 181
Bredt's rule, 48
Bromo compounds, 197
Bromomethylation, 161
N-Bromosuccinimide, 23, 47
Bromotrichloromethane, kinetics of addition to olefins, 172

Bulk chemicals, 58
Brucine, 93
Bucherer reaction, 85
t-Butyl radicals, 170
Butyrospermol, 103

Cactus alkaloids, 66, 122
Cadmium
    derivatives, 35
    organic reagents of
    for preparation of ketones, 46
Calabash alkaloids, 37
Calabash-curare alkaloids, 19, 22, 69, 100, 165
Calophyllolids, 162
Calorimetry, 196, 218, 219
Camphane, 159
Camphor series, 53
Cancer
    advances in research, 1
    chemotherapy of, 75
    mechanisms of induction, 212
    physiological theories of, 109
Cancerigens (see Carcinogens)
Cannizzaro reaction, 85
Carboimide chlorides, 25
Carbazole, 46, 182
Carbazole systems, 145
Carbenes, as intermediates in reactions, 23
α-Carbethoxycycloalkanones
    effect of ring size on, 57
Carbocycles, eight-membered, 48
Carbodiimides, 49
Carbohydrate-protein complexes, 11
Carbohydrate phosphates, 99
Carbohydrate sulfates, 96
Carbohydrates, 2-5, 27, 28, 29, 53, 57, 135, 141, 147, 203, 206
    (see also Sugars and individual listings)
    acids and oxidation products, 135
    anhydro sugars, 135
Carbohydrates and amino acids, complexes of, 63
Carbohydrates
    and mechanisms of replacement reactions, 4
    as components of cardiac glycosides, 2
    biosynthesis of, 212
    biologically-active, 90
    carbonates and thiocarbonates, 5
    carcinogenic, 81, 82
    as photosensitizing agents, 82
    chromatography of, 4
    determination of configuration by boric esters, 3
    esters, 135
    Friedel-Crafts and Grignard reactions in, 3
    formazon reaction in, 5
    halogen oxidation of, 135
    identification and determination of, 135
    infrared spectra, 4
    in the food industry, 119
    I.R. spectroscopy of, 57
    less familiar aspects of, 44
    metabolism of, 73
    nitrogenous derivatives, 135
    of biological interest, 187

of nucleic acids, 187
oligosaccharides, 135
oxidation of, 40, 81
periodate oxidations of, 4
phosphate esters, 135
physicochemical properties and constitution, 5
reactivities of -OH groups in, 3
separation of, 192
stereochemistry of, 4, 100
structure of, 40
sulfonic esters, 3
trityl ethers, 2
unsaturated derivatives, 135
uses of, 57
X-ray investigations of, 43
and disease, 250
carcinogenic, 81, 82
oxidation of, 240

Carbonates, of carbohydrates, 5

Carbon
activated, 108
combustion of, 159
in photosynthesis, 73
quadrivalence of, 110
trivalent, 16

Carbon bonds
dissociation of, 42
properties of, 168

Carbon-carbon alkylations, with amines, 87

Carbon-carbon bonds, oxidative-hydrolytic splitting, 99

Carbon-alkylation
with tert. amines
with quaternary ammonium salts, 17

Carbon compounds
classification and nomenclature, 140
literature and documentation, 140
structure of, historical, 140

Carbon disulfide, 56

Carbon-hydrogen bond rupture, 99

Carbon-hydrogen bonds, polarity, 96

Carbon metabolism, 8

Carbon-metal bonding, 204

Carbon monoxide, 33, 61, 64
and acetylene, 60
synthesis with, 23

Carbon radicals, 21

Carbon rings, small, 23, 70

Carbon suboxide, 40

Carbon-sulfur bonds, cleavage in divalent sulfur compounds, 48

Carbon tetrachloride, reaction with aluminum, 102

Carbonic acid, aromatic polyesters of, 20

Carbonic acid derivatives, 141

Carbonic acids, 197, 198

Carbonium ions, 99, 160, 189

Carbonium reactions, in allylic systems, 103

Carbonyl-aza-aromatic compounds
electronic transitions due to non-bonding electrons in, 51

Carbonyl bridge compounds, 45

Carbonyl compounds, 37, 141, 159
analysis of, 83
as oxidizing agents, 72
bimolecular reduction of, 102
α,β-ethylenic, 39
peroxides of, 22
reduction by hydrides, 20
three-ring, stereochemistry of, 103

Carbonyl-olefination
with triphenylphosphine methylenes (see also Wittig reaction), 23

Carbonyl oxycelluloses, alkaline degradation of, 57

Carbonyls, preparation, 159

Carbonyl sulfide, 51

Carbon dioxide
assimilation, 177
properties of, 250

Carbon monoxide and acetylene, 249

Carbonic acids, nitrogen derivatives, 228

Carbon-carbon bonds, rotational isomerism, 12

Carboxylic acid salts, degradation of, 50

Carboxylic acid silver salts, reactions with halogens

Carboxyl groups, analysis, 83

Carboxylic esters, heterolysis of, 98

Carboxymethylcellulose, 4

Carboxypeptidases, 136

Carbylamines, 228

Carboxylation reactions
participation of chelating metals in, 130

Carboxylic acids
analysis of, 83
anodic syntheses with, 97
association of, 98
chromatography of, 169
conversion to aldehydes, 18, 87
derivatives as antispasmodics, 195
dihydroxy-, 141
end-chain determination of, 176
monobasic, chemistry of, 140
polarization measurements on, 124
production from cyclohexane-1,3-diones, 19

Carboxylic acid derivatives
nucleophilic reactions of, 52

Carcinogenesis, chemical, 176

Carcinogenic activity, and electronic structure, 1, 109

Carcinogenic aminoacid dyes, 1

Carcinogenic carbohydrates, 81, 82

Carcinogens, 1, 7, 54, 63, 69, 81, 82, 93, 102, 196, 249
benzacridines, and various others, 1
correlations in, 54
reactions with macromolecules, 1
thiophenes as, 111

Cardiac genins, 47

Cardiac glycosides, 2, 42, 195

Cardioactive alkaloids, 122

Cardiotonic compounds, 65

Cardiotonic glycosides, 142

Carnitine, 113

β-Carotene, 113

Carotenes, 23, 54, 237

Carotenoid pigments, cis-trans isomerism of, 45, 69

Carotenoid research, 25

Carotenoids, 20, 23, 29, 32, 41, 61, 63, 67, 68, 66, 105, 113, 141, 241, 244
biogenesis, 190
comparative biochemistry, 241
in vitro conversion of, 68
synthetic, 70, 136

Carothers, Wallace H. Collected Papers, 184

Caryophyllene, 102

Castor oil, as starting material, 73

Catachenes, 65

Catalase, 177

Catalysis, 6, 38, 109, 130, 197, 224
    advances in, 90
    by acids and bases, 45
    enzymatic, 247
    heterogeneous, 19, 91, 159, 169
    in industry, 58
    inorganic and organic, 237
    quantum aspect of, 128
    retrospect and prospect, 169

Catalysts
    alloys in dehydrogenation, 169
    copper as hydrogenation, 33
    homogeneous in solution, 221
    noble metals in polymerization, 6
    Raney nickel, 33

Catalytic activation, of hydrogen in various systems, 6

Catalytic chemistry, of hydrocarbons, 102

Catalytic cracking of hydrocarbons, 6

Catalytic dehydrogenation, 150, 169
    mechanism of, 6
    of hydrocarbons, 151
    quantitative, 126

Catalytic, synthesis of ketones, 6

Catalytic reactions, 220
    on alumina, 139

Catechin(s), 68, 175, 181
    stereochemistry of, 166

Cation exchange processes, 126

Cations, alkaline earth; interaction with proteins, 10
    organic, 97

Cell surface chemistry, 236

Cellulose, 66, 73, 180, 194, 203, 227, 239
    and derivatives, 16, 40, 55, 184, 185, 243, 248
    biological transformations, 132
    carboxymethyl-, 4
    degradation of, 132
    molecular constitution, 2

Cellulose acetate plastics, 252

Cellulose derivatives, physical properties, 120

Cellulose ethers, 2, 105

Cellulose esters, of organic acids, 2

Cellulose fibers, 242

Cellulose, molecular weight, 241

Cellulose nitrate, 247

Celluloses, carbonyl oxy-, 57
    oxidized, 107
    relative crystallinity, 3

Cellulosic fibers, dyes for, 58

Cell walls
    chemistry of, 253
    structure of, 249

Centrifuging, 220

Cephalosporins, 137

Cevine, 64

Chain polymers, nature of solid state of, 120

Chain reactions
    induced by peroxides, 233
    initiation of, 190
    problems of, 21

Chelate complexes, of 1,10-phenanthroline, 49

Chelates, magnetochemical studies on, 158

Chelates, metal, 119, 246
    ferric, 180

Chelating agents, 57
    polyamineacetic acid types, 130

Chelating metals, in carboxylation reactions, 130

Chelating resins, 58, 105

Chelation, various aspects, 130

Chemical affinity, 254

Chemical bond, in hydrocarbons, 208

Chemical constitution, and physiological activity, 55

Chemical documentation, 56

Chemical kinetics, 31 (see also kinetics)
    foundations of, 237
    radioactivity applied to, 209

Chemical literature searches, 119

Chemical process industries
    literature resources for, 119

Chemical reactivity, 203

Chemical warfare agents, 132

Chemisorption, 139

Chemists, literature
    training of, 119

Chemotherapeutic activities of sulfanilamide derivatives, 43

Chemotherapeutics, sulfur-containing, 16

Chemotherapy, 26, 90, 204, 206, 231
    in tropical medicine, 89
    of tuberculosis, 89, 212
    problems of, 72

Chitin, 5, 108

Chloramine, syntheses with, 24

Chloramphenicol, 78

Chlorination, aliphatic, 101

Chlorine compounds, 243

Chloroalkanes, tri- and tetra, 99

Chloro compounds, 197

Chlorofluoro compounds, 178

bis-(β-Chloroethyl)amine N-phosphamide esters, 22

β-Chloro alcohols, stereochemistry, 163

Chloromethylation, of diphenylmethane, 161

Chlorophyll, 42, 70, 81, 203
    in 1953, 240
    structure, 42
    total synthesis of, 24

Chlorophyll and related compounds
    absorption spectra, 48

Chloroplast pigments, 252

Chloroplast pigments, paper chromatography of, 76

Chlorothiazide, 128

Chlorovinylarsines, 42

Chloropicrin, 41

Cholesterol
    biosynthesis, 107, 210
    collective volume on, 152
    conversion to steroid hormones, 152
    pathway to estradiol, 15

Choline, 112

Cholinesterases
    active surfaces of, 6
    anti-, 56, 78
    hydrolysis of esters by, 6

Chondrodendrum alkaloids, 165

Chromatographic adsorption, 14

Chromatography, 32, 39, 76, 125, 221, 222, 242, 245, 196

Chromatographic analysis and chloroplast pigments, 252

Chromatography and stereochemistry, 125
    displacement 169
    in amino acid synthesis, 55
    of peptides and proteins, 11
    of sugars, 237
    radial, paper, 175
    frontal analysis, 125

Chromatography, gas liquid, 13, 76, 84, 189, 248
    gas phase, 13, 38, 61
    in gas-solid systems, 129
    ion exchange, 102
    of amino acids and peptides, 169
    of carbohydrates and derivatives, 4
    of carboxylic acids, 169
    of chloroplast pigments, 76
    of dinitrophenylamino acids, 76
    of fats, 129, 169
    of gases and vapors, 169
    of flavonoid pigments, 76
    of larger molecules, 200
    of lipids, 76
    of petroleum hydrocarbons, 169
    of proteins, 114, 169
    of steroids
    paper, 35, 61
    salt concentrations and pH effects, 169
    partition-, 132
    quantitative, systematic, 125
    variable gradient device for, 193
    vapor phase, 103, 214
    symposium volume on (1956), 234

Chromanols, 181

Chromanones, 181

Chromans, 181

Chromenols, 181

Chromium complexes, 121

Chromium compounds, oxidation by, 99

Chromones, 67, 181

Chromophores, effects of alkyl substitution on, 46

Chromylium salts, 42

Chrysene, 229

Chymotripsinogen, 154

Chymotrypsins, 154

Cinchona alkaloids, 121

Cinnolines, 45, 145, 182

Circular electron transfer, 37

Cis-elimination, pyrolytic, 52

Cis-trans isomerization
    of carotenoids and diphenylpolyenes, 45
    of conjugated compounds, 50

Citrus fruits, 107

Claisen rearrangement, 43, 85

Classification, of organic compounds, 72, 220

Cleavage
    steric effects in, 215
    of carbon-sulfur bonds in divalent sulfur compounds, 48
    of ethers, 49
    of sulfonamides, 52
    involving oxygen radicals and cations, 47

Clemmensen reduction, 23, 85

Clinical applications of amino acids and proteins, 241

Coal-tar research, 14

Coatings, surface, 54, 56

Codeine, 166

Coding of organic compounds, 248

Coelenterates, 131

Coenzyme(s)
    A, 8
    dihydrocodehydrase, 175
    folic acid, 8
    nucleotide, 176

Colchicine, 15, 23, 109, 121, 122, 240

Collagen, 241
    constitution of, 136
    optical and chemical studies, 154
    symposium on (1953), 234

Colloidal chemistry of starch, 250

Colloids, 180
    and surface chemistry, 122

Colloidals, organic, 244

Color
    of flowers, 72, 73
    of organic substances, 43
    electron gas theory, 68, 69

Coloring matters, natural, 246

Color photography, 55, 64

Color theory, 18, 96, 109, 136

Coloring matters, symposium on, 136

Combustion agents, 226

Combustion petroleum, 119

Combustion theory, problems of, 21

π-Complex, 160

Complex chemistry, contribution of P. Pfeiffer to, 16

Complex compounds, as catalysts, 16

Complex formation, 89

Complexes, 53, 63, 68, 196
    of amino acids with metals, 11
    of carbonyls, cyanides and olefins, 190

Complexing agents, 189

Composite-cumulene I, 176

Composition tables of organic compounds, 242

Condensation
    of acetoacetic ester, 85

of formaldehyde, 81
of esters, 70
of olefins with aldehydes, 48
of urea-acetaldehyde products, 82

Condensation reactions, 134

Condensation temperatures, determination of, 218

Condensations, 160, 161
　carbonyls with succinic acid, 34

Conductivity, 196, 219

Conessine, 136

Configuration
　and hydrocarbon reactivity, 171
　direct determination of, 107
　of amino acids, 40
　of cycloheptanes, 162
　of non-rigid molecules, 97

Configurational relations in carbon compounds, 103

Configuration (molecular)
　specification and nomenclature, 56

Configurations
　of higher sugars and alcohols, 2
　correlations of, 94

Conformation, 189, 224, 36

Conformational analysis, 57, 75, 98, 163, 215, 223, 224
　of alicyclics, 111

Conformations, 38
　determination of, 25
　of six-membered rings, 94
　of terpenes, 37

Conifer chemistry, 188, 189

Conifer taxonomy, 206

Conifers, flavones of, 162

Conjugated compounds
　1,6-additions to, 52
　cis-trans isomerization of, 50

Conjugated molecules
　aromatic; reaction with organometallics, 47
　electron structure, 97, 158
　free valence in, 93

Conjugated proteins, 172, 234

Conjugated systems
　unsymmetrical 1,6-addition, 52
　in fats, 246

Conjugation, 203
　in ring systems, 138

Constants, physical, 196

Constellation analysis, 232

Constitution of
　cellulose, 194
　wool, 194

Constitution and physical properties of organic compounds, 203

Control, automatic, 218

Conversion, of hydrocarbons into butadiene, 45

Cooling, 220

Coordination compounds, 180, 200, 242
　conferences on, 139, 144
　complex, isomerism of, 200
　enzyme-metal substrates, 132
　of unsaturated hydrocarbons with metals, 139

Coordination polymers, 58

Copolymerization, 31, 48, 184

Copolymers, block and graft, 31

Copper, catalyst in hydrogenation, 33

Cord factor, 176

Cortical hormones, 102, 113

Cortical steroids, 69, 153

Corticotrophins, 210

Cortisone, 29, 35, 78, 93, 105, 113, 153
　from hecogenin, 58
　syntheses of, 67

Cottonseed, pigment of, 52

Coulometric methods, 83

Coumarins, 67, 161, 181, 45

Coumarones, 161

Counter-current distribution, 35, 83, 220
　analytical specificity of, 126

Counter-current fractionation of lipids, 95

Couper, A.S., 110

Covalent bonding, 73

Cozymase, 110

Cracked gases, polymerization of olefins from, 6

Cracking
　of unsymmetrical diaryl ethanes, 170
　theory of catalytic - , 150

Creatine, 40, 131

Creatinine, physico-chemistry of, 40

Critical behavior, of hydrocarbons, 208

Critical properties, of elements and compounds, 49

Crystalbumin, 154

Crystal structure, 40

Crystallization, 220
　from solution, 73

Crystallochemical analysis, 219

Crystallography, 31
　and stereochemistry, 94
　of organic compounds, 140

Crystal morphology, 219

Crystals
　hydrogen bonds in, 159
　liquid, 224
　oriented growths of, 81

Crystals and molecules, 236

Crystals, organic
　dielectric constants, 124

Cularine alkaloids, 122

Cumarins, (see Coumarins)

Cumene hydroperoxide, 172

Cuprammonium glycoside complexes, 3

Curare, 19, 64, 69, 165
   anti-, 165
   synthetic, 165
Curare alkaloids, 78
Curare-like effects, 122
Curariform, 47
Curtius rearrangement, 41, 86
Cyanine dyes, 41, 97
   steric effects in, 214
Cyanines, 34
Cyano compounds, 228
Cyanoethylation, 86
Cyanogen bromide, 87
Cyanogen, 52, 254
Cyanogen compounds, 247
Cyanohydrin synthesis, 2
Cyanuric chloride, 25
Cyclenes, 225
Cyclanes, 225
Cyclic compounds
   complex, 228
   large ring, 60
   eight-membered, 101
Cyclitols, 2, 5, 32
Cyclizations, 166
Cycloammonium rearrangement, 25
Cyclobutadiene
   and diphenylene, 138
   and related compounds, 201
Cyclobutanes, 141
Cyclodehydration, aromatic, 46
Cyclodehydrogenation, aromatic, 248
Cycloglucanes, 21
Cycloheptane, 141
Cyclohexane, 38, 141
   isomers of, 171
   stereochemistry of, 36, 60, 90, 98, 105
   structure and reactivity, 107
   substitution in, 37
Cyclohexane derivatives
   stereoisomerism of, 17, 49
   substitution on, 160
Cyclohexane-1,3-diones, 19, 93
Cyclohexanols, rearrangements of, 159
Cyclohexanones, rearrangements of, 159
Cyclohexenic acids, 163
Cyclohexene
   dicyano-dithia, 25
   reaction with Cl_3C radical, 171
Cyclooctane, 141
Cyclooctatetraene, 201
Cyclopentadiene, 45
   hexachloro-, 58
   metallic compounds of, 19
Cyclopentadienes, 51
Cyclopentadienyl compounds of metals and metalloids, 75, 92, 204
Cyclopentanes, 141

Cyclopentanecarboxylic acids, 163
Cyclopentanone o-carboxylic acid ester
   preparative importance of, 19
Cyclopolyolefins, 63, 201
Cyclopropanes, 141
Cyclopropane derivatives, 101
Cysteine peptides, 157
Cystine, peptides containing-, 136
L-Cystine, N,N'-diglycyl-, 78
Cytochromes, 53, 108
Cytotoxic alkylating agents, 1

Dahlias, flavones, 162
Darzens reaction, 86
Deamination, 15
Decarboxylation, 198
   mechanism of, 97
DDT and related compounds, 73, 247, 253
Defenses, chemical and biological (nonmilitary), 121
Degradation(s) (see specific compounds)
Dehalogenations
   with magnesium, 163
   electrochemical, 102
Dehydroabietic acid, 37
Dehydrocyclization reaction, 49
Dehydrogenation, 9
   alloy catalysts in, 169
   with S, Se, and Pt metals, 15
Dehydrogenases, steroid, 213
Deionization of salt water, 121
Delphinium alkaloids, 123, 190
Demethylation, 137
Demjanov ring expansions, 88
Demulcents, action on nerves, 177
Density, determination of, 196, 218
Depsipeptides, 24
Derris, constituents of, 44
Desoxypregnanes, 232
Desoxyribose, 202
Desulfurization, with Raney nickel, in carbohydrates, 3
Desoxyribonucleic acid, 216
Detergency, 55
Detergents, 95
   synthesis of, 60
   synthetic, analysis of, 13
Detonations and flames, 138
Deuterated paraffin hydrocarbons, 170
   macromolecules, 130
Deuterium, 33, 109
   and hyperconjugation, 164
Deuterium exchanges
   in hydrocarbons, 6
   in peptides, 136
   in proteins, 217, 193

Deuterium isotope effects
Deuterium oxide, acid-base studies with, 129
Developers, photographic, 226
Dextran, 5
Dextrins, Schardinger, 4, 21
Dialysis, of proteins, 193
Diamagnetism, 34, 71, 158
Di- (see also parent compounds)
Diaryl compounds, 22 (see also hydrocarbons)
Diastereoisomers, 102
Diazines, 143, 230
Diazoacetate, ethyl
　reactions of, 106
Diazoaminobenzenes, 22
　tautomerism and hydrogen bonds in, 186
Diazo compounds, 21, 58, 111, 228
　aliphatic, 19, 43, 228
　aromatic, 228
　discovery of, 75
　reduction of, 21
Diazo coupling, kinetics of, 48
Diazo ketones, syntheses using, 24
Diazomethane, 14
Diazonium salts, 88
　action on unsaturated aliphatic compounds, 16
　fluoborates
Diazotization, 54
　mechanism of, 74
Dibenzyl, pyrolysis, 171
Dicarboxy compounds, 41
Dichromylenes, 45
Dielectric constant(s), 124, 219, 224
　of dipolar ion solutions
　of organic crystals and glasses, 124
Dielectrics, 124
Diels-Alder synthesis, 15, 24, 44, 67, 86, 166, 189
　(Diene synthesis)
Diene reactions, kinetics at high temperature, 171
Dienes, conjugated, 175
Diethyl ketone radicals, reactions with oxygen, 172
Diffraction methods, 89
Diffusivity, determination of, 218
Digitalis, 26, 78
　cardiac glycosides of, 58
Digitaloid aglycones and glycosides, 66
Diiodopropyl phosphofluoridate, 137
Dimerizations, in sunlight, 48
Dimethyl formamide, reactions with cyanuric chloride, 25
Dinitrogen tetroxide, reactions in, 75
Dioxanes, 143, 182
　sulfur analogues of, 182
Dioxolanes, unsaturated, polymerization of, 17
1,3-Dioxolane, 182
1,3-Dioxolanes, reduction of diazo compounds with, 21
Diphenylene, 138
Diphenylmethane, chloromethylation of, 161

Diphenylpolyenes, stereochemistry, 45
Diphenyls, 34, 225, 244
　dipole moments of, 158
　stereochemistry, 41, 214
Dipolar ions, dielectric constants, 42
Dipole moment and molecular structure, 42
Dipole moments, 34, 73, 162, 167, 180, 197, 219, 245
　and steric effects, in aromatic molecules, 214
　of esters, 162
　of ethers, 162
　of hydrocarbons, 158
　of diphenyls, 158
　and structure, 158
　tool in structure determination, 44
Dipyrimidopyrazines, (pyrimidopteridines), 155
Dipyrylenes, 45
Directive effects in benzene, 40
Disaccharides, enzymatic syntheses, 3
Displacement reactions, 160
　at saturated carbon, solvolytic, 50
　at unsaturated centers, 94
　in bridged polycyclic systems, 49
Dissociation, by electron impact, 170
Dissociation constants, of monocarboxylic acids, 167, 43
Dissociation of carbon bonds, 42
Dissociation energy of hydrocarbons, 71
Distillation, 220, 224
　azeotropic, 221
　extractive, 221
　vacuum, 221
Disulfides
　in proteins, 157
　scission of bonds in
Dithiocarbamic acids, 34
Dithiocarbamates, 37
Diuracilpyridazine, 155
Diuretic agents, 75, 128
Diuretics
　chemistry of, 128
　non-mercurial, 195
Divalent carbon compounds, structure of, 41
Documentation, mechanical, 56
Doisynolic acids, 47, 210
Double bonds
　Bredt's rule and, 48
　reactions at, 249
Drosophila melanogaster, pteridines, 155
Drugs and alkaloid synthesis, 61
Drugs
　antihistamine, 78
　antimalarial, 63
　chemistry of, 74, 240
　structures of, 74
　synthesis of, 27, 189
　vegetable, 78
Drying, 220
Dye binding methods, in protein analysis, 193
Dye chemistry, inner complex formation in, 16
Dyeing
　coupling reactions in, 23

physical chemistry of, 173
stereochemical problems in, 173
of synthetic polypeptides, 173

Dyes (see also individual entries)
alcian blue, 105
aminoazo, 1
anthraquinone, 56
azo, tricyclic premetallized, 22
bile, 14
cyanine, 143
effects of salts and problems on spectra of, 47
electron gas theory of, 22, 68, 69
for cellulosic fibers, 58
heterocyclic azo, 22
o-hydroxy azo, 22
indigo, 73, 106, 231
in plumage of binds, 69
metal complexes in, 75
naphthol - AS, 18
nitro, 24
organic, 204
Pechmann, 49
photographic, 55, 189
indigo, 229
phthalocyanine, 15, 105
plant, 68
polycyclic aromatic hydrocarbons and heterocycles in, 61
porphyn, 19
recent progress in (1958), 212
sensitization of photographic, 15, 70
steric effects in, 21, 47
sulfur, 16, 45
synthetic, 246, 253
symposium on, 136

Dyson notation, for organic compounds, 73, 240

Elastic materials, Vulkollan, 17

Elastomers, 55, 58, 180, 189

Elbs reaction, 48, 85

Electric moment, in aliphatic compounds, 40

Electrical discharge, products in simple gas atmosphere, 82

Electrical properties, of hydrocarbons, 208

Electrochemical fission, of carbon-halogen bonds, 102

Electrochemical potential, 197

Electrochemistry, 197, 236

Electrochemical reactions, mechanisms of, 90

Electrochemistry, of irreversible oxidation-reduction, 40

Electrodecantation, multimembrane, 193

Electrofugal escape, 23

Electroisomerism, 40

Electrolysis, 220

Electrolyte solutions, 31, 161

Electron absorption spectroscopy, 241

Electron diffraction, 208, 219

Electron donor/acceptor complexes
electron transition in, 24

Electron microscope, 219

Electron resonance spectroscopy, 50, 61

Electron spin resonance, chemical studies by, 13

Electron structure, molecular, quantum theory of, 31

Electron transition
in electron donator/acceptor complexes, 24

π-Electrons, 223
in aromatic compounds, 91

Electrons, low energy, 30

Electronegativity, 50, 74

Electronic concepts of valence, 204

Electronic energy, transfer of, 207

Electronic excitation, change in molecular shape during, 71

Electronic mechanisms, 236, 239, 244

Electronic outline, of organic chemistry, 253

Electronic resonance, in molecular research, 20

Electronic spectra, 214, 250
of aromatic hydrocarbons, 107
of polyatomic free radicals, 127
of pyridine homologs, 170

Electronic spin magnetic resonance, 50, 179

Electronic structure, and carcinogenic activity, 109
of organic compounds, 240

Electronic theory, 243, 249

Electrophilic substitution
aromatic, 70
heterocyclic, 166

Electronic transitions
in unsaturated hydrocarbons, 46
in trisubstituted benzenes, 46

Electronic transition intensities
in aliphatic ketones, 46

Electronic transitions, due to non-bonding electrons, 51

Electronic theory, of reactions, 41

Electronic transition, 125

Electrophoresis, 55, 197, 220
in agar-gel, 193
high voltage, 76
of carbohydrates, 4
paper, 61, 155, 193, 175
of polymers, 82
preparative, 10
of proteins, 82, 193, 236
of pteridines, 155
starch block, 76
starch gel, 76
zonal gradient density, 193
zone-, 11, 12, 220
zone, on filter paper, 13

Elements, thermodynamic properties of, 119

Elimination, 14, 163
steric effects in, 163

Emetamine, 136

Emetine, 136

Emulsion polymerization, 73, 184

Emulsions, 71

End-group determinations, in proteins, 154

Endocrinology, symposium on, 153

Energy transfer, 82

Engines, 180

Enolization, 163
    effect of ring size on, 57
    electronic interpretation of, 72

Enols, 226

Entropies, of branched-paraffin hydrocarbons, 46

Enzymatic degradation, 81

Enzymatic syntheses
    of sucrose and other disaccharides, 3

Enzyme analytical reactions, 84

Enzyme catalysis, 247

Enzyme-metal substrates, 132

Enzyme models, 216

Enzymes, 8, 114, 141, 236 (see also fermentation)
    chemistry and technology, 252
    cholinesterases, 6, 56, 78
    dehydrogenases, 213
    kinetics, 221
    metallo and zinc, 11
    metals and enzyme activity, 132
    models, 18
    oxidative, 175
    photochemistry of, 8
    synthesis of disaccharides, 3
    trypsin, 154
    vitamins and, 60

Ephedra bases, 121

Epinephrine (Adrenaline) and related compounds, 41, 78
(see Hormones)

Epoxidation, with organic peracids, 87

Epoxide reactions, mechanisms of, 52

Epoxide resins, 58 (see also epoxy resins)

Epoxides, 226, 161
    1,2-, 100
    α-, analysis of, 83
    sugar-, 100

Epoxy resins, 184, 185, 245

Equilibrated systems, steric effects in, 215

Equilibrium, 167

Ergosterol, conversion to adrenal cortical hormones, 153

Ergosterol-D-acetate 22:23-dibromide 11-oxygenated
  steroids from-, 153

Ergot alkaloids, 20, 48, 64, 67, 69, 98, 103, 110

Ergothioneine, 113

Erythrina alkaloids, 103, 121, 122, 144, 165, 177
    aromatic, 20, 177

Essential oils, 229

Esters, 198, 227
    acrylic, 250
    aliphatic, condensation of, 160
    alkylation of, 88
    analysis of, 83
    cellulosic, 2
    chemistry of, 140
    condensation of, 70
    dipole moments of, 162
    hydrolysis by cholinesterases, 6
    of carbohydrates, 135
    of fatty acids, unsaturated, 56
    of mineral acids, 226
    of steroids, 114

Estradiol, from cholesterol, 15

Estrogen activity, 34

Estrogens (see also Hormones), 7, 64, 174, 232
    artificial, 51
    doisynolic acids, 47
    in plants, 113
    synthetic, 14, 45, 195
    ultra-violet spectra of, 210

Etamycin, 157

Ethane-ethylene equilibria, 171

Ethanolamines, 72

Ethanol, industrial, 226

Ethereal oils, international catalog, 247

Ethers, 3
    acetylenic, 9, 176
    chemistry of, 140
    cleavage of, 49
    diethyl, autoxidation, 245
    diaryl, 46
    dipole moments of, 162
    ethynyl, 9
    in synthesis, 9
    haloethyl, 49
    of carbohydrates, 135
    of mineral acids, 226
    peroxides of, 22
    reduction of diazo compounds with, 21

Ethyl alcohol, reactions of, 41

Ethylene, 36
    catalytic hydrogenation, 169
    polymers of, 23, 185
    oxidation and other reactions of, 128

Ethylene bond
    additions to, 163
    partial polarity of, 40
    reactions with free radicals, 169

Ethylenediamine tetra-acetic acid (EDTA)
    metal chelates; infrared spectra, 130

Ethylene derivatives, reactions with halogens, 44

Ethylenic ketones, 226

Ethylenimine, 181

Ethyleneiminoquinones, 21

Ethylene oxide, 181

Ethylene-polysulfides, X-ray study of, 109

Ethynyl ethers, 9

Evaporation, 220

Exchange, isotopic, 158
(see under individual compounds)

Excitation, electronic, 71

Excited molecules, 127

Excited states
    in biology, 249
    in chemistry, 249

Excretions, mammalian, 90

Explosions, free-radicals in, 54

Explosive compounds
    relationship between performance and
      constitution of, 47

Explosives, 204

Faraday effect, 219
Fats, 70, 95, 227, 236 (see also lipids)
    autoxidation, 95
    conjugated systems in, 246
    derivatives of, 58
    infra-red spectra, 95
    natural, 27, 66
    synthetic, 109
Fats and oils, 245
Fatty acid anions, combination with proteins, 169
Fatty acid methyl esters, gas-liquid chromatography of, 129
Fatty acids, 35, 70, 95, 97, 246, 249
    acetylenic, 95
    decomposition by γ-particles, 159
    essential, 114
    gas-liquid chromatography of, 129
    synthesis of glycerides, 51
    industrial, 109, 248
    of bacterial origin, 102
    oxygenated, 95
    polyhydric alcohol esters of, 45
    polymorphism, 95
    radiolysis of, 159
    separation of, 65
    structure, 95
    synthesis of, 51
    synthetic, 44
    technology of, 95
    ultraviolet absorption spectra of, 44, 95
    unsaturated, 56, 90, 93
    urea inclusion and, 95
Fatty oils, chromatographic analysis of, 169
Favorskii rearrangement, 34, 88
Fenchylic rearrangement, 163
Fenton's reagent, oxidation of alcohols with, 168
Fermentation
    industries, 231
    L-casei factor, 125
Ferritin, 10
Ferrocene, 74, 98
    preparation by the amine method, 121
Fiber proteins, bridge reactions in, 19
Fiber systems, molecular structure in, 101
Fibers
    nylon, thermal stabilization of, 129
    response to thermal radiation, 129
    synthetic, 63, 74
    synthetic and natural, 185
Fibroins, silk, 11
Filariasis, chemotherapy of, 126
Filtration, 220
Fischer
    indole synthesis, 73
    stereochemical conventions, 2
Fischer-Tropsch process, 6, 150, 244
Fission, electrochemical, 102
Flame propagation, in $CO-O_2$ mixtures, 138
Flames and detonations, 138
Flash photolysis, study of ClO· radicals, 138
Flavandioles, hydroxy-, 65

Flavanes, hydroxy-, 68
Flavans, 175
    stereochemistry of, 166
Flavanols, 181
Flavanones, 161, 181
Flavenes, hydroxy-, 68
Flavins, 143
Flavone glycosides, 162
Flavones, 37, 68, 161, 162, 181
    and anthocyanins, 203
    and related compounds, 132
    iso-, 98, 181
    methylation of, 98
    of Dahlias, 162
    hydroxy-, 3, 161
    infrared spectra, 162
Flavonoid chemistry, unsolved problems in, 103
Flavonoid pigment, chromatography of, 76
Flavonoids, 26, 111
    a new isomerization in, 56
    biosynthesis of, 190
Flavor, and chemical structure, 109
Flavor substances, 106
Flavoring materials, 54
Flavylium salts, 211
Fluorans, 181
Fluoranthene, 48
2-Fluorenamine, chemistry, carcinogenicity and metabolism of, 1
Fluorene, 143, 229
    and derivatives, 43
Fluorescenins, 181
Fluorescence, 63, 197, 240, 249, 219, 222, 224
    of aromatic compounds, 110
    primary processes in, 125
Fluorescence stabilization, of complex molecules, 127
Fluorescyanine, 155
Fluorination, 14
    of hydrocarbons, 151
Fluorine, 56, 70, 74, 89, 102, 178
    action on organic compounds, 46, 178
    in lubricants, 57
    organic derivatives of, 98, 91, 212, 178
    organometallic and organometalloid compounds of, polymers with, 18
    progress in, 110
Fluorine compounds, 74, 93, 105, 242, 251
    aliphatic, 246, 203
    aliphatic, preparation of, 85
    hydrocarbons, 151
    infra-red spectra of, 178
    organic; symposium on, 234
    perfluoro-alkyls, 100
    toluene, ultraviolet spectra of, 170
    thermochemistry of, 111
    thermodynamics of, 111
Fluorocarbon radicals, in metal and nonmetal compounds, 190
Fluoroethylene polymers, 185

Fluoromethane, Raman spectra of, 165

Fluorophosphates, alkyl, 105

Fluorosilicates, reactions with halides, 23

Foam formation, fractionation of mixtures by, 125

Folic acid (pteroyl-glutamic acid), 15, 78, 109, 114, 125
    analogs and antagonists, 7
    coenzymes, 8

Food industry
    analytical methods in, 119
    carbohydrates in, 119

Formaldehyde (see also aldehydes, ketones), 253
    reaction with synthetic protein fibers, 55
    reaction with amino acids and proteins, 10
    polymers, 184
    resins, 16

Formaldehyde condensation, as autocatalysis, 81

Formamide, syntheses with, 23

Formazan reaction, in carbohydrates, 5

Formazans, 17, 50

Formula indexes, rules for, 56

Fractionation procedures, importance in protein studies, 154

Fractionation techniques, small scale, 102

Free atoms, in photochemical reactions, 81

Free energy, of O_2^-, 124

Free radical (see also free radicals; and radicals)
    attack on styrene double bonds, 169
    nature of unsaturated compounds, 70
    polymerization, 75, 184
    reaction, termination in, 24
    reactions, 233

Free radicals (see also radicals), 34, 63, 90, 109, 124, 127, 179, 203, 224, 249, 253
    alkoxy, 52, 74, 138
    alkyl, 74
    alkylperoxy, 74
    aromatic substitution by, 74
    aryl, reaction with heterocycles, 166
    and gas explosions, 54
    and polymerization, 191
    and triplet states, in aromatic vapors, 138
    as intermediates, 93
    associated with the low temperature oxidation of paraffins, 171
    at the decomposition of organic compounds, 42
    characteristics and importance of, 17
    chemistry of, 253
    detection with dropping mercury electrode, 124
    developments in (1946), 89
    developments in (1957), 127
    electronic spectra of, 127
    electronic structure of, 168
    from high-energy irradiation of hydrocarbons, 138
    frozen, 247
    in sensitized ignitions, 138
    in solution, 43, 63, 159, 207, 253
    in the gas phase, 137, 233
    in vapor phase, 74
    influence of structure on, 169
    initiation and addition polymerization, 168
    interaction with aliphatic compounds, 100
    ionization potentials of, 119
    isothermal reactions, 91
    large, instability of, 172
    mass spectrometry of, 100, 127
    mass spectrographic examination of, 22
    nature of, 137
    paramagnetic resonance of, 127
    physical chemical studies of, 71
    propagation and copolymerization, 169
    reactions with aldehydes in liquid phase, 172
    reactions of, 168, 171, 169
    reactivity of, 172
    reactivity in polymerization reactions, 169
    stability, quantum mechanical basis of, 124
    stabilization of, 127
        at low temperature, 127
    structural factors for the reactivity of -methylenic groups toward, 171
    structure and reactivity, 90
    studies by electron-spin resonance, 244
    study by photochemistry, 74
    study of ClO· by flash photolysis, 138
    their role in biological oxidations, 127
    their role in reaction mechanisms, 127
    theory of the structure of, 168
    thermal reactions of, 138

Freezing points, determination of, 218

Friedel, Charles, 73

Friedel-Crafts polymerizations, 105

Friedel-Crafts reaction, 86, 98
    in carbohydrates, 3
    in polycyclic aromatic hydrocarbons, 49

Friedel-Crafts syntheses, 42

Fries reaction, 43, 85

Frontal analysis, in chromatography, 125

Fructose (see also sugars)
    and derivatives, 3

Fuels, substitute, 33

Fulvenes, 49, 93

Functional groups
    analysis via, 251
    microanalysis of, 60

Functions, determination of, 196

Fungal, metabolites, 93, 137

Fungal quinones, 137

Fungi, chemical activity, 241

Fungicides, 243

Furan, 19, 161, 181

Furan resins, 185

Furans, 36, 96 (see also hydrofurans)
    dialkoxydihydro, 9
    diacycloxydihydro, 9
    dibenzo, 181
    dihydro, 160, 181
    tetrahydro, 161
    polymerization of, 25

Furfural, 14, 33, 212

Furoxans, 52

Galactosamine, sulfated, 156
Gallotannins, 68
Gammexane (γ-1, 2, 3, 4, 5, 6-hexachlorocyclohexane) 55
Gangliosides, of brain, 25
Garlic, specific principle of, 8
Garrya alkaloids, 123
Gas chromatography, 13, 38, 61, 76, 84, 189, 248
(gas-liquid chromatography, vapor phase chromatography; see also chromatography)
Gas-liquid chromatographic columns, development of, 128
Gas-liquid chromatography
of fatty acids and fatty acid methyl esters, 129
Gas oils, hydrocarbons in, 150
Gas phase reactions, 31, 251
Gases, handling of, 220
analysis of, 196
Gasolines, hydrocarbons in, 150
Gattermann-Koch reaction, 86
Gatterman synthesis, of aldehydes, 88
Gelatin, peptides from, 105, 154
Gelsemium alkaloids, 136
Genetics, and organic chemistry, 206
Genes, 75
Genins,
cardiac
structure and synthesis of, 47
Geochemistry, 69
Geometric isomerism, 75
Geometry, of giant molecules, 75
Gerhardt (1816-1856), 110
Germanes and organo derivatives, 48, 245
Germicides, quaternary ammonium-, 195
Gibberilic acid, 26
Gibberellins, 69
Glasses, organic, dielectric constants, 124
Gliotoxin, structure of, 211
Globular proteins, aggregation of, 172
Glucagon, 113, 154
chemistry and biology of, 153
Glucose (see also sugars)
active, 40
configuration of, 72
D-, aromatic compounds from, 5
D-, methyl ethers of, 3
Glucosides, 69
D-Glucuronic acid
conjugates of, 4
in metabolism, 4
synthesis of, 4
Glue, 105
Glutathione, 133
Glutose, 2
Glycals, 3
2-hydroxy-, 4

Glycerides (see also fats), 95
acid and alkaline hydrolysis of, 107
composition and structural characteristics of, 44
of fatty acids, 51
of natural fats, 71
synthesis of, 176
synthetic, 44
Glycerin and related compounds, 246
Glycerol, symposium on (1953), 234
Glycerol derivatives
optically active
preparation and properties of, 44
Glycerol phosphates, 137
Glycidic ester, condensation, 86
Glycine, condensation with aromatic aldehydes, 161
Glycocyamidines, 52
Glycogen(s), 5, 8, 73
Glycol hydrates, crystalline, 107
Glycols, 33, 141, 226
industrial, 226
symposium on (1953), 234
Glycoproteins, 10, 32, 135
of plasma, 156
Glycosidases, 135
Glycosides (see also sugars), 27, 35, 68, 135, 177
acid hydrolysis of, 57
alkali-sensitive, 4
cardiac, 42
cardiac, of digitalis, 58
cardioactive, 17, 60, 78
cardioactive, sugars of, 187
digitaloid, 66
flavone, 162
methyl and phenyl of common sugars, 4
plant, 246
spirastano, 232
strophanthus, 78
Glycosidic heart poisons, 68
Glycosylamines, 4
Glycosyl halides, and derivatives, 4
Glycosyl ureides, 5
Gonadotropic hormones, 112
Gossypol, 52
Graft polymers, 31
Grignard compounds, 34
Grignard reactions
in carbohydrates, 3
in ketone synthesis, 87
of non-metallic substances, 245
Grignard reagents, 38, 99, 120
constitution of, 102
reactions with oxinane ring, 48
Grinding, 220
Group V elements, stereochemistry of, 94
Growth hormones, 11
Growth promoters, 60
Growth substances, 70
Guanidine
amino, 43
derivatives, 69

Gums, 251
    and resins, 243
    industrial, 234, 253
    plant, 105, 187
    water soluble, 246
Gutta-percha, 177

Haematoxylin (see also Hematoxylin), 38, 143
Halides
    action of neutrons on, 159
    alkenylmagnesium, 9
    in Wurtz-Fittig reactions, 57
    phosphonitrilic, 9
    reactions of, 97
    reactions with fluorosilicates, 23
β-Haloethylamines, 195
α-Haloethyl ethers, 49

Haloform reaction, 42
Halogen acids, configuration of, 40
Halogen addition, to unsaturated compounds, 108
Halogen, positive, 17
N-Halogenated amides, halogenation with, 102
Halogenation, 223
Halogenated ketones, rearrangements, 160
Halogen compounds
    action of neutrons on, 159
    of hydrocarbons, 140
    as sources for Grignard and lithium reagents, 99
    structure and reactivity, 42
Halogen-metal interconversion reaction, 87
Halogenation, aromatic and heterocyclic compounds, 102
di-α-Halogeno ethers, 23
Halogens
    as electron acceptors, 91
    electropositivity of, 107
    decomposition of salts of carboxylic acids with, 50
    electrochemical dehalogenation, 102
Halohydrins, 33
α-Haloketones, 34
Hammett equation
    for ortho substituents, 214
    tautomerism and, 111
    re-examination of, 49
Hashish, 64
Heart venoms, 15, 232
Heartwood constituents, 93
Heat capacity, of hydrocarbons, 208
Heat conductors, organic, 244
Heating, 220
Hecogenin, cortisone from, 58
Helix-random coil transformations
    in deuterated macromolecules, 130
Helminthiasis, chemotherapy of, 79
Hematoxylin (see also Haemotoxylin), 181

Heme proteins, 10
Hemicelluloses, 5, 91, 187
Hemoproteins, 16, 38
Hemp drugs, 63
Heparin, 4, 172
Heptalene, 201
Herbicides, 58, 59, 236
Hernandine, 166
Herz reaction, 51
Heteroaurins, 177
Heterauxines, 82
Heteroaromatics, infra-red spectra, 100
Heteroatoms, rearrangements concerned with, 134
Heterocyclic
    azo dyes, 22
    compounds in dye synthesis, 66
    nomenclature, 38
Heterocyclic compounds, 176, 181, 182, 204, 236, 247
    action of ozone on, 61
    containing P, As, Sb, Bi and Si, 145
    from levulinic acid, 247
    fungal metabolites, 93
    nitrogen, nitration of, 97
    nomenclature, 229
    of nitrogen, symposium on, 136
    of P, As and Sb, 93
    oxygen containing, 161
    pteridines and purines, 155
    reactions with benzoyl peroxide, 166
    reactions with ethyl diazoacetate, 166
    reactions with reactive methylene groups, 16
    review monographs on, 145-146
    3- and 4-membered, 90
    5-membered, 145
    ultraviolet absorption spectra of, 146
    via acyl-lactone rearrangement, 23
    with unusual hetero atoms, 143
    with four condensed rings, 145
    various classes, 229, 230, 231
    various 5- and 6-membered classes, 143
Heterocyclic nitrogen compounds, 42, 45
Heterocyclic oxo-compounds, 16
Heterocyclic ring systems, 22
Heterogeneous catalysis, 19
    and stereochemistry, 51
Heterogeneous reactions, stereochemistry, 163
Heterosides, 227
Hexachlorocyclohexanes, 55
Hexachlorocyclopentadiene, 58
Hexanone-2, photochemistry of, 38
Hexitol anhydrides, 3
Hexitols, and derivatives, 3
    from unsaturated polyhydric alcohols, 2
Hexosans, 3
Hexoses, 90
    conversion to furans, 3
Heyrovsky (polarography), 43
    (see also polarography)

High energy, use of, 58
High polymers, 54, 58, 91, 161, 180, 184, 241, 246
(see also Polymers, Macromolecules)
advances in, 22
free radicals in, 179
molecular size distribution in, 120
study with X-rays, 180
thermodynamic properties of, 96
High temperature
lubricants, 241
organic conductors, 244
oxygen atoms at, 138
Hindrance, steric, 189 (see also steric effects, etc.)
Hindered internal rotation
studied by nuclear magnetic resonance, 128
Histamine, 64
Hoesch synthesis, 86
Hofmann reaction, 41, 86, 88
Holarrhena alkaloids, 123
Holosides, 227
Homoallylic rearrangements, 163
Homogeneous chemical reactions, 241
Homolytic aliphatic substitution, 233
Homolytic aromatic substitution, 254
Homolytic processes, and stereochemistry, 94
Hop resin acids, 175
Hormones, 27, 28, 75, 112-4, 236
(see also steroids and individual entries)
adrenaline (epinephrine), 41, 78
adrenocortical, 11, 65, 112, 113, 142
chromatography of, 192
cortical, 113
estrogens, 64, 174, 232
gonadotropic, 112
growth, 11
lactogenic, 11
male sex, 42
melanocyte-stimulating, 11, 130, 174
non-benzenoid steroid, 112
of digestive tract, 174
of hypophysis, 112, 174
of invertebrates, 174
of pituitary, 11
of plants, 174, 177
of suprarenal cortex, 174
of suprarenal medula, 174
of the mimosas, 176
of tissues, 174
of thymus, 174
parathyroid, 174
protein, 10
phyto-, 174
progesterones, 47, 174
sexual, 174
steroid, 29, 33
steroid esters, 114
suprarenal, 60, 114
symposium on (1944), 234
thyroid, 74, 113, 174
thyroid stimulating, 113
thyroxine, 55, 71, 126
Hot-atom chemistry, 209
Hot gas effect, on organic materials, 129
C.S. Hudson, collected papers, 243

Humic acids, 248
Hunsdiecker reaction, 50
Hyaluronic acids, 5, 156
Hydantoins, 48
Hydrazine, 236
Hydrazines, 23, 103, 212, 228
Hydrazinophthalazines, hypotensive, 77
Hydrazones, of sugars, 2
Hydride-transfer reaction, 52
Hydrindanes, 65
Hydrindanone, 65
Hydroarylation, of unsaturated compounds, 101
Hydrocarbon radicals
tables of the heats of formation and ionization potentials of, 171
thermal stability and reactivity of, 171
Hydrocarbons, 34, 180
acid-catalyzed reactions, 160
alicyclic, 225
aliphatic, reactions of, 203
alkanes, chemistry of, 140
alkenes, chemistry of, 140
analysis of special 208
aromatic, halogenated, 225
aromatic; steric effects in, 214
arylcycloalkanes, 225
as solvents for U.V. spectroscopy, 19
autoxidation of, 21, 47
base-catalyzed reactions of, 6
behavior under pressure; bibliography, 245
bond energies and resonance energies, 170
butadiene from oxygen derivatives of, 45
catalytic chemistry of, 102
catalytic cracking, 6
catalytic hydrogenation, 151
characterization of, 72
chemistry of, 90
collective volumes on petroleum hydrocarbons, 150-5
conversion into butadiene, 45
critical behavior, 208
data book, 246
density and refractive index of, 208
deuterated, 170
deuterium exchange in, 6
diaryls, atropisomeric, 22
catalytic cracking of, 170
dipole moments of, 158
dissociation energy of, 71
electrical properties, 208
encyclopaedia of, 240
fractionation by adsorption, 125
from petroleum, 101, 250
general theory of oxidation of, 150
halogen derivatives, 140
handbook of, 240
high-energy irradiation in gas phase, 138
high molecular weight, 150
in petroleum, 75
infrared spectra, 33
isomerization of, 42, 240
macromolecules, 58
mechanisms of thermal decomposition, 150
nitration of, 19
nitro-aliphatic, 225
nitro-aromatic, 225
nitrohalogenated aliphatic, 225
nitroso, aliphatic, 225

nomenclature, 38
non-benzenoid, mechanisms of reactions, 150
nuclear radiation chemistry of, 23
optical properties (spectra), 208
oxidation of gaseous, 107
oximation of, 23, 151, 171
phenylalkanes, 142, 225
photo nitrosation of, 23
photosensitized reactions of, 105
physical chemistry of, 208
physical constants, 250
physical properties and structure, 150
polyaryl, 225
polycyclic, 60
polycyclic aromatic, 33
properties of light, 250
polycyclic aromatic, dyes from, 61
purification by selective adsorption, 208
pyrolysis of aromatic, 150
reactions in electrical discharges, 43
reactions in presence of $AlCl_3$, 42
reactions with hydrogen atoms, 172
reactivity of, 171
solid-liquid equilibria, 208
solvent extraction studies, 208
special oxidation reactions of unsaturated, 151
spectra of, 21
surface tension and parachor, 208
symposium on nomenclature of, 234
thermal decomposition of, 171
thermodynamic equilibria, 208
ultraviolet absorption spectra, 44, 150, 208, 241
unsaturated; isomerization, 44
various derivatives, 225

Hydrocolloids
  natural plant, 119
  physical functions of, 121

Hydrocortisone, 105

Hydrocyanic acid, polymeric, 24

Hydroforming, 150

Hydrofuran series, molecular rearrangement in, 17, 160

Hydrogen
  catalytic activation, 6
  in tautomerism, 54
  mobile, 39

Hydrogen
  active
    analysis of, 83

Hydrogenation, 85
  catalysts for, 169
  catalytic, 15, 33, 41
  heats of, 223
  of aromatics, 105
  of ethylene, mechanism, 169
  of esters to alcohols, 87
  of naphthalenes, 229
  of olefins, vapor phase, 49
  mechanism of, 58, 98
  with copper-chromium oxide catalysts, 15
  with Raney-catalysts, 14
  with Raney nickel, 73
  with synthesis gas, 6

Hydrogenation and hydrogenolysis, 203

Hydrogenation-dehydrogenation, 9

Hydrogen bonding, 74, 108, 186
  infrared studies of, 186
  in alcohols, 186
  in inclusion compounds, 75
  in polymers, 75
  in various systems, 186
  studied by infrared absorption, 127

Hydrogen bond, 33, 38, 42, 54, 159, 180, 212, 248

Hydrogen bonds
  energy of, 159
  magnetochemical study of, 158
  proton exchanges in, 128
  stereochemistry of, 94
  thermal properties in crystals, 159

Hydrogen-carbon bond, cleavage, 99

Hydrogen fluoride, its use in reactions, 15

Hydrogen peroxide, oxidation of benzene, 207

Hydrogen sulfide, properties of, 250

Hydrogenolysis
  and hydrogenation, 203
  of benzyl groups, 87

Hydrogen transfer, 110
  with pyridine nucleotides, 213

Hydrolysis
  at carbonyl carbon, mechanism of, 56
  of aliphatic amides, 104
  of glycerides, 107

Hydroperoxides, 172
  (see also peroxides, reactions, free radicals, etc.)

Hydropteridines, 166

Hydropyran series, molecular rearrangement in, 17, 160

Hydroxamic acids, 36, 45

Hydroxy acids, 141, 227
  configuration of, 40

Hydroxy-aldehydes, 141, 227

Hydroxy-amino acids
  chemistry and biology of, 15
  related to collagen, 136

o-Hydroxy azo dyes, 22

Hydroxycarbonylation, 160

Hydroxy flavanes, 68

Hydroxy flavenes, 68

2-Hydroxyglycals, 4

Hydroxy ketones, 227
  naphthalenic, 229

4-Hydroxyquinolines, 47

Hydroxypurines, 156

Hydroxylamines, 228

Hydroxylation, of steroids, 61, 188

Hydroxylation methods, 9

Hydroxylations, with organic peracids, 87

Hydroxyl group
  determination, 83
  hyperconjugation of, 164

Hydroxylysine, 175

Hyperconjugation, 17, 45, 46, 70, 96, 111, 158, 164, 236
  of alkyl groups, 164
  isotope effect, 164
  with hydroxyl groups, 164

Hypertension, chemical
    factors in, 119
Hypnotics, barbituric acid, 195
Hypohalites, organic, 49
Hypophysis, hormones, 112
Hypsochromic shifts, 170

Imidazole, 16
    alkaloids, 121
    and derivatives, 145
Imidazoles, 182, 230
    biologically important, 44
2-Imidazolines, 49
Imidazolidines, 49
Imines, 37, 228
    as intermediates in reactions, 23
Iminoethers, 228
Immunochemistry, 89, 156
    steric factors in, 94
Immunoelectrophoresis, in agar gels, 193
Inclusion compounds, 17, 19, 35, 70, 107
    hydrogen bonding in, 75
    urea and fatty acids, 95
Indanes, <u>gem</u>-diphenyl, rearrangements, 160
Indazoles, 182
Indene, 143
    metallic compounds of, 19
Indicators, effect of salts and proteins on the spectra of, 47
Indigo dyes, 136, 143, 229
Indole, 44
    action of X-rays on, 159
    alkaloids, 15, 65, 93, 98, 121, 122, 136, 144, 176
    derivatives, 145
    effects of X-rays on, 159
    iso-, 182
    synthesis, 73
Indoles, 181
    rearrangements of, 36
Industrial alcohols, 226
Industrial chemistry, 74
Industrial glycols, 226
Industrial organic chemistry, general methods, 231
Infra red, and Raman spectra; theory, 254
Infra red absorption (see also infra red spectra)
    of amino acids, 127
    studies of hydrogen-bonding systems by, 127
    studies in organic phosphorus chemistry, 128
Infra red analysis
    of solid substances, 13
    of structure of amino acids, polypeptides and proteins, 11
Infra red intensities
    and molecular structure, 51
    applied to structure determination, 127
    measurements of, 127
Infra red spectra, 33, 37, 38, 105, 126, 249
    (see also above, and spectra)
    and hydrogen bonds, 186
    applications of, 204
    as analytical tool, 72
    biological applications, 127
    current trends (1960), 200
    in carbohydrate chemistry, 57
    in rubber industry, 58
    in steroids, 57
    in structural analysis, 57
    in textile industry, 57
    near-, 1
    of addition products, 24
    of benzene derivatives, 170
    of biochemicals, 127
        bibliography of, 127
    of ethylene-diamine-tetraacetic acid metal chelates, 130
    of fats, 95
    of fluorocarbons, 178
    of hydrocarbons, 208
    of large molecules, 170
    of penicillin, 148
    of polymers, 12
    of proteins, 193
    of steroids, 107
    of serum lipids, 127
    of tissue lipids, 127
    of transition metal complexes, 200
    theory of, 254
    values of (1944), 89
Inhibition, of vinyl polymerization, 47
Inhibitors
    amine oxidase, 129
    mitosis, 17
    monoamine oxidase, 129
    structure and activity of, 129
Inner complex formation, 16
    in dye chemistry
Inorganic reactions, kinetics, 136
Inositol, phosphoric ethers, 32
Inositols, 15, 99
Insecticides, 28, 61, 65, 67, 72
Insecticides, organic
    mode of action, 246
Insects, active agents of, 82
Instruments, 1, 180
Insulin, 32, 58, 154, 210
    fractionation of, 153
    homogeneity studies with, 130
    ion exchange chromatography of, 130
    in buffers containing urea
Insulin, 63, 174
    structure of, 153
Interaction(s)
    protein-iodine, 50
    1,3-, 163
Interatomic distances
    in proteins and related substances, 43
    tables of, 138
Intermediates, reactive
    in organic chemistry, 245
Intermolecular compounds, 90
Internal complex salts, structure of, 14
Internal rotation, and structure, 247

International congresses of biochemistry, 187
Intramolecular rearrangements, steric effects in, 215
Invertebrate hormones, 174
Iodic acid, analytical applications, 251
Iodides
    photolysis and photo-oxidation of, 168
    photolysis of trifluoromethyl-, 172
Iodination, the chemistry of, 128
Iodo amino acids, 68
Iodo compounds, 197, 44
Iodonium salts
    decomposition, 223
    hydrolysis, 223
Iodo proteins, 68
    natural and artificial, 11
Ion exchange, 64
    adsorbents, 126
    fractionation of proteins, 193
    in industry, 56
    membranes, 126
Ion-exchange chromatography
    of insulin and proteins, 130
    quantitative separation with, 102
Ion-exchange resins, 55, 185
    in analysis, 78
    in medicine and biological research, 126
    non-ionic separations with, 126
    preparation and uses of, 13
    synthesis of, 126
Ion exchangers, 192
Ionic reactions, 19
    half century of, 16
Ions, unstable species, 127
Ionization
    by electron impact, 170
    of organic compounds, 212
Ionizing radiation
    action on lipids, 209
    chemical action of, 22, 24
    methods of protection against, 209
Ionophoresis, preparative, 10
Ipecac alkaloids, 67, 121, 123
Iron
    in homoproteins, 6
    organic compounds of, 110
Irones, 35, 36
Isatin, 45
Isobutylene polymers, 242
Isobutyraldehyde, 242
Isochromans, 162
Isocoumarins, 181
Isoquinolines, 175
Isocyanate-based polymers, 106
Isocyanate chemistry, recent advances in, 50
Isocyanates, 91
    as intermediates, 74
    organic, 47
Isocyanide-metal complexes, 92

Isoflavones, 68
Isoindolenines, in phthalocyanin synthesis, 19
Isomerism
    geometrical, 97
    in prototropic compounds, 40
    rotational, about C-C bonds, 12
Isomerization, 34, 36
    alicyclic-aromatic, 45
    aspects of, 73
    cis-trans, of carotenoids and diphenylpolyenes, 45
    cis-trans, of conjugated compounds, 50
    commercial, 6
    of alkanes, 6
    of alkylbenzenes, 43
    of hydrocarbons, 42
    of flavonoids, 56
    of olefins, 151
    of pure hydrocarbons, 240
    of unsaturated hydrocarbons, 44
    structural, 74
Isomorphism, 15, 33
Isomers, geometric, 54
Isoparaffins, alkylation of
Isoprene chemistry, 41
Isoprene rule, 64, 91
Isoprenoid compounds
    biosynthesis of, 102
    synthesis in plants, 73
Isoquinoline, 45
Isoquinoline alkaloids, 90
Isoquinolines, 44, 87
    biosynthesis of, 121
Isosterism, 33, 73, 82
Isotactic polymers, 20, 58
    from propene, 21
    kinetics of
Isothiocyanates, natural, 69
Isotope effects, 30
    and hyperconjugation, 164
Isotope effect, of deuterium, 50
Isotope labelling, by neutron irradiation, 23
Isotopes, 36, 82
    application of, 70
    compounds labelled with synthesis of, 98
    in catalytic reactions at surfaces, 180
    in photosynthesis, 74
    in reaction mechanisms, 189
    labelling with, 197
    of oxygen, 30
    synthesis with, 247
    use in mechanism studies, 35
    use in reaction mechanisms, 61
    use of, 74, 196
Isotopes, heavy
    in biology, 241
Isotopic exchange, 71, 209
Isotopic tracer techniques, 96
Isotopic tracers, 30, 212
    (symposium on), 234
    i-steroid rearrangement, 160
Ivy
    toxic principle of, 72
    and related plants, 102

Jacobsen reaction, 85
Japp-Klingemann reaction, 88
Jervine, 175

Kanamycin A, 129
Karrer, 60, 65
Kekulé, F.A., 110
Keratins, 11
Kerosenes, 150
Kerr effect, 107, 219
Ketals, of polyols, 3
Ketene(s), 9, 20, 86, 226
Keto acids, 19, 141
β-Keto aldehydes, 87
Keto-enol conversion, 17
11-Ketosteroids, 153
17-Ketosteroids, determination of, 13
α-Ketols, isomerization, 37
Ketals, 47
Ketones
    acylation of, 37, 87
    amino-, 45
    additions to, 37
    β-di-, 87, 242
    catalytic synthesis of, 6
    chemistry of, 140
    cleavage with sodium amide, 88
    condensations with -keto acids, 161
    cyclic, synthesis, 85
    enzymatic reductions of, 213
    ethylenic, 162
    Grignard synthesis of, 87
    primary photochemical process in, 51
    radicals from acetone, 171
    radicals from diethyl ketone, 172
    reactions in sunlight, 46
    reduction of, 160
    tri, 141
    via organo-cadmium reagents, 46
    unsaturated, 19, 45
    various types, 226
    α-halogen-, 36
    unsaturated; spectra, 19
Ketonic acids, 227
Ketonization, 163
Keturonic acids, 240
Kharasch, M.S., 233
Khellin and related products, 48
Kinetic isotope effects, 21
Kinetics, 31, 37, 167, 196
    application of deuterium isotope effect, 129
    in radical polymerizations, 23
    in solution, 99
    of addition polymerization, 99
    of addition of $BrCCl_3$ to olefins, 172
    of amine-catalyzed reactions, 124
    of the bacterial cell, 243
    of Beckmann rearrangement, 45
    of bimolecular reactions, 41
    of calcium-sodium ion exchange, 169
    of diazo coupling reaction, 48
    of decomposition of nitromethane, 51
    of elementary reactions, 43
    of diene reactions, 171
    of olefin oxidation, 96
    of oxidation by permanganate, 51
    of oxygen exchange, 124
    of polymer formation, 75
    of polymerization, 18, 31
    of polymerization of propene to isotactic polymers, 21
    of cumene hydroperoxide-ethylene polyamine reactions, 172
    of trichloromethyl radicals with cyclohexene, 171
Kjeldahl nitrogen determination, 43
Kolbe electrolysis, 104
Kolbe-Schmitt reaction, 51
Kolbe synthesis, 9, 97
    (see also carboxylic acids; synthesis with)
Kojic acid, 4
Koresin, 56

Labelled compounds, 221
    (see also under compounds, and individual isotopes)
Labelled alkaloids, 166
Labelled steroids, 42
Labelled vitamin A, 113
Labile molecule, 168
    in kinetics of hydrocarbon reactions, 168
Lactams, 199
β-Lactams, 88
Lachrymators, 42
Lactic acid
    production from sugars, 247
    steric aspects of reactions of, 213
Lactone acetals, 21
β-Lactones, 88, 149
Lactose, 40
Lanosterol, 153
Lapacol, in chemotherapy, 101
Large ring compounds, theoretical importance of, 20
Large rings, 197
Lead, organic compounds of, 40, 49
Lead tetraacetate
    oxidations with, 14, 21
Lead tetraethyl
    in preparing alkylmercurials, 120
Lecithin, 245
Lectures, the Peter C. Reilly -, 207
Lepra, chemotherapy of, 109
Lethal synthesis, 217
Leuckhart reaction, 86

Levulinic acid, heterocyclic compounds via, 247
Lewis acids, reactions with metal hydrides and borohydrides, 190
Lewisite, 121
Lichen substances, 66
Lichenin, 227
Lieben, Adolf, 72
Ligands
  inorganic, 137
  organic, 137
Light, effect on anthocyanidins, 70
Light microscopy, 219
Light scattering, 219
  molecular weights by, 57
  theory of, 57
Lignin, 20, 27, 33, 38, 41, 66, 67, 105, 188
Lignin sulfonic acids, 64
Lignans, 50, 70, 89
Lignification, 8, 67, 70
Limonin, 65
Linear polymers, synthetic, 43
Line formula notation, 254
Lipid chemistry, 242
Lipids, 10, 27, 28, 29, 56, 57, 67, 76, 95, 176, 204, 209
Lipins, 27
Lipochromes, 41
Lipoic acid, 8, 26
Lipoids, of mycobacteria, 24
Lipo-protein association, 169
Lipoproteins, 10
Liquid ammonia research, 44
Literature and documentation, of organic chemistry, 140
Literature searches, 119
  mechanized systems, 248
Lithium
  organic reagents, 99
  phenyl-, 81
Lithium aluminum hydride, 60, 83, 87
  in organic chemistry, 247
Lithium compounds, 14, 93
Liver "L-casei factor", 125
Lossen rearrangement, 41
Living matter and chemical structure, 61
Lotoflavin problem, 110
Lubricants, 33, 236
  fluorine containing, 57
  high temperature, 241
Lubricating oils
  hydrocarbons in, 150
  oxidation of, 45
Lumi-auxons, 81
Lupin alkaloids, 36, 67, 121, 122
Luteotropin, 112

Lycopodium alkaloids, 122, 123
Lysergic acids, 103
Lysozymes, 154, 189

Macrocyclic compounds, 90, 141, 163
  heterocyclic, 143
Macrolides, 20, 176
Macromolecular chemistry, 82, 247
  constitutional exactness in, 23
Macromolecular substances, with reactive groups, 20
Macromolecules, 35, 54, 61, 63, 71, 89, 161, 180, 191, 248
  bacterial synthesis of, 90
  cross-linked, 23
  structural investigation of, 23
  deoxyribonucleic acids as, 202
  deuterated, 130
  developments and problems of, 22
  hydrocarbon, 58
  in radical polymerization; kinetics, 23
  kinetic properties, 167
  molecular weight of, 196
  natural, 82
  separations of, 90
  with long range periodicities, 102
  reactions with carcinogens, 1
Magnesium compounds, 39
Magnesium-organic compounds
  handbook for, 254
  condensations with, 160
Magnetic resonance
  as a phenomenon, 128
  nuclear, 50, 52
Magnetochemistry, 72, 109, 158, 167, 197, 219, 224
Maillard reaction, 5
Malaria, chemotherapy, 16, 79
Maleic anhydride derivatives
  additions to double bond, 240
Malignant diseases, chemotherapy, 78
Mammalian secretions and excretions, 90
Manganese dioxide oxidations, 99, 100
Mannich reaction, 20, 85, 249
Marine organisms
  compound derived from, 130
  biochemistry and pharmacology of, 130
Marketing of chemicals, 121
Mass spectra
  as analytical tool, 74
  in detecting impurities, 119
  of amino acids and peptides, 62
  of hydrocarbons, 150
  of free radicals and atoms, 22, 100, 127
  of organic phosphates, 119
  of polyatomic molecules, 119
Mass spectrometry, 30, 74, 84, 98, 106, 119, 220
Mayweed constituents, 176
Mechanism (see also kinetics, reactions, reaction mechanisms, etc.)

of electrophylic aromatic substitution, 65
of hydrolysis of carbonyl compounds, 56
of hydrolysis of phosphate esters, 137
of inorganic reactions, 136
of oxidation, 111

Mechanism and structure, in organic chemistry, 241

Mechanisms
of catalysis and biocatalysis, 6
of complex ion reactions, 139
of organic reactions, 63, 140, 236, 252
of hydrocarbon reactions, 208

Medium-sized rings, 21, 163

Medicinal chemistry, 195

Medicinal literature key, 119

Medicinal products, organic, 244

Medicinals, advances in
(1946), 101
(1948), 101

Medicine, impact of chemistry on, 107

Meerwein-Pondorff-Oppenauer reaction, 55

Meerwein-Pondorff-Verley reduction, 14, 85

Meerwein reaction, extension of, 16

Melamine and its derivatives, 51

Melanocyte-stimulating hormone derivatives, 130

Melezitose, 2, 4

Melting points, determination of, 218

Mendeleeff, 38

Menthone chemistry, 40

Mercaptals, 198

Mercaptans, 41, 198, 207
heterocyclic, 166

Mercaptols, 198

Mercurial compounds, 127

Meriquinoid compounds, 18

Merispermaceae plant alkaloids, 67

Meso-ionic compounds, 57, 99

Mesomerism, 17, 33, 54, 73, 74, 109, 214
steric effects, 94

Mesomeric ions, and orbital theory, 168

Metabolism
chemical pathways, 241
of androgens, 210
of carbohydrates, 73
of phosphorus compounds, 28

Metabolites and anti-metabolites, 114

Metabolites, fungal, heterocyclic, 93

Metalations, with organosodium compounds, 51

Metal alkoxides, 92, 119

Metal alkyls
photolyses; importance in photo processes, 125
polymerization with, 23

Metal-amine solutions, reductions with, 99

Metal amines, stereochemistry, 101

Metal-aromatic compounds, 9

Metal-carbon bonds, formation mechanism, 24

Metal carbonyls, 50, 91, 96, 139, 204

Metal chelates, 246

Metal complexes
in dyes and pigments, 75
stability of, 139

Metal compounds
cyclopentadienyl, 75
formation of complexes and reactivity of, 21

Metal hydrides, 241
reactions with Lewis acids, 190

Metal fires, extinguishing with trimethoxyboroxine, 120

Metal ligand bonds, 139

Metal and metalloid compounds, aromatic, 142

Metal-peptide complexes, 133

Metal solutions in liquid ammonia, reactions of, 42

Metals, and enzyme activity, 132
organic reagents for, 234

Metallic compounds, 73
autoxidation of, 23
of heavy metals, 24

Metallic salts, of alcohols, 41

Metallo-carbonyls, 109

Metalloenzymes, zinc and, 11

Metallo-organics
and polymers, 191
complex formation and reactivity of, 190

Metalloides, complexes of, 36

Metalloids, of cyclopentadienyl, 75

Metalloporphyrins, properties of, 50

Methadone, 195

Methane, structure of, 40

Methanol, industrial, 226

Methionine, 26

Methods
in organic chemistry, 54, 196-199
of organic synthesis, 134

Methoxyl group, 50

16-(α and β)-Methyl corticoids, 129

Methyl ethers
of aldopentoses, 3
of fucose, 3
of D-galactose, 3
of D-glucose, 3
of D-mannose, 4
of hexuronic acids, 4
of rhamnose, 3

Methyl groups, 73

Methyl orange, 72

Methyl pentoses, 26

Methyl radicals, 38
preexponential factors for reaction of, 48
reaction with hydrogen, 171

Methylation
biological, 45
of flavones, 98

Methylene, structure of, 168

Methylene blue method, for peroxide determination, 20

α-Methylene groups, reactions with free radicals, 171

Micelles, 71

Michael reaction, 88

Microanalysis, 35
  alkoxyl determination, 200
  new ideas in, 1
  of organic compounds, 60
  quantitative, 14, 80
  ultra-micro, 80
  quantitative; forty years of, 200

Microanalytical methods, 19, 80

Microbial polysaccharides, 135

Microbial products, 147

Microbiological reactions, 213
  in analysis, 70

Microbiological reductions, of ketones, 213

Microchemical methods, 221, 242, 245

Microchemistry, 80, 200

Microorganisms
  drug resistance in, 156
  in organic chemistry, 206
  transformation by, 75

Microscope
  experimentation with, 80
  polarizing, 105

Microscopy, 219

Microsynthesis, 80

Milk oligosaccharides, 32

Mineral oils, constitution of, 247

Miscellaneous
  chemical structure and performance, 55
  "through the looking glass", 54

Miscibilities, 15

Mitosis inhibitors, 17

Mitotic poisons, 81

Mitragyna alkaloids, 136

Mixed crystals, 15

Mixing, 220

Molasses, glucose and other components in, 2

Models, atomic, 196

Molecular association, 40, 74

Molecular assymetry, 109, 215

Molecular biology, principles of, 216

Molecular complexes, 215

Molecular orbital theory, 164

Molecular orientation, in aliphatic compounds, 40

Molecular physics, 61

Molecular rearrangements
  of hydrofuran series, 17
  of hydropyran series, 17

Molecular shapes, 75, 170

Molecular spectra and structure, 242

Molecular spectroscopy, and biological activities, 52

Molecular structure, 224, 250
    and acid-base catalysts, 6
    and bonding, 252
    and nuclear magnetic resonance, 52
    and infrared intensities, 57
    and dipole moment, 42
    of simple molecules, 94
    physical determination of, 31
    from dielectric constants, 40
    from X-ray diffraction, 40

Molecular wave function, 158

Molecular weight, 196
  by light scattering, 57
  determination of, 218

Molybdenum compounds, complexes, 21

Monoacids, 227

Monoamine oxidase inhibitors, 129

Monoalkyl-substituted benzenes, ultraviolet spectra, 46

Monocarboxylic acids, dissociation constants of, 43

Monolayers
  at mobile interfaces, 218
  reactions in, 89

Monosaccharides
  long-chain derivatives of, 52
  reactions with beta-ketone esters, 4
  structure, 135

Monoterpenoids, bicyclic, 142

Morphine, 81, 97, 144, 166
  (see also following items)

Morphine activity
  synthetic medicinals with, 15, 18, 58, 195

Morphine alkaloids, 121, 122

Moth repellants, 15, 61

Molybdenum compounds, 121 or 171

Mould metabolites, 137

Mucilages, 3, 63, 251

Mucoids, 10

Mucopolysaccharides, 2, 54, 156, 187

Mucoproteins, 2, 187

Muscarine, 9, 79

Muscular contraction, chemistry of, 252

Mustard gas, 42, 132

Mustard oil, 69

Musk odor, products with, 60

Mustards, nitrogen, 78

Mutagenic alkylating agents, 156

Mycobacteria, lipoids of, 24

Mycobactorium tuberculosis, polysaccharides of, 156

Mycoseric acid, 162

Mydriatic alkaloids, 122

Name reactions, 252
  (see also reactions, and specific names)

Naphthacene(s), 229
  dihydro, 177

Naphthalene, 229
    aldehydes, 229
    derivatives, 229
    hydrogenated, 229
    hydroxy ketones, 229
    vacuum ultraviolet absorption spectra of, 170

Naphthaphenanthridine alkaloids, 122

Naphthazarin, hydrogen bonds and structure, 186

Naphthenates, 56

Naphthenic acids, 44

Naphthiminazoles, 166

Naphthoic acids, 229

Naphthol-AS dyes, 18

Naphthols, amino, 229

Naphthoquinones, 229
    amino, 61

Naphthydridines, 48

β-Naphthylamine, sensitized fluorescence of, 207

Naphthylamines, 229

Narcotics and analgesics, 122

Natural dyes
    new; biogenesis and physiological significance, 190

Natural fats, 243

Natural gases, hydrocarbons in, 150

Natural pigments, 147
    photodynamically active, 93

Natural products, 61, 65, 66-69
    acetylenic, 99
    ethylenic lactones, 162
    fruit-flavors, 106
    products; synthesis, 175
    reviews on, 147
    steric aspects, 133
    structural relations, 250

Natural resins, 185, 229

Natural substances, 19

Near infrared spectra of, organic compounds, 52

Near ultraviolet absorption spectra of
    monoalkyl-substituted benzenes, 46

Neighbor group effects, 22

Neo-alloocimene, 176

Neomycin, 78

Nepetalic acid, 211

Nereistoxin, chemical properties, 131

Neucleofugal escape, 23

Neuraminic acid, 5, 20, 156

Neurohypophysis, active principles of, 78

Neutron diffraction, 219

Neutrons, action on organic halides, 159

Nickel, Raney, 33

Neutral dyeing, 22

Nicotine, 72

Ninhydrin, 52

Nitramines, 97

Nitrates
    analysis, 83
    esters, 50
    of sugars, 4
    of starch, 5

Nitration, 223
    anomalous, 46
    aromatic, 96
    of aromatic hydrocarbons, 151
    of paraffins and cycloparaffins, 151
    of saturated hydrocarbons, 9
    with nitrogen dioxide

Nitriles, 38
    alkylation of, 88
    di-, 38
    iso-, 198
    preparation of, 47
    and Grignard reagents, 38

Nitroalkanes, chemistry and technology of, 16

Nitro compounds
    aliphatic, 96
    analysis, 83
    ultraviolet absorption spectra, 46

Nitro dyes, color-constitution relationship in, 24

Nitroethane, and 2-nitroethanol, 3

2-Nitroethanol, 3

Nitrogen-carbonyl interactions, transannular, 103

Nitrogen
    heterocyclic, 57
    inorganic, chemistry of, 138

Nitrogen compounds, 91
    heterocyclic, 42
    new, of plants, 176
    various derivatives, 228

Nitrogen determination, Kjeldahl, 43

Nitrogen mustards, 78

Nitrogen-sulfur compounds, 199

Nitrogen tetroxide, reactions with organic compounds, 45

Nitroglycerine, 226

Nitroguanidines, 48

Nitromethane
    properties, thermodynamics, kinetics of decomposition and utilization, 51

Nitroparaffins, 44, 101
    discovery of, 73

Nitrophenols, 226

Nitrones, 43

Nitrosation, 52

Nitrosation reactions, 87

Nitroso compounds, analysis, 83

C-Nitroso compounds, 99

N-Nitrosoacylarylamines,
    as catalysts in addition polymerization, 168

Nitrosophenols, 226

Nitro-substituted molecules
    correlation of resonance structure with ultraviolet absorption in, 46

Nitrosyl chloride, 48

Nitrous acid, 35
    and nitrosation, 52
    reactions with amines, 105

Nomenclature, 82, 224
    chemical, 119
    in stereoisomers, 56
    of heteroatomic acyclic compounds, 227
    Japanese, 75
    heterocyclics, 38
    hydrocarbons, 38
    of terpene hydrocarbons, 119

Nonadecapeptide
    synthesis of, 25

Non-benzenoid aromatic compounds, 89, 93, 201

Nonulosaminic acids, 5, 63

Noradrenaline, 78

Norcamphane derivatives, 228

L-Norleucine, 6-diazo-5-oxo-, 157

Notation
    Dyson system for organic compounds, 240
    live-formula for chemicals, 254

Notation systems, 105

Nuclear dipole-dipole interactions, 128

Nuclear magnetic resonance, 38, 84, 104, 128, 219, 250
    analytical application of, 128
    analysis of the spectra of pyridine and deuterated pyridines, 128
    applications of ^{13}C-spectra, 128
    determination of structures by, 128
    high resolution, 202, 248
    in organic chemistry, 244
    in phosphorus chemistry, 128
    recent studies in England, 128
    requirements and developments in its instrumentation, 128
    studies of hindered internal rotation by, 128
    of proteins, 128
    spectroscopy, 61

NMR and EPR spectroscopy, symposium on (1960), 202

Nuclear quadrupole resonance, 139

Nuclear radiation chemistry, of hydrocarbons, 23

Nuclear reactions, 209

Nuclear resonance, in molecular research, 20

Nuclear spin magnetic resonance, 50

Nucleic acids, 2, 4, 8, 29, 30, 35, 75, 112, 137, 143, 161, 202, 206
    carbohydrates of, 187
    chemical bond in, 202
    chromatography of, 192
    deoxypentose, 202
    deoxyribose, 202
    desoxyribo-, 216
    in cell structures and functions, 10
    microorganisms, 202
    nucleotide sequence in, 137
    pentose, 202
    photochemistry of, 202
    reactions with mutagenic agents, 156
    role in protein synthesis, 132
    structure of, 17, 57, 81

Nucleophilic aromatic substitution, 70, 74, 99, 107
    benzyne as intermediate in, 138

Nucleophilic attack on α-haloketones, 36

Nucleoprotamines, 154

Nucleoproteins, 10, 202

Nucleosides, 143, 202
    bacterial, 5
    desoxy, 111
    pyrimidine, 5, 166
    synthesis of, 103

Nucleotide coenzymes, synthesis of, 8

Nucleotide synthesis, 22

Nucleotides, 34, 58, 66, 89, 90, 91, 143, 176, 202, 212, 252
    bacterial, 5
    desoxy, 111
    poly-, synthesis of, 202
    uridine, 156

Nuclides, use in determining reaction mechanisms, 207

Nylon fibers, thermal stabilization of, 129

Octahydropyrrocolines, 47

Octalin, 163

Octalines, solvolysis of, 177

Odor, 17

Odor and structure, 201

Odor compounds, 66

Oestrogens, synthetic, 78

Oils, essential, 229
    terpenes in, 60

Oils, natural, acyclic constituents of, 27

Oil refinement, methods, 60

Olefin-aldehyde condensation, 48

Olefin autoxidation, 151

Olefin forming elimination reactions
    steric effects in, 215

Olefin hydrocarbons, free energy relations, 42

Olefinic hydrocarbons
    aluminium-organic synthesis of, 17
    thermal stability of, 42

Olefins, 35
    addition compounds of with mercuric salts, 48
    alkylation of phenols by, 21
    analysis of, 83
    coordination compounds with metallic salts, 43
    cyclo poly-, 68, 63
    free radical addition to, 98
    halogen addition to, 96
    isomerization of, 151
    oxidation, 98
    kinetics of, 96
    polymerization of, 6, 51
    qualitative detection by ozonolysis, 75
    reaction at carbon-carbon bond, 249
    reactions with platinum compounds, 22
    special reactions of, 151
    synthesis of aliphatic compounds from, 25
    vapor-phase catalytic hydrogenation of, 49

α-Olefins, polymerization of, 191
    low pressure polymerization of, 22

Oligomers, of polyamides and polyesters, 20

Oligosaccharides, 32, 135
   long-chain derivatives of, 52
   non-reductive, containing galactose, 187
   progress in the field of, 21
   raffinose family of, 4
   synthesis of, 3

Ommochromes, 20, 177

Oppenauer oxidation, 14, 87

Optical activity, 100
   and living matter, 241
   in carbon compounds, 103

Optical properties of organic compounds, 224, 254

Optical rotation, 57, 167
   natural constants, 246

Optical rotatory dispersion, 9, 163, 219
   application of, 103

Optically labile compounds, 94

Orbital theory, 97

Organic acids, analysis, 83
   quantitative, 248

Organic chemical methods, 54

Organic chemistry
   new advances, 247
   recent results, 55
   steric effects in, 215
   structure and mechanism, 244

Organic compounds
   constitution and physical properties, 203
   Dyson system of notation for, 240
   physical constants, 252

Organic dyes, 204 (see also Dyes)

Organic fluorine compounds, 212

Organic ligands, 137

Organic molecules, large, rotation of, 124

Organic peroxides, 97, 244

Organic phosphorus compounds, 212

Organic reagents, in inorganic analysis, 109, 246

Organic sulfur compounds, 203

Organic synthesis, 206

Organoalkali compounds, 41, 45 (see also Alkali Compounds)

Organo-aluminum compounds, 189, 204

Organobismuth compounds, 44 (see Bismuth)

Organoboron compounds, 120

Organocadmium reagents, for preparation of ketones, 46

Organochlorosilanes, redistribution of, 120

Organolead compounds, 40, 49
   see lead

Organoleptic properties, 224

Organoleptic properties, 224

Organoleptic quality, symposium on, 201

Organolithium compounds, 87, 88, 119

Organomagnesium compounds, 34

Organometal compounds, 97
   (see under specific metal, Grignard reagents, etc.)

Organometallic compounds, 33, 35, 38, 63, 92, 111, 119, 139, 190, 203, 204, 226, 250
   containing fluorine, 90
   in chemotherapy, 120
   in ketone synthesis, 87
   preparation of, 49, 50
   preparation of by the diazoalkane method, 50
   steric effects in, 215
   use in active H determination, 83

Organometallic synthesis, new developments in, 20, 206

Organometallics, fluorine containing, 178

Organometalloidal compounds
   preparation of
   by the diazoalkane method, 50

Organosilanes, 245

Organosilicon compounds, 46, 240
   (see Silicon)
   analysis of, 13

Organosilyl metal compounds, 204

Organosodium compounds, 120

Organosulfur compounds, 83

Organotin, 22, 52
   see Tin

Orienting influence in benzene ring, 41

Origin of life on earth, symposium on, 205

Orthoesters
   aliphatic, 249
   of carbohydrates, 2

Osazones, 2, 25, 61

Oses, 227
   stereochemistry of, 39

Osmotic pressure, determination of, 218

Osones, 4

Ovalbumin, properties, 125

Oxalic acid, "active"
   nature of, 168

Oxazines, 143, 183

Oxazole, 182

Oxazole- Is- , 182

Oxazoles, 45

Oxazoles and oxazolones, 149

2,4-Oxazolidinediones, 51

Oxazolidines, 49

Oxazolines, 47

Oxazolones, (5-), 98

Oxidation
   analogy with two-step ionization, 124
   auto- ,
   by chromium and manganese compounds, 99
   by ferricyanide, 51
   by MnO_2, 100
   by permanganate
     kinetics and mechanism, 51
   induced, 244
   influence of substituents on, 171
   mechanism of, 111
   of alcohols with Fenton's reagent
     mechanism of, 168

of aromatic rings, 132
of benzene with H_2O_2, 207
of benzene by H_2O_2 and iron salts, 172
of carbohydrates, 81
of ethylene, 128
of fats, 95
of gaseous hydrocarbons, 107
of hydrocarbons, 171
of liquid aldehydes, 49
of lubrication oils, 45
of olefins, 98
of paraffins, 171
phenol, 175
photo-, 189
processes of, 204
reactions, 99
reactions of free radicals associated with, 171
with periodic acid, 85
with selenium dioxide, 86

Oxidation-reduction
at the dropping mercury electrode, 43
reversible, 40

Oxidations
biological, preparative, 14
investigations via lead tetraacetate, 21
periodate, of carbohydrates, 4
selective, 21
noble metal catalysis, 21
with lead tetraacetate, 14
with periodic acid, 14
with selenium oxide, 14

Oxidative deterioration, of lipids, 56

Oxidizing agents, carbonyl compounds as, 72

Oxides, photo; of "acenes", 229

N-Oxides, aromatic heterocyclic, 99

Oximation, of saturated hydrocarbons, 23

Oximes, 228

Oxindole, 45

Oxine and derivatives, 243

Oxirane ring, reactions with Grignard reagents, 48

17-Oxogenic steroids, determination of, 13

Oxo reaction, 151

17-Oxo steroids, determination of, 13

Oxo synthesis, 70

Oxy-anions in water solution, reactions of, 103

Oxymercuration, of alkenes, 127

Oxygen
determination of, 45
heterocyclic, 57
isotopes, 30, 39
its basic functions in organic compounds, 52

Oxygen atoms, at high temperatures, 138

Oxygen exchange, kinetics, 124

Oxygen radicals, in cleavages and rearrangement, 47

Oxygen reactions, slowness of, 124

11-Oxygenated steroids, 153

Oxyluminescence, 35, 36

Oxytetracycline, 137

Oxytocin, 136, 174, 189

Ozonolysis, qualitative olefin detection by, 75

Ozone, 119
action on aromatic compounds, 61
action on heterocyclic compounds, 61
reactions with organic compounds, 51

Ozonides, 250
peroxides of, 22

Ozonization, 175
of unsaturated compounds, 103

Ozonization reaction, 43

Ozonolysis of aromatics, 34

Paints, fire retardant, 119

Paleobiochemistry, 69

Paludrine, 63

Pancreas, internal secretions of, 153

Pantothenic acid, 8, 14, 32, 66

Papaverine, 35

Paper chromatography, 242
(see also chromatography)
automatic, 126
of polynuclear aromatic substances, 20

Paper electrophoresis, 7, 155, 193

Parachors, 49, 224

Paracyclophanes, 103

Parahydrogen conversion and semi-quinone radicals, 124

Paraffins
behavior on electronic impact, 170
entropies and related properties, 46
free energy relations, 42
halogenation of, 41
oxidation of, 40, 151
thermal stability of, 42
infrared and Raman spectra, 97
nitro-, 73
reactions of, 168
preparation of pure -, 150
reactive, 72

Paramagnetic resonance, 219
of free radicals, 127

Parasympathomimetics, 78

Parathyroid hormones, 174

Parsley plant, glycosides of, 2

Partial polarity, theory of, 40

Particle size, determination of, 218

Partition chromatography, 125, 132
of sugars and derivatives, 169
of steroids, 50
of tertiary amine salts of penicillins, 169

Patentability of compounds, 73

Peanut protein, 11

Pechmann dyes, 49

Pechmann reaction, 87

Pectic substances, 2, 8, 60, 89, 245

Pectins, 5, 243, 246

Pedicin and related compounds, 107

Penaldic acids, 48

Penicillin, 28, 66, 109
   analysis of, 148
   history of, 148
   desthiobenzyl-, 148
Penicillin and derivatives, collaborative monograph on, 148-149
Penicillin tertiary amine salts
   partition chromatography of, 169
Penicillins, 63, 96
Penicilloic acids, 148
Penniloaldehydes, 148
Penniloic acids, 148
Pentacyclic pre-metallized azo dyestuffs, 22
Pentacyclic triperpenoids, 107
Pentaerythritol and derivatives, 47
Pentalene, 201
Pentazenes, 228
Pentazines, 145
Pentitol anhydrides, 3
Pentitols, 2
Pentose sugars, 90
Peptidases
   value in study of protein structure, 154
Peptide antibiotics, 236
Peptide bond formation, 11
Peptide bonds, 176
   N-substituted amides of phosphorus and phosphoric acids in building of, 19
Peptide, synthesis of, 16
Peptides, 29, 30, 35, 56, 91, 93, 103, 130
Peptides and proteins, structure of, 97
Peptides (see also polypeptides)
   antimetabolic activity of, 157
   as antitumor agents, 157
   chromatography of, 169
   column chromatography of, 11
   conformational aspects of, 130
   of low molecular weight, 130
   complex formation with metallic cations, 11
   cyclic; with antibiotic action, 190
   degradation of, 93, 154
   depsi-, 24
   determination of constitution, 20
   deuterium exchange in, 136
   enzymatic reactions in analysis, 62
   identification by X-rays, 62
   mass spectroscopy and, 62
   molecular weight determination of, 130
   naturally occurring, 11
   of ordinary tissues, 154
   related to cystine, 136
   selective cleavage, 154
   separation of, 192
   sequence determination in, 176
   structure of, 79
   sulfur containing, 157
   symposium on, 136
   synthesis of, 10, 11, 18, 21, 23, 68, 79, 99, 130, 136, 175, 176
   synthesis via nitrophenyl ester method, 130
   synthesis; use of mixed anhydrides in, 136

   terminal amino acids in, 10, 99
   thiazoline and thiazolidine rings in, 166
   X-ray studies of, 10
Peracids, 35, 47, 87
Perchlorocyclopentanes, 51
Perfumes, 35, 61, 66, 231
Periodate oxidations of carbohydrates, 4
Periodic acid, analytical applications, 251
   oxidations with, 14
Perkin reaction, 63, 68, 85
Perkin, William, and family, 63, 74
Permutites, 169
Peroxidase, 212
Peroxide effect, 43, 233
Peroxide reactions, mechanisms of, 101
Peroxides, 70, 197
   alkyl, 250
   analysis of, 84
   of carbonyl compounds, 18, 22
   of oxonides, 22
   of ethers, 22
   organic, 240, 244
   organic; in polymerization, 252
   properties of, 171
   quantitative determination of, 20
   transannular, 44
Peroxy radicals, and hydrocarbon oxidation, 138
Persulfate oxidation, Elbs, 48
Pesticides, in tropical agriculture, 119
   pyrethrin, 54
Petrochemical industry, 241
Petrochemicals, 236, 93
Petroleum, 226
Petrochemical reactions, 242
Petroleum
   catalyst technology in, 6
   constituents of, 250
   hydrocarbons in, 75
   porphyrins in, 74
Petroleum acids and bases, 246
Petroleum hydrocarbons
   chromatography of, 169
   purification of, 150
Petroleum products, agricultural applications, 119
Petroleum technology, 119
Petroleum waxes, 150
pH, 197
   effect on dyes, 70
Pharmaceutical literature key, 119
Pharmaceuticals
   advances in (1946), 101
   advances in (1948), 101
Pharmacology, of amino acids and proteins, 241
Phase properties, 167
Phase solubility analysis, 83
Phenanthrene, 229
   diazo-, 146

Phenanthridine(s), 47, 51, 166, 182

Phenanthroline, 251

1,10-Phenanthroline, chelate complexes of, 49

o-Phenanthroline, synthesis of, 42

Phenanthroline indicators, 251

Phenazine dyes, 143

Phenazines, 145, 183

-Phenethylamines, 121

Phenol
synthesis via cumene, 21
oxidation, 175

Phenol-aldehyde condensations, 55

Phenol resins, 16, 17, 250

Phenoldehydrogenation, 175

Phenolic aldehydes, 227

Phenolic derivatives, 227

Phenolic disinfectants, with halogenated benzene nuclei, 18

Phenolic ketones, 227

Phenolic resins, 185, 243, 246

Phenolic substances, hydrogen bonds in, 186

Phenol-formaldehyde condensations, 22

Phenolphthalein, 72

Phenol tautomerism, 98

Phenols, 142, 226
alkylation by olefins, 21
structures and bactericidal properties, 43
industrial aspects, 43

Phenoplasts, 14, 56, 180, 184

Phenothiazine(s), 39, 49, 183

Phenothiazine dyes, 143

Phenoxathiin and its derivatives, 44

Phenoxazines, 143, 183

Phenoxazone dyestuffs, 20, 177

Phenylethanes, 225

Phenylhydrazones, of sugars, 187

Phenyl isothiocyanates, for identifying terminal amino acids, 154

Phenyl-lithium, 81

Phenylmethane dyes
di- and tri- ; steric effects in, 214

Phenylmethanes, 142, 225

β-Phenylserines, 35

Phenylthiohydantoins, in protein analysis, 130

Pheremones, 82

Phlorizin, 161

Phosgene, 40

Phosphagens, of marine animals, 131

Phosphatase, 32

Phosphate esters, 177
solvolysis, 137

Phosphates, 57

Phosphates, fluoro-, alkyl, 105
carbohydrate, 99
glycerol-, 137
hydrolysis of, 57
polyol, 137
sugar, 66
tetraalkyl-monothio-pyro-, 22

Phosphatides, 29, 35, 95, 254

Phosphine, 57
acids, 87
alkylene, 20
oxides, 52
tertiary, 20
triphenyl phosphine methylenes, 33, 175

Phosphite dihalides, triaryl-, 137

Phospho compounds, as new insecticides, 16

Phosphofluoridate, diiodopropyl-, 137

Phospholipids, 95
chromatography of, 57
in foods, 57
structure of, 44

Phosphonic acids, 51, 87

Phosphonic esters, 160

Phosphonitrilic compounds, 106

Phosphonitrilic halides, 9

Phosphoproteins, phosphorus links in, 11

Phosphorescence, 82, 197, 219, 222, 249

Phosphoric acid
amides, 24
anhydrides, 24
esters, 24, 160

Phosphorodiamidic anhydride
tetramethyl, oxidative demethylation of, 137

Phosphorus and its compounds, 228, 253

Phosphorus chemistry
nuclear magnetic resonance and infrared absorption studies, 128

Phosphorus compounds, 38, 89, 108
chemistry and metabolism of, 27, 28
demethylation of, 137
derived from salicyclic acid, 137
electron group polarizability and molecular properties, 129
metabolism of, 28
organic, 245

Phosphorus-fluorine compounds
toxic action of, 251

Phosphorus heterocyclics, 93

Phosphorus oxyacids, 96

Phosphorus, organic derivatives of, 100

Photochemical decomposition of aliphatic ketones in gas-phase, 46

Photochemical reactions
in simple ketones, 50
free atoms in, 81
leading to unstable species, 127
of anthracene, 163
sensitized by polyatomic molecules, 102

Photochemistry, 175, 220
biochemistry of photo-reactive systems, 216
of aldehydes, 107

    of anthracene with carbon tetrachloride, 172
    of 2-hexanone, 38
    of ketones, 46, 107
    of nucleic acids, 202
    of simple unsaturated systems, 9
    preparative, 251
    primary process in, 125
    study of free radical reactions by, 74
    under primitive earth conditions, 207
    use of EPR in, 202
Photochromic phenomena, 21
Photographic agents, 226
Photography, color, 69
Photolysis
    of aliphatic aldehydes and ketones, 107
    of biacetyl, 172
    of organic iodides, 168
    of trifluoromethyl iodide, 172
Photomagnetic phenomena, 21
Photometric analysis, 219
Photo nitrosation, of saturated hydrocarbons, 23
Photo-oxidation, 100, 189
    of anthracenes in solution, 172
    of organic iodides, 168
Photo-oxides of acenes, 229
Photoreception, 129
Photosensitization, with metal vapors, 125
Photosensitized reactions, of hydrocarbons, 105
Photosynthesis, 32, 91, 236, 243
    carbon in, 73
    in the far ultraviolet, 205
    isotope studies of, 174
Phototropy, 40
Phototoxic activity, 82
Phthalan, 181
Phthalazine(s), 47, 145, 182
Phthalic acids, tetrahydro, 51
Phthalideisoquinoline alkaloids, 122, 123
Phthalocyanin synthesis, isoindolenines in, 19
Phthalocyanine dyes, 15, 105
Phthalocyanines, 25, 63
Phycocyanins, 216
Phycoerythrins, 216
Physical aspects, of organic chemistry, 253
Physical chemistry, annual review of, 31
Physical constants
    of organic compounds; determination of, 140
Physical methods, in organic chemistry, 218
Physical organic chemistry, 31, 242, 243
Physical properties of chemical compounds, 119
    (two parts)
Physical properties, steric effects on, 215
Physico-chemical constants of organic compounds, 252
Physics, molecular, 61
Physochemical constants, 38

Physostigmine, synthetic analogs of, 195
Phytochemistry, Lynn index of, 251
Phytohormones, 174
Phytol, 41
α-, and β-Picoline, separation by V.P.C., 57
Phyto-polysaccharides, 135
Picene, 229
Picrines, 143
Pictet-Spengler synthesis, 87
Piezochromic phenomena, 21
Pigment, of cottonseed, 52
Pigments, 249
    carotenoid, 69
    of chloroplasts, 76, 252
    flavonoid, 76
    metal complexes in, 75
    of butterflies, 15
    of ommatin group, 81
    of ommin group, 81
    pyrrol, 143
    tetrapyrrol, 230
    visual, 68
Pinacol rearrangements, 100
Pinene, 159
Piperazine(s), 182
    in chemotherapy of filariasis, 126
Piperidine(s), 36, 181
    analgesics, 195
Plant alkaloids, 242
Plant chemistry
    in Australia, 103
    symposium on (1955), 234
Plant constituents, 241, 244
Plant glycosides, 246
Plant growth substances, 177, 212, 248
    (see also auxins)
Plant gums, 3, 63, 89, 187, 251
Plant heart venoms, 66
Plant hydrocolloids, 119
Plant steroids, 188
Plants
    constituents of, 39
    organic acids of, 27
Plasma proteins, fractionation of, 10
Plasticisers, 185
Plastics, 72, 251
    and coal, 54
    chemical structure, 54
    from acetylene, 54
Plastomers, 161
Platforming and hydroforming, 150
Platinum compounds, reactions with olefins, 22
Plexiglass, 72
Podophyllum, 68
Poisons
    Amanita mushroom-, 176
    arrow-, 15

glycosidic heart, 68
ivy, 72
mitotic, 81
proteins, 81
snake, 82

Polar displacement reactions, mechanism of, 102
Polar factors, in unsaturated compounds, 101
Polarimetry, 197, 219
   spectro-, 61
Polarization, 158
Polarographic analysis, development of, 13, 43
Polarography, 24, 83, 97, 107, 220
Polyacetylene compounds, naturally occurring, 19
Polyacetylenes, 91, 102
Polyacrylonitrile, 58
Polyalkylene sulfides, 102
Polyamides, 36, 184, 185, 243
   oligomers of, 20
Polyamineacetic acid chelating agents, 130
Poly-α-amino acids, 10, 11
Polycarboxylic systems, bridged, 49
Polycarbonates, 20
Polycyclic aromatic hydrocarbons, 49, 166
Polycyclic compounds, 143
   heterocyclic, 143
   stereochemistry, 162
Polycyclic hydrocarbons, 24
Polyenes, 17, 45
   stereochemistry of, 64
Polyepoxides, 19
Polyester resins, 57, 58
   cured, 23
Polyesters, 185
   aromatic, fibers from, 63
   oligomers of, 20
Polyethylene, 151, 185
Polyethylene polyamines, via cumene hydroperoxides, 172
Polyfructosans, and difructose anhydrides, 2
Polyhydric alcohol esters, 45
Polyhydroxy alcohols, 141
Polyketones, 226
Polymer chemistry, contributions of M.S. Kharasch, 233
Polymerization(s), 31, 36, 41, 98, 111, 221
   addition-, 99, 120, 125
   condensation, 46
   emulsion, 73
   free-radicals in, 75, 169
   Friedel-Crafts, 105
   ionic, chain, 17, 99, 184
   kinetics, 18, 36, 245
   linear, 74
   of acrylonitrile, 58
   of aldehydes, 97
   of alkenes, mechanism of, 6
   of alkyls, 51
   of dioxolanes, 17
   of ethylene, 36
   of olefins, by metal catalysts, 51
   of olefins, 6, 22
   of propene, 21
   of tetrahydrofuran, 25
   of unsaturated dioxolanes, 17
   of vinyl esters; stereospecific, 22
   radical, kinetics, 97
   via free radicals, 120, 169
   vinyl, 47, 75, 151
   with metal alkyls, 23
Polymerization catalysts, titanium compounds, 23
Polymerization reactions, theory and fact in, 17
Polymers, 105, 120, 189, 221, 231, 247
   (see also polymerization(s), macromolecules, high polymers)
   and organo-metallic compounds, 191
   analysis of, 185
   biological, 191
   block and branch, mixed, 18
   catalysts in synthesis of high-, 120
   chain degradation of, 191
   containing fluorine, 18
   co-ordination, 58
   degradation of, 58
      mechanism of (symposium), 234
   differential thermal analysis, 84
   effect of oxygen on, 31
   from isocyanates, 106
   gelatin and glue-, 105
   high energy radiation effects on, 129
   high molecular weight, 18, 125, 158, 169, 191
   hydrogen bonding in, 75
   infrared spectra of, 12
   isobutylene, 242
   isotactic, 58, 106
   light-scattering methods for, 13
   living, 106
   of p-xylene, 99
   open-chain and cyclic, 141
   protein, 185
   radiation chemistry of, 75
   recent advances in, 7
   semi-conducting, 58
   stereochemistry of, 94
   structure and properties, 120
   structure by X-ray studies, 72
   structure of, 75
   synthetic, 35, 203
   synthetic linear, 43
   thermally resistant, 24
   thermodynamic properties, 96
   vinyl, 56, 82, 180, 185, 251
Polymethylene, proton magnetic resonance in, 138
Polymorphism, 95
Polymyxin, comparison with "aerosporin", 126
Polymyxin-A, 126
Polynuclear complexes, formation in aqueous solution, 130
Polynucleotides, 132
Polyols, 135, 226
   acetols and ketols of, 3
Polypeptide chains in proteins, 67
Polypeptides, 23
   active, 61
   analytical methods, 193
   chain folding in, 170

cyclic, 157
dyeing of, 173
infrared structure analysis, 11
sequence studies in, 136
structure of, 60
synthetic pathways to naturally occurring, 103
which stimulate plain muscle (symposium 1955), 234

Polyphenyl substances, with fused or separate rings, 109, 225

Polyphosphates, synthesis, 137

Polyphosphoric acid, 9
as cyclizing agent, 18
as reagent in organic chemistry, 51

Poly reactions, 180

Polysaccharides, 135, 212, 253
alkaline degradation of, 5
animal, 135
bacterial, 2
blood-group, 2
constitution of, 40
from seaweeds, 4
from wood cellulose, 4
of gram-negative bacteria, 5
of mycobactericem tuberculosis, 2
methods in structural studies, 5
muco-, 54
related to gums and mucilages, 251
seaweed, 1
size and shape of, 3

Polysaccharides and gums, 253

Polysaccharides and their derivatives symposium volume (1959), 234

Polysulfides, ethylene, 109

Polysulfide polymers, 185

Polythionic acids, 70

Polyurethane resins, 15

Polyurethane foams, 59

Polyvalent iodine, organic compounds of, 44

Polyvinyl resins, 54

Pomeranz-Fritsch reaction, 87

Porphin dyes, 19

Porphyrin, biogenesis,

Porphyrins, 166, 253
formation and significance of, 103
in nature, 67
in petroleum, 74
ionization and coordination behavior, 108
uro-, 82, 155

Potentiometry, 197, 219

Pregnanes, desoxy at C-11, 232

Pressor activity, 187

Pressure reactions of organic gases, 204

Priestley lecture by F.G. Arndt, 236

Prins reaction, 48

Progesterones, 47, 174

Pro-oxidants, 225

Propane, 251

Propane-propylene equilibria, 171

Propene, polymerization, 21

Propenes
1,2-dibromo, 129
1,1,1-trichloro, 233

Propellants, 58

Properties
physical, of chemical compounds, 119 (two parts)

Propylene, 251

Protamines, 12, 154

Protein-protein interaction, 11

Protein structure, 8, 217, 253
function and biosynthesis, 11
X-ray analysis, 10, 11

Protein synthesis, role of nucleic acids in, 132

Proteins, 28, 29, 30, 34, 35, 54, 71, 72, 130, 141, 180, 242

Proteins and peptides, structure of, 97

Proteins and viruses, photochemistry of, 8

Protein(s), 10-11
as polymers, 185
amino acids in, 10, 82, 193
amphoteric properties, 125
analysis of, 10, 130, 193
arrangement of amino acids in, 11
biosynthesis, 12
cell structures and functions, 10
carbohydrate complexes, 11
chain folding in, 170
chemical determination of, 10
chemistry of, 27, 28
chromatography, 114, 169, 192
column chromatography of, 11
combinations with fatty acid anions, 169
complex formation with metallic cations, 11
complexes, 7
configuration in solutions, 108
conjugated, 172
continuity of, 205
counter-current distribution, 11
cross-linking in, 11
crystalline, 124
denaturation of, 10, 11
degradation of, 93
determination of constitution, 20
deuterium and ^{18}O exchange, 193, 217
dialysis of, 193
diffusion coefficients of, 11
dye binding methods, 193
electrophoresis of, 82, 236
enzyme reactions in analysis of, 62
fatty acid derivatives, 169
fibers, 10, 19, 254
food, amino acid composition of, 10
fluorescence of, 172
geometry of, 124
globular, 172
of glyco-, 10
groups, properties, 10
heme, 10
hormones, 10
hydrolysates, 55
infrared analysis of structure, 11
interaction with alkaline earth cations, 10
interactions with organic molecules, 172
interactions with synthetic detergents, 10
interatomic distances in, 43
131-Iodine-labelled, 127

iodine interaction, 50
iodo-, 11, 68
ion-exchange chromatography in urea buffers, 130
isolation, 122
isolation of biologically active, 193
labelled, 172
lyso-, 189
molecular weight determination of, 130
molecular shape and interactions, 172
molecular structure, 82
native, reactions with chemical agents, 70
nuclear magnetic resonance spectra of, 128
nucleo-, 10
optical rotation of, 193
partition chromatography, 154
peanut-, 11
peptide regions of identical structures in, 190
phospho-, phosphorus linkages in, 11
physical chemistry of, 172
physical research on, 81
plasma, fractionation of, 10
poisonous, 81
polarization of, 172
polarized ultra-violet light observations of, 170
polypeptide chains in, 67, 102
purifications of, 14
purified, amino acid composition of, 10
reactions with acids; effect of anions, 125
reactions with alkylating agents, 156
symposia volumes on, 234
reactions with formaldehyde, 10
reactions with mustard gas, 132
sequence analysis in, 193
serum, zone electrophoresis and, 12
simple substances related to, 11
size and shape of, 70
solubility measurements, 122
structural chemistry, 8, 217, 251, 253
structure of, 64
structure of Keratin-myosin, 89
structural, of cells and tissues, 10
study by partition chromatography, 132
sulfur chemistry of, 12
symposium and structures of, 154
synthesis of, 177
synthetic fibers from, 55
thiazoline and thiazolidine rings in, 166
of tumors, 64
terminal amino acids in, 10
the copper, 10
titration curves of, 193
ultraviolet absorption of, 17, 170
X-ray diffraction of, 124

sec-Propyl radicals, 170
Proteolytic activity, 133
Protium-deuterium exchange, 139
Protochlorophyll, 216
Proton magnetic resonance, 139
  in polyethylene and polymethylene, 138
Protons, tunnelling of, 186
Protoberberine alkaloids, 122
Protopine alkaloids, 122
Prototropic compounds, 40
Provitamins, 32
Provitamins A, 112
Pschorr synthesis, 50, 88
Pseudo acids, 124

Psicose, 3
Psychosis, chemical concepts of, 234
Psychotherapeutic drugs, 127
Phthalocyanins, electrical properties, 245
Pteridine, degradation products from L-casei factor, 125
Pteridines, 97, 107, 46, 67, 143
  and derivatives, 155
  biosynthesis, 190
  hydro-, 166
  synthesis of, 155
  symposium on, 154, 155
  ultraviolet absorption spectra of, 155
Pterins, 66
Pteroylglutamic acid, 112, 114
Purification, 196, 220
Purine nucleotides, 136, 212
Purines, 29, 90, 96, 155, 156, 177, 202
Purpurogenone, 137
Pyranes, 161, 229
Pyrans, 36, 96, 181
Pyrazines, 46, 145, 155, 182
Pyrazoles, 182, 230
Pyrazolones, 36
Pyrene, chrysene and picene, 229
Pyrethrins, 15, 54
Pyrethrolone, 59
Pyrethrum, 54
Pyridazines, 21, 145, 182, 230
Pyridine alkaloids, 121, 122
Pyridine and deuterated pyridines
  nuclear magnetic spectra of, 128
Pyridine, 22, 45, 93, 146
Pyridine and derivatives, 146
Pyridine and vitamin B_6, 105
Pyridine homologues, electronic spectra, 170
Pyridine nucleotide action, 103
Pyridine salts, synthesis with, 18
Pyridines, 181
  dihydro-, 36, 175
  enzymatic degradation, 166
  tetrahydro-, 36
Pyridoxal, 105
Pyridoxamine, 105
Pyrimidine, 182
Pyrimidines, 29, 41, 96, 107, 177, 202, 230, 231
Pyrimidine nucleosides, 5, 166
Pyrimidopteridines (dipyrimidopyrazines), 155
Pyrindine, 182
Pyrolysis
  of amine oxides, 88
  of dibenzyl, 171
  of hydrocarbons, 150
Pyrolytic cis elimination, 52
Pyrones, 47, 162, 181

Pyrylium salts, aromatic compounds from, 24
Pyrrocolines, 47
Pyrrole, 240
Pyrrole and derivatives, 230
Pyrrole pigments, 143
    tetra-, 230
Pyrroles, advances in the chemistry of, 15
Pyrrolidine alkaloids, 121, 122
Pyrrolizidine alkaloids, 20, 68, 103, 143, 175
Pyrrol, hydrogen bonding with, 186
Pyrrole, 181
Pyrylenes, di-, 45

Quadruple spectroscopy, chemical applications of, 103
Quantitative analysis
    by means of catalytic hydrogenation, 126
Quasi racemate method, 111
Quasi radicals, 18
Quaternary ammonium salts, carbon-alkylation with, 17
Quaternary bases, 166
Quaternized hydrazine compounds, 51
Quenching, 222
Quinandine, 182
Quinazoline alkaloids, 121
Quinhydrone, 18
Quinhydrone-like compounds, 18
Quinazoline, 182
p-Quinodimethane, its diradical, 168
Quinoid structure, related to lignin, 188
o-Quinol acetates, 176
8-Quinolinol, reactions of, 50
Quinoline, 45, 182
Quinoline alkaloids, 121, 122
Quinoline, iso-, 182
Quinolines, 44
    synthesis, 87
Quinolizidine alkaloids, 166
Quinolizines, 49
Quinols, some aspects of, 110
Quinone derivatives, of chemotherapeutic value, 82
Quinone derivatives, 18
Quinone-imides, 37
Quinone methines, and related compounds, 108
Quinones, 142, 226
Quinones
    as allergens, 64
    as carcinogenics, 64
    biological activity of, 69
    fungal, 137
    natural, 252
    redox potentials and structure, 96
Quinoxalines, 145, 182

Radiation
    as a synthetic tool, 57
    effect on alkylbenzenes, 159
    effect on fatty acids, 159
    effect on halogens, 159
    ionizing, 98
Radiation chemistry, 31, 171 (see also Radiolysis)
    of benzene and benzene-d_6, 171
    of organic solutes, 171
    of organic solutions, 50, 171
    of polymers, 75
    preparative, 21
Radiation damage, free radicals in, 179
Radical polymerizations
    kinetics and constitution of the polymers, 23
Radical reactions
    rate constants and concentration of intermediates, 49
    study of by competitive methods, 138
Radical substitution, in aromatic nuclei, 50
Radicals and related topics, 18
Radicals (see also Free Radicals)
    abstraction, 223
    addition of, 223
        to olefins, 96
    alkyl, 74, 175
    t-butyl, 170
    by decomposition of organic substances, 42
    diethylketone, 172
    electron spin resonance, 179
    formation in the gas phase, 179
    formation by radiation, 159
    formation in the solid phase, 179
    from acetone, 171
    in aqueous medium, 159
    in biological systems, 179
    in gaseous systems, 91
    methyl, 98
    reaction with aldehydes, 172
    radiation damage and, 179
    short-lived, 20
    spectra of, 179
    trapped, chemical and physical aspects of, 179
    trapping from the gas phase, 179
    trapping of, 179
    trichloromethyl, 171
Radioactive gases, 128
Radioactive isotopes, use of, 58, 71
Radioactivity, 220
Radiocarbon
    chemical applications of, 107
    natural, 30
Radiolysis (see also Radiation Chemistry)
    of alkyl benzenes, 159
    of fatty acids, 159
    of organic liquids, 171
Radio-opaque agents, chemical aspect of, 129
Radium, 159
Raman spectra, 37, 42, 158
    and infra-red spectra; theory, 254
    of fluoromethane, 165
    of hydrocarbons, 208
    theory of, 254
Raney nickel, uses of, 6
Rates of reaction, analysis based on, 126
Rauwolfia alkaloids, 18, 67, 68, 79
Reaction kinetics, 31, 32 (see also Kinetics)

Reaction mechanisms, 31, 63, 91, 105, 134, 180, 206, 221, 224
   in flames and detonations, 138
   electric effects on, 63
   study of, 204
   thermodynamic properties and, 98
   use of isotopes in, 36, 61
   use of nuclides in, 207
   quantum mechanics, 160

Reaction rates, 221
   use in analysis, 83
   equilibria and mechanisms, 242

REACTION(S) (See also Catalysis, Condensations, Kinetics, Rearrangements, and specific names and types of reactions such as photolysis, radiolysis, etc.)
   abstraction, by radicals, 223
   acetoacetic ester, 85
   acylation, 134
   addition, 14, 37, 42, 166, 233
     by radicals, 98, 223
     of halogens (thermal) to olefins, 96, 108
     of hydrogen to carbon-carbon bonds, 44
     to multiple bonds, 43
     to unsaturated hydrocarbons, energies of, 42
     steric effects in, 215
   1,3-additions, 43
   1,6-additions, 52
   aliphatic chlorination, 101
   alkylation, 43, 45, 75
   alkylation of aromatic amines, 20
     of aromatic hydrocarbons, 6, 47
     of phenols by olefins, 21
     of saturated hydrocarbons, 151
     reductive, 86
   alkyl polymerizations, 51
   amidomethylations, 21
   amination, 15, 85, 198, 199
   amine-catalyzed, kinetics, 124
   amines with nitrous acid, 105
   amino-aryl insertion, 157
   aminomethylation, 20
   ammonolysis, 43
   anomalous nitration, 46
   aromatic nucleophilic substitutions, 48
   aromatization in the bile acid series, 17
   arylation, homolytic, 51
   auto-oxidation, 16, 41, 49, 75
   atomic and free-radical, 252
   auto-oxidation of aldehydes, 16
   auto-oxidation of hydrocarbons, 47
   auto-oxidation of unsaturated compounds, 19
   base-catalyzed, 6
   Baeyer-Villiger oxidation, 88
   Bart, 85
   Bechamp, 85
   Beckmann, 41, 45, 88
   bimolecular, kinetics of, 41
   bimolecular substitutions, 56
   biological, 221
   biological oxidations and reductions, preparative, 14
   Bischler Napieralski, 87
   bridge, in amino acids, 19
   bromination, with N-bromo compounds, 47
   Bucherer, 85
   Cannizzaro, 85
   carbanionic, 162
   carbene, 23
   carbohydrate oxidations, 40
   carbon alkylation, with quaternary ammonium salts, 17
     with tertiary amines, 17
   carbonyl-olefination with phosphines, 23
   catalytic (see also catalysis), 180
     dehydrogenation, 150
     hydrogenation, 41
   chain-, 21, 190, 233
   Clemmensen, 23
   cleavage and formation of oxygen rings in sugars, 5
   competing, 221
   condensation of aromatic compounds with formaldehyde, 16
   condensation polymerization, 46
   condensations, 34, 160, 161
   Curtius, 41, 86
   cyclization, 37
   cyclodehydration, aromatic, 37
   Darzens, 86
   deamination, 15
   decarboxylation, 97, 198
   degradation of carboxylic acid salts, 50
   degradation of macromolecules, 23, 58
   degradation of polysaccharides, 8
   dehydrocyclization, 49
   dehydrogenation, 9, 15, 150, 169
   dehalogenation, 163
   demethylation, 137
   Demjanov, 88
   desulfurization, 3
   deuterium exchange in proteins, 217
   diazo coupling, kinetics of, 48
   diazotization, 54, 74
   Diels-Alder (Diene), 15, 24, 44, 67, 86, 151, 166, 171, 189
   dimerization in sunlight, 48
   displacement, 49, 50, 94, 160
   effected by microorganisms, 147
   Elbs persulfate oxidation, 48, 85
   electrochemical, 40, 90, 102
   electronic theory of, 41
   electrophylic substitution, 65, 166
   Favorskii (Favorsky), 34, 88
   Fischer-Tropsch, 6, 150, 244
   fluorination, 14
   formazan, 5
   formation of organic compounds on primitive earth, 205
   free radical (see Free Radicals)
   Friedel Crafts, 3, 34, 42, 49, 56, 86, 98, 105
   Fries, 43, 85
   gas phase, 41, 251
   Gattermann, 88
   Gattermann-Koch, 86
   Grignard, 3, 34, 38, 48, 87, 99, 102, 120, 248
   haloform, 42
   halogen-metal interconversion, 87
   halogenation of paraffin hydrocarbons, 41
   Herz, 51
   Hoesch, 86
   Hofmann, 41, 86, 88
   homogenous gas phase, 221
   Hunsdiecker, 50
   hydride-transfer, 52
   hydroacylation of unsaturated compounds, 101
   hydrogenation, 98
   hydrogenation, of alkylbenzenes, 105
   hydrogenation; catalytic, 73
   hydrogenation; mechanism of, 58
   hydrogenation; with Raney-catalysts, 14
   hydrogenation-dehydrogenation, 9
   hydrogenation and hydrogenolysis, 203
   hydrogenation of olefins; catalytic, vapor-phase, 49
   hydrogenations; with copper-chromium oxide catalysts, 15
   hydrogen addition to carbon-carbon bonds, 44
   hydroxylations, 9, 87
   hydroxylation of steroids, 61, 188
   in dyeing processes, 23
   in monolayers, 89
   ionic, 19
   half century of, 16

isomerization of alkanes, 6
isotopic exchange between $CH_3\cdot$ radicals and CH_4, 138
irreversible oxidation-reduction, 40
isomerization of -ketols, 37
isotopic exchange, 209
Japp-Klingemann, 88
keto-enol conversion, 17
kinetics of, 167
Kolbe-Schmitt, 51
Leuckhart, 86
listed by name, 252
Lobry de Bruyn-von Ekenstein, 5
Maillard, 5
Mannich, 20, 249
mechanisms of, 252
Meerwein, 16
Meerwein-Ponndorff-Oppenauer, 55
Meerwein-Ponndorff reduction, 14, 85
Metalation with organosodium compounds, 51
methylation; biological, 45
Michael, 88
Michaelis-Becker, with halogeno ketones, 137
"Name"-, 252
Nef, 49
ninhydrin, 52
nitration of saturated hydrocarbons, 19
nitrosation, 52
nucleophilic reactions of carboxylic acid derivatives, 52
nucleophilic substitutions, 72
occurring with Walden inversions, 72
of absolute asymmetric synthesis and asymmetric catalysis, 205
of aldehydes with amines, 43
of aliphatic acid chlorides, 49
of aliphatic hydrocarbons; mechanism of, 73
of alkali compounds, stereochemistry of, 21
of allylic compounds, 50
of aluminum chloride in organic chemistry, 252
of aluminum with carbon tetrachloride, 102
of amino acids with formaldehyde, 10
of aromatic compounds, 203
of benzimidazoles, 21, 65
of benzyne, 21, 65, 138, 204
of biuret, 50
of borontrichloride with organic compounds, 51
of carbohydrates, 2-5
of carbonium ions, 160
of carbon monoxide with oxygen, 138
of complex ions, 139
of cumene hydroperoxide and polyethylene polyamines (kinetics), 172
of cyanuric chloride with dimethyl formamide, 25
of diazomethane, 88
of diazonium salts on unsaturated aliphatic compounds, 16
of dienes, kinetics, 171
epoxide, mechanisms of, 52
of ethyl alcohol, 41
of ethyl diazoacetate, 106
of ethylene, 128
of ethylene derivatives with halogens, 44
of fluorosilicates with halides, 23
of free radicals, 140
of free radicals associated with oxidation of paraffins, 171
of free radicals in solution, 207
of free radicals; study by photochemistry, 74
of free radicals with aldehydes; in liquid phase, 172
of halogens and silver salts of carboxylic acids, 46, 88
of heterocyclic compounds with methylene groups, 16
of halogens with compounds containing carbonyl groups, 40
of hydantoins, 48

of hydrazines, 23, 103, 212, 228
of hydride transfer, 52
of hydrocarbons (see Hydrocarbons)
of hydrocarbons in electrical discharges, 43
of hydrocarbons in presence of aluminum chloride, 42
of hydrocarbons with H atoms, 172
of hydrogen and oxygen at room temperature, Hg-photo-catalyzed, 138
of hydroxylamines, 228
of ions in the gas phase, 111
of lead tetra-acetate with sugars, 5
of metals in liquid ammonia, 42
of methyl radical with hydrogen, 171
of monomeric styrenes, 47
of monosaccharides, 4
of ninhydrin, 52
of nitramines, 97
of nitrogen tetroxide with organic compounds, 45
of nitrous acid with amines, 105
of nitriles, 38, 47
of nitroalkanes, 3, 16, 44, 51, 73, 83, 96, 101
of non-enolizable ketones in sunlight, 46
of -OH groups in carbohydrates, 3
of olefins (see under Olefins)
of organic cations, 97
of organic compounds, 243
of organic compounds with fluorine, 46
of organic gases under pressure, 204
of organometallic compounds with solutions of metals in liquid ammonia, 48
of oxirane ring with Grignard reagents, 48
of oxy-anions in water solution, 103
of ozone and heterocyclic compounds, 61
of ozone with organic compounds, 61
of ozone with unsaturated compounds, 103
of paraffins and cycloparaffins, 151
of pentaerythritol and its derivatives, 47
of peroxides, 97, 204
of phosphate esters, 137
proteins with mustard gas, 132
of pteridines, 155
of 8-quinolinol, 50
of radicals; in polymerization, 168, 169
of radicals from acetone with oxygen, 171
of radicals from diethyl ketone with oxygen, 172
of resonance hybrid(s); prediction, 74
of saturated halides with olefins, 151
of sulfonamides; cleavage and rearrangement, 52
of sulfur with aliphatic and araliphatic compounds, 22
of sulfur dioxide and unsaturated hydrocarbons, 72
of terpene hydrocarbons, 41
of thiocyanogen, 86
of triphenylenes, 52
of unsaturated ketones with amino compounds, 45
of value in synthesis, 134
olefins from carbonyl compounds, via triphenyl phosphine methylenes, 23
ozonolysis of aromatic compounds, 61
of ylides, 16
olefin-aldehyde condensation, 48
Oppenauer oxidation, 14, 87
oxidation (see under Oxidation, also below)
oxidation of o-xylene, 151
oxidation of phenols, 175
oxidation, use of selenium oxide, 33
oxidation - reduction at the dropping-mercury electrode, 43
oxidation with permanganate; kinetics and mechanism, 51
oxidations by ferricyanide, 51

oxidations of unsaturated hydrocarbons, 151
"oxo", 33, 151
ozonization, 34, 43, 51, 61, 75, 103, 119, 175, 250
oxidation of liquid aldehydes, 49
oxymercuriation of alkenes, 127
Pechmann, 87
Perkin, 63,
periodate oxidations of carbohydrates, 4
Pictet-Spengler, 87
phenol-aldehyde condensations, 55
phenol-dehydrogenation, biochemical, 175
photochemical decomposition of aliphatic ketones, 46
photochemical addition of RSH to olefins, 207
photochemical, preparative, 251
polar displacement; mechanism of, 102
polymerization, radical catalyzed, 97
polymerization, theory and fact in, 17
polymer degradation, 58
Prins, 48
Pschorr synthesis, 88
pyrolytic cis elimination, 52
pyrolytic, of hydrocarbons, 150
radical reactions; kinetics and concentration of intermediates, 49
radical substitution in aromatic nuclei, 50
rapid, 221, 222
the redistribution-, 203
redox, 101
reduction of carbonyl compounds with complex hydrides, 20
reduction of diazo compounds, 21
reduction in metal-ammonia solutions, 96
reductions with lithium, 119
Reformatskii, 75
Reimer-Tiemann, 52
related to Perkin reaction, 85
reversible oxidation-reduction, 40
reviewed in "Organic Reactions", 85-88
ring closure, 37
ring expansions, 88
Rosenmund reduction, 86
Sandmeyer, 17, 46, 97
Schmidt, 86
Skraup, 87
selective oxidation with metals, 21
Serini, 64
solvolytic displacement at saturated carbon, 50
Sommelet, 87
stereochemical, control of, 102
Stobbe condensation, 87
Strecker degradation of amino acids, 48
substitution in aromatic ring systems, 41, 44, 69
substitution in furan types, 41
substitution of cyclohexanes, 160
substitution on substituted benzenes and pyridines; rules for, 16
substitution on aliphatic compounds, 14
sulfonation of aliphatic compounds, 15
sulfurization of unsaturated compounds, 46
sulfoxidation of alkanes, 16
thermal, involving free radicals, 138
thiocyanation; methods of, 14
transamination, 15
transannular elimination, 21, 103, 189
transannular substitutions, 189
transposition, 160
Ullman, 45
unsymmetrical 1,6-addition to conjugated systems, 52
vinyl polymerization, 151
von Braun, 87
Walden inversion, 159
with free radicals in solution, 43
with hydrogen fluoride, 15
with ozone, 175
Willgerodt reaction, 86
Wittig reaction, 9, 23, 38
Wohl-Ziegler reaction, 47
Wolff-Kishner reaction, 86
Wurtz-Fittig reaction, 57

Reactors, future developments of, 82

Reagents, organic
    analytical, 253
    for metals, symposium volume on, 234
    in inorganic analysis, 246
    specific and selective, 200

Rearrangement(s), 160
    acyl, in proteins, 154
    allylic, 50, 102, 159
    Amadori, 4
    aromatic, 97, 159
    Beckmann, 41, 45, 88
    benzidine, 89
    benzilic acid, 100
    benzpinacol, 73
    bornylic, 163
    Claisen, 43
    concepts in, 90
    Curtius, 41
    cycloammonium, 25
    Favorskii, 88
    fenchylic, 163
    gem-diphenylindanes, 160
    Hoffmann, 41
    homoallylic, 163
    intramolecular, 224
    i-steroid, 160
    involving oxygen radicals and cations, 47
    Lossen, 41
    molecular, 159, 203
    of acyl-lactones, 23
    of alkyl and aryl groups, 102
    of alkylcyclohexanols, 162
    of carboxylic groups, 24
    of dimethylaminocyclohexanones, 159
    of hydrofuranes, 160
    of hydropyrans, 160
    of ketones, 160
    of substituted benzpinacols, 73
    of sulfur compounds, 160
    pinacol, 100
    peroxide effects in, 43
    steric effects in, 215
    study by mass spectra, 119
    of sulfonamides, 52
    Wagner, 160

Recent progress
    in analytical chemistry (1958), 212
    in dyes (1958), 212

Recording, automatic, 218

Redistribution reaction, 203

Redox potentials, of quinones, 96

Redox reactions, factors for mechanism, 101

Reduction(s)
    biological, preparative, 14
    by complex metal hydrides, 241
    by lithium, 119
    by lithium aluminum hydride, 87
    by metal/amine solutions, 99
    Clemmensen, 23

  of aromatic diazo compounds with ethers, 1,3-
   dioxolanes and tertiary amines, 21
  of carbonyl compounds, 102

Reduction indicators
 formazans, 17
 tetrazolium salts, 17

Reductones, 60, 240

Reformatsky (Reformatskii) reaction, 75, 85

Refractometric analysis, in structure evaluation, 72

Refractometry, 197, 219

Relaxin, 174

Reimer-Tiemann reaction, 52

Reissert compounds, 50

Research
 in industry, 58
 modern methods, 58

Reserpines, 26

Resin acids, 47

Resins, 72, 251
 acrylic, 72
 alkyd, 185
 amino, 185
 analysis of, 84
 artificial, 229
 chelating, 58, 105
 complexing, 58
 cured polyester, 23
 epoxy, 58, 185
 formaldehyde, 16
 furan, 185
 ion exchange, 13, 78, 185
 natural, 185, 229
 phenolic, 16, 185, 250
 polyester, 57, 58
 polyurethane, 15
 thermosetting, 55

Resolution, of racemic α-amino acids, 11

Resolutions, 197

Resonance, 73, 180
 electron and nuclear, 13, 138
 in organic chemistry, 253
 nuclear and magnetic, 32
 significance of, 204
 theory of, 75, 206
 ultraviolet absorption spectra and, 46

Resonance energies, estimates for hydrocarbons, 170

Resonance hybrid, 74

Resonance structures, nitro-substituted molecules, 46

Respiratory stimulants, 122

Retardation, of vinyl polymerization, 47

Retene, 43

Retene and phenanthrene, 229

Retinene, cis-trans isomers, 133

Rhodamines, 181

Ribonuclease
 chromatographic purification, 154
 structure of, 130

Ribose, 3, 103, 202
 desoxy-, 202

Ribosomes, synthetic aspects of, 130

Ring closure reactions, 37

Ring index, the 248

Rings
 expansion of, 160
 medium sized, 162

Ring systems
 bridged, 141
 with urotropine structure, 18

Roger Adams, symposium, 211

Rosenmund reaction, 85, 86

Rotation
 about single bonds, potential energies of, 170
 hindered, 170
 internal, 247
 restricted, 101
 restricted, in ethane, 171
 of large organic molecules, 124

Rotatory dispersion, 37

Rotatory power, in steroids, 55

Rotenoids, 15

Rotenone, structure of, 41

Rotenone bearing plants, constituents of, 44

Rubber, 55, 61, 64, 141, 151, 251

Rubber(s)
 as polymer, 185
 chemistry of, 40
 halogenated, 248
 I.R. spectroscopy in, 58
 natural, 23, 245
 structure of, 54
 synthetic, 72
 synthetic, 33, 161

Rubrene, 229

Runge, Friedlieb, 74

Sabatier
 contribution to catalysis, 90

Saccharification, of wood, 3

Saccharases, yeast, 176

Saccharides (see sugars)

Saccharinic acids, 4, 57
 four-carbon-, 5

Salicylates, pharmacology of, 78

Salicyloins, 161

Saline water conversion,

Sandmeyer reaction, 17, 46, 97

Sapogenin(s), 142, 161

Saponines, 66

Saponins, neutral, 232

Sarmentogenin, 153

Schardinger dextrins, 4, 21

Schiemann reaction, 86

Schmidt reaction, 86

Schradan, biochemistry of, 56

Scilla Maritima, cardiotonic compounds of, 70

Scission
    of carbon-sulfur bonds,
    of sulfur-sulfur bonds, 52

Sclerothiorine, 161

Screening, 220

Seaweed polysaccharides, 4, 187

Sebacic acid, 60

Secretions, mammalian, 90

Selective hydrogenation of oils and fats, 245

Selenium,
    analogs of alcohols and phenols, 226
    organic chemistry of, 48

Selenium compounds, 2, 43, 198, 226, 227, 230

Selenium dioxide, 14, 33, 45

Selenium heterocycles, 230

Seleno-sugars, 2

Selenols, 226

Semicarbazides, 36

Semiconductors, organic, 106

Semimicro methods, 221

Semiquinone radicals, 124

Semiquinones, 42

Senecio alkaloids, 17, 121, 122

Sennosides, 66

Separation energies, of molecules, 82

Separation methods, 105, 177, 220

Sequestration of metals, 251

Serini reaction, 64

Serotonin, neurochemistry of, 127

Serum lipids, infrared spectroscopy of, 127

Serum proteins, zone electrophoresis, 12

Sesquiterpenes, 67, 103, 142, 228

Sesquiterpenoid lactones, 103

Sex hormones, 142

Sexogens, activity and structure, 210

Short-lived substances, absorption spectroscopy of, 170

Silanes, 13, 37
    aryl, 120
    tetrachloro-, 57

Silicate derivatives, alkanolamine, 120

Silicic acid(s), 5
    lipid chromatography on, 76

Silicic science, 242

Silico-organic compounds, 240

Silicon
    analysis of organic compounds of, 13
    orthoesters of, 105

Silicon compounds, 46, 49, 50, 58, 63, or 68, 72, 228, 245, 249
    nomenclature of, 72
    surface activity of, 58

Silicones, 18, 70, 185, 243, 249, 250, 253
    symposium volume on (1960), 234

Silk, structure of, 24

Silk fibroins, 11

Silks, artificial, 227

Silver perchlorate, aromatic molecular complexes with, 144

Silyl, organo, metallic derivatives of, 100

Single bonds, potential energies for rotation about, 170

Sinomenine, 121

Skraup synthesis, 87

Small-ring compounds, 103

Snake venoms, 68, 64

Soaps, 71
    and related products, 231

Sodium acetylides, 120

Sodium amide, cleavage of ketones, 88

Sodium nitromalonaldehyde, 52

Solanum alkaloids, 121, 123

Solubility, 196
    determination of, 218
    relations of hydrocarbons and other liquids, 208
    of proteins, 172

Solustibosan, 16

Solvent(s), 221
    purification for spectroscopic work, 19
    organic, manufacture, 212
    removal, 220

Solvolysis, 223
    effect on spectra, 164
    of octalines, 177
    of substituted carbinyl chlorides, 214

Sommelet reaction, 87

Sorbose, 3

Spatial structure of compounds, 15

Spectra (see also infra-red, Raman, microwave and ultraviolet spectra)
    absorption of
    alkylbenzenes, 46
    and structure, 33, 47
    electronic, 31, 111
    effect of solvolysis on, 164
    Hertzian, 33
    infrared, 167, 222, 224
    infrared, of fats, 95
    infrared, of heteroaromatics, 100
    infrared, of polymers, 12
    infrared, of serum lipids, 127
    infrared, of steroids, 112
    infrared, of acetylenes and olefins, 97
    infrared, of paraffins, 97
    microwave, 167
    molecular, 158
    of conjugated carbonyl compounds, 214
    of short-lived substances, 170
    pure solvents for, 19
    Raman, 167, 197, 222, 224
    Raman, of acetylene and olefins, 97
    Raman, of fluoromethane, 165
    Raman, of paraffins, 97
    U.V., of fatty acids, 95
    U.V., of trisubstituted benzenes, 165

Spectrophotometry, 219

Spectroscopy, 12, 31, 60, 140, 219, 222
    e.p.r. (electron-paramagnetic resonance), 202
    infrared, 105, 197
    infrared and Raman spectra, analytical applications, in petroleum industry; analysis, 83   150
    in study of free radicals, 91
    mass-, 196
    micro, 219
    micro-wave, 197, 219
    molecular electronic, 32
    nuclear magnetic resonance- (NMR), 202
    nuclear quadrupole, 139
    Raman, 167, 197, 222, 224
    ultraviolet, 167, 197, 222, 224
    vibrational, study of rotational isomerism by, 12
    vibration-rotation, 32
    visible, 167, 197, 222, 224

Spectropolarimetry, 61

Sphingosine, 103

Spirans, 229

Spiro compounds, 141

Spiropyrans, 47

Spirostano glycosides, 232

Spot test analysis, 105, 189

Squalene, 157
    synthesis of all-trans, 188

Stains
    formazans, 17
    tetrazolium salts, 17

Starch and derivatives, 2, 8, 21, 40, 56, 64, 73, 89, 122, 204, 243, 249

Starch
    biological transformations, 132
    colloid chemistry of, 250
    constitution, synthesis and degradation of, 67
    fractionation of, 2
    X-ray analysis, 227

Starch esters, 2

Starch gels, zone electrophoresis in, 12

Starch industry, 245

Starch nitrate, 5

Starch products, 227

Stereochemical control of reactions, 102

Stereochemical conventions, historical aspects of E. Fischer's, 2

Stereochemical correlations, 133
    and quasiracemate method, 111

Stereochemical problems, 60

Stereochemical research, 102

Stereochemistry, 35, 36, 37, 38, 41, 65, 70, 78, 94, 160, 162, 163, 180, 189, 206, 223, 248
    bases of, 89
    and crystallography, 94
    and heterogeneous catalysis, 51
    and hemolytic-processes, 94
    and reaction kinetics, 94
    and spectral properties, 94
    application of deuterium isotope effect in, 129
    in carbonium ion reactions, 160
    in high polymers, 94
    nomenclature, 111
    of α-acyl-cycloalkanones, 57
    of additions, 163, 215
    of alkali compound reactions, 21
    of alkaloids, 56
    of alicyclic hydrocarbon, 225
    of alkyldiphenyls, 214
    of amino acids, 10
    of β-amino acids, 157
    of bicycloheptanes, 163
    of bicyclohexanes, 163
    of bicyclo(3, 3, 0)-octane, 162
    of bimolecular substitution reactions, 56
    of C-20 steroids, 153
    of carbon compounds, 140
    of carbohydrates, 100
    of carotenoids and diphenylpolymers, 45
    of catechins, 166
    of complex compounds, 94
    of cyclic carbohydrate derivatives, 4
    of cyclohexane, 98, 105
    of diphenyls and analogous compounds, 41, 214
    of displacements at unsaturated centers, 94
    of electrophilic substitution, 111
    of flavans, 166
    of group VI$_B$ elements, 99
    of heterocyclic reactions, 163
    of homolytic substitution, 111
    of hydrogen bond, 94
    of labile compounds, 89'
    of metal ammines, 101
    of nucleoside synthesis, 156
    of oses, 39
    of polycyclic systems, 162
    of polyenes, 64
    of salicyloins, 161
    of terpene biosynthesis, 133
    of three-ring carbonyl compounds, 103
    specification of assymetric configuration, 65

Stereoisomers, 102
    nomenclature, 56

Stereoisomerism, 74, 203
    and biological action, 78
    of cyclohexane derivatives, 49
    of hydrindanes and hydrindanones, 65

Stereospecific catalyses, 20

Stereospecific polymerization
    of alpha-olefins, kinetics of, 6

Stereospecific reactions, notations for, 102

Steric effects
    across single bonds, 65
    and basicity of aromatic hydrocarbons, 214
    and mesomerism, 94
    and ultraviolet absorption spectra, 214
    front, back and internal strains, 102
    calculation of magnitude of, 215
    in azo and indigo dyes, 136
    in conjugated systems (symposium), 214
    in organic chemistry (coll. volume on), 215
    quantitative theory of, 101
    separation of from polar and resonance effects in reactivity, 215

Steric factors
    in drug action, 133
    in immunochemistry, 94

Steric hindrance, 96, 99, 224
    in solids, 72
    to planarity in dye molecules, 47

Steric rearrangements, 159

Sternutators, 42

Steroid alkaloids, 71
    holarrhena, solanum and veratrum group, 123

Steroid antibiotics, 236

Steroid compounds, with progestational activity, 128

Steroid dehydrogenases, 213

Steroid hormones, 29
    analysis for, 254
    non-benzenoid, 112
    symposium (1950), 234

Steroid stereochemistry, 207, 212

Steroid saponins, 142

Steroidal alkaloids, 66, 98

Steroidal olefins, trisubstituted characterization, 153

Steroidal sapogenins, conversion to 11-oxygenated steroids, 153

Steroids, 28, 33, 34, 37, 75, 81, 82, 90, 111, 153, 203, 206, 210, 240, 245, 251
    (see also hormones and individual listings)
    action of X-rays on, 153
    and cortisone, 113
    A-nor-, 163
    aromatization of A-ring in, 232
    characterization by spectroscopy, 210
    chemistry of, 27, 28, 76
    complete synthesis of natural, 17
    of the ergosterin type, 15
    of progesterone series, 47
    cortical, 64
    desoxypregnanes, 232
    esters, 114
    ergosterol, 153
    excretion of, 210
    estradiol, 15

    C-21, from plants, 188
    16-hydroxylated, 210
    hydroxylation in position 9, 188
    hydroxylation of, 61
    infrared spectra and structure of, 107
    introduction of the 11-keto function into, 153
    in marine organisms, 131
    in proteins, 251
    I.R. spectroscopy of, 57
    isotopic, 210
    17-ketogenic, determination of, 13
    11-keto, 153
    17-keto, determination of, 13
    metabolism of, 29
    microbiological synthesis, 210
    11-oxygenated, 210
    17-oxogenic, determination of, 13
    17-oxosteroids, determination of, 13
    partition chromatography of, 50
    progesterones, 47, 174
    radioactively-labeled, 112
    relation to aromatic carcinogens, 93
    status of studies (1960), 26
    stereochemistry of, 17
    steric aspects of biosynthesis, 133
    structure by infrared spectroscopy, 112
    synthesis of adrenal cortical-, 210
    synthesis of, 81
    their transformation into aromatic compounds, 14
    total synthesis, 24, 93, 107
    ultraviolet absorption spectra of, 49
    unsaturated, 15

Sterol alkaloids, 232

Sterol research, history of, 24

Sterols, 35, 82, 89, 95, 112, 157, 229, 232
    chemistry of, 27
    chromatography of, 76
    of invertebrates, 131

Stimulants (see also alkaloids)
    respiratory, 122
    uterine, 122

Stobbe condensation, 87

Strain theory, 225
    in alicyclic compounds, 203

Strains, front, back, internal (FBI), 102

Streaming bifrefringence, 219

Strecker degradation, of amino acids, 48

Streptomycin, 2, 56, 78

Streptomycin problem, chromatography in, 125

Strophanthus glycosides, 78

Structural analysis
    methods in, 81

Structural chemistry, 19, 21
    radioactivity applied to, 209
    theory, 75, 91

Structural theory, Butlerov and, 75

Structure and chemistry, 240

Structure-activity
    relations, 55, 56, 79, 251
    in β-haloethylamine adrenergic blocking agents, 195

Structure
    and isotopic exchange, 158
    and living matter, 61
    and odor, 201
    and organo-leptic quality, 201
    determination by reduction, 99
    determination of, 40
    direct determination of, 107
    molecular, 71, 72, 73
    of drugs, 74
    of molecules and crystals, 248
    of polymers, 72
    protein, by X-ray diffraction, 10

Structure determination
    by dipole moments, 44
    by electron and X-ray diffraction, 208
    by infrared intensity, 127
    by nuclear magnetic resonance, 109
    by physical methods, 109

Strychnine, 93, 189

Strychnos alkaloids, 16, 37, 69, 200, 121, 122, 165

Styrene, monomers and polymers, 185

Styrene double bond, reactivity toward free radical attack, 169

Styrenes
    reactions, 47
    substituted-, 47

Sublimation, 221

Substituted benzenes
    infrared spectra of, 170
    vacuum ultraviolet absorption spectra of, 170

Substitution, 14

aromatic nucleophilic, 48, 99
aromatic, steric effects in, 214
at elements other than carbon, 244
electrophilic, 70, 166
homolytic, 223
in allylic compounds, 50
in aromatic systems, 40
in benzene nucleus, 44, 48
in furan derivatives, 41
nucleophilic, 70, 223
radical; aromatic, 50
studies with isotopes, 21
at saturated carbon; steric effects in, 215

Substitution reactions, 90
of the aromatic ring, 69

Succinic acid, 34

Sucrose
enzymatic synthesis, 3
relation to melezitose, 4
structure, 2

Sugar
aconitic acid from, 3
industrial applications, 212

Sugar cane, 55

Sugar epoxides, 100

Sugar metabolism
syntheses of intermediate products of, 21

Sugar nitrates, 4

Sugar phosphates, 66

Sugar products, color and turbidity of, 4

Sugars, 68 (see also carbohydrates and specific entries)
amino, 3, 5, 20, 70, 177
2-amino-deoxy-, 5
anhydro-, 2
benzyl ethers, 4
biochemical reductions with, 3
configuration of, 40
2 and 3-deoxyribose, 202
determination on glass fiber paper, 24
3,6-didesoxyhexoses, 25
enzymatic synthesis of, 3
formation and cleavage of oxygen rings in, 4
hydrazone and osozone derivatives, 2
methyl and phenyl glycosides, 4
of cardioglycosides, 187
phenylhydrazone derivatives of, 187
thio- and seleno-, 2

Sugars and derivatives
separation by partition chromatography, 169

Sugars and polysaccharides, 247

Sulfamic acid, 43

Sulfamide, 43

Sulfanilamide, 72

Sulfanilamide derivatives
structure and chemotherapeutic activities of, 43

Sulfenamides, 46, 198

Sulfenic acids, 46, 198

Sulfenyl chloride, trichloromethane-, 51

Sulfenyl compounds, 46

Sulfide, β, β'-dichlorodiethyl-, 42, 132
(see also mustard gas)

Sulfides, 198
di-, 198
ethylene, 198
poly-, 198

Sulfinic acids, 198
preparation of, 48

Sulfochlorination, 198

Sulfonamides, 248
cleavage and rearrangement of, 52

Sulfonamide, derivatives of pteridines, 155

Sulfonation,
of arenes and haloarenes, 86
of aromatic hydrocarbons, 157

Sulfones, 198

Sulfonic acid derivatives, as moth repellants, 61

Sulfonic acid esters, 198

Sulfonic acid halides, 198

Sulfonic acids, 198
lignin-, 69

Sulfonic esters, of carbohydrates, 3

Sulfonium compounds, 198

Sulfonyl group, 34

Sulfonylthioureas, 48

Sulfonylureas, 48

Sulfoxides, 198

Sulfoximines, 198

Sulfur
analogs of alcohols and phenols, 226
analogs of dioxanes, 182
inorganic chemistry of (symposium), 139
organic chemistry of, 41, 252
organic compounds of; biological aspects, 63
reactions with araliphatic and aliphatic compounds,
removal of, with Raney nickel, 3   22
bivalent chemistry of, 249
of proteins, 12

Sulfur compounds, 198 (see also thio- and specific entries)
analysis of, 83
antifungal, 245
chemistry and metabolism of, 27, 28
cleavage of carbon-sulfur bonds in, 48
metabolism of, 28
natural, 82
nomenclature of, 198
organic, 203
rearrangements of, 160
related to alcohols, 140

Sulfur-chain compounds, structures of, 9

Sulfur-containing compounds
amino acids, 16
heterocycles, 230
peptides, 157

Sulfur derivatives, acidic, 227

Sulfur dioxide
reactions with unsaturated hydrocarbons, 72
versatility as catalyst

Sulfur dyes, 45, 143
constitution of, 16

Sulfur-fluorine compounds, 9
Sulfur-nitrogen compounds, 199, 228
Sulfur outer shell, expansion of, 52
Sulfur-sulfur bond, scission of, 52
Sulfuric acid, organic compounds in, 98
Sulfurization of unsaturated compounds, 46
Sultams, 49
Sultones, 49
Suprarenal hormones, 60, 114
Surface active agents, 125
Surface chemistry, 122, 236
    of cells, 236
Surface coatings, 54, 56
Surface films, 167
Surface phenomena, in fertilization, 177
Surface tension, 196, 218
Surfaces, study by isotopes, 180
Symposium
    on antibiotics and mould metabolites, 137
    on aromatic chemistry, 138
    on chemistry of coordinate compounds, 144
    on electron and nuclear resonance (1958), 138
    on free radicals in the gas phase, 137
    on inorganic chemistry of nitrogen, 138
    on inorganic chemistry of sulfur, 139
    on phosphoric esters and related compounds, 137
    on stability constants, 137
Synthesis
    lethal, 217
    involving metal carbonyls, 139
    of acetylenes
    of nucleotides, 30
    principles of
Synthetic analgesics, 244
Synthetic dyes, 246, 253
Synthetic fibers, 56, 60
Synthetic photochemistry, problems relating to, 17

Tables, anti-composition, 56
Tagatose, 3
Tanning, physical chemistry of, 173
Tanning agents, 241, 252
    ellagic, 68
Tanning processes, 231, 242
    protein-chemical aspects of, 10
Tannins, 65
    and tanning agents, 241
    natural, 19, 42
Tartaric acids, 109
Taurobetaine, 131
Tautomerism, 54, 75, 98, 111, 189
    in heterocyclic mercaptans, 166
Tea, 55
Tellurium compounds, 198, 226

Temperature, measurement of, 218
Terephtalic acid, 24, 59
Terpene, 81
Terpene hydrocarbons
    nomenclature, 119
    thermal reactions of, 41
Terpenes, 15, 53, 63, 73, 157, 204, 225, 250, 251
    and steroids, 144
    biogenesis of, 64
    conformation of, 37
    constituents of essential oils, 60
    di-, 67
    in gorgonians, 131
    physical approach to structure, 212
    sesqui-, 99
    steric aspects of biosynthesis, 133
    tri-, 28, 66, 176
        nomenclature of, 111
    tri-tetracyclic, 67, 98
        biogenesis of, 103
        butyrospermol, 103
    theory in, 206
Terpenoids, 141, 147
    di-, alkaloids, 123
    di-, 52, 96, 142
    tri-, 92, 142
Terphenyls, 51 (see Hydrocarbons, polycyclic)
Terramycin, 78, 126 (see Antibiotics)
Tertiary amines
    reduction of diazo compounds with, 21
Testosterone, (see Steroids, Hormones)
    19 nor-17-ethynyl-, 128
Tetrazines, 145, 228
Tetrazoles, 46
Tetrazolium salts, 17, 50, 74
Tetronic acids, 100
Textile chemistry in 1948, 101
Textile fibers, 194
Textiles
    radiation and high-temperature behavior of, 129
Theoretical chemistry, 58
    in Russia, 74
Theoretical organic chemistry, 40, 93, 101, 242, 236
Theories, modern
    of organic chemistry, 253
Therapeutics, 55
Thermal analysis, 196
Thermal decomposition (see also Pyrolysis)
    of hydrocarbons, 171
Thermal diffusion, 220
Thermal reactions, of free-radicals, 138
Thermal stabilization, of nylon fibers, 129
Thermal stability, and aromatic character, 24
Thermochemistry, 31, 164
    of alkoxyl radicals, 52
    of fluorocarbons, 111
Thermochromic phenomena, 21

Thermodynamic equilibria, in hydrocarbons, 208
Thermodynamic methods, 196
Thermodynamic properties, 98, 167
    of formic acid, 48
    of high polymers, 96
    of the elements, 119
    of organic compounds, 244
Thermodynamics, 31
    of addition polymerization, 99
    of fluorocarbons, 111
    of hydrocarbons and related substances, 250
    of nitromethane, 51
Thermoplasts, 20
Thiadiazine, 230
Thialdines, 230
Thials, 46
Thiapyrans, 181
Thiapyrones, 181
Thiazines, 143, 183
Thiazoles, 87, 182
    card catalog of, 249
    in industry and medicine, 54
Thiazolidine rings, in peptides and proteins, 166
Thiazolidines, 149
Thiazoline rings, in peptides and proteins, 166
Thioamides, 34, 228
    iso-, 34
Thiocarbonates, of carbohydrates, 5
Thiocarbonyl group, 103
Thiochromans, 181
Thioctic acid, 26
Thiocyanates, 54
Thiocyanation, methods of, 14
Thiocyanogen, 86
Thiocyanogen compounds, 14
Thioethers, 9, 198
Thioimides, 228
Thiol acids, 198
Thiol aldehydes, 198
Thioketones, 198
Thiolsulfinic acid esters, 198
Thiolsulfones, 198
Thiols, 226
    o-aminoaryl-, 51
Thionaphthene, 181
Thiones, 46
Thiophene, 70, 73, 145, 181, 252
    dibenzo, 181
Thiophene compounds, 73, 145
    biologically active, 77
Thiophenes, 87
    as carcinogens, 111
    condensed, 111
    tetrahydro, 87
Thiophenols, 198

Thiosemicarbazides, as antitubercular drugs, 26
Thiosugars, 2
Thiourea, use in separating paraffins, 150
Thioureas, 49
Thyroid gland, 89, 126
Thyroid hormones, 74, 113, 174
Thyroid stimulating hormones, 113
Thyroxine, 55, 66
    its formation in iodinated proteins, 126
Tiffenau-Demjanov ring expansions, 88
Tiglic acids, 50
Tin compounds, 52, 106, 120, 127 (
    (see also organometallics)
Tissue lipids, infrared studies of, 127
Titanium compounds, 120, 121
    as polymerization catalysts, 23
Titanium, orthoesters of, 105
Toad venoms, 15, 66, 142
Tobacco
    alkaloids of, 44
    constituents of, 52
Tobacco mosaic virus
    structural aspects of, 12
Tobacco smoke
    constituents of, 52
Toxic principle of ivy, 72
Toxicity of phosphorus and fluorine compounds, 212, 251
Tracers (see Isotopes, Labeled compounds and specific entries)
Transamination, 15
Transannular effects
    in elimination and substitution reactions, 103
    in paracyclophanes and related compounds, 103
Transannular elimination, studies with isotopes, 21
Transannular interactions, nitrogen-carbonyl, 103
Transannular peroxides, 44
Transference numbers, 219
Transition metals (see also organometallics)
    acetylides of, 23, 139
    alkyl and aryl derivatives of, 103
    alkyls and aryls of, 50
    arene complexes of, 204
    complex acetylides of, 23, 139
    complexes, infrared spectra of, 200
    hydride complexes of, 24
    organic compounds of, 103, 110
1,2,4-Triazine derivatives, as tuberculostatics, 18
Triazines, 56, 145
    aromatic, 48, 228
    diamino, 56
s-Triazines, 146
Triazoles, vicinal, 47
Trichloromethyl radicals
    interactions with cyclohexene
    kinetics, 171
Triethanolamine, 240

Trifluoroacetic anhydride, and related compounds, 50
Trifluoromethyl group, in medicinal chemistry, 77
Trifluoromethyl iodide, photolysis of, 172
Trimethoxyboroxine, fire extinguisher, 120
Trimethylene oxide, 181
Trimethylsulfonylmethane, 37
Triphenylenes, 52
Triphenylmethane derivatives, 33
Trityl ethers, of carbohydrates, 2
Trivalent carbon, 16
Tropane alkaloids, 61, 121, 122, 177
Tropane derivatives, 18
Tropical agriculture, pesticides in, 119
Tropism, of the mimosas, 176
Tropolene, and its derivatives, 17
Tropolone(s), 35, 49, 97, 190, 201
    natural, 68, 177
Tropone compounds, pharmacology of, 79
Troponoids, 68
    natural, 177
Tropones, 49, 201
Tropylium, 223
Tropylium ion, 20
Trypanocides, 55
Trypsin, 154
Trypsinogen, 154
Tryptophane, syntheses of, 16
Tryptophanes, degradation products of, 177
Tuberculosis, chemotherapy of, 17, 26, 73, 78, 89, 212
D-Tubocurarin, synthetic analog of, 176
Tumors
    chemistry of, 81
    mammary, steroids and - , 210
    proteins of, 69
Turanose, 2
Tythricine, 109

Ullmann synthesis of biaryls, 45
Ultracentrifuge, determinations with, 218
Ultramicro-chemistry, 80
Ultra-sonic waves, 175, 197
Ultraviolet absorption spectra, 17, 167, 197, 204
    (see also Spectra)
    of anthracene derivatives, 47
    of aromatic amino acids in proteins, 170
    of aromatic compounds, 241
    of aromatic hydrocarbons, 44, 241
    of estrogens, 210
    of fatty acids, 44, 95
    of fluorinated toluenes, 170
    of hydrocarbons, 150, 208
    of nitro compounds, 46
    of polycyclic heterocyclic compounds, 146
    of proteins, 17, 170
    of pteridines, 155
    resonance structure and, 46
    of steroids, 49
    of substituted benzenes and naphthalenes, 165, 170
    steric effects and, 214
Ultraviolet light (see Photochemistry)
    chemical action of, 240
Ultraviolet spectroscopy
    hydrocarbons as solvents for, 19
Unsaturated compounds, 203
    (see also Olefins, Hydrocarbons and specific entries)
    aliphatic, action of diazonium salts on, 16
    hydroarylation of, 101
    free-radical nature of, 70
    halogen addition to, 96, 108
    ozonization of, 103
    polar factors in, 101
Unsaturated fatty acids, 56
Unsaturated hydrocarbons
    electronic transitions in, 46
    energetics of additions, 42
    isomerization of, 44
    reactions with sulfur dioxide, 72
Unsaturated ketones
    derivatives with amino compounds, 45
    spectroscopic studies of, 19
Unsaturated steroids, synthesis of, 15
Unsaturated systems, 9
Unstable species (see also Free Radicals)
Urea
    acetaldehyde condensation products, 82
    addition products, 16
    herbicides, 58
    inclusion compounds of fatty acids, 95
    isolation from natural sources, 74
    use in separating paraffins, 150
Ureas, methyl
    hydrogen bonds in, 186
Ureides, glycosyl
Urethan elastomers, synthesis of, 25
Uridine nucleotides, 156
Uroporphyrins, 82, 155
Urothione, 155
Urotropine structure, ring systems with, 18
Uterine stimulants, 122

Valence
    electronic concepts of, 204
    index of free, 158
    theory, 154
    Kekule's
    status (1941), 89
Valency, 248 (see also chemical affinity)
van der Waals-London energies, 159
Vapor phase chromatography (see Chromatography)
Vapor pressure, 196, 244
    determination of, 218
Vasopressins, 187, 174

Vegetable drugs, 78, 236

Vegetable oils, dictionary of, 246

Venoms (see also Poisons and specific entries)
    heart, 15, 66
    from plants, 15
    of snakes, 64, 68
    of toad, 15, 66

Veratramine, 175

Veratrum alkaloids, 99, 102, 121, 123

Vibrational energy transfer
    from collisional deactivation of simple molecules, 127

Vibrational spectroscopy
    study of rotational isomerism by, 12

Vibrations and electronic transition, 125

Vinyl acetate, monomeric and polymeric, 57

Vinylacetylene, 16

Vinyl compounds, 38

Vinyl esters, stereospecific polymerization of, 22

Vinylmagnesium compounds, 38, 163

Vinylmetallic compounds, 204

Vinylogy, principle of, 42

Vinyl polymerization, 75, 151
    inhibition and retardation of, 47

Vinyl polymers, 56, 82, 180, 251
    reaction mechanism of the formation of, 82

Vinyl, polymers and copolymers, 185

Violets, odoriferous compounds from, 66

Virus infection, chemotherapy of, 78

Viruses, 75, 211
    photochemistry of, 8
    tobacco mosaic, 12

Viscosity, determination of, 218

Visual processes, 133

Vitamin A, 20, 37, 41, 54, 60, 63, 90, 105, 112
    constitution and activity of, 16
    determination of, 78
    labelled, 113
    recent results in, 25
    synthesis and properties of, 25, 67

Vitamin B_6, 66, 105, 113

Vitamin B_{12}, 38, 58, 63, 68, 78, 102, 107, 110, 113, 114, 132, 143, 156, 251
    determination of, 13
    group, 26
    X-ray analysis of, 68

Vitamin C, 41

Vitamin D, 54, 67, 68, 176, 232

Vitamin D_3, total synthesis, 232

Vitamin E, 113

Vitamin K_2, 22

Vitamin P, 112

Vitamin research, history of, 24

Vitamins, 8, 33, 35, 43, 54, 72, 73, 109, 112-4, 236, 250, 252, 192,
    antihemorragic, 109
    antirachitic, 25
    as constituents of enzymes, 60
    B_2-complex, 54
    biochemistry of the B group, 254
    chemistry and technology, 253
    of the B-group, 89
    of the D-group, 91
    structure and activity, 33

Vitamins B, 71, 143

Vitamins K, 22, 44, 109, 113

Vomicine, 93

von Braun reaction, 87

Vulcanization, 122

Vulkollan, 17
    synthesis of, 25

Wagner rearrangement, 160

Walden inversion, in nucleophilic substitution, 159

War gases, new developments in the chemistry of, 48

Water repellants, alkyl methoxysilane, 120

Wave mechanics, 91, 167

Waxes, 95, 105

Weighing, 218

Willgerodt reaction, 86

Willstatter, memorial lecture, 90

Wittig reaction, 9, 23, 38

Wohl-Ziegler reaction, 47

Wolff-Kishner reduction, 86

Wood, 64
    biochemistry of, 188
    chemistry of, 240
    carbonization, 227

Wood cellulose, polysaccharides from, 4

Wood chemistry, 60, 242, 248, 250, 252, 253
    symposium volume (1952), 234

Wood extractives, 56

Wood oils, 241

Wood saccharification, 3

Wool, 134
    selective absorption of optical antipodes by, 173
    wax, 97, 253

Wurtz-Fittig reaction, mechanism of, 57

Xanthenes, 181

Xanthones, 181

Xanthydrols, 181

Xanthylenes, di-, 45

Xanthylium salts, 181

X-ray, 197

X-ray analysis, 84, 105
    of aminoacids and peptides, 10
    of carbohydrates, 43
    of molecular structure, 57
    of polymer structure, 72

of starch, 227
of vitamin B_{12}, 68

X-ray crystallography
of biochemical substances, 28, 29
of penicillin, 148
of sterols, 112

X-ray diffraction, 208, 167
in liquids, 40
of proteins, 193
protein structure by, 10

X-ray microscopy, 219

X-rays, 224
action on indole, 159
action on steroids, 153
determination of conformations with, 25
identification of peptides by, 62
study of high polymers, 180
study of plastics with, 54

Xylan, 3

o-Xylene, oxidation to phthalic anhydride, 151

p-Xylene, 99

Ylid, reactions, 16
Ylides, 16

Zinc compounds, biogenic, 20

Zirconium, orthoesters of, 105

Zone electrophoresis, 11, 12, 13, 172
of carbohydrates, 4

ADDRESSES OF PUBLISHERS

Academic Press Inc.
111 Fifth Avenue
New York 3, N.Y.

Akademie-Verlag, G.M.B.H.
Leipziger. Str.
Berlin, W.1.
Germany.

American Association for the
    Advancement of Science
1515 Massachusetts Avenue, N.W.
Washington 5, D.C.

American Book Company
55 Fifth Avenue
New York 3, N.Y.

American Chemical Society
1155 16th Street, N.W.
Washington 6, D.C.

American Petroleum Institute
1155 16th Street, N.W.
Washington 6, D.C.

E.J. Arnold & Son, Ltd.,
Butterley Street
Leeds 10 - England.

Edward Arnold (Publishers) Ltd.,
41 Maddox Street
London, W.1. - England.

The Athlone Press of the
University of London
2 Gower Street
London, W.C.1. - England.

Baillière, Tindall & Cox Ltd.,
7 & 8 Henrietta Street
London, W.C.2. - England.

J.A. Barth Verlag
Salomonstr. 18 B
Leipzig C.1.
Germany.

Birkhäuser Verlag A.G.
Basel 10
Switzerland.

Blackie & Son Ltd.,
16-18 William IV Street
London, W.C.2. - England.

McGraw Hill Book Company
330 West 42nd Street
New York 36, N.Y.

Burgess Publishing Company
426 South Sixth Street
Minneapolis 15 - Minn.

Butterworths Scientific Publications
88 Kingsway
London, W.C.2. - England.

Cambridge University Press
Bentley House
200 Euston Road
London, N.W.1. - England.

Carnegie Press
Carnegie Institute of Technology
Pittsburgh 13 - Penn.

The Catholic University of
    America Press
620 Michigan Avenue, N.E.
Washington 17, D.C.

Chapman & Hall Ltd.,
37-39 Essex Street
Strand
London, W.C.2. - England.

Chemical Publishing Company Inc.
212 Fifth Avenue
New York 10, N.Y.

Chemical Society (London)
Burlington House
Piccadilly
London, W.1. - England.

Chemie-Verlag, G.M.B.H.
Weinheim/Bergstr.
Pappelallee 3
Germany.

J. & A. Churchill Ltd.,
104 Gloucester Place
London, W.1. - England.

Clarendon Press
Oxford - England
(see Oxford University Press).

Cornell University Press
124 Roberts Place
Ithaca, N.Y.

Thomas Y. Crowell Company
432 Park Avenue South
New York 16, N.Y.

The Dow Chemical Company
Girard Tr. Co. Bl.
Philadelphia - Penn.

The Dow Chemical Company
Midland - Michigan.

Dunod
92 Rue Bonaparte
Paris 6^e - France.

J.W. Edwards (Publishers) Inc.
2500 South State Street
Ann Arbor - Michigan.

Elsevier Publishing Company
New York.
(see Elsevier - Amsterdam).

Elsevier Publishing Company N.V.
Spuistraat 110-2
Amsterdam - The Netherlands.

F. Enke Verlag
Hasenbergsteige 3
Stuttgart - Germany.

Fachbuchverlag
Karl-Heine Strasse 16
Leipzig W.31 - Germany.

VEB Gustav Fischer
Villengang 2
Jena - Germany.

W.H. Freeman & Company
660 Market Street
San Francisco 4 - California.

Gauthier-Villars
55 Quai des Grandss-Augustins
Paris 6^e - France.

Walter de Gruyter & Company
    Verlag
Genthinerstr. 13
Berlin W. 35 - Germany.

P. Hasse & Son
Loenstraede 8
Copenhagen - Denmark.

C. Hanser Verlag
Kolbergerstr. 22
München - Germany.

George G. Harrap & Company Ltd.,
1 & 2 High Holborn
London, W.C.1. - England.

W. Heffer & Sons Ltd.,
Cambridge - England.

Heywood & Company Ltd.,
Drury House
Russell Street
London, W.C.2. - England.

Hilger & Watts Ltd.,
98 St. Pancras Way
Camden Road
London, N.W.1. - England.

S. Hirzel Verlag in Verw
Schuhmachergässchen 1/3
Leipzig C.1. - Germany.

Holt, Rinehart & Winston Inc.
383 Madison Avenue
New York 17, N.Y.

Hutchinson Scientific & Technical
    Publications
178-202 Great Portland Street
London, W.1. - England.

Iliffe & Sons Ltd.,
Dorset House
Stamford Street
London, S.E.1. - England.

Imperial Chemical Industries Ltd.,
Imperial Chemical House
Millbank
London, S.W.1. - England.

Interscience Publishers Inc.
250 Fifth Avenue
New York 1, N.Y.

ADDRESSES OF PUBLISHERS (CONTINUED)

Iowa State University Press
Press Building
Ames - Iowa.

S. Karger A.G.
Arnold Boecklinstrasse 25
Basel - Switzerland.

Paul Lechevalier
87 Bld. Raspail
Paris 6 - France.

H.K. Lewis & Company Ltd.,
136 Gower Street
London, W.C.1. - England.

Little, Brown & Company
34 Beacon Street
Boston 6 - Mass.

Livingstone Ltd., (E. & S.)
15, 16 & 17 Teviot Place
Edinburgh - Scotland.

Longmans, Green & Company Ltd.,
6 & 7 Clifford Street
Piccadilly
London, W.I. - England.

Alex. MacLaren & Sons
268 Argyle Street
Glasgow, C.2. - Scotland.

The Macmillan Company
60 Fifth Avenue
New York 11, N.Y.

Massachusetts College of Pharmacy
179 Longwood Avenue
Boston 15 - Mass.

Masson et Cie
120 Bld. St. Germain
Paris 6^e - France.

Olin Mathieson Chemical Corporation
Mathieson Building
Baltimore - Maryland.

McDowell, Obolensky, Inc.
219 East 61st Street
New York 21, N.Y.

McGraw-Hill Book Company Inc.
330 West 42nd Street
New York 36, N.Y.

Methuen & Company Ltd.,
36 Essex Street
London, W.C.2. - England.

Michigan State University Press
Box 752
East Lansing - Michigan.

Frederick Muller Ltd.,
Ludgate House
Fleet Street
London, E.C.4. - England.

Munksgaard Ltd.,
Nörregade 6
Copenhagen - Denmark.

National Bureau of Standards
Washington 25, D.C.

George Newnes Ltd.,
Tower House
Southampton Street
London, W.C.2. - England.

New York Academy of Sciences
2 East 63rd Street
New York 21, N.Y.

R. Oldenbourg Verlag
Rosenheimerstr. 145
München 8 - Germany.

Oliver & Boyd Ltd.,
Tweeddale Court
14 High Street
Edinburgh - Scotland.

Oxford University Press
J.G.N. Brown
Amen House
Warwick Square
London, E.C.4. - England.

Paul Parey
Lindstr. 44/47
Berlin S.W. 68 - Germany.

Pennsylvania State University Press
University Park
Pennsylvania.

Pergamon Press Inc.
122 East 55th Street
New York 22, N.Y.
         and
Headington Hill Hall
Oxford - England.

Pharmaceutical Society of Great
   Britain
17 Bloomsbury Square
London, W.C.1. - England.

Prentice-Hall Inc.,
Englewood Cliffs, N.J.
         and
70 Fifth Avenue
New York 11, N.Y.

Princeton University Press
Princeton - New Jersey.

Purdue University Press
Lafayette - Indiana.

Reinhold Publishing Corporation
430 Park Avenue
New York 22, N.Y.

Editions de la Revue Scientifique
4 Rue Pomereu
Paris 16 - France.

Royal Australian Chemical Inst.
314 Albert Street
East Melbourne C.2.
Victoria - Australia.

Royal Institute of Chemistry
30 Russell Square
London, W.C.1. - England.

Rutgers University Press
30 College Avenue
New Brunswick - New Jersey.

Benno Schwabe & Company
Steinentorstrasse 13
Basel - Switzerland.

Schwabe-Beyer Verlag G.M.B.H.
Adolfsallee 49-53
Wiesbaden - Germany.

Smith Agricultural Chemical Co.
618 North Champion
Columbus - Ohio.

G.F. Smith Company
867 McKinley Avenue
Columbus - Ohio.

Société de Chimie Physique
École de Physique et de Chimie
10 Rue Vauquelin
Paris V - France.

Société de Productions
   Documentaires
28 Rue St. Dominique
Paris 7e - France.

Society of Chemical Industry
14 Belgrave Square
London, S.W.1. - England.

Springer-Verlag
Berlin-Göttingen-Heidelberg
Heidelberger Platz 3
Berlin-Wilmersdorf - Germany.

Springer-Verlag
Molkerbastei 5
Wien 1 - Austria.

E. & F.N. Spon, Ltd.,
22 Henrietta Street
London, W.C.2. - England.

Dr. Dietrich Steinkopff
Holzhofallee 35
Darmstadt - Germany.

Sugar Research Foundation Inc.
52 Wall Street
New York, N.Y.

Verlag Technik, VEB
Oranienburgerstr. 13-14
Berlin, C.2. - Germany.

Temple Press Ltd.,
Bowling Green Lane
London, W.C.1. - England.

ADDRESSES OF PUBLISHERS (CONTINUED)

Tennessee Eastman Company
Eastman Road
Kingsport - Tenn.

Texas Gulf Sulphur Company
75 East 45th Street
New York, N.Y.

Texas - U.S. Chemical Company
260 Madison Avenue
New York 16, N.Y.

G. Thieme Verlag
Herdweg, 63
Stuttgart-Nord
Germany.

VEB Georg Thieme
Hainstr. 17-19
Leipzig C.1. - Germany.

Charles C. Thomas, Publisher
301-327 E. Lawrence Avenue
Springfield - Illinois.

University of London Press Ltd.,
Little Paul's House
Warwick Square
London, E.C.4. - England.

University of Notre Dame Press
Notre Dame - Indiana.

University of North Carolina Press
Chapel Hill
North Carolina.

University of Pennsylvania Press
3436 Walnut Street
Philadelphia 4 - Penn.

University of Wisconsin Press
430 Sterling Ct.
Madison 6 - Wisconsin.

United States Department of Commerce
Washington 25, D.C.

University of Oklahoma Press
Norman - Oklahoma.

Urban & Schwarzenberg G.M.B.H.
Frankgasse 4
Wien IX - Austria.

U.S. Government Printing Office
N. Capitol & H Streets, N.W.
Washington 25, D.C.

D. Van Nostrand Company Inc.
24 West 40th Street
New York 18, N.Y.
and
D. Van Nostrand Company
(Canada) Ltd.,
25 Hollinger Road
Toronto 16 - Ontario.

F. Vieweg & Sohn Verlag
Braunschweig
Germany.

Wayne State University Press
5047 Second Boulevard
Detroit 2 - Michigan.

John Wiley & Sons Inc.
440 Park Avenue South
New York 16, N.Y.

Wissenschaftlicher Verlag
G.M.B.H.
Birkenwaldstr. 44
Stuttgart-Nord
Germany.

The Williams & Wilkins Co.
428 East Preston Street
Baltimore 2 - Maryland.

Z
5524
O 8
I 5
1940-60